Chemical Process Safety

Third Edition

Contents

7 Concepts to Prevent Fires and Explosions 309

Preface

The third edition of *Chemical Process Safety* is designed to enhance the process of teaching and applying the fundamentals of chemical process safety. It is appropriate for an industrial reference, a senior-level undergraduate course, or a graduate course in chemical process safety. It can be used by anyone interested in improving chemical process safety, including chemical and mechanical engineers and chemists. More material is presented than can be accommodated in a three-credit course, providing instructors with the opportunity to emphasize their topics of interest.

The primary objective of this textbook is to present the important technical fundamentals of chemical process safety. The emphasis on the fundamentals will help the student and practicing scientist to *understand* the concepts and apply them accordingly. This application requires a significant quantity of fundamental knowledge and technology.

The third edition has been rewritten to include new process safety technology, new references, and updated data that have appeared since the first edition was published in 1990 and the second edition in 2002. It also includes our combined experiences of teaching process safety in both industry and academia during the past 20 years.

The third edition contains two new chapters. Chapter 8, "Chemical Reactivity," was added due to the recommendations from the US Chemical Safety Board (CSB) as a result of the T2 Laboratories accident investigation. Chapter 13, "Safety Procedures and Designs," was added to consolidate some material that was scattered throughout the previous editions and to present a more complete and detailed discussion. We removed the chapter on accident investigations that appeared in the first and second editions; much of the content was moved to Chapter 13.

We continue to believe that a textbook on safety is possible only with both industrial and academic inputs. The industrial input ensures that the material is industrially relevant. The academic input ensures that the material is presented on a fundamental basis to help professors and students understand the concepts. Although the authors are (now) both from universities, one has over 30 years of relevant experience in industry (J.F.L.), and the other (D.A.C.) has accumulated significant industrial and government consulting experience since the writing of the first edition.

Since the first edition was published, many universities have developed courses or course content in chemical process safety. This new emphasis on process safety is the result of the positive influences from industry and the Accreditation Board for Engineering and Technology (ABET). Based on faculty feedback, this textbook is an excellent application of the fundamental topics that are taught in the first three years of undergraduate education.

Although professors normally have little background in chemical process safety, they have found that the concepts in this text and the accompanying problems and solutions are easy to learn and teach. Professors have also found that industrial employees are enthusiastic and willing to give specific lectures on safety to enhance their courses.

This textbook is designed for a dedicated course in chemical process safety. However, we continue to believe that chemical process safety should be part of every undergraduate and graduate course in chemistry and chemical and mechanical engineering, just as it is a part of all the industrial experiences. This text is an excellent reference for these courses. This textbook can also be used as a reference for a design course.

Some will remark that our presentation is not complete or that some details are missing. The purpose of this book, however, is not to be complete but to provide a starting point for those who wish to learn about this important area. This book, for example, has a companion text titled *Health and Environmental Risk Analysis* that extends the topics relevant to risk analysis.

We are indebted to our many friends who helped us learn the fundamentals of chemical process safety and its application. Several of these friends have passed on – including G. Boicourt, J. Wehman, and W. Howard. We especially wish to thank S. Grossel, industrial consultant; B. Powers, retired from Dow Chemical Company; D. Hendershot, retired from Rohm and Haas; R. Welker, retired from the University of Arkansas; R. Willey of Northeastern University; R. Darby, retired from Texas A&M University; and Tom Spicer of the University of Arkansas. R. Willey of Northeastern University and V. Wilding of BYU provided very useful reviews of the entire manuscript. Several reviewers provided helpful comments on Chapter 8, "Chemical Reactivity," including S. Horsch, H. Johnstone, and C. Mashuga of Dow Chemical Company; R. Johnson of Unwin Corporation; J. Keith of Michigan Technological University; and A. Theis of Fauske and Associates.

We also acknowledge and thank all the members of the Safety and Chemical Engineering Education (SACHE) Committee of the Center for Chemical Process Safety and the Safety and Loss Prevention Committee of the American Institute of Chemical Engineers. We are honored to be members of both committees. The members of these committees are the experts in safety; their enthusiasm and knowledge have been truly educational and a key inspiration to the development of this text.

Finally, we continue to acknowledge our families, who provided patience, understanding, and encouragement throughout the writing of these three editions.

We hope that this textbook helps prevent chemical plant and university accidents and contributes to a much safer future.

Daniel A. Crowl and Joseph F. Louvar

About the Authors

Daniel A. Crowl is the Herbert H. Dow Professor for Chemical Process Safety at Michigan Technological University. Professor Crowl received his B.S. in fuel science from Pennsylvania State University and his M.S. and Ph.D. in chemical engineering from the University of Illinois.

He is coauthor of the textbook *Chemical Process Safety: Fundamentals with Applications*, First and Second Editions, published by Prentice Hall. He is also author/editor of several AIChE books on process safety and editor of the safety section in the eighth edition of *Perry's Chemical Engineer's Handbook*.

Professor Crowl has won numerous awards, including the Bill Doyle award from AIChE, the Chemical Health and Safety Award from ACS, the Walton/Miller award from the Safety and Health Division of AIChE, and the Gary Leach Award from the AIChE Board.

Professor Crowl is a Fellow of AIChE, ACS Safety and Health Division, and CCPS.

Joseph F. Louvar has a B.S., M.S., and Ph.D. in chemical engineering. He is currently a professor at Wayne State University after having retired from the BASF Corporation. While working at the BASF Corporation, he was a director of BASF's chemical engineering department; his responsibilities included the production of specialty chemicals, and he managed the implementation and maintenance of five processes that handled highly hazardous chemicals that were covered by Process Safety Management. As a professor at Wayne State University, he teaches chemical process safety, risk assessment, and process design.

Professor Louvar is the author of many safety-related publications and the coauthor of two books, *Chemical Process Safety: Fundamentals with Applications*, First and Second Editions, and *Health and Environmental Risk Analysis: Fundamentals with Applications*. Both books are published by Prentice Hall. Professor Louvar has been the chair of the Loss Prevention Committee and the Safety and Health Division. He is the CCPS staff consultant for the Undergraduate Education Committee, commonly known as the Safety and Chemical Engineering Education Committee (SACHE), and he is the coeditor of AIChE's journal for process safety, *Process Safety Progress*.

Nomenclature

a	velocity of sound (length/time)
A	area (length^2) or Helmholtz free energy (energy/mole); or process component availability; or arrhenius reaction rate pre-exponential constant (time^{-1})
A_t	tank cross sectional area (length^2)
ΔA	change in Helmoltz free energy (energy/mole)
B	adiabatic reactor temperature increase (dimensionless)
C	mass concentration (mass/volume) or capacitance (Farads)
C_0	discharge coefficient (unitless), or concentration at the source (mass/volume)
C_1	concentration at a specified time (mass/volume)
C_m	concentration of dense gas (volume fraction)
C_p	heat capacity at constant pressure (energy/mass deg)
C_{ppm}	concentration in parts per million by volume
C_V	heat capacity at constant volume (energy/mass deg)
C_{vent}	deflagration vent constant (pressure$^{1/2}$)
C_x	concentration at location x downwind from the source (mass/volume)
$\langle C \rangle$	average or mean mass concentration (mass/volume)
d	diameter (length)
d_p	particle diameter (length)
d_f	diameter of flare stack (length)
D	diffusion coefficient (area/time)
D_c	characteristic source dimension for continuous releases of dense gases (length)
D_i	characteristic source dimension for instantaneous releases of dense gas (length)
D_0	reference diffusion coefficient (area/time)

D_{m}	molecular diffusivity (area/time)
D_{tid}	total integrated dose due to a passing puff of vapor (mass time/volume)
E_{a}	activation energy (energy/mole)
ERPG	emergency response planning guideline (see Table 5-6)
EEGL	emergency exposure guidance levels (see Section 5.5)
f	Fanning friction factor (unitless) or frequency (1/time)
$f(t)$	failure density function
f_{v}	mass fraction of vapor (unitless)
F	frictional fluid flow loss term (energy mass) or force or environment factor
FAR	fatal accident rate (fatalities/10^8 hours)
FEV	forced expired volume (liters/sec)
FVC	forced vital capacity (liters)
g	gravitational acceleration (length/time^2)
g_{c}	gravitational constant (mass length/force time^2)
g_{o}	initial cloud buoyancy factor (length/time^2)
g_x	buoyancy factor at location x (length/time^2)
G	Gibbs free energy (energy/mole) or mass flux (mass/area time)
G_{T}	mass flux during relief (mass/area time)
ΔG	change in Gibbs free energy (energy/mole)
h	specific enthalpy (energy/mass)
h_{L}	fluid level above leak in tank (length)
h_{L}^{0}	initial fluid level above leak in tank (length)
h_{s}	leak height above ground level (length)
H	enthalpy (energy/mole) or height (length)
H_{f}	flare height (length)
H_{r}	effective release height in plume model (length)
ΔH	change in enthalpy (energy/mole)
ΔH_{c}	heat of combustion (energy/mass)
ΔH_{r}	release height correction given by Equation 5-65
ΔH_{v}	enthalpy of vaporization (energy/mass)
I	sound intensity (decibels)
ID	pipe internal diameter (length)
IDLH	immediately dangerous to life and health (see Section 5.5)
I_0	reference sound intensity (decibels)
I_{s}	streaming current (amps)
ISOC	in-service oxygen concentration (volume percent oxygen)
j	number of inerting purge cycles (unitless)
J	electrical work (energy)
k	non-ideal mixing factor for ventilation (unitless), or reaction rate (concentration^{1-m}/time)
k_1, k_2	constants in probit a equations
k_{s}	thermal conductivity of soil (energy/length time deg)
K	mass transfer coefficient (length/time)
K_{b}	backpressure correction for relief sizing (unitless)
K_{f}	excess head loss for fluid flow (dimensionless)

K_i, K_∞	constants in excess head loss, given by Equation 4-38
K_G	explosion constant for vapors (length pressure/time)
K_j	eddy diffusivity in *x*, *y* or *z* direction (area/time)
K_P	overpressure correction for relief sizing (unitless)
K_{St}	explosion constant for dusts (length pressure/time)
K_V	viscosity correction for relief sizing (unitless)
K_0	reference mass transfer coefficient (length/time)
K^*	constant eddy diffusivity (area/time)
L	length
LEL	lower explosion limit (volume %)
LFL = *LEL*	lower flammability limit (volume %)
LOC	limiting oxygen concentration (volume percent oxygen)
LOL	lower flammable limit in pure oxygen (volume %)
m	mass
m_f	mass fraction
m_0	total mass contained in reactor vessel (mass)
m_{LR}	mass of limiting reactant in Equation (8-34) (mass)
m_T	total mass of reacting mixture in Equation (8-34) (mass)
m_{TNT}	mass of TNT
m_v	mass of vapor
M	molecular weight (mass/mole)
M_0	reference molecular weight (mass/mole)
*M*a	Mach number (unitless)
MOC, MSOC	Minimum oxygen concentration or maximum safe oxygen concentration. See LOC
MTBC	mean time between coincidence (time)
MTBF	mean time between failure (time)
n	number of moles or, reaction order
OSFC	out of service fuel concentration (volume percent fuel)
p	partial pressure (force/area)
p_d	number of dangerous process episodes
p_s	scaled overpressure for explosions (unitless)
P	total pressure or probability
P_b	backpressure for relief sizing (psig)
PEL	permissable exposure level (see Section 2.8)
PFD	probability of failure on demand
P_g	gauge pressure (force/area)
P_{max}	maximum pressure for relief sizing (psig)
P_s	set pressure for relief sizing (psig)
P^{sat}	saturation vapor pressure
q	heat (energy/mass) or heat intensity (energy/area time)
q_f	heat intensity of flare (energy/time area)
q_g	heat flux from ground (energy/area time)
q_s	specific energy release rate at set pressure during reactor relief (energy/mass)
Q	heat (energy) or electrical charge (coulombs)

Q_m	mass discharge rate (mass/time)
Q_m^*	instantaneous mass release (mass)
Q_v	ventilation rate (volume/time)
r	radius (length)
R	electrical resistance (ohms) or reliability
$\overline{R}$	Sachs scaled distance, defined by Equation 6-29 (unitless)
R_d	release duration for heavy gas releases (time)
RHI	reaction hazard index defined by Equation 14-1
r_f	vessel filling rate (time^{-1})
R_g	ideal gas constant (pressure volume/mole deg)
Re	Reynolds number (unitless)
S	entropy (energy/mole deg) or stress (force/area)
S_m	material strength (force/area)
SPEGL	short term public exposure guideline (see Section 5.5)
t	time
t_d	positive phase duration of a blast (time)
t_e	emptying time
t_p	time to form a puff of vapor
t_v	vessel wall thickness (length)
t_w	worker shift time
Δt_v	venting time for reactor relief
T	temperature (deg)
T_d	material decomposition temperature (deg)
T_i	time interval
TLV	threshold limit value (ppm or mg/m^3 by volume)
T_m	maximum temperature during reactor relief (deg)
T_s	saturation temperature at set pressure during reactor relief (deg)
TWA	time weighted average (ppm or mg/m^3 by volume)
TXD	toxic dispersion method (see Section 5.5)
u	velocity (length/time)
u_d	dropout velocity of a particle (length/time)
$\overline{u}$	average velocity (length/time)
$\langle u \rangle$	mean or average velocity (length/time)
U	internal energy (energy/mole) or overall heat transfer coefficient (energy/area deg time) or process component unavailability
UEL	upper explosion limit (volume %)
$UFL = UEL$	upper flammability limit (volume %)
UOL	upper flammable limit in pure oxygen (volume %)
v	specific volume (volume/mass)
v_f	specific volume of liquid (volume/mass)
v_g	specific volume of vapor (volume/mass)
v_{fg}	specific volume change with liquid vaporization (volume/mass)
V	total volume or electrical potential (volts)
V_c	container volume
W	width (length)

W_e	expansion work (energy)
W_s	shaft work (energy)
x	mole fraction or Cartesian coordinate (length), or reactor conversion (dimensionless), or distance from the source (length)
x_t	is the distance from the source to the transition (length),
x_v	is the virtual distance (length), and
x_{nb}	is the distance used in the neutrally buoyant model to compute the concentration downwind of the transition. (length)
X_f	distance from flare at grade (length)
y	mole fraction of vapor (unitless) or Cartesian coordinate (length)
Y	probit variable (unitless)
Y_G	gas expansion factor (unitless)
z	height above datum (length) or Cartesian coordinate (length) or compressibility (unitless)
z_e	scaled distance for explosions (length/mass$^{1/3}$)

Greek Letters

α	velocity correction factor (unitless) or thermal diffusivity (area/time)
β	thermal expansion coefficient (deg^{-1})
δ	double layer thickness (length)
ε	pipe roughness (length) or emissivity (unitless)
ε_r	relative dielectric constant (unitless)
ε_0	permittivity constant for free space (charge^2/force length^2)
η	explosion efficiency (unitless)
Φ	nonideal filling factor (unitless), or phi-factor for calorimeter thermal inertia (dimensionless)
γ	heat capacity ratio (unitless)
γ_c	conductivity (mho/cm)
Γ	dimensionless activation energy
χ	function defined by Equation 9-10
λ	frequency of dangerous episodes
λ_d	average frequency of dangerous episodes
μ	viscosity (mass/length/time) or mean value or failure rate (faults/time)
μ_V	vapor viscosity (mass/length/time)
Ψ	overall discharge coefficient used in Equation 10-15 (unitless)
ρ	density (mass/volume)
ρ_L	liquid density (mass/volume)
ρ_{ref}	reference density for specific gravity (mass/volume)
ρ_V	vapor density (mass/volume)
ρ_x	density at distance x downwind from source (mass/volume)
σ	standard deviation (unitless)
$\sigma_x, \sigma_y, \sigma_z$	dispersion coefficient (length)
τ	relaxation time, or dimensionless reaction time
τ_i	inspection period for unrevealed failures

τ_0	operation period for a process component
τ_r	period required to repair a component
τ_u	period of unavailability for unrevealed failures
ζ	zeta potential (volts)

Subscripts

a	ambient
ad	adiabatic
c	combustion
f	formation or liquid
g	vapor or gas
H	higher pressure
i	initiating event
j	purges
L	lower pressure
m	maximum
s	set pressure
o	initial or reference

Superscripts

$^\circ$	standard
$'$	stochastic or random variable

CHAPTER 1

Introduction

In 1987, Robert M. Solow, an economist at the Massachusetts Institute of Technology, received the Nobel Prize in economics for his work in determining the sources of economic growth. Professor Solow concluded that the bulk of an economy's growth is the result of technological advances.

It is reasonable to conclude that the growth of an industry is also dependent on technological advances. This is especially true in the chemical industry, which is entering an era of more complex processes: higher pressure, more reactive chemicals, and exotic chemistry.

More complex processes require more complex safety technology. Many industrialists even believe that the development and application of safety technology is actually a constraint on the growth of the chemical industry.

As chemical process technology becomes more complex, chemical engineers will need a more detailed and fundamental understanding of safety. H. H. Fawcett said, "To know is to survive and to ignore fundamentals is to court disaster."[1] This book sets out the fundamentals of chemical process safety.

Since 1950, significant technological advances have been made in chemical process safety. Today, safety is equal in importance to production and has developed into a scientific discipline that includes many highly technical and complex theories and practices. Examples of the technology of safety include

- Hydrodynamic models representing two-phase flow through a vessel relief
- Dispersion models representing the spread of toxic vapor through a plant after a release, and

[1] H. H. Fawcett and W. S. Wood, *Safety and Accident Prevention in Chemical Operations,* 2nd ed. (New York: Wiley, 1982), p. 1.

- Mathematical techniques to determine the various ways that processes can fail and the probability of failure

Recent advances in chemical plant safety emphasize the use of appropriate technological tools to provide information for making safety decisions with respect to plant design and operation.

The word "safety" used to mean the older strategy of accident prevention through the use of hard hats, safety shoes, and a variety of rules and regulations. The main emphasis was on worker safety. Much more recently, "safety" has been replaced by "loss prevention." This term includes hazard identification, technical evaluation, and the design of new engineering features to prevent loss. The subject of this text is loss prevention, but for convenience, the words "safety" and "loss prevention" will be used synonymously throughout.

Safety, hazard, and *risk* are frequently used terms in chemical process safety. Their definitions are

- *Safety* or *loss prevention:* the prevention of accidents through the use of appropriate technologies to identify the hazards of a chemical plant and eliminate them before an accident occurs.
- *Hazard:* a chemical or physical condition that has the potential to cause damage to people, property, or the environment.
- *Risk:* a measure of human injury, environmental damage, or economic loss in terms of both the incident likelihood and the magnitude of the loss or injury.

Chemical plants contain a large variety of hazards. First, there are the usual mechanical hazards that cause worker injuries from tripping, falling, or moving equipment. Second, there are chemical hazards. These include fire and explosion hazards, reactivity hazards, and toxic hazards.

As will be shown later, chemical plants are the safest of all manufacturing facilities. However, the potential always exists for an accident of catastrophic proportions. Despite substantial safety programs by the chemical industry, headlines of the type shown in Figure 1-1 continue to appear in the newspapers.

1-1 Safety Programs

A successful safety program requires several ingredients, as shown in Figure 1-2. These ingredients are

- **S**ystem
- **A**ttitude
- **F**undamentals
- **E**xperience
- **T**ime
- **Y**ou

Figure 1-1 Headlines are indicative of the public's concern over chemical safety.

First, the program needs a system (1) to record what needs to be done to have an outstanding safety program, (2) to do what needs to be done, and (3) to record that the required tasks are done. Second, the participants must have a positive attitude. This includes the willingness to do some of the thankless work that is required for success. Third, the participants must understand and use the fundamentals of chemical process safety in the design, construction, and operation of their plants. Fourth, everyone must learn from the experience of history or be doomed to repeat it. It is especially recommended that employees (1) read and understand

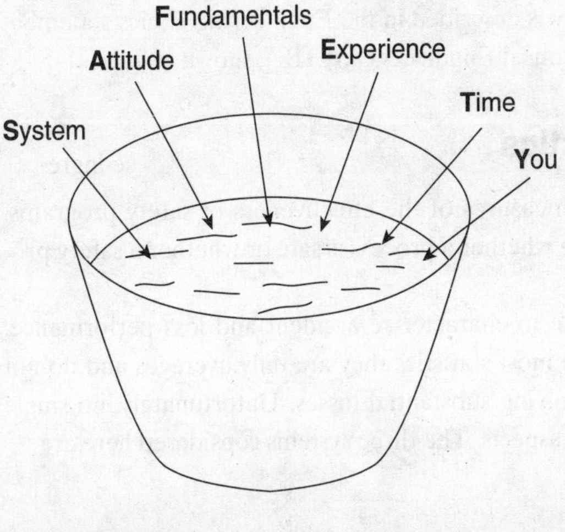

Figure 1-2 The ingredients of a successful safety program.

case histories of past accidents and (2) ask people in their own and other organizations for their experience and advice. Fifth, everyone should recognize that safety takes time. This includes time to study, time to do the work, time to record results (for history), time to share experiences, and time to train or be trained. Sixth, everyone (you) should take the responsibility to contribute to the safety program. A safety program must have the commitment from all levels within the organization. Safety must be given importance equal to production.

The most effective means of implementing a safety program is to make it everyone's responsibility in a chemical process plant. The older concept of identifying a few employees to be responsible for safety is inadequate by today's standards. All employees have the responsibility to be knowledgeable about safety and to practice safety.

It is important to recognize the distinction between a good and an outstanding safety program.

- A *good* safety program identifies and eliminates existing safety hazards.
- An *outstanding* safety program has management systems that prevent the existence of safety hazards.

A good safety program eliminates the existing hazards as they are identified, whereas an outstanding safety program prevents the existence of a hazard in the first place.

The commonly used management systems directed toward eliminating the existence of hazards include safety reviews, safety audits, hazard identification techniques, checklists, and proper application of technical knowledge.

1-2 Engineering Ethics

Most engineers are employed by private companies that provide wages and benefits for their services. The company earns profits for its shareholders, and engineers must provide a service to the company by maintaining and improving these profits. Engineers are responsible for minimizing losses and providing a safe and secure environment for the company's employees. Engineers have a responsibility to themselves, fellow workers, family, community, and the engineering profession. Part of this responsibility is described in the Engineering Ethics statement developed by the American Institute of Chemical Engineers (AICHE), shown in Table 1-1.

1-3 Accident and Loss Statistics

Accident and loss statistics are important measures of the effectiveness of safety programs. These statistics are valuable for determining whether a process is safe or whether a safety procedure is working effectively.

Many statistical methods are available to characterize accident and loss performance. These statistics must be used carefully. Like most statistics they are only averages and do not reflect the potential for single episodes involving substantial losses. Unfortunately, no single method is capable of measuring all required aspects. The three systems considered here are

Table 1-1 American Institute of Chemical Engineers Code of Professional Ethics

Fundamental principles
Engineers shall uphold and advance the integrity, honor, and dignity of the engineering profession by 1. using their knowledge and skill for the enhancement of human welfare; 2. being honest and impartial and serving with fidelity the public, their employers, and clients; 3. striving to increase the competence and prestige of the engineering profession.
Fundamental canons
1. Engineers shall hold paramount the safety, health, and welfare of the public in the performance of their professional duties. 2. Engineers shall perform services only in areas of their competence. 3. Engineers shall issue public statements only in an objective and truthful manner. 4. Engineers shall act in professional matters for each employer or client as faithful agents or trustees, and shall avoid conflicts of interest. 5. Engineers shall build their professional reputations on the merits of their services. 6. Engineers shall act in such a manner as to uphold and enhance the honor, integrity, and dignity of the engineering profession. 7. Engineers shall continue their professional development throughout their careers and shall provide opportunities for the professional development of those engineers under their supervision.

- OSHA incidence rate,
- Fatal accident rate (FAR), and
- Fatality rate, or deaths per person per year

All three methods report the number of accidents and/or fatalities for a fixed number of workers during a specified period.

OSHA stands for the Occupational Safety and Health Administration of the United States government. OSHA is responsible for ensuring that workers are provided with a safe working environment. Table 1-2 contains several OSHA definitions applicable to accident statistics.

The OSHA incidence rate is based on cases per 100 worker years. A worker year is assumed to contain 2000 hours (50 work weeks/year × 40 hours/week). The OSHA incidence rate is therefore based on 200,000 hours of worker exposure to a hazard. The OSHA incidence rate is calculated from the number of occupational injuries and illnesses and the total number of employee hours worked during the applicable period. The following equation is used:

$$\begin{array}{c}\text{OSHA incidence rate}\\ \text{(based on injuries}\\ \text{and illness)}\end{array} = \frac{\begin{array}{c}\text{Number of injuries and}\\ \text{illnesses} \times 200{,}000\end{array}}{\begin{array}{c}\text{Total hours worked by}\\ \text{all employees during}\\ \text{period covered.}\end{array}} \qquad (1\text{-}1)$$

Table 1-2 Glossary of Terms Used by OSHA and Industry to Represent Work-Related Losses[a,b]

Term	Definition
First aid	Any one-time treatment and any follow-up visits for the purpose of observation of minor scratches, cuts, burns, splinters, and so forth that do not ordinarily require medical care. Such one-time treatment and follow-up visits for the purpose of observation are considered first aid even though provided by a physician or registered professional personnel.
Incident rate	Number of occupational injuries and/or illnesses or lost workdays per 100 full-time employees.
Lost workdays	Number of days (consecutive or not) after but not including the day of injury or illness during which the employee would have worked but could not do so, that is, during which the employee could not perform all or any part of his or her normal assignment during all or any part of the workday or shift because of the occupational injury or illness.
Medical treatment	Treatment administered by a physician or by registered professional personnel under the standing orders of a physician. Medical treatment does not include first aid treatment even though provided by a physician or registered professional personnel.
Occupational injury	Any injury such as a cut, sprain, or burn that results from a work accident or from a single instantaneous exposure in the work environment.
Occupational illness	Any abnormal condition or disorder, other than one resulting from an occupational injury, caused by exposure to environmental factors associated with employment. It includes acute and chronic illnesses or diseases that may be caused by inhalation, absorption, ingestion, or direct contact.
Recordable cases	Cases involving an occupational injury or occupational illness, including deaths.
Recordable fatality cases	Injuries that result in death, regardless of the time between the injury and death or the length of the illness.
Recordable nonfatal cases without lost workdays	Cases of occupational injury or illness that do not involve fatalities or lost workdays but do result in (1) transfer to another job or termination of employment or (2) medical treatment other than first aid or (3) diagnosis of occupational illness or (4) loss of consciousness or (5) restriction of work or motion.
Recordable lost workday cases due to restricted duty	Injuries that result in the injured person not being able to perform their regular duties but being able to perform duties consistent with their normal work.
Recordable cases with days away from work	Injuries that result in the injured person not being able to return to work on their next regular workday.
Recordable medical cases	Injuries that require treatment that must be administered by a physician or under the standing orders of a physician. The injured person is able to return to work and perform his or her regular duties. Medical injuries include cuts requiring stitches, second-degree burns (burns with blisters), broken bones, injury requiring prescription medication, and injury with loss of consciousness.

[a]*Injury Facts,* 1999 ed. (Chicago: National Safety Council, 1999), p. 151.
[b]OSHA regulations, 29 CFR 1904.12.

An incidence rate can also be based on lost workdays instead of injuries and illnesses. For this case

$$\begin{array}{c}\text{OSHA incidence rate}\\ \text{(based on lost}\\ \text{workdays)}\end{array} = \frac{\begin{array}{c}\text{Number of lost}\\ \text{workdays} \times 200{,}000\end{array}}{\begin{array}{c}\text{Total hours worked by}\\ \text{all employees during}\\ \text{period covered.}\end{array}} \tag{1-2}$$

The definition of a lost workday is given in Table 1-2.

The OSHA incidence rate provides information on all types of work-related injuries and illnesses, including fatalities. This provides a better representation of worker accidents than systems based on fatalities alone. For instance, a plant might experience many small accidents with resulting injuries but no fatalities. On the other hand, fatality data cannot be extracted from the OSHA incidence rate without additional information.

The FAR is used mostly by the British chemical industry. This statistic is used here because there are some useful and interesting FAR data available in the open literature. The FAR reports the number of fatalities based on 1000 employees working their entire lifetime. The employees are assumed to work a total of 50 years. Thus the FAR is based on 10^8 working hours. The resulting equation is

$$\text{FAR} = \frac{\begin{array}{c}\text{Number of}\\ \text{fatalities} \times 10^8\end{array}}{\begin{array}{c}\text{Total hours worked by all}\\ \text{employees during period covered.}\end{array}} \tag{1-3}$$

The last method considered is the fatality rate or deaths per person per year. This system is independent of the number of hours actually worked and reports only the number of fatalities expected per person per year. This approach is useful for performing calculations on the general population, where the number of exposed hours is poorly defined. The applicable equation is

$$\text{Fatality rate} = \frac{\begin{array}{c}\text{Number of}\\ \text{fatalities per year}\end{array}}{\begin{array}{c}\text{Total number of people in}\\ \text{applicable population.}\end{array}} \tag{1-4}$$

Both the OSHA incidence rate and the FAR depend on the number of exposed hours. An employee working a ten-hour shift is at greater total risk than one working an eight-hour shift. A FAR can be converted to a fatality rate (or vice versa) if the number of exposed hours is known. The OSHA incidence rate cannot be readily converted to a FAR or fatality rate because it contains both injury and fatality information.

Table 1-3 Accident Statistics for Selected Industries

	OSHA incident rates (U.S.)					
	Recordable[a]	Days away from work[a]	Fatality[b, 2]		FAR (U.K.)[c]	
Industrial activity	**2007**	**2007**	**2000**	**2005**	**1974–78**	**1987–90**
Agriculture[1]	6.1	3.2	24.1	27	7.4	3.7
Chemical and allied products	3.3	1.9	2.5	2.8	2.4	1.2
Coal mining	4.7	3.2	50	26.8	14.5	7.3
Construction	5.4	2.8	10	11.1	10	5.0
Vehicle manufacturing	9.3	5.0	1.3	1.7	1.2	0.6
All manufacturing	5.6	3.0	3.3	2.4	2.3	1.2

[a]*Injury Facts* (Chicago: National Safety Council, 2009), p. 62.
[b]Fatal occupational injuries, total hours worked, and rates of fatal occupational injuries, 2000, *www.bls.gov/iif/oshwc/cfoi/cfoi_rates_2000.pdf.*
S. Mannan, ed., *Lees' Loss Prevention in the Process Industries*, 3rd ed., Vol. 1 (London: Butterworth Heinemann), p. 2/12.
[1]Crop and animal products.
[2]Fatalities per 100,000 employed.

Example 1-1

A process has a reported FAR of 2. If an employee works a standard 8-hr shift 300 days per year, compute the deaths per person per year.

Solution

$$\text{Deaths per person per year} = (8 \text{ hr/day}) \times (300 \text{ days/yr}) \times (2 \text{ deaths}/10^8 \text{ hr})$$
$$= 4.8 \times 10^{-5}.$$

Typical accident statistics for various industries are shown in Table 1-3. A FAR of 1.2 is reported in Table 1-3 for the chemical industry. Approximately half these deaths are due to ordinary industrial accidents (falling down stairs, being run over), the other half to chemical exposures.[2]

The FAR figures show that if 1000 workers begin employment in the chemical industry, 2 of the workers will die as a result of their employment throughout all of their working lifetimes. One of these deaths will be due to direct chemical exposure. However, 20 of these same

[2]T. A. Kletz, "Eliminating Potential Process Hazards," *Chemical Engineering* (Apr. 1, 1985).

Table 1-4 Fatality Statistics for Common Nonindustrial Activities[a,b]

Activity	FAR (deaths/10^8 hours)	Fatality rate (deaths per person per year)
Voluntary activity		
Staying at home	3	
Traveling by		
Car	57	17×10^{-5}
Bicycle	96	
Air	240	
Motorcycle	660	
Canoeing	1000	
Rock climbing	4000	4×10^{-5}
Smoking (20 cigarettes/day)		500×10^{-5}
Involuntary activity		
Struck by meteorite		6×10^{-11}
Struck by lightning (U.K.)		1×10^{-7}
Fire (U.K.)		150×10^{-7}
Run over by vehicle		600×10^{-7}

[a]Frank P. Lees, *Loss Prevention in the Process Industries* (London: Butterworths, 1986), p. 178.
[b]Frank P. Lees, *Loss Prevention in the Process Industries,* 2nd ed. (London: Butterworths, 1996), p. 9/96.

1000 people will die as a result of nonindustrial accidents (mostly at home or on the road) and 370 will die from disease. Of those that perish from disease, 40 will die as a direct result of smoking.[3]

Table 1-4 lists the FARs for various common activities. The table is divided into voluntary and involuntary risks. Based on these data, it appears that individuals are willing to take a substantially greater risk if it is voluntary. It is also evident that many common everyday activities are substantially more dangerous than working in a chemical plant.

For example, Table 1-4 indicates that canoeing is much more dangerous than traveling by motorcycle, despite general perceptions otherwise. This phenomenon is due to the number of exposed hours. Canoeing produces more fatalities per hour of activity than traveling by motorcycle. The total number of motorcycle fatalities is larger because more people travel by motorcycle than canoe.

Example 1-2

If twice as many people used motorcycles for the same average amount of time each, what will happen to (a) the OSHA incidence rate, (b) the FAR, (c) the fatality rate, and (d) the total number of fatalities?

[3]Kletz, "Eliminating Potential Process Hazards."

Solution

a. The OSHA incidence rate will remain the same. The number of injuries and deaths will double, but the total number of hours exposed will double as well.

b. The FAR will remain unchanged for the same reason as in part a.

c. The fatality rate, or deaths per person per year, will double. The fatality rate does not depend on exposed hours.

d. The total number of fatalities will double.

Example 1-3

If all riders used their motorcycles twice as much, what will happen to (a) the OSHA incidence rate, (b) the FAR, (c) the fatality rate, and (d) the total number of fatalities?

Solution

a. The OSHA incidence rate will remain the same. The same reasoning applies as for Example 1-2, part a.

b. The FAR will remain unchanged for the same reason as in part a.

c. The fatality rate will double. Twice as many fatalities will occur within this group.

d. The number of fatalities will double.

Example 1-4

A friend states that more rock climbers are killed traveling by automobile than are killed rock climbing. Is this statement supported by the accident statistics?

Solution

The data from Table 1-4 show that traveling by car (FAR = 57) is safer than rock climbing (FAR = 4000). Rock climbing produces many more fatalities per exposed hour than traveling by car. However, the rock climbers probably spend more time traveling by car than rock climbing. As a result, the statement might be correct but more data are required.

Recognizing that the chemical industry is safe, why is there so much concern about chemical plant safety? The concern has to do with the industry's potential for many deaths, as, for example, in the Bhopal, India, tragedy. Accident statistics do not include information on the total number of deaths from a single incident. Accident statistics can be somewhat misleading in this respect. For example, consider two separate chemical plants. Both plants have a probability of explosion and complete devastation once every 1000 years. The first plant employs a single operator. When the plant explodes, the operator is the sole fatality. The second plant employs 10 operators. When this plant explodes all 10 operators succumb. In both cases the FAR and OSHA incidence rate are the same; the second accident kills more people, but there are a correspondingly larger number of exposed hours. In both cases the risk taken by an individual operator is the same.[4]

It is human nature to perceive the accident with the greater loss of life as the greater tragedy. The potential for large loss of life gives the perception that the chemical industry is unsafe.

[4]Kletz, "Eliminating Potential Process Hazards."

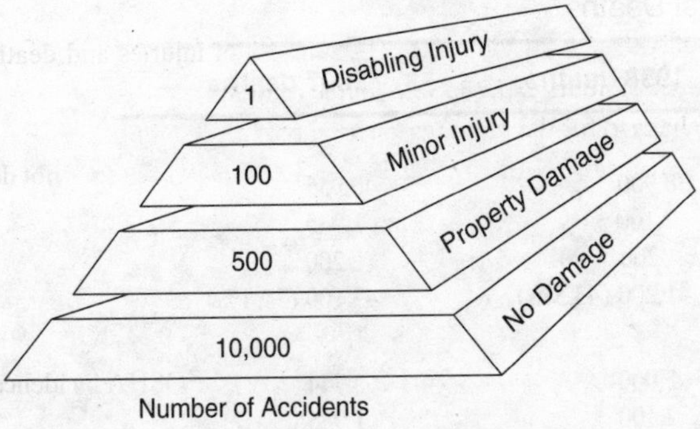

Figure 1-3 The accident pyramid.

Loss data[5] published for losses after 1966 and in 10-year increments indicate that the total number of losses, the total dollar amount lost, and the average amount lost per incident have steadily increased. The total loss figure has doubled every 10 years despite increased efforts by the chemical process industry to improve safety. The increases are mostly due to an expansion in the number of chemical plants, an increase in chemical plant size, and an increase in the use of more complicated and dangerous chemicals.

Property damage and loss of production must also be considered in loss prevention. These losses can be substantial. Accidents of this type are much more common than fatalities. This is demonstrated in the accident pyramid shown in Figure 1-3. The numbers provided are only approximate. The exact numbers vary by industry, location, and time. "No Damage" accidents are frequently called "near misses" and provide a good opportunity for companies to determine that a problem exists and to correct it before a more serious accident occurs. It is frequently said that "the cause of an accident is visible the day before it occurs." Inspections, safety reviews, and careful evaluation of near misses will identify hazardous conditions that can be corrected before real accidents occur.

Safety is good business and, like most business situations, has an optimal level of activity beyond which there are diminishing returns. As shown by Kletz,[6] if initial expenditures are made on safety, plants are prevented from blowing up and experienced workers are spared. This results in increased return because of reduced loss expenditures. If safety expenditures increase, then the return increases more, but it may not be as much as before and not as much as achieved by spending money elsewhere. If safety expenditures increase further, the price of the product increases and sales diminish. Indeed, people are spared from injury (good humanity), but the cost is decreased sales. Finally, even higher safety expenditures result in uncompetitive product pricing: The company will go out of business. Each company needs to determine an appropriate level for safety expenditures. This is part of risk management.

From a technical viewpoint, excessive expenditures for safety equipment to solve single safety problems may make the system unduly complex and consequently may cause new safety

[5] *The 100 Largest Losses, 1972–2001: Large Property Damage Losses in the Hydrocarbon-Chemical Industries*, 20th ed., Marsh's Risk Consulting Practice, Feb. 2003.

[6] Kletz, "Eliminating Potential Process Hazards."

Table 1-5 All Accidental Deaths[a]

Type of death	1998 deaths	2007 deaths
Motor-vehicle		
Public nonwork	38,900	40,955
Work	2,100	1,945
Home	200	200
Subtotal	41,200 (43.5%)	43,100 (35.4%)
Work		
Non-motor-vehicle	3,000	2,744
Motor-vehicle	2,100	1,945
Subtotal	5,100 (5.4%)	4,689 (3.9%)
Home		
Non-motor-vehicle	28,200	43,300
Motor-vehicle	200	200
Subtotal	28,400 (30.0%)	43,500 (35.7%)
Public	20,000 (21.1%)	30,500 (25%)
All classes	94,700	121,789

[a]*Injury Facts*, 2009, p. 2.

problems because of this complexity. This excessive expense could have a higher safety return if assigned to a different safety problem. Engineers need to also consider other alternatives when designing safety improvements.

It is also important to recognize the causes of accidental deaths, as shown in Table 1-5. Because most, if not all, company safety programs are directed toward preventing injuries to employees, the programs should include off-the-job safety, especially training to prevent accidents with motor vehicles.

When organizations focus on the root causes of worker injuries, it is helpful to analyze the manner in which workplace fatalities occur (see Figure 1-4). Although the emphasis of this book is the prevention of chemical-related accidents, the data in Figure 1-4 show that safety programs need to include training to prevent injuries resulting from transportation, assaults, mechanical and chemical exposures, and fires and explosions.

1-4 Acceptable Risk

We cannot eliminate risk entirely. Every chemical process has a certain amount of risk associated with it. At some point in the design stage someone needs to decide if the risks are

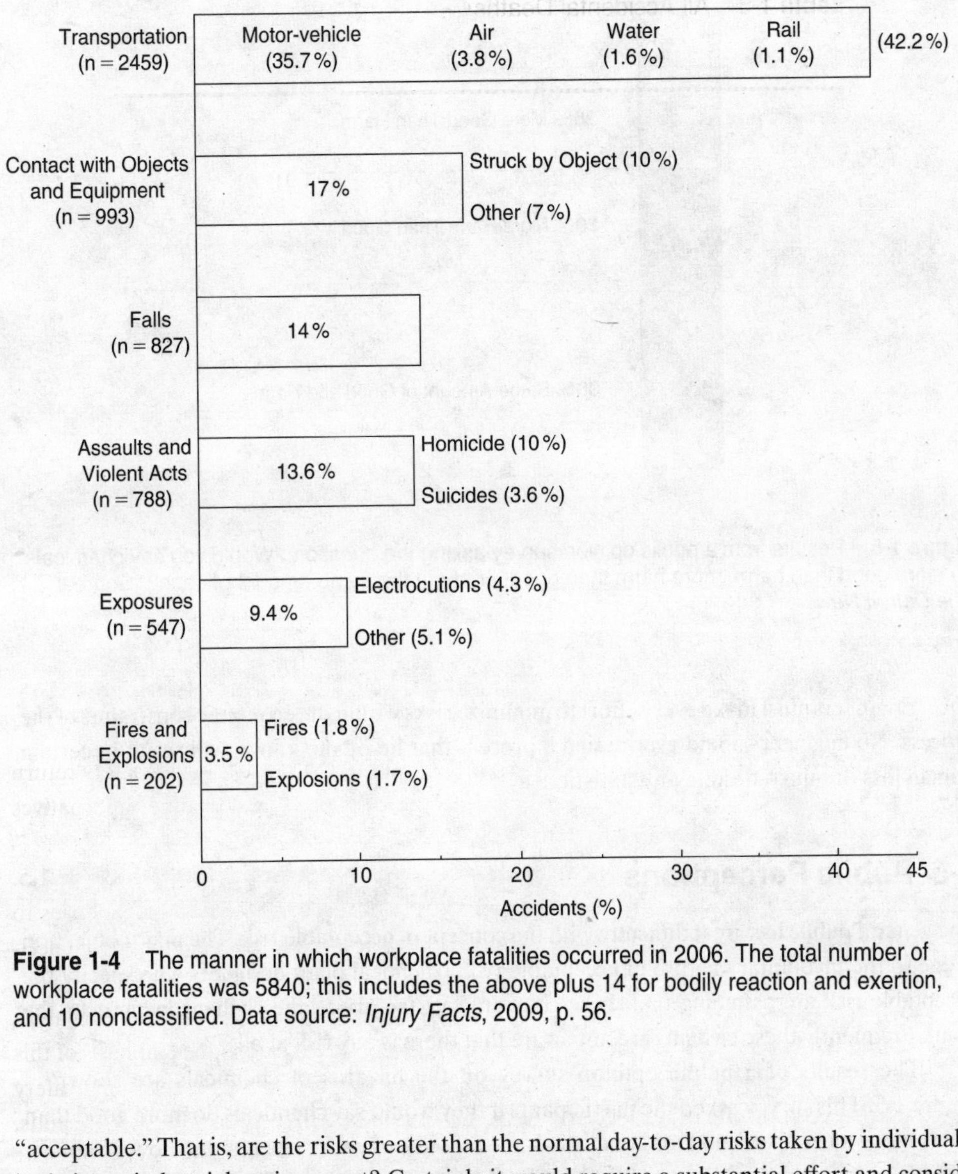

Figure 1-4 The manner in which workplace fatalities occurred in 2006. The total number of workplace fatalities was 5840; this includes the above plus 14 for bodily reaction and exertion, and 10 nonclassified. Data source: *Injury Facts*, 2009, p. 56.

"acceptable." That is, are the risks greater than the normal day-to-day risks taken by individuals in their nonindustrial environment? Certainly it would require a substantial effort and considerable expense to design a process with a risk comparable to being struck by lightning (see Table 1-4). Is it satisfactory to design a process with a risk comparable to the risk of sitting at home? For a single chemical process in a plant composed of several processes, this risk may be too high because the risks resulting from multiple exposures are additive.[7]

[7]Modern site layouts require sufficient separation of plants within the site to minimize risks of multiple exposures.

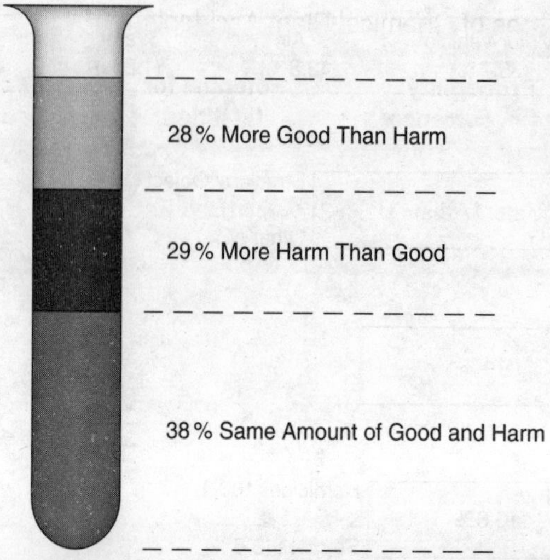

Figure 1-5 Results from a public opinion survey asking the question, "Would you say chemicals do more good than harm, more harm than good, or about the same amount of each?" Source: *The Detroit News.*

Engineers must make every effort to minimize risks within the economic constraints of the process. No engineer should ever design a process that he or she knows will result in certain human loss or injury, despite any statistics.

1-5 Public Perceptions

The general public has great difficulty with the concept of acceptable risk. The major objection is due to the involuntary nature of acceptable risk. Chemical plant designers who specify the acceptable risk are assuming that these risks are satisfactory to the civilians living near the plant. Frequently these civilians are not aware that there is any risk at all.

The results of a public opinion survey on the hazards of chemicals are shown in Figure 1-5. This survey asked the participants if they would say chemicals do more good than harm, more harm than good, or about the same amount of each. The results show an almost even three-way split, with a small margin to those who considered the good and harm to be equal.

Some naturalists suggest eliminating chemical plant hazards by "returning to nature." One alternative, for example, is to eliminate synthetic fibers produced by chemicals and use natural fibers such as cotton. As suggested by Kletz,[8] accident statistics demonstrate that this will result in a greater number of fatalities because the FAR for agriculture is higher.

[8]Kletz, "Eliminating Potential Process Hazards."

Table 1-6 Three Types of Chemical Plant Accidents

Type of accident	Probability of occurrence	Potential for fatalities	Potential for economic loss
Fire	High	Low	Intermediate
Explosion	Intermediate	Intermediate	High
Toxic release	Low	High	Low

Example 1-5

List six different products produced by chemical engineers that are of significant benefit to mankind.

Solution

Penicillin, gasoline, synthetic rubber, paper, plastic, concrete.

1-6 The Nature of the Accident Process

Chemical plant accidents follow typical patterns. It is important to study these patterns in order to anticipate the types of accidents that will occur. As shown in Table 1-6, fires are the most common, followed by explosion and toxic release. With respect to fatalities, the order reverses, with toxic release having the greatest potential for fatalities.

Economic loss is consistently high for accidents involving explosions. The most damaging type of explosion is an unconfined vapor cloud explosion, where a large cloud of volatile and flammable vapor is released and dispersed throughout the plant site followed by ignition and explosion of the cloud. An analysis of the largest chemical plant accidents (based on worldwide accidents and 1998 dollars) is provided in Figure 1-6. As illustrated, vapor cloud explosions

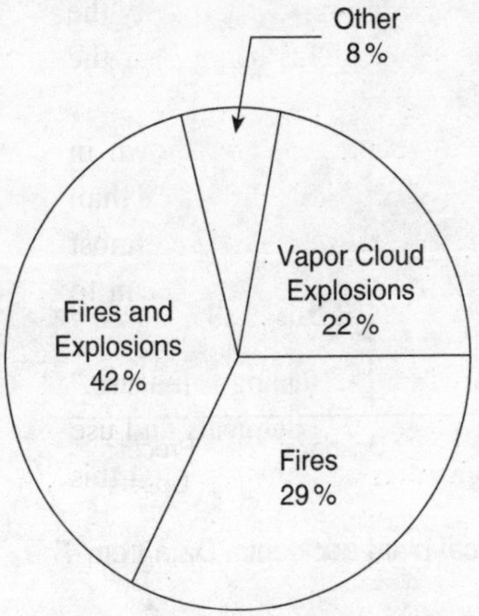

Figure 1-6 Types of loss for large hydrocarbon-chemical plant accidents. Data from *The 100 Largest Losses, 1972–2001.*

account for the largest percentage of these large losses. The "other" category of Figure 1-6 includes losses resulting from floods and windstorms.

Toxic release typically results in little damage to capital equipment. Personnel injuries, employee losses, legal compensation, and cleanup liabilities can be significant.

Figure 1-7 presents the causes of losses for these largest accidents. By far the most frequent cause is mechanical failures, such as pipe failures due to corrosion, erosion, and high pressures, and seal/gasket failures. Failures of this type are usually due to poor maintenance or the poor utilization of the principles of inherent safety (Section 1-7) and process safety management (Section 3-1). Pumps, valves, and control equipment will fail if not properly maintained. The second largest cause is operator error. For example, valves are not opened or closed in the proper sequence or reactants are not charged to a reactor in the correct order. Process upsets caused by, for example, power or cooling water failures account for 3% of the losses.

Human error is frequently used to describe a cause of losses. Almost all accidents, except those caused by natural hazards, can be attributed to human error. For instance, mechanical failures could all be due to human error as a result of improper maintenance or inspection. The term "operator error," used in Figure 1-7, includes human errors made on-site that led directly to the loss.

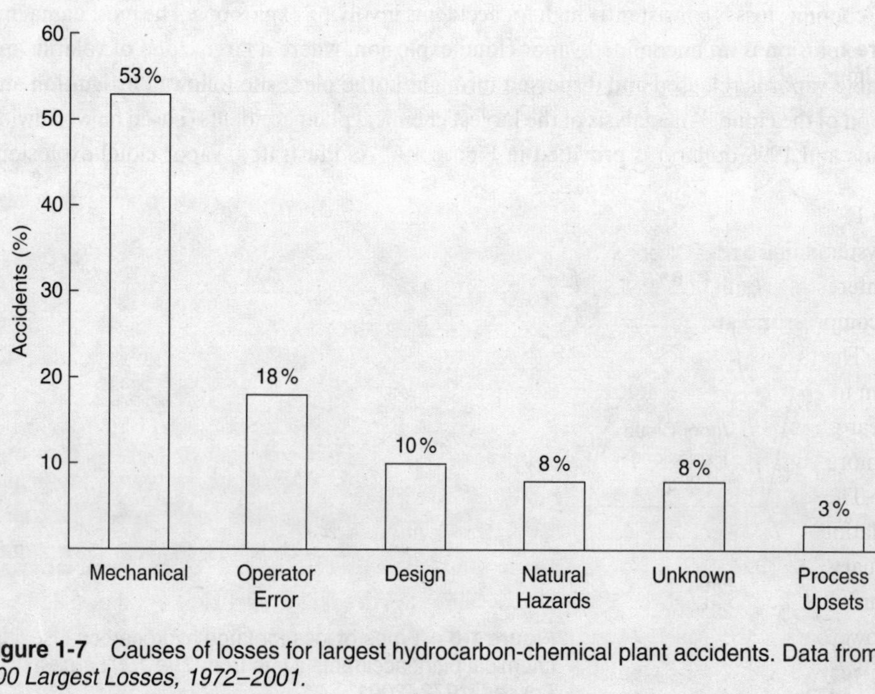

Figure 1-7 Causes of losses for largest hydrocarbon-chemical plant accidents. Data from *The 100 Largest Losses, 1972–2001.*

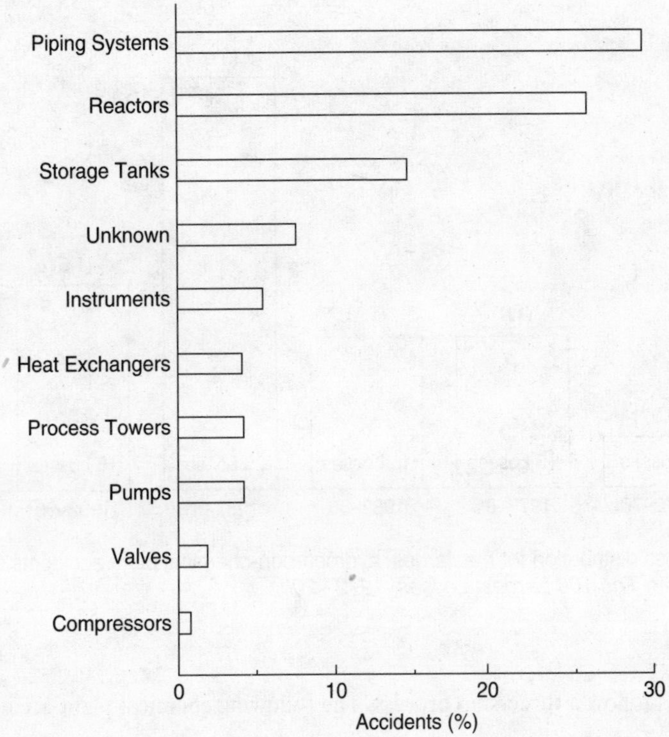

Figure 1-8 Hardware associated with the largest hydrocarbon-chemical plant accidents. Data from *The 100 Largest Losses, 1972–2001*.

Figure 1-8 presents a survey of the type of hardware associated with large accidents. Piping system failure represents the bulk of the accidents, followed by storage tanks and reactors. An interesting result of this study is that the most complicated mechanical components (pumps and compressors) are minimally responsible for large losses.

The loss distribution for the hydrocarbon and chemical industry over 5-year intervals is shown in Figure 1-9. The number and magnitude of the losses increase over each consecutive 10-year period for the past 30 years. This increase corresponds to the trend of building larger and more complex plants.

The lower losses between 1992 and 1996 are likely the temporary result of governmental regulations that were implemented in the United States during this time; that is, on February 24, 1992, OSHA published its final rule "Process Safety Management of Highly Hazardous Chemicals (PSM)." This rule became effective on May 26, 1992. As shown, however, the lower losses between 1992 and 1996 were probably a start-up benefit of PSM because in the last 5-year period (1997-01) the losses went up again.

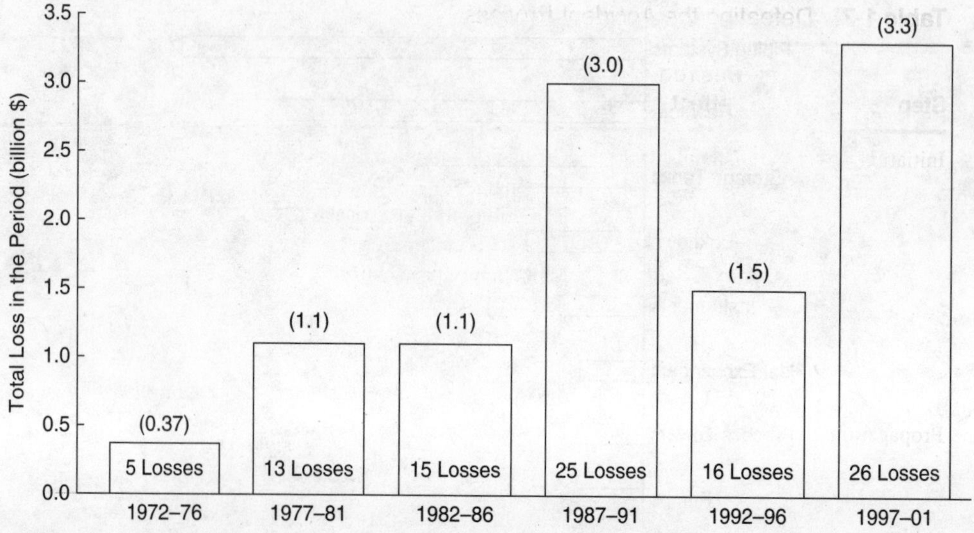

Figure 1-9 Loss distribution for the largest hydrocarbon-chemical plant accidents over a 30-year period. Data from *The 100 Largest Losses, 1972–2001.*

Accidents follow a three-step process. The following chemical plant accident illustrates these steps.

A worker walking across a high walkway in a process plant stumbles and falls toward the edge. To prevent the fall, he grabs a nearby valve stem. Unfortunately, the valve stem shears off and flammable liquid begins to spew out. A cloud of flammable vapor rapidly forms and is ignited by a nearby truck. The explosion and fire quickly spread to nearby equipment. The resulting fire lasts for six days until all flammable materials in the plant are consumed, and the plant is completely destroyed.

This disaster occurred in 1969[9] and led to an economic loss of $4,161,000. It demonstrates an important point: Even the simplest accident can result in a major catastrophe.

Most accidents follow a three-step sequence:

- Initiation (the event that starts the accident)
- Propagation (the event or events that maintain or expand the accident), and
- Termination (the event or events that stop the accident or diminish it in size)

In the example the worker tripped to initiate the accident. The accident was propagated by the shearing of the valve and the resulting explosion and growing fire. The event was terminated by consumption of all flammable materials.

[9] *One Hundred Largest Losses: A Thirty-Year Review of Property Losses in the Hydrocarbon-Chemical Industries* (Chicago: M & M Protection Consultants, 1986), p. 3.

Table 1-7 Defeating the Accident Process

Step	Desired effect	Procedure
Initiation	Diminish	Grounding and bonding Inerting Explosion proof electrical Guardrails and guards Maintenance procedures Hot work permits Human factors design Process design Awareness of dangerous properties of chemicals
Propagation	Diminish	Emergency material transfer Reduce inventories of flammable materials Equipment spacing and layout Nonflammable construction materials Installation of check and emergency shutoff valves
Termination	Increase	Fire-fighting equipment and procedures Relief systems Sprinkler systems Installation of check and emergency shutoff valves

Safety engineering involves eliminating the initiating step and replacing the propagation steps with termination events. Table 1-7 presents a few ways to accomplish this. In theory, accidents can be stopped by eliminating the initiating step. In practice this is not effective: It is unrealistic to expect elimination of all initiations. A much more effective approach is to work on all three areas to ensure that accidents, once initiated, do not propagate and will terminate as quickly as possible.

Example 1-6

The following accident report has been filed[10].

> Failure of a threaded 1½″ drain connection on a rich oil line at the base of an absorber tower in a large (1.35 MCF/D) gas producing plant allowed the release of rich oil and gas at 850 psi and −40°F. The resulting vapor cloud probably ignited from the ignition system of engine-driven recompressors. The 75′ high × 10′ diameter absorber tower eventually collapsed across the pipe rack and on two exchanger trains. Breaking pipelines added more fuel to the fire. Severe flame impingement on an 11,000-horsepower gas turbine–driven compressor, waste heat recovery, and super-heater train resulted in its near total destruction.

Identify the initiation, propagation, and termination steps for this accident.

[10] *One Hundred Largest Losses,* p. 10.

Solution

Initiation:	Failure of threaded 1½″ drain connection
Propagation:	Release of rich oil and gas, formation of vapor cloud, ignition of vapor cloud by recompressors, collapse of absorber tower across pipe rack
Termination:	Consumption of combustible materials in process

As mentioned previously, the study of case histories is an especially important step in the process of accident prevention. To understand these histories, it is helpful to know the definitions of terms that are commonly used in the descriptions (see Table 1-8).

1-7 Inherent Safety

An inherently safe plant[11,12] relies on chemistry and physics to prevent accidents rather than on control systems, interlocks, redundancy, and special operating procedures to prevent accidents. Inherently safer plants are tolerant of errors and are often the most cost effective. A process that does not require complex safety interlocks and elaborate procedures is simpler, easier to operate, and more reliable. Smaller equipment, operated at less severe temperatures and pressures, has lower capital and operating costs.

In general, the safety of a process relies on multiple layers of protection. The first layer of protection is the process design features. Subsequent layers include control systems, interlocks, safety shutdown systems, protective systems, alarms, and emergency response plans. Inherent safety is a part of all layers of protection; however, it is especially directed toward process design features. The best approach to prevent accidents is to add process design features to prevent hazardous situations. An inherently safer plant is more tolerant of operator errors and abnormal conditions.

Although a process or plant can be modified to increase inherent safety at any time in its life cycle, the potential for major improvements is the greatest at the earliest stages of process development. At these early stages process engineers and chemists have the maximum degree of freedom in the plant and process specifications, and they are free to consider basic process alternatives, such as changes to the fundamental chemistry and technology.

The following four words are recommended to describe inherent safety:

- Minimize (intensification)
- Substitute (substitution)
- Moderate (attenuation and limitation of effects)
- Simplify (simplification and error tolerance)

[11] Center for Chemical Process Safety (CCPS), *Guidelines for Engineering Design for Process Safety* (New York: American Institute of Chemical Engineers, 1993).

[12] Center for Chemical Process Safety (CCPS), *Inherently Safer Chemical Processes: A Life Cycle Approach*, 2nd ed. (Hoboken, NJ: John Wiley & Sons, 2009).

Table 1-8 Definitions for Case Histories[a]

Term	Definition
Accident	The occurrence of a sequence of events that produce unintended injury, death, or property damage. "Accident" refers to the event, not the result of the event.
Hazard	A chemical or physical condition that has the potential for causing damage to people, property, or the environment.
Incident	The loss of containment of material or energy; not all events propagate into incidents; not all incidents propagate into accidents.
Consequence	A measure of the expected effects of the results of an incident.
Likelihood	A measure of the expected probability or frequency of occurrence of an event. This may be expressed as a frequency, a probability of occurrence during some time interval, or a conditional probability.
Risk	A measure of human injury, environmental damage, or economic loss in terms of both the incident likelihood and the magnitude of the loss or injury.
Risk analysis	The development of a quantitative estimate of risk based on an engineering evaluation and mathematical techniques for combining estimates of incident consequences and frequencies.
Risk assessment	The process by which the results of a risk analysis are used to make decisions, either through a relative ranking of risk reduction strategies or through comparison with risk targets.
Scenario	A description of the events that result in an accident or incident. The description should contain information relevant to defining the root causes.

[a]Center for Chemical Process Safety (CCPS), *Guidelines for Consequence Analysis.*

The types of inherent safety techniques that are used in the chemical industry are illustrated in Table 1-9 and are described more fully in what follows.

Minimizing entails reducing the hazards by using smaller quantities of hazardous substances in the reactors, distillation columns, storage vessels, and pipelines. When possible, hazardous materials should be produced and consumed in situ. This minimizes the storage and transportation of hazardous raw materials and intermediates.

Vapor released from spills can be minimized by designing dikes so that flammable and toxic materials will not accumulate around leaking tanks. Smaller tanks also reduce the hazards of a release.

While minimization possibilities are being investigated, substitutions should also be considered as an alternative or companion concept; that is, safer materials should be used in place of hazardous ones. This can be accomplished by using alternative chemistry that allows the use of less hazardous materials or less severe processing conditions. When possible,

Table 1-9 Inherent Safety Techniques

Type	Typical techniques
Minimize (intensification)	Change from large batch reactor to a smaller continuous reactor Reduce storage inventory of raw materials Improve control to reduce inventory of hazardous intermediate chemicals Reduce process hold-up
Substitute (substitution)	Use mechanical pump seals vs. packing Use welded pipe vs. flanged Use solvents that are less toxic Use mechanical gauges vs. mercury Use chemicals with higher flash points, boiling points, and other less hazardous properties Use water as a heat transfer fluid instead of hot oil
Moderate (attenuation and limitation of effects)	Use vacuum to reduce boiling point Reduce process temperatures and pressures Refrigerate storage vessels Dissolve hazardous material in safe solvent Operate at conditions where reactor runaway is not possible Place control rooms away from operations Separate pump rooms from other rooms Acoustically insulate noisy lines and equipment Barricade control rooms and tanks
Simplify (simplification and error tolerance)	Keep piping systems neat and visually easy to follow Design control panels that are easy to comprehend Design plants for easy and safe maintenance Pick equipment that requires less maintenance Pick equipment with low failure rates Add fire- and explosion-resistant barricades Separate systems and controls into blocks that are easy to comprehend and understand Label pipes for easy "walking the line" Label vessels and controls to enhance understanding

toxic or flammable solvents should be replaced with less hazardous solvents (for example, water-based paints and adhesives and aqueous or dry flowable formulations for agricultural chemicals).

Another alternative to substitution is moderation, that is, using a hazardous material under less hazardous conditions. Less hazardous conditions or less hazardous forms of a material include (1) diluting to a lower vapor pressure to reduce the release concentration, (2) refrigerating to lower the vapor pressure, (3) handling larger particle size solids to minimize dust, and (4) processing under less severe temperature or pressure conditions.

Containment buildings are sometimes used to moderate the impact of a spill of an especially toxic material. When containment is used, special precautions are included to ensure worker protection, such as remote controls, continuous monitoring, and restricted access.

Simpler plants are friendlier than complex plants because they provide fewer opportunities for error and because they contain less equipment that can cause problems. Often, the reason for complexity in a plant is the need to add equipment and automation to control the hazards. Simplification reduces the opportunities for errors and misoperation. For example, (1) piping systems can be designed to minimize leaks or failures, (2) transfer systems can be designed to minimize the potential for leaks, (3) process steps and units can be separated to prevent the domino effect, (4) fail-safe valves can be added, (5) equipment and controls can be placed in a logical order, and (6) the status of the process can be made visible and clear at all times.

The design of an inherently safe and simple piping system includes minimizing the use of sight glasses, flexible connectors, and bellows, using welded pipes for flammable and toxic chemicals and avoiding the use of threaded pipe, using spiral wound gaskets and flexible graphite-type gaskets that are less prone to catastrophic failures, and using proper support of lines to minimize stress and subsequent failures.

1-8 Seven Significant Disasters

The study of case histories provides valuable information to chemical engineers involved with safety. This information is used to improve procedures to prevent similar accidents in the future.

The seven most cited accidents (Flixborough, England; Bhopal, India; Seveso, Italy; Pasadena, Texas; Texas City, Texas; Jacksonville, Florida; and Port Wentworth, Georgia) are presented here. All these accidents had a significant impact on public perceptions and the chemical engineering profession that added new emphasis and standards in the practice of safety. Chapter 14 presents case histories in considerably more detail.

The Flixborough accident is perhaps the most documented chemical plant disaster. The British government insisted on an extensive investigation.

Flixborough, England

The accident at Flixborough, England, occurred on a Saturday in June 1974. Although it was not reported to any great extent in the United States, it had a major impact on chemical engineering in the United Kingdom. As a result of the accident, safety achieved a much higher priority in that country.

The Flixborough Works of Nypro Limited was designed to produce 70,000 tons per year of caprolactam, a basic raw material for the production of nylon. The process uses cyclohexane, which has properties similar to gasoline. Under the process conditions in use at Flixborough (155°C and 7.9 atm), the cyclohexane volatilizes immediately when depressurized to atmospheric conditions.

The process where the accident occurred consisted of six reactors in series. In these reactors cyclohexane was oxidized to cyclohexanone and then to cyclohexanol using injected air in the presence of a catalyst. The liquid reaction mass was gravity-fed through the series of reactors. Each reactor normally contained about 20 tons of cyclohexane.

Several months before the accident occurred, reactor 5 in the series was found to be leaking. Inspection showed a vertical crack in its stainless steel structure. The decision was made to remove the reactor for repairs. An additional decision was made to continue operating by connecting reactor 4 directly to reactor 6 in the series. The loss of the reactor would reduce the yield but would enable continued production because unreacted cyclohexane is separated and recycled at a later stage.

The feed pipes connecting the reactors were 28 inches in diameter. Because only 20-inch pipe stock was available at the plant, the connections to reactor 4 and reactor 6 were made using flexible bellows-type piping, as shown in Figure 1-10. It is hypothesized that the bypass pipe section ruptured because of inadequate support and overflexing of the pipe section as a result of internal reactor pressures. Upon rupture of the bypass, an estimated 30 tons of cyclohexane volatilized and formed a large vapor cloud. The cloud was ignited by an unknown source an estimated 45 seconds after the release.

The resulting explosion leveled the entire plant facility, including the administrative offices. Twenty-eight people died, and 36 others were injured. Eighteen of these fatalities occurred in the main control room when the ceiling collapsed. Loss of life would have been substantially greater had the accident occurred on a weekday when the administrative offices were filled with employees. Damage extended to 1821 nearby houses and 167 shops and factories. Fifty-three civilians were reported injured. The resulting fire in the plant burned for over 10 days.

This accident could have been prevented by following proper safety procedures. First, the bypass line was installed without a safety review or adequate supervision by experienced engineering personnel. The bypass was sketched on the floor of the machine shop using chalk!

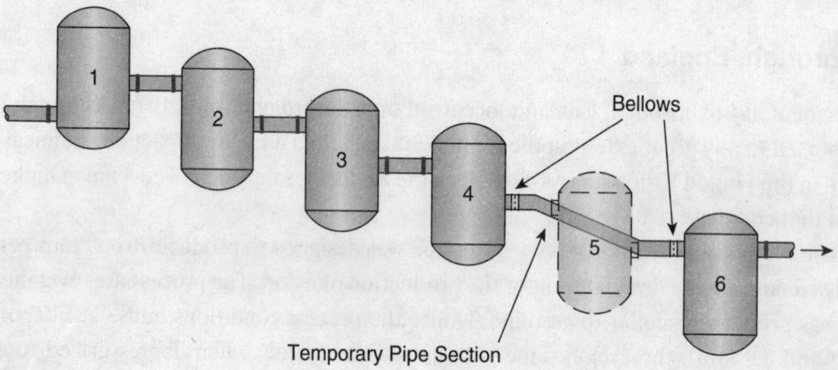

Figure 1-10 A failure of a temporary pipe section replacing reactor 5 caused the Flixborough accident.

Second, the plant site contained excessively large inventories of dangerous compounds. This included 330,000 gallons of cyclohexane, 66,000 gallons of naphtha, 11,000 gallons of toluene, 26,400 gallons of benzene, and 450 gallons of gasoline. These inventories contributed to the fires after the initial blast. Finally, the bypass modification was substandard in design. As a rule, any modifications should be of the same quality as the construction of the remainder of the plant.

Bhopal, India

The Bhopal, India, accident, on December 3, 1984, has received considerably more attention than the Flixborough accident. This is due to the more than 2000 civilian casualties that resulted.

The Bhopal plant is in the state of Madhya Pradesh in central India. The plant was partially owned by Union Carbide and partially owned locally.

The nearest civilian inhabitants were 1.5 miles away when the plant was constructed. Because the plant was the dominant source of employment in the area, a shantytown eventually grew around the immediate area.

The plant produced pesticides. An intermediate compound in this process is methyl isocyanate (MIC). MIC is an extremely dangerous compound. It is reactive, toxic, volatile, and flammable. The maximum exposure concentration of MIC for workers over an 8-hour period is 0.02 ppm (parts per million). Individuals exposed to concentrations of MIC vapors above 21 ppm experience severe irritation of the nose and throat. Death at large concentrations of vapor is due to respiratory distress.

MIC demonstrates a number of dangerous physical properties. Its boiling point at atmospheric conditions is 39.1°C, and it has a vapor pressure of 348 mm Hg at 20°C. The vapor is about twice as heavy as air, ensuring that the vapors will stay close to the ground once released.

MIC reacts exothermically with water. Although the reaction rate is slow, with inadequate cooling the temperature will increase and the MIC will boil. MIC storage tanks are typically refrigerated to prevent this problem.

The unit using the MIC was not operating because of a local labor dispute. Somehow a storage tank containing a large amount of MIC became contaminated with water or some other substance. A chemical reaction heated the MIC to a temperature past its boiling point. The MIC vapors traveled through a pressure relief system and into a scrubber and flare system installed to consume the MIC in the event of a release. Unfortunately, the scrubber and flare systems were not operating, for a variety of reasons. An estimated 25 tons of toxic MIC vapor was released. The toxic cloud spread to the adjacent town, killing over 2000 civilians and injuring an estimated 20,000 more. No plant workers were injured or killed. No plant equipment was damaged.

The exact cause of the contamination of the MIC is not known. If the accident was caused by a problem with the process, a well-executed safety review could have identified the problem. The scrubber and flare system should have been fully operational to prevent the release. Inventories of dangerous chemicals, particularly intermediates, should also have been minimized.

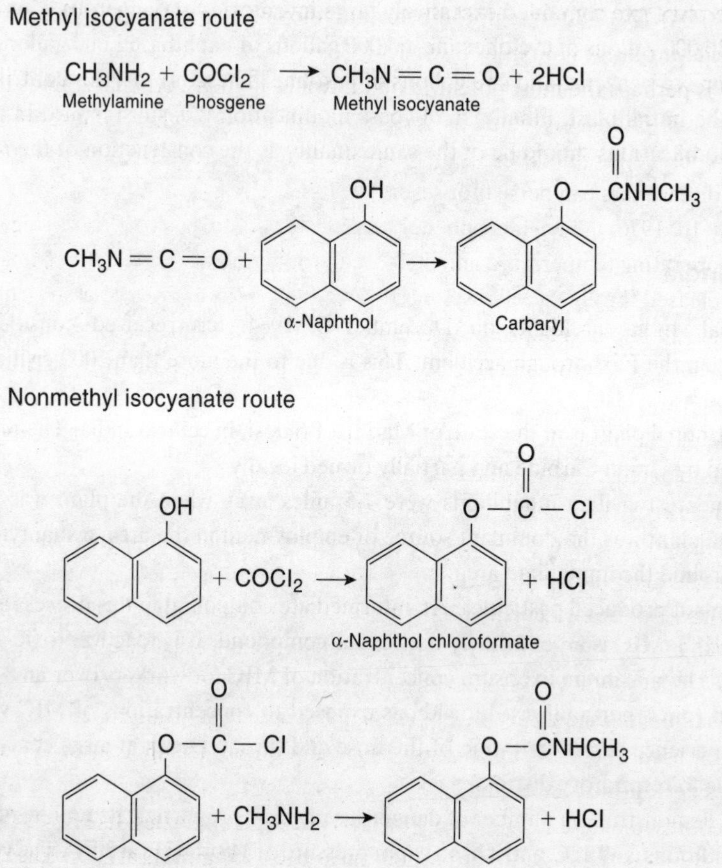

Figure 1-11 The upper reaction is the methyl isocyanate route used at Bhopal. The lower reaction suggests an alternative reaction scheme using a less hazardous intermediate. Adapted from *Chemical and Engineering News* (Feb. 11, 1985), p. 30.

The reaction scheme used at Bhopal is shown at the top of Figure 1-11 and includes the dangerous intermediate MIC. An alternative reaction scheme is shown at the bottom of the figure and involves a less dangerous chloroformate intermediate. Another solution is to redesign the process to reduce the inventory of hazardous MIC. One such design produces and consumes the MIC in a highly localized area of the process, with an inventory of MIC of less than 20 pounds.

Seveso, Italy

Seveso is a small town of approximately 17,000 inhabitants, 15 miles from Milan, Italy. The plant was owned by the Icmesa Chemical Company. The product was hexachlorophene, a bactericide, with trichlorophenol produced as an intermediate. During normal operation, a small amount of TCDD (2,3,7,8-tetrachlorodibenzoparadioxin) is produced in the reactor as an undesirable side-product.

TCDD is perhaps the most potent toxin known to humans. Animal studies have shown TCDD to be fatal in doses as small as 10^{-9} times the body weight. Because TCDD is also insoluble in water, decontamination is difficult. Nonlethal doses of TCDD result in chloracne, an acne-like disease that can persist for several years.

On July 10, 1976, the trichlorophenol reactor went out of control, resulting in a higher than normal operating temperature and increased production of TCDD. An estimated 2 kg of TCDD was released through a relief system in a white cloud over Seveso. A subsequent heavy rain washed the TCDD into the soil. Approximately 10 square miles were contaminated.

Because of poor communications with local authorities, civilian evacuation was not started until several days later. By then, over 250 cases of chloracne were reported. Over 600 people were evacuated, and an additional 2000 people were given blood tests. The most severely contaminated area immediately adjacent to the plant was fenced, the condition it remains in today.

TCDD is so toxic and persistent that for a smaller but similar release of TCDD in Duphar, India, in 1963 the plant was finally disassembled brick by brick, encased in concrete, and dumped into the ocean. Less than 200 g of TCDD was released, and the contamination was confined to the plant. Of the 50 men assigned to clean up the release, 4 eventually died from the exposure.

The Seveso and Duphar accidents could have been avoided if proper containment systems had been used to contain the reactor releases. The proper application of fundamental engineering safety principles would have prevented the two accidents. First, by following proper procedures, the initiation steps would not have occurred. Second, by using proper hazard evaluation procedures, the hazards could have been identified and corrected before the accidents occurred.

Pasadena, Texas

A massive explosion in Pasadena, Texas, on October 23, 1989, resulted in 23 fatalities, 314 injuries, and capital losses of over $715 million. This explosion occurred in a high-density polyethylene plant after the accidental release of 85,000 pounds of a flammable mixture containing ethylene, isobutane, hexane, and hydrogen. The release formed a large gas cloud instantaneously because the system was under high pressure and temperature. The cloud was ignited about 2 minutes after the release by an unidentified ignition source.

The damage resulting from the explosion made it impossible to reconstruct the actual accident scenario. However, evidence showed that the standard operating procedures were not appropriately followed.

The release occurred in the polyethylene product takeoff system, as illustrated in Figure 1-12. Usually the polyethylene particles (product) settle in the settling leg and are removed through the product takeoff valve. Occasionally, the product plugs the settling leg, and

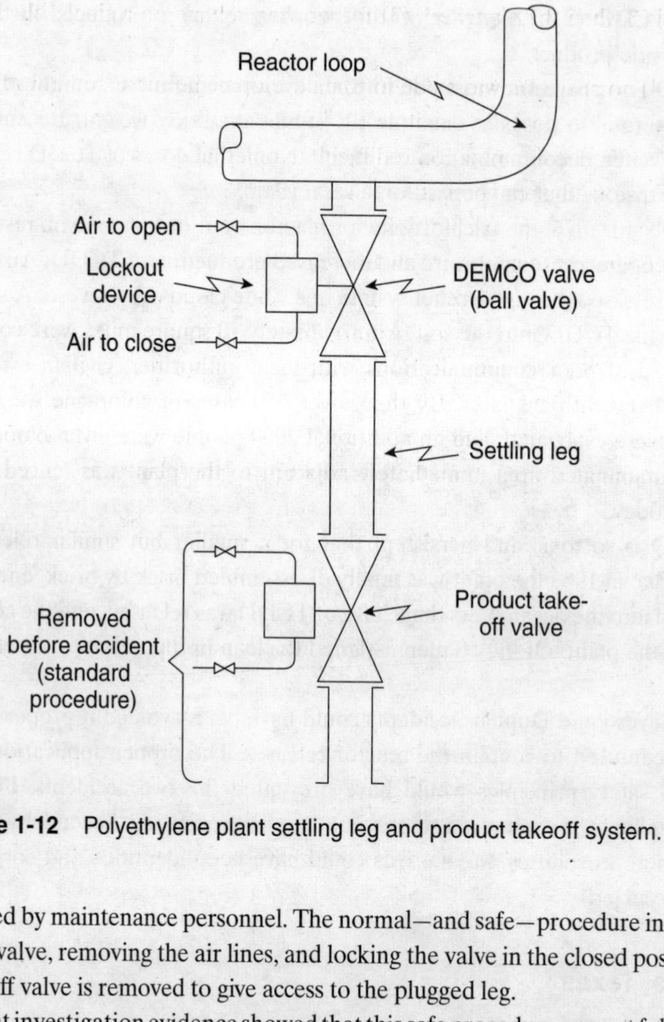

Figure 1-12 Polyethylene plant settling leg and product takeoff system.

the plug is removed by maintenance personnel. The normal—and safe—procedure includes closing the DEMCO valve, removing the air lines, and locking the valve in the closed position. Then the product takeoff valve is removed to give access to the plugged leg.

The accident investigation evidence showed that this safe procedure was not followed; specifically, the product takeoff valve was removed, the DEMCO valve was in the open position, and the lockout device was removed. This scenario was a serious violation of well-established and well-understood procedures and created the conditions that permitted the release and subsequent explosion.

The OSHA investigation[13] found that (1) no process hazard analysis had been performed in the polyethylene plant, and as a result, many serious safety deficiencies were ignored or overlooked; (2) the single-block (DEMCO) valve on the settling leg was not designed to fail to a safe

[13]Occupational Safety and Health Administration, *The Pasadena Accident: A Report to the President* (Washington, DC: US Department of Labor, 1990).

closed position when the air failed; (3) rather than relying on a single-block valve, a double block and bleed valving arrangement or a blind flange after the single-block valve should have been used; (4) no provision was made for the development, implementation, and enforcement of effective permit systems (for example, line opening); and (5) no permanent combustible gas detection and alarm system was located in the region of the reactors.

Other factors that contributed to the severity of this disaster were also cited: (1) proximity of high-occupancy structures (control rooms) to hazardous operation, (2) inadequate separation between buildings, and (3) crowded process equipment.

Texas City, Texas

A petroleum refinery had large explosions on March 23, 2005, that killed 15 workers and injured about 180.[14] The explosions were the result of a sudden release of flammable liquid and vapor from an open vent stack in the refinery's isomerization (ISOM) unit. The ISOM unit converts pentane and hexane into isopentane and isohexane (gasoline additive). The unit works by heating the pentane and hexane in the presence of a catalyst. This unit includes a splitter tower and associated process equipment, which is used to prepare the hydrocarbon feed of the isomerization reactor.

This accident was during the startup of this ISOM process unit. In this startup, hydrocarbons were pumped into the splitter tower for three hours without any liquid being removed and transferred to storage (which should have happened). As a result, the 164-foot-tall tower was overfilled. The resulting high pressure activated three pressure relief valves, and the liquid was discharged to a vented blowdown drum. The blowdown drum overfilled with hydrocarbons, producing a geyser-like release from the vented stack. The flammable hydrocarbons pooled on the ground, releasing vapors that ignited, resulting in multiple explosions and fires. Many of those killed were working in or around two contractor office trailers located near a blowdown drum.

The CSB investigation identified the following major findings: (1) the occupied trailers were sited in an unsafe location (all 15 fatalities occurred in or around two contractor trailers); (2) the ISOM unit should not have been started up because there were existing and known problems that should have been repaired before a startup (known equipment malfunctions included a level indicator and alarm, and a control valve); and (3) previously there were at least four other serious releases of flammables out of this blowdown drum vent, and even though these serious near-misses revealed the existing hazard, no effective investigations were conducted nor were appropriate design changes made (a properly designed flare system would have burned these effluents to prevent this unsafe release of the flammable liquid and combustible vapors).

[14]D. Holmstrom, F. Altamirano, J. Banks, G. Joseph, M. Kaszniak, C. Mackenzie, R. Shroff, H. Cohen, and S. Wallace, "CSB Investigation of the Explosions and Fire at the BP Texas City Refinery on March 23, 2005," *Process Safety Progress* (2006), 25(4): 345–349.

Jacksonville, Florida

CSB investigated an accident[15] that occurred in a chemical manufacturing plant (gasoline additive) on December 19, 2007. A powerful explosion and fire killed 4 employees and injured 32, including 4 employees and 28 members of the public who were working in surrounding businesses. This plant blended and sold printing solvents and started to manufacture methylcyclopentadienyl manganese tricarbonyl (MCMT) in a 2500-gallon batch reactor in January of 2004.

The accident occurred while the plant was producing its 175th batch of MCMT. The process included two exothermic reactions, the first a necessary step in the production of MCMT, and the second an unwanted side reaction that occurs at about 390°F, which is slightly higher than the normal operating temperature. The reactor cooling failed (line blockage or valve failure), and the temperature increased, setting off both runaway reactions uncontrollably. About ten minutes after the initial cooling failure, the reactor burst and its contents exploded due to the uncontrolled high temperatures and pressures. The pressure burst the reactor and the reactor's contents exploded with a TNT equivalent to 1400 pounds of TNT. Debris from the reactor was found up to one mile away, and the explosion damaged buildings within one-quarter mile of the facility.

CSB found that (1) the cooling system was susceptible to only single-point failures due to the lack of design redundancy, (2) the reactor relief system was incapable of relieving the pressure from the runaway reactions, and (3) despite a number of previous and similar near-misses the company employees failed to recognize the hazards of the runaway reactions associated with this manufacturing process (even though the two owners of the company had undergraduate degrees in chemistry and chemical engineering).

The CSB recommendations in this accident investigation report focused on improving the education of chemical engineering students on the hazards of reactive chemicals.

Port Wentworth, Georgia

On February 7, 2008, a series of sugar dust explosions at a sugar manufacturing facility resulted in 14 fatalities and 36 injuries.[16] This refinery converted raw sugarcane into granulated sugar. A system of screw and belt conveyors and bucket elevators transported granulated sugar from the refinery to storage silos, and to specialty sugar processing areas.

A recently installed steel cover panel on the belt conveyor allowed explosive concentrations of sugar dust to accumulate inside the enclosure. The first dust explosion occurred in this enclosed steel belt conveyor located below the sugar silos. An overheated bearing in the steel belt conveyor was the most likely ignition source. This primary explosion dispersed sugar dust that

[15]"Investigation Report—T2 Laboratories, Inc. Runaway Reaction," U.S. Chemical Safety and Hazard Investigation Board, Report No. 2008-3-I-FL, Sept. 2009.

[16]"Investigation Report—Sugar Dust Explosion and Fire," U.S. Chemical Safety and Hazard Investigation Board, Report No. 2008-05-I-GA, Sept. 2009.

had accumulated on the floors and elevator horizontal surfaces, propagating more explosions throughout the buildings. Secondary dust explosions occurred throughout the packing buildings, parts of the refinery, and the loading buildings. The pressure waves from the explosions heaved thick concrete floors and collapsed brick walls, blocking stairwell and other exit routes.

The CSB investigation identified three major causes: (1) The conveying equipment was not designed to minimize the release of sugar dust and eliminate all ignition sources in the work areas; (2) housekeeping practices were poor; and (3) the company failed to correct the ongoing and known hazardous conditions, despite the well-known and broadly published hazards associated with combustible dusts.

Prior to this Port Wentworth accident, CSB undertook a study[17] in 2005 concerning the extent of the industrial dust explosion problem. They identified 200 fires and explosions due to dusts over a 25-year period that took 100 lives and caused 600 injuries. The tragic event in Port Wentworth demonstrates that dust explosions in industry continue to be a problem.

Suggested Reading

General Aspects of Chemical Process Safety

Robert M. Bethea, *Explosion and Fire at Pasadena, Texas* (New York: American Institute of Chemical Engineers, 1996).

Howard H. Fawcett and William S. Wood, eds., *Safety and Accident Prevention in Chemical Operations,* 2nd ed. (New York: Wiley, 1982), ch. 1.

Dennis C. Hendershot, "A History of Process Safety and Loss Prevention in the American Institute of Chemical Engineers," *Process Safety Progress* (June 2009), 28(2): 105–113.

S. Mannan, ed. *Lees' Loss Prevention in the Process Industries*, 3rd ed. (London: Butterworth-Heinemann, 2005).

Bhopal

Chemical and Engineering News (Feb. 11, 1985), p. 14.

A. Sam West, Dennis Hendershot, John F. Murphy, and Ronald Willey, "Bhopal's Impact on the Chemical Industry," *Process Safety Progress* (Dec. 2004), 23(4): 229–230.

Ronald J. Willey, Dennis C. Hendershot, and Scott Berger, "The Accident in Bhopal: Observations 20 Years Later," *Process Safety Progress* (Sept. 2007), 26(3): 180–184.

Seveso

Chemical and Engineering News (Aug. 23, 1976), p. 27.

Dennis C. Hendershot and John F. Murphy, "Expanding Role of the Loss Prevention Professional: Past, Present, and Future," *Process Safety Progress* (March 2007), 26(1): 18–26.

[17] "CSB Reports Chemical Dust Explosions Are a Serious Problem," *www.csb.gov/newsroom/detail.aspx?nid=272&SID=0&pg=1&F*.

Walter B. Howard, "Seveso: Cause; Prevention," *Plant/Operations Progress* (Apr. 1985), 4(2): 103–104.
J. Sambeth, "What Really Happened at Seveso," *Chemical Engineering* (May 16, 1983), pp. 44–47.

Flixborough

Robert M. Bethea, *Process Safety Management with Case Histories: Flixborough, Pasadena, and Other Incidents* (New York: American Institute of Chemical Engineers, 1994).
Dennis C. Hendershot and John F. Murphy, "Expanding Role of the Loss Prevention Professional: Past, Present, and Future," *Process Safety Progress* (Mar. 2007), 26(1): 18–26.
Trevor A. Kletz, "The Flixborough Explosion — Ten Years Later," *Plant/Operations Progress* (July 1984), 3(3): 133–135.
S. Mannan, ed. *Lees' Loss Prevention in the Process Industries*, 3rd ed., vol. 3, Appendix 2, Pages 1–18. (London: Butterworth-Heinemann, 2005).

General Case Histories

T. Kletz, *Learning from Accidents*, 3rd ed. (Boston: Butterworth-Heinemann, 2001).
T. Kletz, *What Went Wrong? Case Histories of Process Plant Disasters and How They Could Have Been Avoided*, 5th ed. (Boston: Butterworth-Heinemann, 2009).

Problems

1-1. An employee works in a plant with a FAR of 4. If this employee works a 4-hr shift, 200 days per year, what is the expected deaths per person per year?

1-2. Three process units are in a plant. The units have FARs of 0.5, 0.3, and 1.0, respectively.

- **a.** What is the overall FAR for the plant, assuming worker exposure to all three units simultaneously?
- **b.** Assume now that the units are far enough apart that an accident in one would not affect the workers in another. If a worker spends 20% of his time in process area 1, 40% in process area 2, and 40% in process area 3, what is his overall FAR?

1-3. A worker is told her chances of being killed by a particular process are 1 in every 500 years. Should the worker be satisfied or alarmed? What is the FAR (assuming normal working hours) and the deaths per person per year? What should her chances be, assuming an average chemical plant?

1-4. A plant employs 1500 full-time workers in a process with a FAR of 5. How many industrial-related deaths are expected each year?

1-5. Consider Example 1-4. How many hours must be traveled by car for each hour of rock climbing to make the risk of fatality by car equal to the risk of fatality by rock climbing?

1-6. Identify the initiation, propagation, and termination steps for the following accident reports.[18] Suggest ways to prevent and contain the accidents.

[18] *One Hundred Largest Losses.*

a. A contractor accidentally cut into a 10-in propane line operating at 800 psi at a natural gas liquids terminal. The large vapor cloud estimated to cover an area of 44 acres was ignited about 4–5 min later by an unknown source. Liquid products from 5 of 26 salt dome caverns fed the fire with an estimated 18,000–30,000 gal of LPGs for almost 6 hr before being blocked in and the fires extinguished. Both engine-driven fire pumps failed, one because intense radiated heat damaged its ignition wires and the other because the explosion broke a sight glass fuel gauge, spilling diesel fuel, which ignited, destroying the fire pump engine.

b. An alkylation unit was being started up after shutdown because of an electrical outage. When adequate circulation could not be maintained in a deisobutanizer heater circuit, it was decided to clean the strainer. Workers had depressurized the pipe and removed all but three of the flange bolts when a pressure release blew a black material from the flange, followed by butane vapors. These vapors were carried to a furnace 100 ft away, where they ignited, flashing back to the flange. The ensuing fire exposed a fractionation tower and horizontal receiver drums. These drums exploded, rupturing pipelines, which added more fuel. The explosions and heat caused loss of insulation from the 8-ft × 122-ft fractionator tower, causing it to weaken and fall across two major pipelines, breaking piping – which added more fuel to the fire. Extinguishment, achieved basically by isolating the fuel sources, took 2½ hours.

The fault was traced to a 10-in valve that had been prevented from closing the last ¾-inch by a fine powder of carbon and iron oxide. When the flange was opened, this powder blew out, allowing liquid butane to be released.

1-7. A university has 1200 full-time employees. In a particular year this university had 38 reportable lost-time injuries with a resulting 274 lost workdays. Compute the OSHA incidence rate based on injuries and lost workdays.

1-8. Water will flash into vapor almost explosively if heated under certain conditions.

a. What is the ratio in volume between water vapor at 300 K and liquid water at 300 K at saturated conditions?

b. Hot oil is accidentally pumped into a storage vessel. Unfortunately, the tank contains residual water, which flashes into vapor and ruptures the tank. If the tank is 10 m in diameter and 5 m high, how many kilograms of water at 300 K are required to produce enough water vapor to pressurize the tank to 8 in of water gauge pressure, the burst pressure of the tank?

1-9. The Weather Channel reports that, on average, about 42 Americans are killed by lightning each year. The current population of the U.S. is about 300 million people. Which accident index is suitable for this information: FAR, OSHA incident rate, or deaths per person per year? Why? Calculate the value of the selected index and compare it to published values.

1-10. The plant has been down for extensive maintenance and repair. You are in charge of bringing the plant up and on-line. There is considerable pressure from the sales department to deliver product. At about 4 AM a problem develops. A slip plate or blind has accidentally been left in one of the process lines. An experienced maintenance person suggests that she can remove the slip plate without depressurizing the line. She said that she routinely performed this operation years ago. Since you are in charge, what would you do?

1-11. The CSB video "Preventing Harm from Sodium Hydrosulfide" presents an incident involving sodium hydrosulfide (NaSH) and hydrogen sulfide (H_2S). Go on-line and find at least two material safety data sheets (MSDS) for both of these chemicals. Tabulate the following physical properties for these chemicals at room temperature and pressure, if available: physical state density, PEL, TLV, and vapor pressure. List any other concerns that might be apparent from the MSDS. Which of these properties are of major concern in using these chemicals?

1-12. One of the categories of inherent safety is simplification/error tolerance. What instrumentation could you add to the tank described in Problem 1-25 to eliminate problems?

1-13. Gasoline tank trucks are load restricted in that the tank must never be between 20% and 80% full when traveling. Or it must be below 20% and above 80%. Why?

1-14. Pumps can be shut-in by closing the valves on the inlet and outlet sides of the pump. This can lead to pump damage and/or a rapid increase in the temperature of the liquid shut inside the pump. A particular pump contains 4 kg of water. If the pump is rated at 1 HP, what is the maximum temperature increase expected in the water in °C/hr? Assume a constant water heat capacity of 1 kcal/kg/°C. What will happen if the pump continues to operate?

1-15. In 1891 the copper industry in Michigan employed 7702 workers. In that year there were 28 fatalities in the mines. Estimate the FAR for this year, assuming that the workers worked 40-hour weeks and 50 weeks per year. Compare the result to the published FAR for the chemical industry.

1-16. Another way of measuring accident performance is by the LTIR, or lost-time injury rate. This is identical to the OSHA incidence rate based on incidents in which the employee is unable to continue their normal duties. A plant site has 1200 full-time employees working 40 hr/week and 50 weeks/yr. If the plant had 2 lost-time incidents last year, what is the LTIR?

1-17. Based on workplace fatalities (Figure 1-4) and assuming you are responsible for a safety program of an organization, what would you emphasize?

1-18. Based on the causes of the largest losses (Figure 1-7), what would you emphasize in a safety program?

1-19. After reviewing the answers to Problems 1-17 and 1-18, can inherent safety help?

1-20. A column was used to strip low-volatile materials from a high-temperature heat transfer fluid. During a maintenance procedure, water was trapped between two valves. During normal operation, one valve was opened and the hot oil came in contact with the cold water. The result was almost sudden vaporization of the water, followed by considerable damage to the column. Consider liquid water at 25°C and 1 atm. How many times does the volume increase if the water is vaporized at 100°C and 1 atm?

1-21. What is the worst thing that could happen to you as a chemical engineer in industry?

1-22. A cover plate on a pump housing is held in place by eight bolts. A pipefitter is instructed to repair the pump. The fitter removes all eight bolts only to find the cover plate stuck on the housing. A screwdriver is used to pry off the cover. The cover flies off suddenly, and toxic liquid sprays throughout the work area. Clearly the pump unit should have been isolated, drained, and cleaned before repair. There is, however, a better procedure for removing the cover plate. What is this procedure?

1-23. An explosion has occurred in your plant and an employee has been killed. An investigation shows that the accident was the fault of the dead employee, who manually charged the wrong ingredient to a reactor vessel. What is the appropriate response from the following groups?

a. The other employees who work in the process area affected.
b. The other employees elsewhere in the plant site.
c. Middle management.
d. Upper management.
e. The president of the company.
f. The union.

1-24. A large storage tank is filled manually by an operator. The operator first opens a valve on a supply line and carefully watches the level on a level indicator until the tank is filled (a long time later). Once the filling is complete, the operator closes the valve to stop the filling. Once a year the operator is distracted and the tank is overfilled. To prevent this, an alarm was installed on the level gauge to alert the operator to a high-level condition. With the installation of the alarm, the tank now overfills twice per year. Can you explain?

1-25. The liquid level in a tank 10 m in height is determined by measuring the pressure at the bottom of the tank. The level gauge was calibrated to work with a liquid having a specific gravity of 0.9. If the usual liquid is replaced with a new liquid with a specific gravity of 0.8, will the tank be overfilled or underfilled? If the actual liquid level is 8 m, what is the reading on the level gauge? Is it possible that the tank will overflow without the level gauge indicating the situation?

CHAPTER 2

Toxicology

Because of the quantity and variety of chemicals used by the chemical process industries, chemical engineers must be knowledgeable about

- The way toxicants enter biological organisms
- The way toxicants are eliminated from biological organisms
- The effects of toxicants on biological organisms, and
- Methods to prevent or reduce the entry of toxicants into biological organisms

The first three areas are related to toxicology. The last area is essentially *industrial hygiene,* a topic considered in Chapter 3.

Many years ago, toxicology was defined as the science of poisons. Unfortunately, the word *poison* could not be defined adequately. Paracelsus, an early investigator of toxicology during the 1500s, stated the problem: "All substances are poisons; there is none which is not a poison. The right dose differentiates a poison and a remedy." Harmless substances, such as water, can become fatal if delivered to the biological organism in large enough doses. A fundamental principle of toxicology is

There are no harmless substances, only harmless ways of using substances.

Today, toxicology is more adequately defined as the qualitative and quantitative study of the adverse effects of toxicants on biological organisms. A toxicant can be a chemical or physical agent, including dusts, fibers, noise, and radiation. A good example of a physical agent is asbestos fiber, a known cause of lung damage and cancer.

The *toxicity* of a chemical or physical agent is a property of the agent describing its effect on biological organisms. *Toxic hazard* is the likelihood of damage to biological organisms based on exposure resulting from transport and other physical factors of usage. The toxic hazard of a substance can be reduced by the application of appropriate industrial hygiene techniques. The toxicity, however, cannot be changed.

2-1 How Toxicants Enter Biological Organisms

For higher-order organisms the path of the chemical agent through the body is well defined. After the toxicant enters the organism, it moves into the bloodstream and is eventually eliminated or it is transported to the target organ. The damage is exerted at the target organ. A common misconception is that damage occurs in the organ where the toxicant is most concentrated. Lead, for instance, is stored in humans mostly in the bone structure, but the damage occurs in many organs. For corrosive chemicals the damage to the organism can occur without absorption or transport through the bloodstream.

Toxicants enter biological organisms by the following routes:

- Ingestion: through the mouth into the stomach
- Inhalation: through the mouth or nose into the lungs
- Injection: through cuts into the skin
- Dermal absorption: through skin membrane

All these entry routes are controlled by the application of proper industrial hygiene techniques, summarized in Table 2-1. These control techniques are discussed in more detail in Chapter 3 on industrial hygiene. Of the four routes of entry, the inhalation and dermal routes are the most significant to industrial facilities. Inhalation is the easiest to quantify by the direct measurement of airborne concentrations; the usual exposure is by vapor, but small solid and liquid particles can also contribute.

Injection, inhalation, and dermal absorption generally result in the toxicant entering the bloodstream unaltered. Toxicants entering through ingestion are frequently modified or excreted in bile.

Toxicants that enter by injection and dermal absorption are difficult to measure and quantify. Some toxicants are absorbed rapidly through the skin.

Figure 2-1 shows the expected blood-level concentration as a function of time and route of entry. The blood-level concentration is a function of a wide range of parameters, so large variations in this behavior are expected. Injection usually results in the highest blood-level

Table 2-1 Entry Routes for Toxicants and Methods for Control

Entry route	Entry organ	Method for control
Ingestion	Mouth or stomach	Enforcement of rules on eating, drinking, and smoking
Inhalation	Mouth or nose	Ventilation, respirators, hoods, and other personal protection equipment
Injection	Cuts in skin	Proper protective clothing
Dermal absorption	Skin	Proper protective clothing

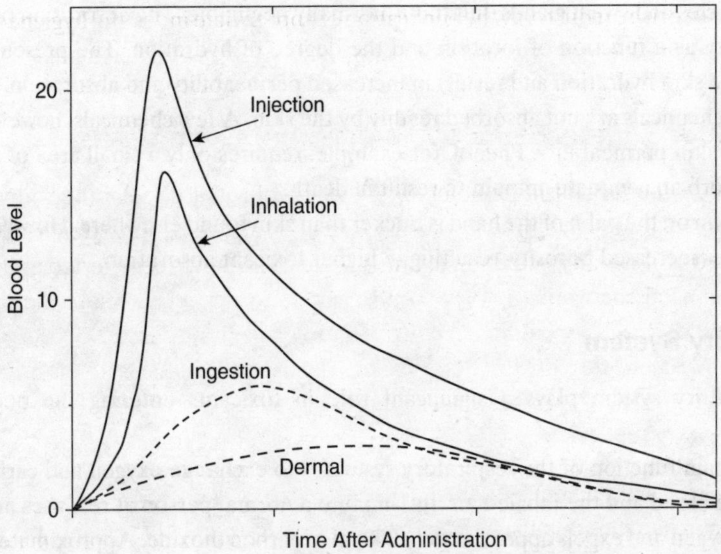

Figure 2-1 Toxic blood-level concentration as a function of route of exposure. Wide variations are expected as a result of rate and extent of absorption, distribution, biotransformation, and excretion.

concentration, followed by inhalation, ingestion, and absorption. The peak concentration generally occurs earliest with injection, followed by inhalation, ingestion, and absorption.

The gastrointestinal (GI) tract, the skin, and the respiratory system play significant roles in the various routes of entry.

Gastrointestinal Tract

The GI tract plays the most significant role in toxicants entering the body through ingestion. Food or drink is the usual mechanism of exposure. Airborne particles (either solid or liquid) can also lodge in the mucus of the upper respiratory tract and be swallowed.

The rate and selectivity of absorption by the GI tract are highly dependent on many conditions. The type of chemical, its molecular weight, molecule size and shape, acidity, susceptibility to attack by intestinal flora, rate of movement through the GI tract, and many other factors affect the rate of absorption.

Skin

The skin plays important roles in both the dermal absorption and injection routes of entry. Injection includes both entry by absorption through cuts and mechanical injection with hypodermic needles. Mechanical injection can occur as a result of improper hypodermic needle storage in a laboratory drawer.

The skin is composed of an outer layer called the stratum corneum. This layer consists of dead, dried cells that are resistant to permeation by toxicants. Absorption also occurs through the hair follicles and sweat glands, but this is normally negligible. The absorption properties of the skin vary as a function of location and the degree of hydration. The presence of water increases the skin hydration and results in increased permeability and absorption.

Most chemicals are not absorbed readily by the skin. A few chemicals, however, do show remarkable skin permeability. Phenol, for example, requires only a small area of skin for the body to absorb an adequate amount to result in death.

The skin on the palm of the hand is thicker than skin found elsewhere. However, this skin demonstrates increased porosity, resulting in higher toxicant absorption.

Respiratory System

The respiratory system plays a significant role in toxicants entering the body through inhalation.

The main function of the respiratory system is to exchange oxygen and carbon dioxide between the blood and the inhaled air. In 1 minute a normal person at rest uses an estimated 250 ml of oxygen and expels approximately 200 ml of carbon dioxide. Approximately 8 L of air are breathed per minute. Only a fraction of the total air within the lung is exchanged with each breath. These demands increase significantly with physical exertion.

The respiratory system is divided into two areas: the upper and the lower respiratory system. The upper respiratory system is composed of the nose, sinuses, mouth, pharynx (section between the mouth and esophagus), larynx (the voice box), and the trachea or windpipe. The lower respiratory system is composed of the lungs and its smaller structures, including the bronchi and the alveoli. The bronchial tubes carry fresh air from the trachea through a series of branching tubes to the alveoli. The alveoli are small blind air sacs where the gas exchange with the blood occurs. An estimated 300 million alveoli are found in a normal lung. These alveoli contribute a total surface area of approximately 70 m^2. Small capillaries found in the walls of the alveoli transport the blood; an estimated 100 ml of blood is in the capillaries at any moment.

The upper respiratory tract is responsible for filtering, heating, and humidifying the air. Fresh air brought in through the nose is completely saturated with water and regulated to the proper temperature by the time it reaches the larynx. The mucus lining the upper respiratory tract assists in filtering.

The upper and lower respiratory tracts respond differently to the presence of toxicants. The upper respiratory tract is affected mostly by toxicants that are water soluble. These materials either react or dissolve in the mucus to form acids and bases. Toxicants in the lower respiratory tract affect the alveoli by physically blocking the transfer of gases (as with insoluble dusts) or reacting with the wall of the alveoli to produce corrosive or toxic substances. Phosgene gas, for example, reacts with the water on the alveoli wall to produce HCl and carbon monoxide.

Upper respiratory toxicants include hydrogen halides (hydrogen chloride, hydrogen bromide), oxides (nitrogen oxides, sulfur oxides, sodium oxide), and hydroxides (ammonium hydroxide, sodium dusts, and potassium hydroxides). Lower respiratory toxicants include monomers (such as acrylonitrile), halides (fluorine, chlorine, bromine), and other miscellaneous substances such as hydrogen sulfide, phosgene, methyl cyanide, acrolein, asbestos dust, silica, and soot.

Dusts and other insoluble materials present a particular difficulty to the lungs. Particles that enter the alveoli are removed slowly. For dusts the following simple rule usually applies: The smaller the dust particles, the farther they penetrate into the respiratory system. Particles greater than 5 μm in diameter are usually filtered by the upper respiratory system. Particles with diameters between 2 and 5 μm generally reach the bronchial system. Particles less than 1 μm in diameter can reach the alveoli.

2-2 How Toxicants Are Eliminated from Biological Organisms

Toxicants are eliminated or rendered inactive by the following routes

- Excretion: through the kidneys, liver, lungs, or other organs
- Detoxification: by changing the chemical into something less harmful by biotransformation
- Storage: in the fatty tissue

The kidneys are the dominant means of excretion in the human body. They eliminate substances that enter the body by ingestion, inhalation, injection, and dermal absorption. The toxicants are extracted by the kidneys from the bloodstream and are excreted in the urine.

Toxicants that are ingested into the digestive tract are frequently excreted by the liver. In general, chemical compounds with molecular weights greater than about 300 are excreted by the liver into bile. Compounds with lower molecular weights enter the bloodstream and are excreted by the kidneys. The digestive tract tends to selectively detoxify certain agents, whereas substances that enter through inhalation, injection, or dermal absorption generally arrive in the bloodstream unchanged.

The lungs are also a means for elimination of substances, particularly those that are volatile. Chloroform and alcohol, for example, are excreted partially by this route.

Other routes of excretion are the skin (by means of sweat), hair, and nails. These routes are usually minor compared to the excretion processes of the kidneys, liver, and lungs.

The liver is the dominant organ in the detoxification process. The detoxification occurs by biotransformation, in which the chemical agents are transformed by reaction into either harmless or less harmful substances. Biotransformation reactions can also occur in the blood, intestinal tract wall, skin, kidneys, and other organs.

The final mechanism for elimination is storage. This process involves depositing the chemical agent mostly in the fatty areas of the organism but also in the bones, blood, liver, and kidney. Storage can create a future problem if the organism's food supply is reduced and the fatty deposits are metabolized; the stored chemical agents will be released into the bloodstream, resulting in possible damage.

For massive exposures to chemical agents, damage can occur to the kidneys, liver, or lungs, significantly reducing the organism's ability to excrete the substance.

Table 2-2 Various Responses to Toxicants

Effects that are irreversible
Carcinogen causes cancer
Mutagen causes chromosome damage
Reproductive hazard causes damage to reproductive system
Teratogen causes birth defects
Effects that may or may not be reversible
Dermatotoxic affects skin
Hemotoxic affects blood
Hepatotoxic affects liver
Nephrotoxic affects kidneys
Neurotoxic affects nervous system
Pulmonotoxic affects lungs

2-3 Effects of Toxicants on Biological Organisms

Table 2-2 lists some of the effects or responses from toxic exposure.

The problem is to determine whether exposures have occurred before substantial symptoms are present. This is accomplished through a variety of medical tests. The results from these tests must be compared to a medical baseline study, performed before any exposure. Many chemical companies perform baseline studies on new employees before employment.

Respiratory problems are diagnosed using a spirometer. The patient exhales as hard and as fast as possible into the device. The spirometer measures (1) the total volume exhaled, called the forced vital capacity (FVC), with units in liters; (2) the forced expired volume measured at 1 second (FEV_1), with units in liters per second; (3) forced expiratory flow in the middle range of the vital capacity (FEV 25–75%), measured in liters per second; and (4) the ratio of the observed FEV_1 to FVC × 100 (FEV_1/FVC%).

Reductions in expiration flow rate are indicative of bronchial disease, such as asthma or bronchitis. Reductions in FVC are due to reduction in the lung or chest volume, possibly as a result of fibrosis (an increase in the interstitial fibrous tissue in the lung). The air remaining in the lung after exhalation is called the residual volume (RV). An increase in the RV is indicative of deterioration of the alveoli, possibly because of emphysema. The RV measurement requires a specialized tracer test with helium.

Nervous system disorders are diagnosed by examining the patient's mental status, cranial nerve function, motor system reflexes, and sensory systems. An electroencephalogram (EEG) tests higher brain and nervous system functions.

Changes in skin texture, pigmentation, vascularity, and hair and nail appearance are indicative of possible toxic exposures.

Blood counts are also used to determine toxic exposures. Measurements of the red and white blood cells, hemoglobin content, and platelet count are performed easily and inexpensively. However, blood counts are frequently insensitive to toxic exposure; marked changes are seen only after substantial exposure and damage.

Kidney function is determined through a variety of tests that measure the chemical content and quantity of urine. For early kidney damage proteins or sugars are found in the urine.

Liver function is determined through a variety of chemical tests on the blood and urine.

2-4 Toxicological Studies

A major objective of a toxicological study is to quantify the effects of the suspect toxicant on a target organism. For most toxicological studies animals are used, usually with the hope that the results can be extrapolated to humans. Once the effects of a suspect agent have been quantified, appropriate procedures are established to ensure that the agent is handled properly.

Before undertaking a toxicological study, the following items must be identified:

- The toxicant
- The target or test organism
- The effect or response to be monitored
- The dose range
- The period of the test

The toxicant must be identified with respect to its chemical composition and its physical state. For example, benzene can exist in either liquid or vapor form. Each physical state preferentially enters the body by a different route and requires a different toxicological study.

The test organism can range from a simple single cell up through the higher animals. The selection depends on the effects considered and other factors such as the cost and availability of the test organism. For studies of genetic effects, single-cell organisms might be satisfactory. For studies determining the effects on specific organs such as the lungs, kidneys, or liver, higher organisms are a necessity.

The dose units depend on the method of delivery. For substances delivered directly into the organism (by ingestion or injection), the dose is measured in milligrams of agent per kilogram of body weight. This enables researchers to apply the results obtained from small animals such as mice (fractions of a kilogram in body weight) to humans (about 70 kg for males and 60 kg for females). For gaseous airborne substances the dose is measured in either parts per million (ppm) or milligrams of agent per cubic meter of air (mg/m^3). For airborne particulates the dose is measured in milligrams of agent per cubic meter of air (mg/m^3) or millions of particles per cubic foot (mppcf).

The period of the test depends on whether long- or short-term effects are of interest. Acute toxicity is the effect of a single exposure or a series of exposures close together in a short period of time. Chronic toxicity is the effect of multiple exposures occurring over a long period of time. Chronic toxicity studies are difficult to perform because of the time involved; most toxicological studies are based on acute exposures. The toxicological study can be complicated by latency, an exposure that results in a delayed response.

2-5 Dose versus Response

Biological organisms respond differently to the same dose of a toxicant. These differences are a result of age, sex, weight, diet, general health, and other factors. For example, consider the effects of an irritant vapor on human eyes. Given the same dose of vapors, some individuals will barely notice any irritation (weak or low response), whereas other individuals will be severely irritated (high response).

Consider a toxicological test run on a large number of individuals. Each individual is exposed to the same dose and the response is recorded. A plot of the type shown in Figure 2-2 is prepared with the data. The fraction or percentage of individuals experiencing a specific response is plotted. Curves of the form shown in Figure 2-2 are frequently represented by a normal or Gaussian distribution, given by the equation

$$f(x) = \frac{1}{\sigma\sqrt{2\pi}} e^{-\frac{1}{2}\left(\frac{x-\mu}{\sigma}\right)^2}, \tag{2-1}$$

where

$f(x)$ is the probability (or fraction) of individuals experiencing a specific response,
x is the response,
σ is the standard deviation, and
μ is the mean.

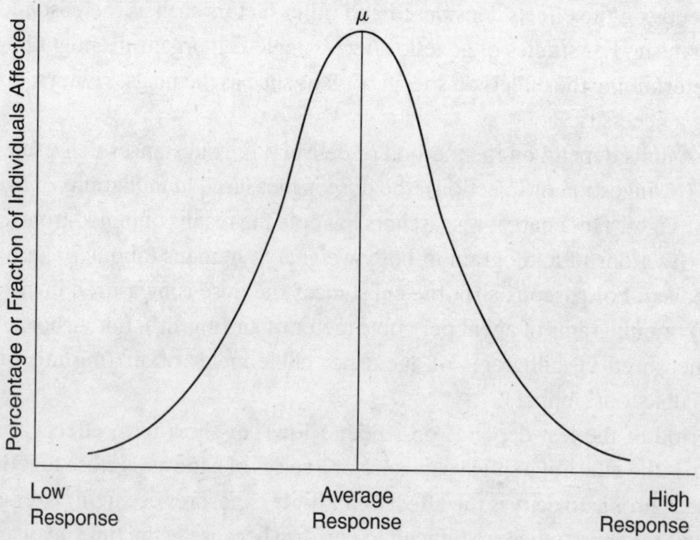

Figure 2-2 A Gaussian or normal distribution representing the biological response to exposure to a toxicant.

The standard deviation and mean characterize the shape and the location of the normal distribution curve, respectively. They are computed from the original data $f(x_i)$ using the equations

$$\mu = \frac{\sum_{i=1}^{n} x_i f(x_i)}{\sum_{i=1}^{n} f(x_i)}, \tag{2-2}$$

$$\sigma^2 = \frac{\sum_{i=1}^{n} (x_i - \mu)^2 f(x_i)}{\sum_{i=1}^{n} f(x_i)}, \tag{2-3}$$

where n is the number of data points. The quantity σ^2 is called the variance.

The mean determines the location of the curve with respect to the x axis, and the standard deviation determines the shape. Figure 2-3 shows the effect of the standard deviation on the shape. As the standard deviation decreases, the distribution curve becomes more pronounced around the mean value.

The area under the curve of Figure 2-2 represents the percentage of individuals affected for a specified response interval. In particular, the response interval within 1 standard deviation of the mean represents 68% of the individuals, as shown in Figure 2-4a. A response interval of 2 standard deviations represents 95.5% of the total individuals (Figure 2-4b). The area under the entire curve represents 100% of the individuals.

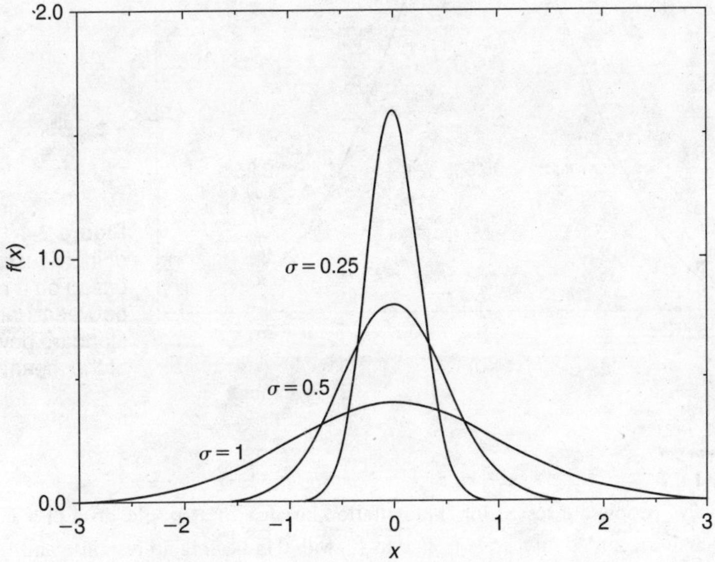

Figure 2-3 Effect of the standard deviation on a normal distribution with a mean of 0. The distribution becomes more pronounced around the mean as the standard deviation decreases.

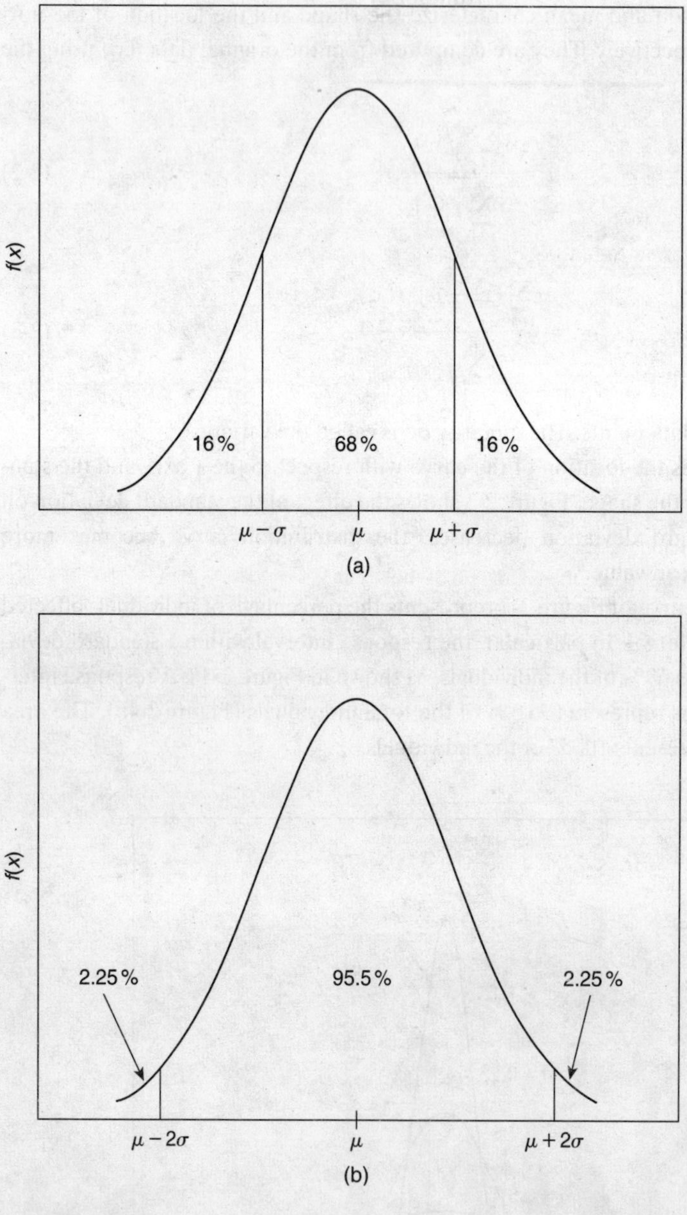

Figure 2-4 Percentage of individuals affected based on a response between 1 and 2 standard deviations of the mean.

Example 2-1

Seventy-five people are tested for skin irritation because of a specific dose of a substance. The responses are recorded on a scale from 0 to 10, with 0 indicating no response and 10 indicating a high response. The number of individuals exhibiting a specific response is given in the following table:

Response	Number of individuals affected
0	0
1	5
2	10
3	13
4	13
5	11
6	9
7	6
8	3
9	3
10	2
	75

a. Plot a histogram of the number of individuals affected versus the response.

b. Determine the mean and the standard deviation.

c. Plot the normal distribution on the histogram of the original data.

Solution

a. The histogram is shown in Figure 2-5. The number of individuals affected is plotted versus the response. An alternative method is to plot the percentage of individuals versus the response.

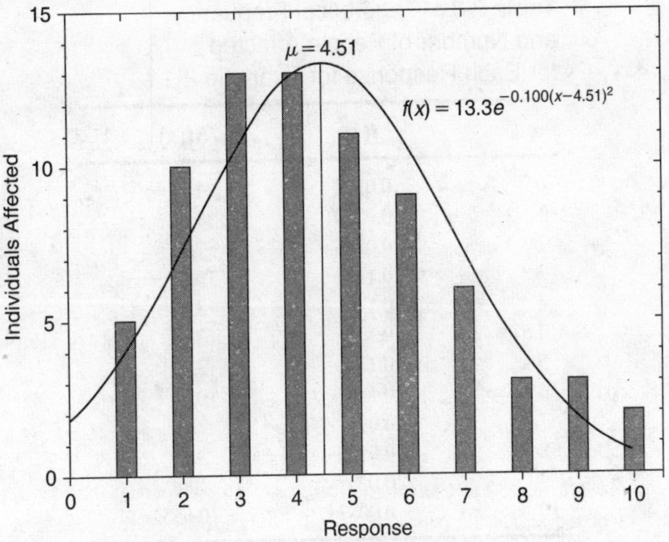

Figure 2-5 Percentage of individuals affected based on response.

b. The mean is computed using Equation 2-2:

$$\mu = \frac{(0\times0)+(1\times5)+(2\times10)+(3\times13)+(4\times13)+(5\times11)+(6\times9)+(7\times6)+(8\times3)+(9\times3)+(10\times2)}{75}$$

$$= \frac{338}{75} = 4.51.$$

The standard deviation is computed using Equation 2-3:

$$\sigma^2 = [(1 - 4.51)^2(5) + (2 - 4.51)^2(10) + (3 - 4.51)^2(13)$$
$$+ (4 - 4.51)^2(13) + (5 - 4.51)^2(11) + (6 - 4.51)^2(9)$$
$$+ (7 - 4.51)^2(6) + (8 - 4.51)^2(3) + (9 - 4.51)^2(3)$$
$$+ (10 - 4.51)^2(2)]/75 = 374.7/75 = 5.00,$$

$$\sigma = \sqrt{\sigma^2} = \sqrt{5.00} = 2.24.$$

c. The normal distribution is computed using Equation 2-1. Substituting the mean and standard deviations, we find

$$f(x) = \frac{1}{(2.24)\sqrt{6.28}} e^{-\frac{1}{2}\left(\frac{x-4.51}{2.24}\right)^2}$$

$$= 0.178e^{-0.100(x-4.51)^2}.$$

The distribution is converted to a function representing the number of individuals affected by multiplying by the total number of individuals, in this case 75. The corresponding values are shown in Table 2-3 and Figure 2-5.

Table 2-3 Theoretical Frequency and Number of People Affected for Each Response for Example 2-1

x	*f*(*x*)	75*f*(*x*)
0	0.0232	1.74
1	0.0519	3.89
2	0.0948	7.11
3	0.1417	10.6
4	0.173	13.0
4.51	0.178	13.3
5	0.174	13.0
6	0.143	10.7
7	0.096	7.18
8	0.0527	3.95
9	0.0237	1.78
10	0.00874	0.655

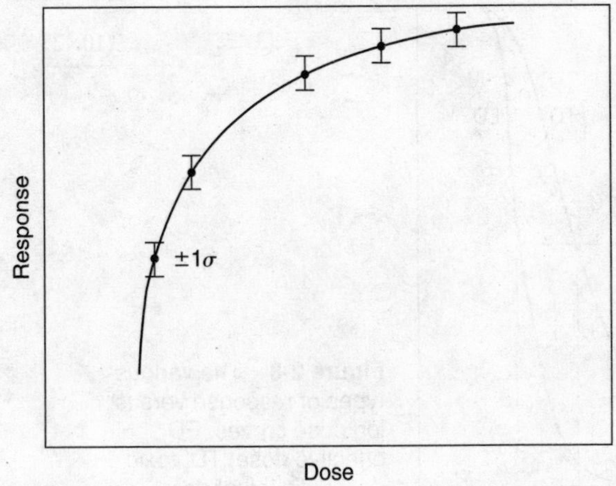

Figure 2-6 Dose-response curve. The bars around the data points represent the standard deviation in response to a specific dose.

The toxicological experiment is repeated for a number of different doses, and normal curves similar to Figure 2-3 are drawn. The standard deviation and mean response are determined from the data for each dose.

A complete dose-response curve is produced by plotting the cumulative mean response at each dose. Error bars are drawn at $\pm\sigma$ around the mean. A typical result is shown in Figure 2-6.

For convenience, the response is plotted versus the logarithm of the dose, as shown in Figure 2-7. This form provides a much straighter line in the middle of the response curve than the simple response versus dose form of Figure 2-6.

If the response of interest is death or lethality, the response versus log dose curve of Figure 2-7 is called a lethal dose curve. For comparison purposes the dose that results in 50%

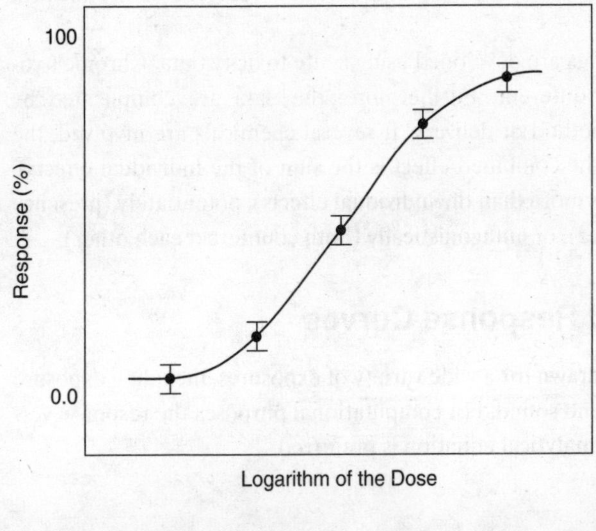

Figure 2-7 Response versus log dose curve. This form presents a much straighter function than the one shown in Figure 2-6.

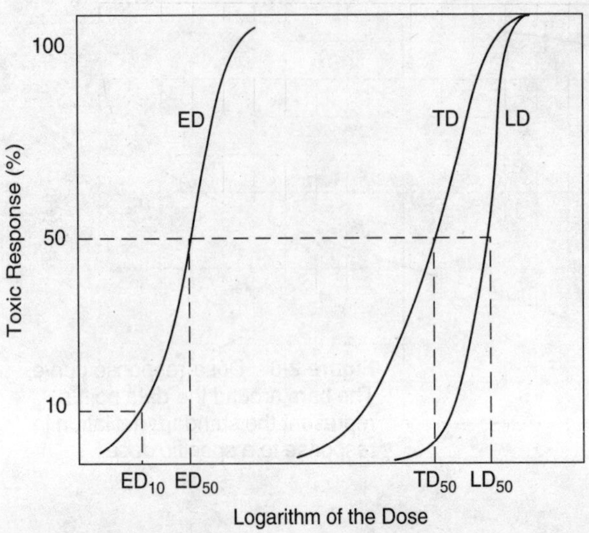

Figure 2-8 The various types of response versus log dose curves. ED, effective dose; TD, toxic dose; LD, lethal dose. For gases, LC (lethal concentration) is used.

lethality of the subjects is frequently reported. This is called the LD_{50} dose (lethal dose for 50% of the subjects). Other values such as LD_{10} or LD_{90} are sometimes also reported. For gases, LC (lethal concentration) data are used.

If the response to the chemical or agent is minor and reversible (such as minor eye irritation), the response–log dose curve is called the effective dose (ED) curve. Values for ED_{50}, ED_{10}, and so forth are also used.

Finally, if the response to the agent is toxic (an undesirable response that is not lethal but is irreversible, such as liver or lung damage), the response–log dose curve is called the toxic dose, or TD curve.

The relationship between the various types of response–log dose curves is shown in Figure 2-8.

Most often, response-dose curves are developed using acute toxicity data. Chronic toxicity data are usually considerably different. Furthermore, the data are complicated by differences in group age, sex, and method of delivery. If several chemicals are involved, the toxicants might interact additively (the combined effect is the sum of the individual effects), synergistically (the combined effect is more than the individual effects), potentiately (presence of one increases the effect of the other), or antagonistically (both counteract each other).

2-6 Models for Dose and Response Curves

Response versus dose curves can be drawn for a wide variety of exposures, including exposure to heat, pressure, radiation, impact, and sound. For computational purposes the response versus dose curve is not convenient; an analytical equation is preferred.

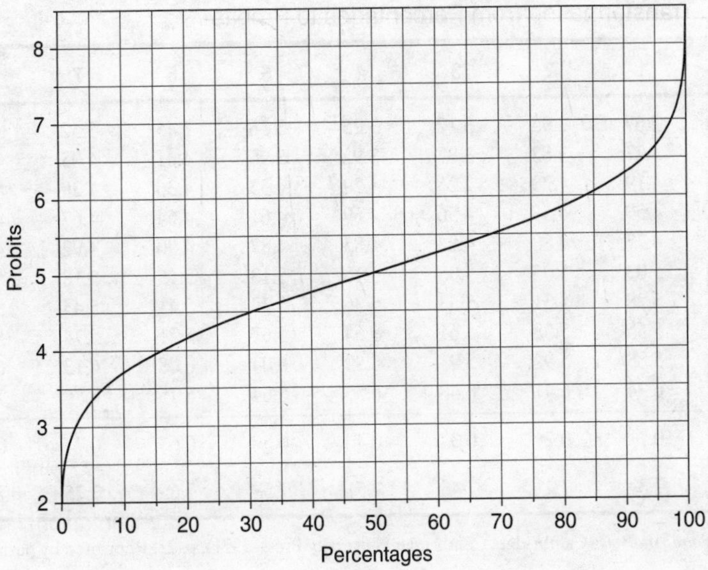

Figure 2-9 The relationship between percentages and probits. Source: D. J. Finney, *Probit Analysis,* 3rd ed. (Cambridge: Cambridge University Press, 1971), p. 23. Reprinted by permission.

Many methods exist for representing the response-dose curve.[1] For single exposures the probit (probit = probability unit) method is particularly suited, providing a straight-line equivalent to the response-dose curve. The probit variable Y is related to the probability P by[2]

$$P = \frac{1}{(2\pi)^{1/2}} \int_{-\infty}^{Y-5} \exp\left(-\frac{u^2}{2}\right) du. \tag{2-4}$$

Equation 2-4 provides a relationship between the probability P and the probit variable Y. This relationship is plotted in Figure 2-9 and tabulated in Table 2-4.

The probit relationship of Equation 2-4 transforms the sigmoid shape of the normal response versus dose curve into a straight line when plotted using a linear probit scale, as shown in Figure 2-10. Standard curve-fitting techniques are used to determine the best-fitting straight line.

Table 2-5 lists a variety of probit equations for a number of different types of exposures. The causative factor represents the dose V. The probit variable Y is computed from

$$Y = k_1 + k_2 \ln V. \tag{2-5}$$

[1]Phillip L. Williams, Robert C. James, and Stephen M. Roberts, eds., *The Principles of Toxicology: Environmental and Industrial Applications*, 2nd ed. (New York: John Wiley & Sons, 2000).

[2]D. J. Finney, *Probit Analysis* (Cambridge: Cambridge University Press, 1971), p. 23.

Table 2-4 Transformation from Percentages to Probits[a]

%	0	1	2	3	4	5	6	7	8	9
0	—	2.67	2.95	3.12	3.25	3.36	3.45	3.52	3.59	3.66
10	3.72	3.77	3.82	3.87	3.92	3.96	4.01	4.05	4.08	4.12
20	4.16	4.19	4.23	4.26	4.29	4.33	4.36	4.39	4.42	4.45
30	4.48	4.50	4.53	4.56	4.59	4.61	4.64	4.67	4.69	4.72
40	4.75	4.77	4.80	4.82	4.85	4.87	4.90	4.92	4.95	4.97
50	5.00	5.03	5.05	5.08	5.10	5.13	5.15	5.18	5.20	5.23
60	5.25	5.28	5.31	5.33	5.36	5.39	5.41	5.44	5.47	5.50
70	5.52	5.55	5.58	5.61	5.64	5.67	5.71	5.74	5.77	5.81
80	5.84	5.88	5.92	5.95	5.99	6.04	6.08	6.13	6.18	6.23
90	6.28	6.34	6.41	6.48	6.55	6.64	6.75	6.88	7.05	7.33
%	0.0	0.1	0.2	0.3	0.4	0.5	0.6	0.7	0.8	0.9
99	7.33	7.37	7.41	7.46	7.51	7.58	7.65	7.75	7.88	8.09

[a]D. J. Finney, *Probit Analysis* (Cambridge: Cambridge University Press, 1971), p. 25. Reprinted by permission.

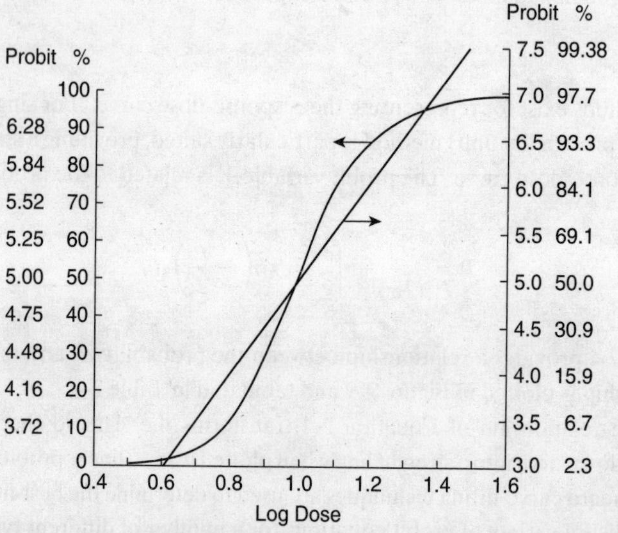

Figure 2-10 The probit transformation converts the sigmoidal response versus log dose curve into a straight line when plotted on a linear probit scale. Source: D. J. Finney, *Probit Analysis,* 3rd ed. (Cambridge: Cambridge University Press, 1971), p. 24. Reprinted by permission.

Table 2-5 Probit Correlations for a Variety of Exposures (The causative variable is representative of the magnitude of the exposure.)

Type of injury or damage	Causative variable	Probit parameters k_1	k_2
Fire[a]			
Burn deaths from flash fire	$t_e I_e^{4/3}/10^4$	−14.9	2.56
Burn deaths from pool burning	$tI^{4/3}/10^4$	−14.9	2.56
Explosion[a]			
Deaths from lung hemorrhage	p^o	−77.1	6.91
Eardrum ruptures	p^o	−15.6	1.93
Deaths from impact	J	−46.1	4.82
Injuries from impact	J	−39.1	4.45
Injuries from flying fragments	J	−27.1	4.26
Structural damage	p^o	−23.8	2.92
Glass breakage	p^o	−18.1	2.79
Toxic release[b]			
Ammonia deaths	$\Sigma C^{2.0}T$	−35.9	1.85
Carbon monoxide deaths	$\Sigma C^{1.0}T$	−37.98	3.7
Chlorine deaths	$\Sigma C^{2.0}T$	−8.29	0.92
Ethylene oxide deaths[c]	$\Sigma C^{1.0}T$	−6.19	1.0
Hydrogen chloride deaths	$\Sigma C^{1.0}T$	−16.85	2.0
Nitrogen dioxide deaths	$\Sigma C^{2.0}T$	−13.79	1.4
Phosgene deaths	$\Sigma C^{1.0}T$	−19.27	3.69
Propylene oxide deaths	$\Sigma C^{2.0}T$	−7.42	0.51
Sulfur dioxide deaths	$\Sigma C^{1.0}T$	−15.67	1.0
Toluene	$\Sigma C^{2.5}T$	−6.79	0.41

t_e = effective time duration (s)
I_e = effective radiation intensity (W/m^2)
t = time duration of pool burning (s)
I = radiation intensity from pool burning (W/m^2)
p^o = peak overpressure (N/m^2)
J = impulse (N s/m^2)
C = concentration (ppm)
T = time interval (min)

[a]Selected from Frank P. Lees, *Loss Prevention in the Process Industries* (London: Butterworths, 1986), p. 208.

[b]Center for Chemical Process Safety (CCPS), *Guidelines for Consequence Analysis of Chemical Releases* (New York: American Institute of Chemical Engineers, 2000), p. 254.

[c]Richard W. Prugh, "Quantitative Evaluation of Inhalation Toxicity Hazards," in *Proceedings of the 29th Loss Prevention Symposium* (American Institute of Chemical Engineers, July 31, 1995).

For spreadsheet computations a more useful expression for performing the conversion from probits to percentage is given by

$$P = 50\left[1 + \frac{Y - 5}{|Y - 5|}\,\text{erf}\left(\frac{|Y - 5|}{\sqrt{2}}\right)\right], \tag{2-6}$$

where erf is the error function.

Example 2-2

Determine the percentage of people who will die as a result of burns from pool burning if the probit variable Y is 4.39. Compare results from Table 2-4 and Equation 2-6.

Solution

The percentage from Table 2-4 is 27%. The same percentage can be computed using Equation 2-6, as follows:

$$P = 50\left[1 + \frac{4.39 - 5}{|4.39 - 5|}\,\text{erf}\left(\frac{|4.39 - 5|}{\sqrt{2}}\right)\right]$$

$$= 50\left[1 - \text{erf}\left(\frac{0.61}{\sqrt{2}}\right)\right] = 50[1 - \text{erf}(0.4314)]$$

$$= 50[1 - 0.458] = 27.1\%,$$

where the error function is a mathematical function found in spreadsheets, Mathcad, and other software programs.

Example 2-3

Eisenberg[3] reported the following data on the effect of explosion peak overpressures on eardrum rupture in humans:

Percentage affected	Peak overpressure (N/m^2)
01	16,500
10	19,300
50	43,500
90	84,300

Confirm the probit correlation for this type of exposure, as shown in Table 2-5.

Solution

The percentage is converted to a probit variable using Table 2-4. The results are:

Percentage	Probit
01	2.67
10	3.72
50	5.00
90	6.28

[3] N. A. Eisenberg, *Vulnerability Model: A Simulation System for Assessing Damage Resulting from Marine Spills,* NTIS Report AD-A015-245 (Springfield, VA: National Technical Information Service, 1975).

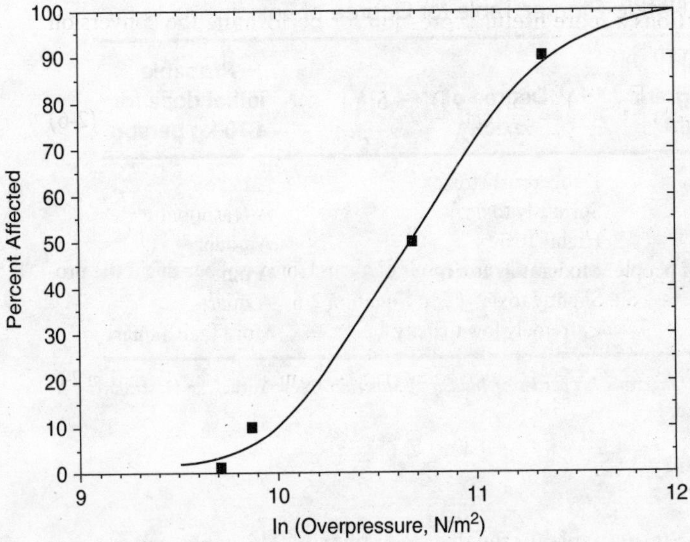

Figure 2-11 Percentage affected versus the natural logarithm of the peak overpressure for Example 2-3.

Figure 2-11 is a plot of the percentage affected versus the natural logarithm of the peak overpressure. This demonstrates the classical sigmoid shape of the response versus log dose curve. Figure 2-12 is a plot of the probit variable (with a linear probit scale) versus the natural logarithm of the peak overpressure. The straight line verifies the values reported in Table 2-5. The sigmoid curve of Figure 2-11 is drawn after converting the probit correlation back to percentages.

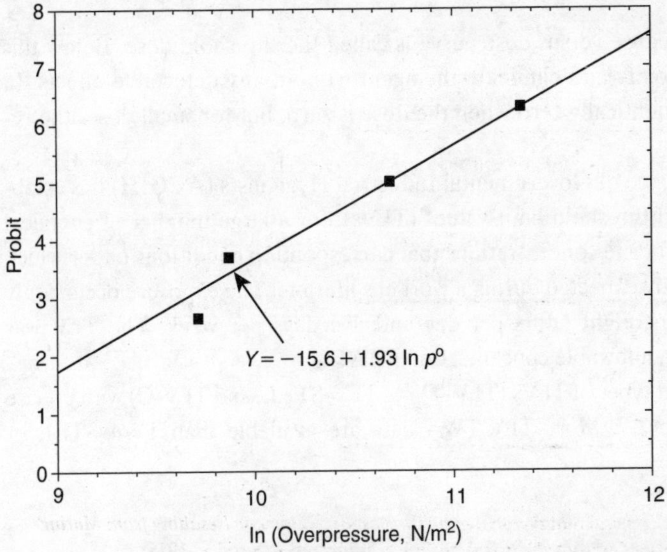

Figure 2-12 Probit versus the natural logarithm of the peak overpressure for Example 2-3.

Table 2-6 Hodge-Sterner Table for Degree of Toxicity[a]

Experimental LD_{50} per kilogram of body weight	Degree of toxicity	Probable lethal dose for a 70-kg person
<1.0 mg	Dangerously toxic	A taste
1.0–50 mg	Seriously toxic	A teaspoonful
50–500 mg	Highly toxic	An ounce
0.5–5 g	Moderately toxic	A pint
5–15 g	Slightly toxic	A quart
>15 g	Extremely low toxicity	More than a quart

[a]N. Irving Sax, *Dangerous Properties of Industrial Materials* (New York: Van Nostrand Reinhold, 1984), p. 1.

2-7 Relative Toxicity

Table 2-6 shows the Hodge-Sterner table for the degree of toxicity. This table covers a range of doses from 1.0 mg/kg to 15,000 mg/kg.

Toxicants are compared for relative toxicity based on the LD, ED, or TD curve. If the response-dose curve for chemical A is to the right of the response-dose curve for chemical B, then chemical A is more toxic. Care must be taken when comparing two response-dose curves when partial data are available. If the slopes of the curves differ substantially, the situation shown in Figure 2-13 might occur. If only a single data point is available in the upper part of the curves, it might appear that chemical A is always more toxic than chemical B. The complete data show that chemical B is more toxic at lower doses.

2-8 Threshold Limit Values

The lowest value on the response versus dose curve is called the threshold dose. Below this dose the body is able to detoxify and eliminate the agent without any detectable effects. In reality the response is only identically zero when the dose is zero, but for small doses the response is not detectable.

The American Conference of Governmental Industrial Hygienists (ACGIH) has established threshold doses, called threshold limit values (TLVs), for a large number of chemical agents. The TLV refers to airborne concentrations that correspond to conditions under which no adverse effects are normally expected during a worker's lifetime. The exposure occurs only during normal working hours, eight hours per day and five days per week. The TLV was formerly called the maximum allowable concentration (MAC).

There are three different types of TLVs (TLV-TWA, TLV-STEL, and TLV-C) with precise definitions provided in Table 2-7. More TLV-TWA data are available than TWA-STEL or TLV-C data.

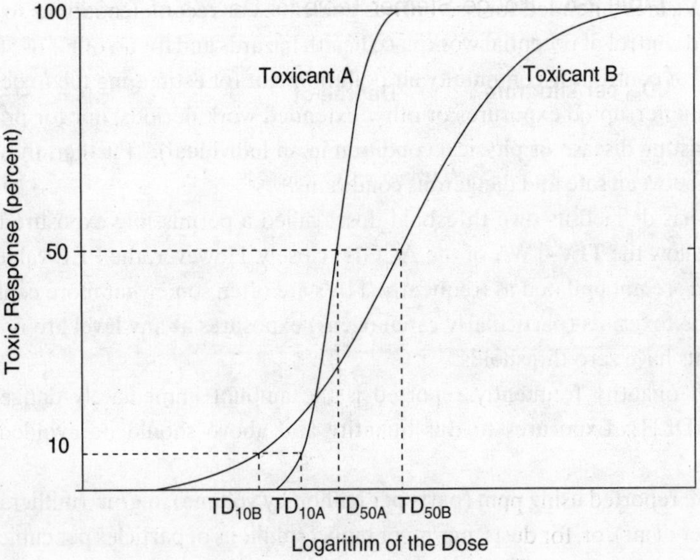

Figure 2-13 Two toxicants with differing relative toxicities at different doses. Toxicant A is more toxic at high doses, whereas toxicant B is more toxic at low doses.

Table 2-7 Definitions for Threshold Limit Values (TLVs)[a]

TLV type	Definition
TLV-TWA	Threshold limit value–time-weighted average The concentration for a conventional 8-hour workday and a 40-hour workweek, to which it is believed that nearly all workers may be repeatedly exposed, day after day, for a working lifetime without adverse effect.
TLV-STEL	Threshold limit value–short-term exposure limit A 15-minute TWA exposure that should not be exceeded at any time during a workday, even if the 8-hour TWA is within the TLV-TWA. The TLV-STEL is the concentration to which it is believed that workers can be exposed continuously for a short period of time without suffering (1) irritation, (2) chronic or irreversible tissue damage, (3) dose-rate-dependent toxic effects, or (4) narcosis of sufficient degree to increase the likelihood of accidental injury, impaired self-rescue, or materially reduced work efficiency. Exposures above the TLV-TWA up to the TLV-STEL should be less than 15 minutes, should occur no more than four times per day, and there should be at least 60 minutes between successive exposures in this range.
TLV-C	Threshold limit value–ceiling The concentration that should not be exceeded during any part of the working exposure.

[a]ACGIH, *2009 TLVs and BEIs* (Cincinnati, OH: American Conference of Governmental Industrial Hygienists, 2009).

The TLVs are "intended for use only as guidelines or recommendations to assist in the evaluation and control of potential workplace health hazards and for no other use (e.g., neither for evaluating or controlling community air pollution; nor for estimating the toxic potential of continuous, uninterrupted exposures or other extended work periods; nor for proving or disproving an existing disease or physical condition in an individual)." Further, these values are not fine lines between safe and dangerous conditions.[4]

OSHA has defined its own threshold dose, called a permissible exposure level (PEL). PEL values follow the TLV-TWA of the ACGIH closely. However, the PEL values are not as numerous and are not updated as frequently. TLVs are often somewhat more conservative.

For some toxicants (particularly carcinogens) exposures at any level are not permitted. These toxicants have zero thresholds.

Another quantity frequently reported is the amount immediately dangerous to life and health (IDLH). Exposures to this quantity and above should be avoided under any circumstances.

TLVs are reported using ppm (parts per million by volume), mg/m^3 (milligrams of vapor per cubic meter of air), or, for dusts, mg/m^3 or mppcf (millions of particles per cubic foot of air). For vapors, mg/m^3 is converted to ppm using the equation

$$C_{\text{ppm}} = \text{Concentration in ppm} = \frac{22.4}{M}\left(\frac{T}{273}\right)\left(\frac{1}{P}\right)(\text{mg/m}^3)$$

$$= 0.08205\left(\frac{T}{PM}\right)(\text{mg/m}^3), \qquad (2\text{-}7)$$

where

T is the temperature in degrees Kelvin,
P is the absolute pressure in atm, and
M is the molecular weight in gm/gm-mole.

TLV and PEL values for a variety of toxicants are provided in Appendix G.

Please note that even though the PELs are legal limits and the TLVs are guidelines, every effort should be made to reduce the workplace exposure concentrations as much as possible.

2-9 National Fire Protection Association (NFPA) Diamond

Another method that is used to characterize the hazardous properties of chemicals is the National Fire Protection Association (NFPA) diamond.

The NFPA is a professional society that was established in 1896 to reduce worldwide fatalities and injuries due to fires and other hazards. Their primary function is to promote consensus codes and standards, including the National Electrical Code (NEC).

[4] ACGIH, *2009 TLVs and BEIs.*

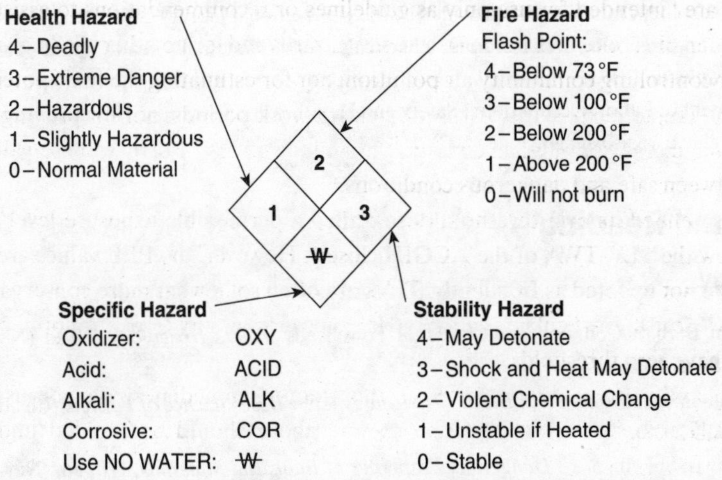

Figure 2-14 The NFPA Diamond used to identify chemical hazards.

The NFPA diamond frequently appears on chemical containers and storage vessels. The main purpose of the diamond is to provide a quick means for emergency response personnel to recognize the chemical hazards that they may face during a fire or other emergency. However, it is also useful for routine operations where hazards recognition is important. NFPA diamonds are frequently found on chemical containers in laboratories.

The NFPA diamond consists of 4 separate areas shown in Figure 2-14. The respective areas correspond to health, fire, stability, and special hazards. In the past the word reactivity was used instead of stability, but chemical stability is a more accurate description of the hazard facing emergency response personnel during a fire incident.

The simplicity of the NFPA diamond is that the respective hazards are indicated by a number, with the number 0 representing minimal hazard and the number 4 representing the greatest hazard. Figure 2-14 shows how the numbers are assigned.

Appendix G contains NFPA numbers for a variety of common chemicals.

On-Line Resources

American Conference of Governmental Industrial Hygienists (ACGIH), *www.acgih.org*.

NIOSH Pocket Guide to Chemical Hazards. This is a free database of chemical hazards. *www.cdc.gov/niosh/npg/*.

Society of Toxicology. This is a professional organization of scientists from academic institutions, government, and industry representing toxicologists. *www.toxicology.org*.

TOXNET, Toxicology Data Network provided by the U.S. National Library of Medicine. This includes free databases on toxicology, hazardous chemicals, environmental health, and toxic releases. *www.toxnet.nlm.nih.gov*.

U.S. Department of Labor, Occupational Safety and Health Administration. This includes all regulations and PEL values. *www.osha.gov*.

Suggested Reading

Toxicology

Eula Bingham, Barbara Cohrssen, and Charles H. Powell, eds., *Patty's Toxicology*, 5th ed. (New York: John Wiley and Sons, 2001).

Curtis D. Klassen, ed., *Casarett and Doull's Toxicology—The Basic Science of Poisons*, 7th ed. (New York: McGraw-Hill, 2008).

Richard J. Lewis, Sr., ed., *Sax's Dangerous Properties of Industrial Materials*, 11th ed. (New York: Wiley Interscience, 2004).

Probit Analysis

D. J. Finney, *Probit Analysis* (Cambridge: Cambridge University Press), 1971.

Sam Mannan, ed., *Lees' Loss Prevention in the Process Industries*, 3rd ed. (Amsterdam: Elsevier, 2005), pp. 18/49–18/58.

Threshold Limit Values

Documentation of the Threshold Limit Values and Biological Exposure Indices, 7th ed. (Cincinnati, OH: American Conference of Governmental Industrial Hygienists, 2010).

ACGIH, *2009 TLVs and BEIs* (Cincinnati, OH: American Conference of Governmental Industrial Hygienists, 2009).

Problems

2-1. Finney[5] reported the data of Martin[6] involving the toxicity of rotenone to the insect species *Macrosiphoniella sanborni.* The rotenone was applied in a medium of 0.5% saponin, containing 5% alcohol. The insects were examined and classified one day after spraying. The obtained data were:

[5]Finney, *Probit Analysis*, p. 20.

[6]J. T. Martin, "The Problem of the Evaluation of Rotenone-Containing Plants. VI. The Toxicity of l-Elliptone and of Poisons Applied Jointly, with Further Observations on the Rotenone Equivalent Method of Assessing the Toxicity of Derris Root," *Ann. Appl. Biol.* (1942), 29: 69–81.

Dose of rotenone (mg/l)	Number of insects	Number affected
10.2	50	44
7.7	49	42
5.1	46	24
3.8	48	16
2.6	50	6
0	49	0

a. From the given data, plot the percentage of insects affected versus the natural logarithm of the dose.

b. Convert the data to a probit variable, and plot the probit versus the natural logarithm of the dose. If the result is linear, determine a straight line that fits the data. Compare the probit and number of insects affected predicted by the straight-line fit to the actual data.

2-2. A blast produces a peak overpressure of 47,000 N/m^2. What fraction of structures will be damaged by exposure to this overpressure? What fraction of people exposed will die as a result of lung hemorrhage? What fraction will have eardrums ruptured? What conclusions about the effects of this blast can be drawn?

2-3. In Example 2-1, part c, the data were represented by the normal distribution function

$$f(x) = 0.178e^{-0.100(x-4.51)^2}$$

Use this distribution function to determine the fraction of individuals demonstrating a response in the range of 2.5 to 7.5.

2-4. Use the NIOSH web site to determine and compare the PEL, IDLH concentration, and TLV for ethylene oxide, benzene, ethanol, ethylene trichloride, fluorine, and hydrogen chloride.

2-5. Use the probit equation (Equation 2-5) to determine the expected fatalities for people exposed for 2 hours to each of the IDLH concentrations of ammonia, chlorine, ethylene oxide, and hydrogen chloride.

2-6. The Immediately Dangerous to Life and Health (IDLH) concentration is defined as the concentration "that poses a threat of exposure to airborne contaminants when that exposure is likely to cause death or immediate or delayed adverse health effects or prevent escape from such an environment." The IDLH implies a 30-min maximum exposure time.

a. The IDLH for chlorine gas is 10 ppm. Use the probit equation for chlorine deaths to estimate the fraction of fatalities due to exposure at the IDLH for 30 min.

b. Estimate the maximum exposure or evacuation time to result in no more than 1% fatalities at the IDLH level.

2-7. Determine the concentration of ethylene oxide that will cause a 50% fatality rate if the exposure occurs for 30 min.

2-8. Use Equation 2-7 to convert the TLV in ppm to the TLV in mg/m^3 for benzene, carbon monoxide, and chlorine. Assume 25°C and 1 atm.

2-9. Use the NIOSH web site to determine and compare the PEL, IDLH concentration, and LC_{50} for ammonia, carbon monoxide, and ethylene oxide.

2-10. Use Equation 2-6 to convert probits of 3.72, 5.0, and 6.28 to percentage affected, and compare with the values shown in Table 2-4.

2-11. Determine the duration times, in minutes, in which a group of 100 people can be exposed to 1500 ppm of carbon monoxide to result in (a) 0% fatalities and (b) 50% fatalities.

2-12. Using the probit equations provided in Table 2-5:

a. Determine the explosion overpressure (in psi) where 50% fatalities due to lung hemorrhage are expected.

b. Determine the explosion overpressure (in psi) where 50% of the structures are damaged.

c. Compare the results of parts a and b. Why is the overpressure of part b frequently used as the minimum overpressure for fatalities?

2-13. Determine the potential deaths resulting from the following exposure to chlorine:

a. 200 ppm for 15 min.

b. 100 ppm for 5 min.

c. 50 ppm for 2 min.

2-14. If 500 workers in a plant are exposed to the following concentrations of ammonia for the given number of hours, how many deaths will be expected?

a. 1000 ppm for 1 hr.

b. 2000 ppm for 2 hr.

c. 300 ppm for 3 hr.

d. 150 ppm for 2 hr.

2-15. Use the NIOSH web site to determine the number of deaths that occurred in 1992 as a result of asbestos.

2-16. Use the NIOSH web site (*www.cdc.gov/niosh*) to acquire the meaning and definition of IDLH concentration.

2-17. How much acetone liquid (in milliliters) is required to produce a vapor concentration of 200 ppm in a room of dimension 3 × 4 × 10 m? The temperature is 25°C and the pressure is 1 atm. The following physical property data are for acetone: molecular weight, 58.1; and specific gravity, 0.7899.

2-18. Estimate the exposure concentration in ppm that will result in fatalities for 80% of the exposed individuals if they are exposed to phosgene for 4 min.

2-19. Use the NIOSH web site to determine and compare the PEL and the IDLH concentration of ethylene oxide and ethanol.

2-20. The NIOSH web site states that deaths occur as a result of ammonia exposures between 5000 and 10,000 ppm over a 30-min period. Compare the result to the results from the probit equation (Table 2-5).

2-21. Determine the potential deaths resulting from the following exposure to chlorine:

a. 200 ppm for 150 min.

b. 100 ppm for 50 min.

c. 50 ppm for 20 min.

2-22. A group of 100 people is exposed to phosgene in two consecutive periods as follows: (a) 10 ppm for 30 min and (b) 1 ppm for 300 min. Determine the expected number of fatalities.

2-23. Humans breathe about 500 ml of air per breath and take about 12 breaths per minute during normal activities. If a person is exposed to an atmosphere containing benzene at a concentration of 10 ppm (by volume), how many grams of benzene will be deposited in the lungs during an 8-hour shift if all the benzene that enters remains in the lungs? How many drops of liquid is that? A drop of liquid contains about 0.05 cm^3. The specific gravity of benzene is 0.879. If you were the worker, would this be acceptable?

2-24. Use the NIOSH web site to determine an escape time period for a person subjected to an IDLH concentration.

CHAPTER 3

Industrial Hygiene

Industry and society are continuing to focus on reducing personnel and environmental damage resulting from accidents. Many of the results in this area are due to civic concern and ethics, sometimes manifested in laws and regulations. In this chapter we describe the relationship between laws and regulations as an introduction to industrial hygiene.

Industrial hygiene is a science devoted to the identification, evaluation, and control of occupational conditions that cause sickness and injury. Industrial hygienists are also responsible for selecting and using instrumentation to monitor the workplace during the identification and control phases of industrial hygiene projects.

Typical projects involving industrial hygiene are monitoring toxic airborne vapor concentrations, reducing toxic airborne vapors through the use of ventilation, selecting proper personal protective equipment to prevent worker exposure, developing procedures for the handling of hazardous materials, and monitoring and reducing noise, heat, radiation, and other physical factors to ensure that workers are not exposed to harmful levels.

The four phases in any industrial hygiene project are *anticipation, identification, evaluation,* and *control:*

- Anticipation: expectation of the presence of workplace hazards and worker exposures
- Identification: determination of the presence of workplace exposures
- Evaluation: determination of the magnitude of the exposure
- Control: application of appropriate technology to reduce workplace exposures to acceptable levels

In chemical plants and laboratories the industrial hygienist works closely with safety professionals as an integral part of a safety and loss prevention program. After identifying and evaluating the hazards, the industrial hygienist makes recommendations relevant to control techniques. The industrial hygienist, safety professionals, and plant operations personnel work together to ensure that the control measures are applied and maintained. It has been clearly demonstrated that toxic chemicals can be handled safely when principles of industrial hygiene are appropriately applied.

3-1 Government Regulations

Laws and Regulations

Laws and regulations are major tools for protecting people and the environment. Congress is responsible for passing laws that govern the United States. To put these laws into effect, Congress authorizes certain government organizations, including the Environmental Protection Agency (EPA), Occupational Safety and Health Administration (OSHA), and the Department of Homeland Security (DHS) to create and enforce regulations.

Creating a Law

A law is created with a three-step process:

Step 1: A member of Congress proposes a bill. A bill is a document that, if approved, becomes a law.

Step 2: If both houses of Congress approve the bill, it is sent to the president, who has the option to either approve it or veto it. If approved, it becomes a law that is called an act.

Step 3: The complete text of the law is published in the United States Code (USC).[1] The code is the official record of all federal laws.

Creating a Regulation

After the law is official, how is it put into practice? Laws often do not include the details for compliance. For example, the USC requires the appropriate respirator protection, but it does not specify the detailed types or limitations of respirators. To make the laws work on a day-to-day level, Congress authorizes governmental organizations, including the EPA, OSHA, and DHS, to create regulations and/or standards.

Regulations set specific rules about what is legal and what is not legal. For example, a regulation relevant to the Clean Air Act will specify levels of specific toxic chemicals that are safe, quantities of the toxic chemicals that are legally emitted into the air, and what penalties are

[1] *www4.law.cornell.edu/uscode.*

given if the legal limits are exceeded. After the regulation is in effect, the EPA has the responsibility (1) to help citizens comply with the law and (2) to enforce the regulation.

The process for creating a regulation and/or standard has two steps:

Step 1: The authorized organization or agency decides when a regulation is needed. The organization then researches, develops, and proposes a regulation. The proposal is listed in the *Federal Register* (FR) so that the public can evaluate it and send comments to the organization. These comments are used to revise the regulation.

Step 2: After a regulation is rewritten, it is posted in the *Federal Register* as a final rule, and it is simultaneously codified by publishing it in the *Code of Federal Regulations* (CFR).

In 1970 the U.S. Congress enacted a health and safety law that continues to have a significant impact on the practices of industrial hygiene in the chemical industry: the Occupational Safety and Health Act of 1970 (OSHAct). To appreciate the significance of the OSHAct, it is helpful to review regulations and practices[2] before 1970.

Before 1936 regulations concerning occupational health were poorly administered by state and local governmental agencies. During this era, staffs and funds were too small to carry out effective programs. In 1936 the federal government enacted the Walsh-Healy Act to establish federal safety and health standards for activities relating to federal contracts. This 1936 act also initiated significant research related to the cause, recognition, and control of occupational disease. The concepts promulgated by the Walsh-Healy Act, although not adequate by today's standards, were the forerunners of our current occupational health and safety regulations.

Between 1936 and 1970 a number of states enacted their own safety and health regulations. Although some progress was made, these regulations were never sufficiently supported to carry out a satisfactory program. This produced relatively inconsistent and ineffective results.

The OSHAct of 1970 was developed to solve these problems and to give a nationally consistent program with the funding necessary to manage it effectively. This act defined clear procedures for establishing regulations, conducting investigations for compliance, and developing and maintaining safety and health records.

As a result of the OSHAct, sufficient funding was committed to create and support the Occupational Safety and Health Administration (OSHA), which manages and administers the government's responsibilities specified in the OSHAct, and the National Institute for Occupational Safety and Health (NIOSH), which conducts research and technical assistance programs for improving the protection and maintenance of workers' health. Examples of NIOSH responsibilities include (1) measuring health effects of exposure in the work environment, (2) developing criteria for handling toxic materials, (3) establishing safe levels of exposure, and (4) training professionals for administering the programs of the act.

[2] J. B. Olishifski, ed., *Fundamentals of Industrial Hygiene*, 2nd ed. (Chicago: National Safety Council, 1979), pp. 758–777.

Table 3-1 A Few Laws from the United States Code (USC) and Regulations from the Code of Federal Regulations (CFR)

Number	Description
29 USC 651	Occupational Safety and Health Act (1970)
42 USC 7401	Clean Air Act (1970)
33 USC 1251	Clean Water Act (1977)
42 USC 7401	Clean Air Act Amendments (1990)
15 USC 2601	Toxic Substances Control Act II (1992)
42 USC 300f	Safe Drinking Water Act Amendment (1996)
40 CFR 280.20	Underground Storage Tank Leak Tests (1988)
40 CFR 370.30	Annual Toxic Release Report, SARA 313 (1989)
29 CFR 1910.120	Training, Hazardous Materials Technician, HAZMAT (1989)
29 CFR 1910.1450	Exposure to Hazardous Chemicals in Laboratories (1990)
40 CFR 370.20	Annual Inventory of Hazardous Chemicals, SARA 311 (1991)
29 CFR 1910.119	Process Safety Management (1992)
40 CFR 68.65	Risk Management Program (1996)
29 CFR 1910.134	Respirator Program (1998)
42 USC 7401	Chemical Safety Information, Site Security and Fuels Regulatory Act (1999)
49 USC 40101	Transportation and Security Act (2001)
6 USC 101	Homeland Security Act (2002)
42 USC 301	Federal Food, Drug and Cosmetic Act (2002)
42 USC 13201	Energy Policy Act (2005)
29 CFR 1910 Subpart S	Electrical Standard (2007)
6 CFR 27	Chemical Facility Anti-Terrorism Standards (CFATS) (2007)

NIOSH develops data and information regarding hazards, and OSHA uses these data to promulgate standards. Some laws and regulations particularly relevant to the chemical industry are shown in Table 3-1. As illustrated in this table, the distinction between laws (USC) and regulations (CFR) is global versus detail.

The OSHAct makes employers responsible for providing safe and healthy working conditions for their employees. OSHA is authorized, however, to conduct inspections, and when violations of the safety and health standards are found, they can issue citations and financial penalties. Highlights of OSHA enforcement rights are illustrated in Table 3-2.

Table 3-2 Highlights of OSHA's Right of Enforcement

Employers must admit OSHA compliance officers into their plant sites for safety inspections with no advance notice. A search warrant may be required to show probable cause.
OSHA's right of inspection includes safety and health records.
Criminal penalties can be invoked.
OSHA officers finding conditions of imminent danger may request plant shutdowns.

The implications, interpretations, and applications of the OSHAct will continue to develop as standards are promulgated. Especially within the chemical industry, these standards will continue to create an environment for improving process designs and process conditions relevant to the safety and health of workers and the surrounding communities.

Government regulation will continue to be a significant part of the practice of chemical process safety. Since the OSHAct was signed into law, substantial new legislation controlling the workplace and community environment has been enacted. Table 3-3 provides a summary of relevant safety legislation. Table 3-4 summarizes the important parts of the current OSHAct.

Table 3-3 Federal Legislation Relevant to Chemical Process Safety[a]

Date	Abbreviation	Act
1899	RHA	River and Harbor Act
1906	FDCA	Federal Food, Drug, and Cosmetic Act
1947	FIFRA	Federal Insecticide, Fungicide, and Rodenticide Act
1952	DCA	Dangerous Cargo Act
1952	FWPCA	Federal Water Pollution Control Act
1953	FFA	Flammable Fabrics Act
1954	AEA	Atomic Energy Act
1956	FWA	Fish and Wildlife Act of 1956
1960	FHSA	Federal Hazardous Substances Labeling Act
1965	SWDA	Solid Waste Disposal Act
1966	MNMSA	Metal and Non-Metallic Mine Safety Act
1969	NEPA	National Environmental Policy Act
1969	CMHSA	Federal Coal Mine Health and Safety Act
1970	CAA	Clean Air Act
1970	PPPA	Poison Prevention Packaging Act of 1970
1970	WQI	Water Quality Improvement Act of 1970
1970	RSA	Federal Railroad Safety Act of 1970
1970	RRA	Resource Recovery Act of 1970
1970	OSHA	Occupational Safety and Health Act
1972	NCA	Noise Control Act of 1972
1972	FEPCA	Federal Environmental Pollution Control Act
1972	HMTA	Hazardous Materials Transportation Act
1972	CPSA	Consumer Product Safety Act
1972	MPRSA	Marine Protection, Research, and Sanctuary Act of 1972
1972	CWA	Clean Water Act
1972	CZMA	Coastal Zone Management Act
1973	ESA	Endangered Species Act of 1973
1974	SDWA	Safe Drinking Water Act
1974	TSA	Transportation Safety Act of 1974
1974	ESECA	Energy Supply and Environmental Coordination Act
1976	TSCA	Toxic Substances Control Act

(*continues*)

Table 3-3 *(continued)*

Date	Abbreviation	Act
1976	RCRA	Resource Conservation and Recovery Act
1977	FMSHA	Federal Mine Safety and Health Act
1977	SMCRA	Surface Mine Control and Reclamation Act
1978	UMTCA	Uranium Mill Tailings Control Act
1978	PTSA	Port and Tanker Safety Act
1980	CERCLA	Comprehensive Environmental Response, Compensation, and Liability Act of 1980 (Superfund)
1984	HSWA	Hazardous and Solid Waste Amendments
1986	AHERA	Asbestos Hazard Emergency Response Act
1986	SARA	Superfund Amendments and Reauthorization Act
1986	EPCRA	Emergency Planning and Community Right-to-Know Act
1986	TSCA	Toxic Substances Control Act
1987	WQA	Water Quality Act
1990	OPA	Oil Pollution Act of 1990
1990	CAAA	Clean Air Act Amendments
1990	PPA	Pollution Prevention Act of 1990
1992	TSCA-II	Residential Lead-Based Paint Hazard Abatement Act
1992	—	Federal Facility Compliance Act
1993	NEPA	National Environmental Policy Act
1994	HMTAA	Hazardous Materials Transportation Act Amendments
1996	SDWA	Safe Drinking Water Act Amendment
1996	FQPA	Food Quality Protection Act
1996	EPCRA	Emergency Planning and Community Right-to-Know Act
1996	FFDCA	Federal Food, Drug and Cosmetic Act
1996	FIFRA	Insecticide, Fungicide, and Rodenticide Act
1999	—	Community Safety Information, Site Security and Fuels Regulatory Act
2001	TSA	Transportation and Security Act
2002	HAS	Homeland Security Act
2005	—	Energy Policy Act
2007	CFATS	Chemical Facility Anti-Terrorism Standards

[a]Information from the EPA and OSHA web sites: *www.epa.gov* and *www.osha.gov*.

Table 3-4 Parts of the OSHAct Relevant to Chemical Engineering Practice[a]

Part	Title
1910.95	Occupational noise exposure
1910.97	Non-ionizing radiation
1910 Subpart H	Hazardous materials
1910.106	Flammable and combustible liquids
1910.110	Storage and handling of liquefied petroleum gases
1910.119	Process safety management of highly hazardous chemicals

Table 3-4 *(continued)*

Part	Title
1910.120	Hazardous waste operations and emergency response
1910 Subpart I	Personal protective equipment
1910.133	Eye and face protection
1910.134	Respiratory protection
1910.135	Head protection
1910.136	Foot protection
1910.138	Hand protection
1910 Subpart L	Fire protection
1910 Subpart N	Materials handling and storage
1910 Subpart O	Machinery and machine guarding
1910 Subpart P	Hand and portable tools and other hand equipment
1910 Subpart Q	Welding, cutting and brazing
1910 Subpart S	Electrical
1910 Subpart Z	Toxic and hazardous substances–this includes regulations for specific chemicals
1910.1200	Hazard communication
1910.1450	Occupational exposure to hazardous chemicals in laboratories

[a]These are all part of 29 CRF 1910. See *www.osha.gov* for details.

OSHA: Process Safety Management

On February 24, 1992, OSHA published the final rule "Process Safety Management of Highly Hazardous Chemicals." This standard is performance oriented; that is, it sets general requirements for the management of hazardous chemicals. Process safety management (PSM) was developed after the Bhopal accident (1984), to prevent similar accidents. It is recognized by industry and the government as an excellent regulation that will reduce the number and magnitude of accidents–if it is understood and practiced as intended.

The PSM standard has 14 major sections: employee participation, process safety information, process hazard analysis, operating procedures, training, contractors, pre-startup safety review, mechanical integrity, hot work permits, management of change, incident investigations, emergency planning and response, audits, and trade secrets. A brief description of each section is given in what follows.

Employee participation requires active employee participation in all the major elements of PSM. Employers must develop and document a plan of action to specify this participation.

Process safety information is compiled and made available to all employees to facilitate the understanding and identification of hazards. This information includes block flow diagrams or process flow diagrams, process chemistry, and process limitations, such as temperatures, pressures, flows, and compositions. Consequences of process deviations are also required. This process safety information is needed before training, process hazards analysis, management of change, and accident investigations.

Process hazard analysis (PHA) must be performed by a team of experts, including engineers, chemists, operators, industrial hygienists, and other appropriate and experienced specialists. The PHA needs to include a method that fits the complexity of the process, a hazards and operability (HAZOP) study for a complex process, and for less complex processes a less rigorous process, such as what-if scenarios, checklists, failure mode and effects analysis, or fault trees.

Employers must ensure that the recommendations from the PHA are acted on in a timely manner. Every PSM process needs an updated PHA at least every five years after the initial analysis is completed.

Operating procedures that facilitate the safe operation of the plant must be documented. These instructions must be clearly written and consistent with the process safety information. They need to cover, at a minimum, initial startup, normal operations, temporary operations, emergency shutdown, emergency operations, normal shutdown, startup after normal and emergency shutdowns, operating limits and consequences of deviations, safety and health considerations, hazardous properties of the chemicals, exposure precautions, engineering and administrative controls, quality control specifications for all chemicals, special or unique hazards, and safety control systems and functions. Safe work practices also need to be documented, such as hot work, lockout/tagout, and confined space. These operating procedures are updated frequently, with the frequency being set by the operating personnel.

An effective *training* program helps employees understand the hazards associated with the tasks they perform. Maintenance and operations personnel receive initial training and refresher training. Operators need to understand the hazards associated with every task, including emergency shutdowns, startups, and normal operations. Refresher training is given every three years and more often if necessary; the operators decide on the frequency of the refresher training.

Contractors are trained to perform their tasks safely to the same extent as employees. Even when selecting contractors, the employees need to consider the contractors' safety performance in addition to their skills.

A pre-startup safety review is a special safety review that is conducted after a modification to the process or operating conditions has been made and before the startup. In this review a team of reviewers ensures that (1) the system is constructed in accordance with the design specifications, (2) the safety, maintenance, operating, and emergency procedures are in place, (3) the appropriate training is completed, and (4) the recommendations from the PHA are implemented or resolved.

The mechanical integrity section of the PSM standard ensures that the equipment, piping, relief systems, controls, and alarms are mechanically sound and operational. The requirements include (1) written procedures to maintain functioning systems, (2) training regarding preventive maintenance, (3) periodic inspections and testing based on vendor recommendations, (4) a process to correct deficiencies, and (5) a process to ensure that all equipment and spare parts are suitable.

The PSM standard ascertains that a system is in place to prepare and issue *hot work permits* before conducting hot work activities (welding, grinding, or using spark-producing equipment). The permit requires dates authorized for hot work, the equipment involved in the work, a system to maintain and document certification, identification of openings where sparks may drop, the types and numbers of fire extinguishers, identification of fire watches, an inspection before the work, authorization signatures, identification of flammable materials in the area, verification that the surrounding area is not explosive, verification that combustible materials are removed or covered appropriately, identification and closure of open vessels or ducts, and verification that welded walls are not flammable.

Under the *management of change* section of the PSM standard employees are required to develop and implement documented procedures to manage changes in the process chemistry, process equipment, and operating procedures. Before a change occurs (except for replacement-in-kind), it must be reviewed to ascertain that it will not affect the safety of the operation. After the change has been made, all the affected employees are trained, and a pre-startup review is conducted.

The PSM standard mandates *incident investigation.* Employers must investigate all incidents that have or could have resulted in a major release or accident within 48 hours of the event. The regulation requires an investigation team composed of people, including operators, who are knowledgeable about the system. After the investigation, the employers are required to appropriately use the investigation recommendations.

The intent of the PSM element for *emergency planning and response* is to require employers to respond effectively to the release of highly hazardous chemicals. Although the regulation requires this activity for companies with more than 10 employees, this element should be part of a program for even the smallest organizations that handle hazardous chemicals.

Under the *audits* section of the PSM standard employers are required to certify that they have evaluated their compliance with the standard at least every three years. The recommendations from the audit must be followed. The audit reports need to be retained as long as the process exists.

The *trade secrets* section of the PSM standard ensures that all contractors are given all the information relevant to operating in the plant safely. Some personnel may need to sign secrecy agreements before they receive this information.

EPA: Risk Management Plan

On June 20, 1996, the EPA published the Risk Management Plan (RMP) as a final rule.[3] This regulation is also a response to the Bhopal accident. It is recognized by industry and the government as an excellent regulation that will reduce the number and magnitude of accidents—if it is understood and practiced as intended.

[3] *Code of Federal Regulations,* 40 CFR 68, subpart B (Washington, DC: US Government Printing Office, June 20, 1996).

The RMP regulation is aimed at decreasing the number and magnitude of accidental releases of toxic and flammable substances. Although the RMP is similar to the PSM regulation in many respects, the RMP is designed to protect off-site people and the environment, whereas PSM is designed to protect on-site people. The RMP is required for plant sites that use more than a specified threshold quantity of regulated highly hazardous chemicals. The RMP is a site responsibility (the site may have several processes), whereas PSM covers every covered process on the site.

The RMP has the following elements:

- Hazard assessment
- Prevention program
- Emergency response program
- Documentation that is maintained on the site and submitted to federal, state, and local authorities. This information is also shared with the local community.

The RMP document is updated when the process or chemistry changes or when a governmental audit requests an update. The first three parts of the regulation are described briefly in the following paragraphs. The fourth part, documentation, is self-explanatory.

Hazard assessment is a consequence analysis for a range of potential hazardous chemical releases, including the history of such releases at the facility. The releases must include the worst-case scenario and the more likely but significant accident release scenarios. A risk matrix can be used to characterize the worst-case and more likely scenarios.

The EPA requires the following consequence analyses: (1) A single worst-case release scenario is analyzed for all covered flammable materials on the site, and only one flammable substance is analyzed for other more likely scenarios; and (2) a single worst-case release scenario is analyzed for all toxic substances on the site, and more likely releases are analyzed for each toxic substance covered by the rule.

The worst-case scenario is based on releasing the entire contents of a vessel or piping system in a 10-minute period under worst-case meteorological conditions (F stability and 1.5 m/s wind speed). Passive mitigation measures (for example, dikes) can be used in the calculation process; therefore the release rate for liquid spills corresponds to the evaporation rate.

Alternative release cases for toxic substances cover scenarios with toxic concentrations beyond the fenceline. Alternative cases for flammable substances cover scenarios that may cause substantial damage off-site and on-site. The release scenarios that have a potential to reach the public are of the greatest concern. Those with no off-site potential damage are not required to be reported.

Dispersion model calculations are normally used to estimate downwind concentrations; these concentrations are the basis for determining the consequences resulting from toxicity, fires, and/or explosions. For those not interested in using dispersion models, the standard includes lookup tables for all the listed substances to help a facility determine the impact distances for specific release scenarios.

Table 3-5 Comparison of the PSM and RMP Prevention Programs

PSM program (OSHA)	RMP (EPA)
Process safety information	Process safety information
Process hazards analysis	Hazard evaluation
Operating procedures	Standard operating procedures
Employee participation	(No equivalence)
Training	Training
Contractors	(No equivalence)
Pre-startup review	Pre-startup review
Mechanical integrity	Maintenance
Hot work permit	(No equivalence)
Management of change	Management of change
Incident investigations	Accident investigations
Emergency planning and response	Emergency response
Compliance audits	Safety audits
Trade secrets	(No equivalence)
(No equivalence)	Risk assessment

The RMP requires only an analysis of the consequence and not the probability. Therefore the results are not a true determination of risk, because risk is composed of both consequence and probability. A more detailed description of the required consequence analyses can be found elsewhere.[4]

The second requirement of the RMP is a *prevention program.* The prevention program has 11 elements, compared to the 14 elements of the PSM standard. As shown in Table 3-5, many of these elements are duplicated. Fortunately, the EPA made a deliberate attempt to retain the same requirements wherever possible, although differences exist because the EPA and OSHA have different responsibilities. The first column in Table 3-5 lists each element of the PSM program, and the second column shows the corresponding element of the prevention program (some elements have no equivalence).

The *emergency response program* delineates the steps to be taken by the facility's employees in response to accidental releases of hazardous materials. It also establishes procedures for notifying the local community and the appropriate emergency response agencies. Training is for all employees on the topics relevant to emergency response. The requirements include drills to test the plan and to evaluate its effectiveness, and the plan must be revised based on the findings of these drills.

The plan must be coordinated with local emergency response plans developed by Local Emergency Planning Committees (LEPCs) and local emergency response agencies. As with

[4]Daniel A. Crowl, "Consequence Modeling for the EPA Risk Management Plan (RMP)," *Process Safety Progress* (Spring 1997), pp. 1–5.

similar OSHA regulations, the Resource Conservation and Recovery Act (RCRA), and the Spill Prevention Control under the Clean Water Act, the emergency response plan must be maintained at the facility and must include descriptions of all mitigating systems.

DHS: Chemical Facility Anti-Terrorism Standards (CFATS)

In 2006 Congress passed a law requiring the U.S. Department of Homeland Secuity (DHS) to establish risk-based performance standards for the security of chemical facilities. Subsequently, on April 9, 2007, DHS issued an interim rule called the Chemical Facility Anti-Terrorism Standards (CFATS). The details are provided in the Code of Federal Regulations 6 CFR 27. This rule applies to any facility that manufactures, uses, stores, distributes, or otherwise possesses certain chemicals at or above a specified quantity.

Chemical plants contain assets, which include any person, environment, facility, material, information, business reputation, or activity that has a positive value for the company. The asset that is of the most concern with respect to chemical plants is the quantity of hazardous materials. A threat is any indication, circumstance, or event with the potential to cause the loss of, or damage to, an asset. A vulnerability is any weakness that can be exploited by an adversary to gain access to an asset. An adversary is any group, organization, or government that conducts, intends to conduct, or has the capability to conduct activities detrimental to critical assets.[5]

Table 3-6 identifies some of the security issues of concern to chemical plants. The purpose of the CFATS rule is to identify to DHS all chemical facilities that are high-risk with respect to terrorism and to ensure that these facilities have an effective security risk management plan.

The rule works as follows. The rule 6 CFR 27 includes Appendix A, which is a list of chemicals and threshold quantities. If a facility has these chemicals in quantities that exceed the threshold, they are required to complete a Chemical Security Assessment Tool (CSAT) Top Screen. The CSAT Top Screen is done on-line. DHS evaluates the Top Screen and makes a preliminary classification whether the facility poses a high risk. DHS ranks high-risk facilities into four tiers, 1 through 4, with tier 1 having the highest risk. All preliminarily tiered chemical facilities must subsequently conduct a Security Vulnerability Assessment (SVA) and submit it to DHS.

A security vulnerability assessment (SVA) is a process used to identify security issues arising from the facility's activities, ranging from intentional release of chemicals, sabotage, to theft or diversion of chemicals that can be used as, or converted into, weapons. The SVA identifies these security issues and also allows the facility to estimate the likelihood of the facility's vulnerabilities being successfully exploited. DHS evaluates the SVA and assigns a final tier ranking to the facility.

Chemical facilities in all four tiers are required to develop and implement a Site Security Plan (SSP) that meets criteria published in the risk-based performance standards. DHS

[5]David A. Moore, "Security," *Perry's Chemical Engineers' Handbook*, 8th ed., Don W. Green and Robert H. Perry, eds. (New York: McGraw-Hill), pp. 23–104 to 23–109.

Table 3-6 Security Issues of Concern to Chemical Plants

Security issue	**Example terrorist objective**
Intentional loss of containment	Release of chemicals to the atmosphere, resulting in toxic exposure, fire, or explosion. This results in harm to the public, to workers, and to the environment. The chemical plant can also be damaged or destroyed, causing direct or indirect economic damage.
Theft of chemicals	Use of the chemicals as primary or secondary[a] improvised weapons against a third party.
Contamination or spoilage of a product or process	Immediate or delayed harm to people or the environment, or to cause economic injury.
Degradation of the asset	Mechanical or physical damage or cyber disruption. This causes severe direct or indirect economic damages.
Acquisition of chemicals under false pretense	Purchase of chemicals through normal purchasing channels by misrepresentation of purpose. Use of the chemicals as primary or secondary[a] improvised weapons against a third party.

[a]A supporting or auxiliary weapon, with the purpose of supporting or supplementing the primary weapon.
Adapted from David A. Moore, "Security," pp. 23–104 to 23–109.

conducts inspections and/or audits at tiered facilities, with the highest-risk facilities being inspected more frequently. The SSP must detail physical, procedural, and cyber measures that the site takes to reduce or eliminate the vulnerabilities.

Security strategies for chemical facilities usually involve the following countermeasures for each security threat:[6] deterrence, detection, delay, response, and awareness.

Deterrence prevents or discourages security breaches by means of fear or doubt. Security guards, lighting, and barriers are examples of deterrence countermeasures.

Cameras, monitoring, and intrusion alarms detect an adversary attempting to commit a security event. They may also provide the identity of the adversary, real-time observation, and possibly aid in apprehension of the adversary.

The countermeasure of delay is designed to slow the progress of an adversary either coming into or out of a restricted area. Delay may provide the time required to interdict the attack or to apprehend the adversary.

Response includes both facility response capability and the demonstrated capability of off-site responders, such as police and fire fighters. Response is not limited to armed interdiction by police and/or security personnel but also includes all the traditional hazardous materials response capability normally associated with safety and environmental stewardship. On-site response capabilities include fire fighting, security, medical response, spill containment, and the capability to quickly reduce inventory, to name a few.

[6]Center for Chemical Process Safety (CCPS), *Guidelines for Managing and Analyzing the Security Vulnerabilities of Fixed Chemical Sites* (New York: American Institute of Chemical Engineers, 2002).

Awareness includes knowledge of your customers and the purpose of their purchase. This security strategy is designed mostly to prevent acquisition of chemicals under false pretense but can also identify inquiries from adversaries posing as customers in order to obtain information about your facility, raw materials, intermediates, or products.

3-2 Industrial Hygiene: Anticipation and Identification

One of the major responsibilities of the industrial hygienist is to anticipate, identify, and solve potential health problems within plants. Chemical process technology, however, is so complex that this task requires the concerted efforts of industrial hygienists, process designers, operators, laboratory personnel, and management. The industrial hygienist helps the effectiveness of the overall program by working with these plant personnel. For these reasons industrial hygiene (particularly identification) must be a part of the education process of chemists, engineers, and managers.

Many hazardous chemicals are handled safely on a daily basis within chemical plants. To achieve this operating success, *all* potential hazards must be identified and controlled. When toxic and/or flammable chemicals are handled, the potentially hazardous conditions may be numerous – in large plants there may be thousands. To be safe under these conditions requires discipline, skill, concern, and attention to detail.

The identification step requires a thorough study of the chemical process, operating conditions, and operating procedures. The sources of information include process design descriptions, operating instructions, safety reviews, equipment vendor descriptions, information from chemical suppliers, and information from operating personnel. The quality of this identification step is often a function of the number of resources used and the quality of the questions asked. The different resources may have different operating and technical emphases unique to pieces of equipment or specific chemicals. In this identification step it is often necessary to collate and integrate the available information to identify new potential problems resulting from the combined effects of multiple exposures.

During the identification step, the potential hazards and methods of contact are identified and recorded. As illustrated in Table 3-7, the potential hazards are numerous, especially because the listed hazards can also act in combination. This list of potential hazards together with the required data for hazard identification (see Table 3-8) is commonly used during the identification step of industrial hygiene projects.

Table 3-9 is a list of odor thresholds for various chemicals. This is one approach to identify the presence of chemical vapors in the workplace. Individuals vary greatly with respect to odor detection so great variability in this is expected. Also, some chemicals, like methyl ethyl ketone, anesthetize the olfactory organs with continued exposure, reducing the ability to detect the odor. In many cases the odor threshold is below the threshold limit value (TLV). For instance, chlorine has an odor threshold of 0.05 ppm while the TLV is 0.5 ppm (Appendix G). In this case the odor is noticed at a concentration well below the TLV. For some chemicals the reverse case is true. For instance, ethylene oxide has an odor threshold of 851 ppm while the TLV is 1 ppm. In this case once the odor is detected, the exposure limit has been greatly exceeded.

Table 3-7 Identification of Potential Hazards[a]

Potential hazards	
Liquids	Noise
Vapors	Radiation
Dusts	Temperature
Fumes	Mechanical
Entry mode of toxicants	
Inhalation	Ingestion
Body absorption (skin or eyes)	Injection
Potential damage	
Lungs	Skin
Ears	Eyes
Nervous system	Liver
Kidneys	Reproductive organs
Circulatory system	Other organs

[a]Olishifski, *Fundamentals of Industrial Hygiene*, pp. 24–26.

Table 3-8 Data Useful for Health Identification

Threshold limit values (TLVs)
Odor threshold for vapors
Physical state
Vapor pressure of liquids
Sensitivity of chemical to temperature or impact
Rates and heats of reaction
Hazardous by-products
Reactivity with other chemicals
Flammable and explosive concentrations of chemicals, dusts, and vapors
Noise levels of equipment
Types and degree of radiation

Determining the potential for hazards to result in an accident (risk assessment) is frequently part of the identification step (see Chapter 12). This list of potential hazards and their risk is used during the evaluation and control phase of the project. Resources for evaluating the hazards and developing control methods are allocated on a priority basis, giving the appropriate time and attention to the most significant hazards.

Table 3-9 Odor Thresholds for Various Chemicals[a]

Chemical species	Odor threshold (ppm)
Acetaldehyde	0.186
Acetic acid	0.016
Acrolein	0.174
Acrylic acid	0.4
Acrylonitrile	16.6
Ammonia	5.75
Aniline	0.676
Bromine	0.066
Butane	204
Butyraldehyde	0.009
Camphor	0.051
Chlorine	0.05
Chloroform	11.7
Cumene	0.024
Diethylamine	0.186
Ethyl alcohol	0.136
Ethylamine	0.324
Ethylene oxide	851
Ethyl ether	2.29
Ethyl mercaptan	0.001
Fluorine	0.126
Hydrogen chloride	0.77
Hydrogen sulfide	0.0005
Isopropyl ether	0.055
Methyl alcohol	141
Methylene chloride	0.912
Methyl ethyl ketone (MEK)	0.27
Methyl isocyanate	2.1
Methyl mercaptan	0.001
Ozone	0.051
Phenol	0.011
Phosgene	0.55
Styrene	3.44
Toluene	0.16
Trichloroethylene	1.36
Vinyl acetate	0.603
Vinyl chloride	0.253

[a]Data from *2010 Respirator Selection Guide* (St. Paul, MN: 3M Corporation, 2010).

Material Safety Data Sheets

One of the most important references used during an industrial hygiene study involving toxic chemicals is the material safety data sheet (MSDS). A sample MSDS is shown in Figure 3-1. The MSDS lists the physical properties of a substance that may be required to determine the potential hazards of the substance.

MSDSs are available from (1) the chemical manufacturer, (2) a commercial source, or (3) a private library developed by the chemical plant.

The industrial hygienist or safety professional must interpret the physical and toxicological properties to determine the hazards associated with a chemical. These properties are also used to develop a strategy for the proper control and handling of these chemicals.

Example 3-1

A survey of a laboratory is made and the following chemical species are identified: sodium chloride, toluene, hydrochloric acid, phenol, sodium hydroxide, benzene, and ether. Identify the potential hazards in this laboratory.

Solution

Sax[7] provided the technical information required to solve this problem. The following table summarizes the results:

Chemical	Description and potential hazard
Sodium chloride	Common table salt. No hazard.
Toluene	Clear, colorless liquid with a slight fire hazard and moderate explosion hazard. Entry into the body is mostly by vapor inhalation. Irritant to skin and eyes.
Hydrochloric acid	Clear, colorless liquid with no fire or explosion hazard. It is a moderate irritant to the skin, eyes, and mucous membranes and by ingestion and inhalation. Highly reactive with a wide variety of substances.
Phenol	A white, crystalline mass that is most frequently found in solution form. It is a moderate fire hazard. Emits toxic fumes when heated. Absorbed readily through the skin. Exposures to skin areas as small as 64 in^2 have resulted in death in less than 1 hr.
Sodium hydroxide	A skin and eye irritant. Corrosive action on all body tissues. Reacts violently with a number of substances.
Benzene	Clear, colorless liquid with a dangerous fire hazard and a moderate explosion hazard. It is a possible carcinogen. Entry into the body is mostly by inhalation, but it is also absorbed through the skin. High concentrations produce a narcotic effect.
Ether	A wide variety of organic compounds that are mostly narcotic in effect. Large doses can cause death. Most ethers are dangerously flammable and explosive.

[7] R. J. Lewis, ed., *Sax's Dangerous Properties of Industrial Materials,* 11th ed. (New York: Wiley, 2004).

MATERIAL SAFETY DATA SHEET — S-210 31:9203

Material Safety Data Sheet
May be used to comply with
OSHA's Hazard Communication Standard,
29 CFR 1910.1200. Standard must be
consulted for specific requirements.

U.S. Department of Labor
Occupational Safety and Health Administration
(Non-Mandatory Form)
Form Approved
OMB No. 1218-0072

IDENTITY *(As Used on Label and List)*	Note: *Blank spaces are not permitted. If any item is not applicable, or no information is available, the space must be marked to indicate that.*

Section I

Manufacturer's Name	Emergency Telephone Number
Address *(Number, Street, City, State, and ZIP Code)*	Telephone Number for Information
	Date Prepared
	Signature of Preparer *(optional)*

Section II — Hazardous Ingredients/Identity Information

Hazardous Components (Specific Chemical Identity; Common Name(s))	OSHA PEL	ACGIH TLV	Other Limits Recommended	% *(optional)*

Section III — Physical/Chemical Characteristics

Boiling Point		Specific Gravity (H_2O = 1)	
Vapor Pressure (mm Hg.)		Melting Point	
Vapor Density (AIR = 1)		Evaporation Rate (Butyl Acetate = 1)	
Solubility in Water			
Appearance and Odor			

Section IV — Fire and Explosion Hazard Data

Flash Point (Method Used)	Flammable Limits	LEL	UEL
Extinguishing Media			
Special Fire Fighting Procedures			
Unusual Fire and Explosion Hazards			

(Reproduce locally) OSHA 174, Sept. 1985

Figure 3-1 Material safety data sheet. Most companies use their own MSDS format.

31:9204 REFERENCE FILE

Section V — Reactivity Data

Stability	Unstable		Conditions to Avoid
	Stable		

Incompatibility (*Materials to Avoid*)

Hazardous Decomposition or Byproducts

Hazardous Polymerization	May Occur		Conditions to Avoid
	Will Not Occur		

Section VI — Health Hazard Data

Route(s) of Entry: Inhalation? Skin? Ingestion?

Health Hazards (*Acute and Chronic*)

Carcinogenicity: NTP? IARC Monographs? OSHA Regulated?

Signs and Symptoms of Exposure

Medical Conditions
Generally Aggravated by Exposure

Emergency and First Aid Procedures

Section VII — Precautions for Safe Handling and Use

Steps to Be Taken in Case Material Is Released or Spilled

Waste Disposal Method

Precautions to Be Taken in Handling and Storing

Other Precautions

Section VIII — Control Measures

Respiratory Protection (*Specify Type*)

Ventilation	Local Exhaust		Special
	Mechanical (*General*)		Other

Protective Gloves	Eye Protection

Other Protective Clothing or Equipment

Work/Hygienic Practices

Page 2 ☆ USGPO 1986-491-529/45775

Figure 3-1 (*continued*)

3-3 Industrial Hygiene: Evaluation

The evaluation phase determines the extent and degree of employee exposure to toxicants and physical hazards in the workplace environment.

During the evaluation phase, the various types of existing control measures and their effectiveness are also studied. Control techniques are presented in more detail in Section 3-4.

During the evaluation study, the likelihood of large and small leaks must be considered. Sudden exposures to high concentrations, through large leaks, may lead to immediate acute effects, such as unconsciousness, burning eyes, or fits of coughing. There is rarely lasting damage to individuals if they are removed promptly from the contaminated area. In this case ready access to a clean environment is important.

Chronic effects, however, arise from repeated exposures to low concentrations, mostly by small leaks or volatilization of solid or liquid chemicals. Many toxic chemical vapors are colorless and odorless (or the toxic concentration might be below the odor threshold). Small leaks of these substances might not become obvious for months or even years. There may be permanent and serious impairments from such exposures. Special attention must be directed toward preventing and controlling low concentrations of toxic gases. In these circumstances some provision for continuous evaluation is necessary; that is, continuous or frequent and periodic sampling and analysis is important.

To establish the effectiveness of existing controls, samples are taken to determine the workers' exposure to conditions that may be harmful. If problems are evident, controls must be implemented immediately; temporary controls such as personal protective equipment can be used. Longer term and permanent controls are subsequently developed.

After the exposure data are obtained, it is necessary to compare actual exposure levels to acceptable occupational health standards, such as TLVs, PELs, or IDLH concentrations. These standards together with the actual concentrations are used to identify the potential hazards requiring better or more control measures.

Evaluating Exposures to Volatile Toxicants by Monitoring

A direct method for determining worker exposures is by continuously monitoring the air concentrations of toxicants on-line in a work environment. For continuous concentration data $C(t)$ the TWA (time-weighted average) concentration is computed using the equation

$$\text{TWA} = \frac{1}{8}\int_0^{t_w} C(t)\,dt, \tag{3-1}$$

where

$C(t)$ is the concentration (in ppm or mg/m^3) of the chemical in the air and

t_w is the worker shift time in hours.

The integral is always divided by 8 hours, independent of the length of time actually worked in the shift. Thus, if a worker is exposed for 12 hours to a concentration of chemical equal to the TLV-TWA, then the TLV-TWA has been exceeded, because the computation is normalized to 8 hours.

Continuous monitoring is not the usual situation because most facilities do not have the necessary equipment available.

The more usual case is for intermittent samples to be obtained, representing worker exposures at fixed points in time. If we assume that the concentration C_i is fixed (or averaged) over the period of time T_i, the TWA concentration is computed by

$$\text{TWA} = \frac{C_1T_1 + C_2T_2 + \cdots + C_nT_n}{8\ \text{hr}}. \tag{3-2}$$

All monitoring systems have drawbacks because (1) the workers move in and out of the exposed workplace and (2) the concentration of toxicants may vary at different locations in the work area. Industrial hygienists play an important role in the selection and placement of workplace monitoring equipment and the interpretation of the data.

If more than one chemical is present in the workplace, one procedure is to assume that the effects of the toxicants are additive (unless other information to the contrary is available). The combined exposures from multiple toxicants with different TLV-TWAs is determined from the equation

$$\sum_{i=1}^{n} \frac{C_i}{(\text{TLV-TWA})_i}, \tag{3-3}$$

where

n is the total number of toxicants,

C_i is the concentration of chemical i with respect to the other toxicants, and

$(\text{TLV-TWA})_i$ is the TLV-TWA for chemical species i.

If the sum in Equation 3-3 exceeds 1, then the workers are overexposed.

The mixture TLV-TWA can be computed from

$$(\text{TLV-TWA})_{\text{mix}} = \frac{\sum_{i=1}^{n} C_i}{\sum_{i=1}^{n} \frac{C_i}{(\text{TLV-TWA})_i}}. \tag{3-4}$$

If the sum of the concentrations of the toxicants in the mixture exceeds this amount, then the workers are overexposed.

For mixtures of toxicants with different effects (such as an acid vapor mixed with lead fume) the TLVs cannot be assumed to be additive.

Example 3-2

Air contains 5 ppm of diethylamine (TLV-TWA of 5 ppm), 20 ppm of cyclohexanol (TLV-TWA of 50 ppm), and 10 ppm of propylene oxide (TLV-TWA of 2 ppm). What is the mixture TLV-TWA and has this level been exceeded?

Solution

From Equation 3-4,

$$(\text{TLV-TWA})_{\text{mix}} = \frac{5 + 20 + 10}{\frac{5}{5} + \frac{20}{50} + \frac{10}{2}}$$

$$= 5.5 \text{ ppm.}$$

The total mixture concentration is 5 + 20 + 10 = 35 ppm. The workers are overexposed under these circumstances.

An alternative approach is to use Equation 3-3:

$$\sum_{i=1}^{3} \frac{C_i}{(\text{TLV-TWA})_i} = \frac{5}{5} + \frac{20}{50} + \frac{10}{2} = 6.4.$$

Because this quantity is greater than 1, the TLV-TWA has been exceeded.

Example 3-3

Determine the 8-hr TWA worker exposure if the worker is exposed to toluene vapors as follows:

Duration of exposure (hr)	Measured concentration (ppm)
2	110
2	330
4	90

Solution

Using Equation 3-2,

$$\text{TWA} = \frac{C_1T_1 + C_2T_2 + C_3T_3}{8}$$

$$= \frac{110(2) + 330(2) + 90(4)}{8} = 155 \text{ ppm.}$$

Because the TLV for toluene is 20 ppm, the worker is overexposed. Additional control measures need to be developed. On a temporary and immediate basis all employees working in this environment need to wear the appropriate respirators.

Example 3-4

Determine the mixture TLV at 25°C and 1 atm pressure of a mixture derived from the following liquid:

Component	Mole percent	Species TLV (ppm)
Heptane	50	400
Toluene	50	20

Solution

The solution requires the concentration of the heptane and toluene in the vapor phase. Assuming that the composition of the liquid does not change as it evaporates (the quantity is large), the vapor composition is computed using standard vapor-liquid equilibrium calculations. Assuming that Raoult's and Dalton's laws apply to this system under these conditions, the vapor composition is determined directly from the saturation vapor pressures of the pure components. Himmelblau[8] provided the following data at the specified temperature:

$$P^{\text{sat}}_{\text{heptane}} = 46.4 \text{ mm Hg},$$

$$P^{\text{sat}}_{\text{toluene}} = 28.2 \text{ mm Hg}.$$

Using Raoult's law, the partial pressures in the vapor are determined:

$$p_i = x_i P^{\text{sat}}_t,$$

$$p_{\text{heptane}} = (0.5)(46.4 \text{ mm Hg}) = 23.2 \text{ mm Hg},$$

$$p_{\text{toluene}} = (0.5)(28.2 \text{ mm Hg}) = 14.1 \text{ mm Hg}.$$

The total pressure of the toxicants is (23.2 + 14.1) = 37.3 mm Hg. From Dalton's law the mole fractions on a toxicant basis are

$$y_{\text{heptane}} = \frac{23.2 \text{ mm Hg}}{37.3 \text{ mm Hg}} = 0.622,$$

$$y_{\text{toluene}} = 1 - 0.622 = 0.378.$$

The mixture TLV is computed using Equation 3-4:

$$\text{TLV}_{\text{mix}} = \frac{1}{\dfrac{0.622}{400} + \dfrac{0.378}{20}} = 48.9 \text{ ppm}.$$

Because the vapor will always be the same concentration, the TLVs for the individual species in the mixture are

$$\text{TLV}_{\text{heptane}} = (0.622)(48.9 \text{ ppm}) = 30.4 \text{ ppm},$$

$$\text{TLV}_{\text{toluene}} = (0.378)(48.9 \text{ ppm}) = 18.5 \text{ ppm}.$$

[8]David M. Himmelblau and James B. Riggs, *Basic Principles and Calculations in Chemical Engineering,* 7th ed. (Englewood Cliffs, NJ: Prentice Hall, 2004), app. G.

If the actual concentration exceeds these levels, more control measures will be needed. For mixtures of vapors the individual species' TLVs in the mixture are significantly reduced from the TLVs of the pure substance.

Evaluating Worker Exposures to Dusts

Industrial hygiene studies include any contaminant that may cause health injuries; dusts, of course, fit this category. Toxicological theory teaches that dust particles that present the greatest hazard to the lungs are normally in the respirable particle size range of 0.2–0.5 μm (see Chapter 2). Particles larger than 0.5 μm are usually unable to penetrate the lungs, whereas those smaller than 0.2 μm settle out too slowly and are mostly exhaled with the air.

The main reason for sampling for atmospheric particulates is to estimate the concentrations that are inhaled and deposited in the lungs. Sampling methods and the interpretation of data relevant to health hazards are relatively complex; industrial hygienists, who are specialists in this technology, should be consulted when confronted with this type of problem.

Dust evaluation calculations are performed in a manner identical to that used for volatile vapors. Instead of using ppm as a concentration unit, mg/m^3 or mppcf (millions of particles per cubic foot) is more convenient.

Example 3-5

Determine the TLV for a uniform mixture of dusts containing the following particles:

Type of dust	Concentration (wt.%)	TLV (mppcf)
Dust A	70	20
Dust B	30	2.7

Solution

From Equation 3-4:

$$\text{TLV of mixture} = \frac{1}{\dfrac{C_1}{\text{TLV}_1} + \dfrac{C_2}{\text{TLV}_2}}$$

$$= \frac{1}{\dfrac{0.70}{20} + \dfrac{0.30}{2.7}}$$

$$= 6.8 \text{ mppcf.}$$

Special control measures will be required when the actual particle count (of the size range specified in the standards or by an industrial hygienist) exceeds 6.8 mppcf.

Evaluating Worker Exposures to Noise

Noise problems are common in chemical plants; this type of problem is also evaluated by industrial hygienists. If a noise problem is suspected, the industrial hygienist should immediately make the appropriate noise measurements and develop recommendations.

Noise levels are measured in decibels. A decibel (dB) is a relative logarithmic scale used to compare the intensities of two sounds. If one sound is at intensity I and another sound is at intensity I_o, then the difference in intensity levels in decibels is given by

$$\text{Noise intensity (dB)} = -10 \log_{10}\left(\frac{I}{I_o}\right). \tag{3-5}$$

Thus a sound 10 times as intense as another has an intensity level 10 dB greater.

An absolute sound scale (in dBA for absolute decibels) is defined by establishing an intensity reference. For convenience, the hearing threshold is set at 0 dBA. Table 3-10 contains dBA levels for a variety of common activities.

Some permissible noise exposure levels for single sources are provided in Table 3-11.

Noise evaluation calculations are performed identically to calculations for vapors, except that dBA is used instead of ppm and hours of exposure is used instead of concentration.

Table 3-10 Sound Intensity Levels for a Variety of Common Activities

Source of noise	Sound intensity level (dB)
Riveting (painful)	120
Punch press	110
Passing truck	100
Factory	90
Noisy office	80
Conventional speech	60
Private office	50
Average residence	40
Recording studio	30
Whisper	20
Threshold of good hearing	10
Threshold of excellent youthful hearing	0

Table 3-11 Permissible Noise Exposures[a]

Sound level (dBA)	Maximum exposure (hr)
85	16
88	10.6
90	8
91	7
92	6
94	4.6
95	4
97	3
100	2
102	1.5
105	1
110	0.5
115	0.25

[a]Combined from OSHA CFR 1910.05 and B. A. Plog and P. J. Quinlan, *Fundamentals of Industrial Hygiene*, 5th ed. (Itasca, IL: National Safety Council, 2001).

Example 3-6

Determine whether the following noise level is permissible with no additional control features:

Noise level (dBA)	Duration (hr)	Maximum allowed (hr)
85	3.6	16
95	3.0	4
110	0.5	0.5

Solution

From Equation 3-3:

$$\sum_{i=1}^{3} \frac{C_i}{(\text{TLV-TWA})_i} = \frac{3.6}{16} + \frac{3}{4} + \frac{0.5}{0.5} = 1.97.$$

Because the sum exceeds 1.0, employees in this environment are immediately required to wear ear protection. On a longer-term basis, noise reduction control methods should be developed for the specific pieces of equipment with excessive noise levels.

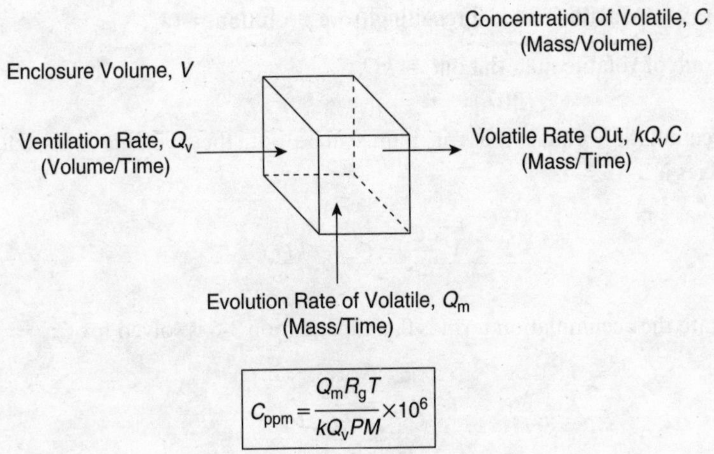

Figure 3-2 Mass balance for volatile vapor in an enclosure.

Estimating Worker Exposures to Toxic Vapors

The best procedure to determine exposures to toxic vapors is to measure the vapor concentrations directly. For design purposes estimates of vapor concentrations are frequently required in enclosed spaces, above open containers, where drums are filled, and in the area of spills.

Consider the enclosed volume shown in Figure 3-2. This enclosure is ventilated by a constant volume airflow. Volatile vapors are evolved within the enclosure. An estimate of the concentration of volatile in the air is required.

Let

C be the concentration of volatile vapor in the enclosure (mass/volume),
V be the volume of the enclosure (volume),
Q_v be the ventilation rate (volume/time),
k be the nonideal mixing factor (unitless), and
Q_m be the evolution rate of volatile material (mass/time).

The nonideal mixing factor k accounts for conditions in the enclosure that are less than well mixed. It follows that

$$\text{Total mass of volatile in volume} = VC,$$

$$\text{Accumulation of mass of volatile} = \frac{d(VC)}{dt} = V\frac{dC}{dt},$$

Mass rate of volatile material resulting from evolution = Q_m,

Mass rate of volatile material out = kQ_vC.

Because accumulation equals mass in minus mass out, the dynamic mass balance on the volatile species is

$$V\frac{dC}{dt} = Q_m - kQ_vC. \tag{3-6}$$

At steady state the accumulation term is 0, and Equation 3-6 is solved for C:

$$C = \frac{Q_m}{kQ_v}. \tag{3-7}$$

Equation 3-7 is converted to the more convenient concentration units of ppm by direct application of the ideal gas law. Let m represent mass, ρ represent mass density, and the subscripts v and b denote the volatile and bulk gas species, respectively. Then:

$$C_{ppm} = \frac{V_v}{V_b} \times 10^6 = \left(\frac{m_v/\rho_v}{V_b}\right) \times 10^6 = \left(\frac{m_v}{V_b}\right)\left(\frac{R_gT}{PM}\right) \times 10^6, \tag{3-8}$$

where

R_g is the ideal gas constant,
T is the absolute ambient temperature,
P is the absolute pressure, and
M is the molecular weight of the volatile species.

The term m_v/V_b is identical to the concentration of volatile computed using Equation 3-7. Substituting Equation 3-7 into Equation 3-8 yields

$$\boxed{C_{ppm} = \frac{Q_mR_gT}{kQ_vPM} \times 10^6.} \tag{3-9}$$

Equation 3-9 is used to determine the average concentration (in ppm) of any volatile species in an enclosure given a source term Q_m and a ventilation rate Q_v. It can be applied to the following types of exposures: a worker standing near a pool of volatile liquid, a worker standing near an opening to a storage tank, or a worker standing near an open container of volatile liquid.

Equation 3-9 includes the following important assumptions:

- The calculated concentration is an average concentration in the enclosure. Localized conditions could result in significantly higher concentrations; workers directly above an open container might be exposed to higher concentrations.

- A steady-state condition is assumed; that is, the accumulation term in the mass balance is zero.

The nonideal mixing factor varies from 0.1 to 0.5 for most practical situations.[9] For perfect mixing $k = 1$.

Example 3-7

An open toluene container in an enclosure is weighed as a function of time, and it is determined that the average evaporation rate is 0.1 g/min. The ventilation rate is 100 ft³/min. The temperature is 80°F and the pressure is 1 atm. Estimate the concentration of toluene vapor in the enclosure, and compare your answer to the TLV for toluene of 50 ppm.

Solution

Because the value of k is not known directly, it must be used as a parameter. From Equation 3-9

$$kC_{\text{ppm}} = \frac{Q_{\text{m}} R_{\text{g}} T}{Q_{\text{v}} P M} \times 10^6.$$

From the data provided

$$\begin{aligned}
Q_{\text{m}} &= 0.1 \text{ g/min} = 2.20 \times 10^{-4} \text{ lb}_{\text{m}}/\text{min},\\
R_{\text{g}} &= 0.7302 \text{ ft}^3 \text{ atm/lb-mol °R},\\
T &= 80°\text{F} = 540°\text{R},\\
Q_{\text{v}} &= 100 \text{ ft}^3/\text{min},\\
M &= 92 \text{ lb}_{\text{m}}/\text{lb-mol},\\
P &= 1 \text{ atm}.
\end{aligned}$$

Substituting into the equation for kC_{ppm}:

$$\begin{aligned}
kC_{\text{ppm}} &= \frac{(2.20 \times 10^{-4} \text{ lb}_{\text{m}}/\text{min})(0.7302 \text{ ft}^3 \text{ atm/lb-mol°R})(540°\text{R})}{(100 \text{ ft}^3/\text{min})(1 \text{ atm})(92 \text{ lb}_{\text{m}}/\text{lb-mol})} \times 10^6\\
&= 9.43 \text{ ppm}.
\end{aligned}$$

Because k varies from 0.1 to 0.5, the concentration is expected to vary from 18.9 ppm to 94.3 ppm. Actual vapor sampling is recommended to ensure that the TLV of 20 ppm is not exceeded.

Estimating the Vaporization Rate of a Liquid

Liquids with high saturation vapor pressures evaporate faster. As a result, the evaporation rate (mass/time) is expected to be a function of the saturation vapor pressure. In reality,

[9] R. Craig Matthiessen, "Estimating Chemical Exposure Levels in the Workplace," *Chemical Engineering Progress* (Apr. 1986), p. 30.

for vaporization into stagnant air, the vaporization rate is proportional to the difference between the saturation vapor pressure and the partial pressure of the vapor in the stagnant air; that is,

$$Q_m \alpha (P^{sat} - p), \tag{3-10}$$

where

P^{sat} is the saturation vapor pressure of the pure liquid at the temperature of the liquid and
p is the partial pressure of the vapor in the bulk stagnant gas above the liquid.

A more generalized expression for the vaporization rate is available[10]:

$$Q_m = \frac{MKA(P^{sat} - p)}{R_g T_L}, \tag{3-11}$$

where

Q_m is the evaporation rate (mass/time),
M is the molecular weight of the volatile substance,
K is a mass transfer coefficient (length/time) for an area A,
R_g is the ideal gas constant, and
T_L is the absolute temperature of the liquid.

For many situations, $P^{sat} \gg p$, and Equation 3-11 is simplified to

$$\boxed{Q_m = \frac{MKAP^{sat}}{R_g T_L}.} \tag{3-12}$$

Equation 3-12 is used to estimate the vaporization rate of volatile from an open vessel or from a spill of liquid.

The vaporization rate or source term, determined by Equation 3-12, is used in Equation 3-9 to estimate the concentration (in ppm) of a volatile in an enclosure resulting from evaporation of a liquid:

$$C_{ppm} = \frac{KATP^{sat}}{kQ_v PT_L} \times 10^6. \tag{3-13}$$

[10]Steven R. Hanna and Peter J. Drivas, *Guidelines for the Use of Vapor Cloud Dispersion Models*, 2nd ed. (New York: American Institute of Chemical Engineers, 1996).

For most situations $T = T_L$, and Equation 3-13 is simplified to

$$C_{\text{ppm}} = \frac{KAP^{\text{sat}}}{kQ_vP} \times 10^6. \tag{3-14}$$

The gas mass transfer coefficient is estimated using the relationship[11]

$$K = aD^{2/3}, \tag{3-15}$$

where

a is a constant and
D is the gas-phase diffusion coefficient.

Equation 3-15 is used to determine the ratio of the mass transfer coefficients between the species of interest K and a reference species K_o:

$$\frac{K}{K_o} = \left(\frac{D}{D_o}\right)^{2/3}. \tag{3-16}$$

The gas-phase diffusion coefficients are estimated from the molecular weights M of the species[12]:

$$\frac{D}{D_o} = \sqrt{\frac{M_o}{M}}. \tag{3-17}$$

Equation 3-17 is combined with Equation 3-16, giving

$$K = K_o\left(\frac{M_o}{M}\right)^{1/3}. \tag{3-18}$$

Water is most frequently used as a reference substance; it has a mass transfer coefficient[13] of 0.83 cm/s.

Example 3-8

A large open tank with a 5-ft diameter contains toluene. Estimate the evaporation rate from this tank assuming a temperature of 77°F and a pressure of 1 atm. If the ventilation rate is 3000 ft^3/min, estimate the concentration of toluene in this workplace enclosure.

[11] Louis J. Thibodeaux, *Environmental Chemodynamics*, 2nd ed. (New York: Wiley, 1996), p. 85.
[12] Gordon M. Barrow, *Physical Chemistry,* 2nd ed. (New York: McGraw-Hill, 1966), p. 19.
[13] Matthiessen, "Estimating Chemical Exposure," p. 33.

Solution

The molecular weight of toluene is 92. The mass transfer coefficient is estimated from Equation 3-18 using water as a reference:

$$K = (0.83 \text{ cm/s})\left(\frac{18}{92}\right)^{1/3} = 0.482 \text{ cm/s} = 0.949 \text{ ft/min}.$$

The saturation vapor pressure is given in Example 3-4:

$$P^{\text{sat}}_{\text{toluene}} = 28.2 \text{ mm Hg} = 0.0371 \text{ atm}.$$

The pool area is

$$A = \frac{\pi d^2}{4} = \frac{(3.14)(5 \text{ ft})^2}{4} = 19.6 \text{ ft}^2.$$

The evaporation rate is computed using Equation 3-12:

$$Q_{\text{m}} = \frac{MKAP^{\text{sat}}}{R_{\text{g}}T_{\text{L}}}$$

$$= \frac{(92 \text{ lb}_{\text{m}}/\text{lb-mol})(0.949 \text{ ft/min})(19.6 \text{ ft}^2)(0.0371 \text{ atm})}{(0.7302 \text{ ft}^3 \text{ atm/lb-mol°R})(537\text{°R})}$$

$$= 0.162 \text{ lb}_{\text{m}}/\text{min}.$$

The concentration is estimated using Equation 3-14 with k as a parameter:

$$kC_{\text{ppm}} = \frac{KAP^{\text{sat}}}{Q_{\text{v}}P} \times 10^6$$

$$= \frac{(0.949 \text{ ft/min})(19.6 \text{ ft}^2)(0.0371 \text{ atm})}{(3000 \text{ ft}^3/\text{min})(1 \text{ atm})} \times 10^6$$

$$= 230 \text{ ppm}.$$

The concentration will range from 460 ppm to 2300 ppm, depending on the value of k. Because the TLV for toluene is 20 ppm, additional ventilation is recommended, or the amount of exposed surface area should be reduced. The amount of ventilation required to reduce the worst-case concentration (2300 ppm) to 50 ppm is

$$Q_{\text{v}} = (3000 \text{ ft}^3/\text{min})\left(\frac{2300 \text{ ppm}}{20 \text{ ppm}}\right) = 345{,}000 \text{ ft}^3/\text{min}.$$

This represents an impractical level of general ventilation. Potential solutions to this problem include containing the toluene in a closed vessel or using local ventilation at the vessel opening.

Estimating Worker Exposures during Vessel Filling Operations

For vessels being filled with liquid, volatile emissions are generated from two sources, as shown in Figure 3-3. These sources are

- Evaporation of the liquid, represented by Equation 3-14, and
- Displacement of the vapor in the vapor space by the liquid filling the vessel

The net generation of volatile is the sum of the two sources:

$$Q_m = (Q_m)_1 + (Q_m)_2, \tag{3-19}$$

where

$(Q_m)_1$ represents the source resulting from evaporation and
$(Q_m)_2$ represents the source resulting from displacement.

The source term $(Q_m)_1$ is computed using Equation 3-12. $(Q_m)_2$ is determined by assuming that the vapor is completely saturated with the volatile. An adjustment is introduced later for less than saturated conditions. Let

V_c be the volume of the container (volume),
r_f be the constant filling rate of the vessel (time^{-1}),

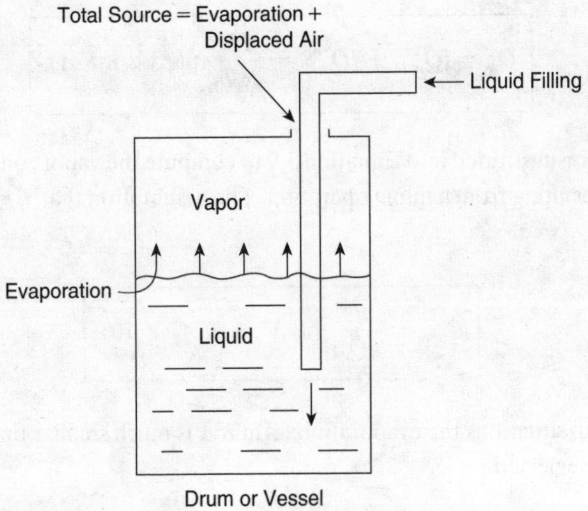

Figure 3-3 Evaporation and displacement from a filling vessel.

P^{sat} be the saturation vapor pressure of the volatile liquid, and
T_L be the absolute temperature of the container and liquid.

It follows that $r_f V_c$ is the volumetric rate of bulk vapor being displaced from the drum (volume/time). Also, if ρ_v is the density of the volatile vapor, $r_f V_c \rho_v$ is the mass rate of volatile displaced from the container (mass/time). Using the ideal gas law,

$$\rho_v = \frac{MP^{\text{sat}}}{R_g T_L}, \tag{3-20}$$

and it follows that

$$(Q_m)_2 = \frac{MP^{\text{sat}}}{R_g T_L} r_f V_c. \tag{3-21}$$

Equation 3-21 can be modified for container vapors that are not saturated with the volatile. Let ϕ represent this adjustment factor; then,

$$(Q_m)_2 = \frac{MP^{\text{sat}}}{R_g T_L} \phi r_f V_c. \tag{3-22}$$

For splash filling (filling from the top of a container with the liquid splashing to the bottom), $\phi = 1$. For subsurface filling[14] (by a dip leg to the bottom of the tank), $\phi = 0.5$.

The net source term resulting from filling is derived by combining Equations 3-12 and 3-22 with Equation 3-19:

$$\boxed{Q_m = (Q_m)_1 + (Q_m)_2 = \frac{MP^{\text{sat}}}{R_g T_L}(\phi r_f V_c + KA).} \tag{3-23}$$

This source term is substituted into Equation 3-9 to compute the vapor concentration (in ppm) in an enclosure resulting from a filling operation. The assumption that $T = T_L$ is also invoked. The result is

$$\boxed{C_{\text{ppm}} = \frac{P^{\text{sat}}}{kQ_v P}(\phi r_f V_c + KA) \times 10^6.} \tag{3-24}$$

For many practical situations the evaporation term KA is much smaller than the displacement term and can be neglected.

[14]Matthiessen, "Estimating Chemical Exposure," p. 33.

Example 3-9

Railroad cars are being splash-filled with toluene. The 10,000-gal cars are being filled at the rate of one every 8 hr. The filling hole in the tank car is 4 in. in diameter. Estimate the concentration of toluene vapor as a result of this filling operation. The ventilation rate is estimated at 3000 ft^3/min. The temperature is 77°F and the pressure is 1 atm.

Solution

The concentration is estimated using Equation 3-24. From Example 3-8, $K = 0.949$ ft/min and $P^{\text{sat}} = 0.0371$ atm. The area of the filling hole is

$$A = \frac{\pi d^2}{4} = \frac{(3.14)(4\text{ in})^2}{(4)(144\text{ in}^2/\text{ft}^2)} = 0.0872\text{ ft}^2.$$

Thus

$$KA = (0.949\text{ ft/min})(0.0872\text{ ft}^2) = 0.0827\text{ ft}^3/\text{min}.$$

The filling rate r_{f} is

$$r_{\text{f}} = \left(\frac{1}{8\text{ hr}}\right)\left(\frac{1\text{ hr}}{60\text{ min}}\right) = 0.00208\text{ min}^{-1}.$$

For splash filling the nonideal filling factor ϕ is 1.0. The displacement term in Equation 3-24 is

$$\phi r_{\text{f}} V_{\text{c}} = (1.0)(0.00208\text{ min}^{-1})(10{,}000\text{ gal})\left(\frac{\text{ft}^3}{7.48\text{ gal}}\right) = 2.78\text{ ft}^3/\text{min}.$$

As expected, the evaporation term is small compared to the displacement term. The concentration is computed from Equation 3-24, using k as a parameter:

$$kC_{\text{ppm}} = \frac{P^{\text{sat}}\phi r_{\text{f}} V_{\text{c}}}{Q_{\text{v}}P} = \frac{(0.0371\text{ atm})(2.78\text{ ft}^3/\text{min})}{(3000\text{ ft}^3/\text{min})(1\text{ atm})} \times 10^6$$
$$= 34.4\text{ ppm}.$$

The actual concentration could range from 69 ppm to 344 ppm, depending on the value of k. Sampling to ensure that the concentration is below 20 ppm is recommended. For subsurface filling, $\phi = 0.5$, and the concentration range is reduced to 35–172 ppm.

3-4 Industrial Hygiene: Control

After potential health hazards are identified and evaluated, the appropriate control techniques must be developed and installed. This requires the application of appropriate technology for reducing workplace exposures.

The types of control techniques used in the chemical industry are illustrated in Table 3-12.

Table 3-12 Chemical Plant Industrial Hygiene Methods

Type and explanation	Typical techniques
Inherently safer	
Eliminate or reduce hazard	Eliminate chemical entirely. Reduce chemical inventories, including raw materials, intermediates, and products. Replace chemical with less hazardous chemical. Decrease temperature and pressure of chemical. Reduce pipeline size to reduce hold-up inventory.
Enclosures	
Enclose room or equipment and place under negative pressure.	Enclose hazardous operations such as sample points. Seal rooms, sewers, ventilation, and the like. Use analyzers and instruments to observe inside equipment. Shield high-temperature surfaces.
Local ventilation	
Contain and exhaust hazardous substances.	Use properly designed hoods. Use hoods for charging and discharging. Use ventilation at drumming station. Use local exhaust at sample points. Keep exhaust systems under negative pressure.
Dilution ventilation	
Design ventilation systems to control low-level toxics.	Design locker rooms with good ventilation and special areas or enclosures for contaminated clothing. Design ventilation to isolate operations from rooms and offices. Design filter press rooms with directional ventilation.
Wet methods	
Use wet methods to minimize contamination with dusts.	Clean vessels chemically vs. sandblasting. Use water sprays for cleaning. Clean areas frequently. Use water sprays to shield trenches or pump seals.
Good housekeeping	
Keep toxicants and dusts contained.	Use dikes around tanks and pumps. Provide water and steam connections for area washing. Provide lines for flushing and cleaning. Provide well-designed sewer system with emergency containment.
Personal protection	
As last line of defense.	Use safety glasses and face shields. Use aprons, arm shields, and space suits. Wear appropriate respirators; airline respirators are required when oxygen concentration is less than 19.5%.

Table 3-13 Personal Protective Equipment, Not Including Respirators[a]

Type	Description
Hard hat	Protects head from falling equipment and bumps
Safety glasses	Impact-resistant lenses with side shields
Chemical splash goggles, gas-tight	Suitable for liquids and fumes
Steel-toed safety shoes	Protects against dropped equipment
Wraparound face shield	Resistant to most chemicals
Vinyl apron	Resists most chemicals
Splash suit	Viton or butyl rubber for nonflammable exposures
Umbilical cord suit	Used with external air supply
Rubber oversleeves	Protects forearms
PVC-coated gloves	Resists acids and bases
PVC and nitrile knee boots	Resists acids, oils, and greases
Ear plugs	Protects against high noise levels

[a] *Lab Safety Supply Catalog* (Janesville, WI: Lab Safety Supply Inc.). Manufacturers' technical specifications must always be consulted.

Designing control methods is an important and creative task. During the design process, the designer must pay particular attention to ensure that the newly designed control technique provides the desired control and that the new control technique itself does not create another hazard, sometimes even more hazardous than the original problem.

The two major control techniques are environmental controls and personal protection. Environmental control reduces exposure by reducing the concentration of toxicants in the workplace environment. This includes enclosure, local ventilation, dilution ventilation, wet methods, and good housekeeping, as discussed previously. Personal protection prevents or reduces exposure by providing a barrier between the worker and the workplace environment. This barrier is usually worn by the worker, hence the designation "personal." Typical types of personal protective equipment are listed in Table 3-13.

Respirators

Respirators are routinely found in chemical laboratories and plants. Respirators should be used only

- On a temporary basis, until regular control methods can be implemented
- As emergency equipment, to ensure worker safety in the event of an accident
- As a last resort, in the event that environmental control techniques are unable to provide satisfactory protection

Respirators always compromise worker ability. A worker with a respirator is unable to perform or respond as well as a worker without one. Various types of respirators are listed in Table 3-14.

Table 3-14 Respirators Useful to the Chemical Industry[a]

Exposure	Type	Example of a commercial brand	Limitations
Dust	Mouth and nose dust mask	MSA Comfo Classic half-mask	$O_2 > 19.5\%$ N- and R-series filters Less than 8 hours usage Total dust loading <200 mg Concentrations less than IDLH Exposure limits must be known for chemicals
Chemical vapors	Mouth and nose with chemical cartridge	MSA Comfo Classic half-mask	$O_2 > 19.5\%$ Concentrations less than IDLH. Concentrations must not exceed 10 times exposure limit. Must prevent cartridge breakthrough. Many cartridges available for chemicals. Exposure limits must be known for chemicals
Chemical vapors	Full face mask with chemical cartridge	MSA Advantage series MSA Gas Mask	$O_2 > 19.5\%$ Concentrations less than IDLH. Concentrations must not exceed 50 times exposure limit. Must prevent cartridge breakthrough. Many cartridges available for chemicals. Exposure limits must be known for chemicals.
Chemical vapors and dusts	Self-contained breathing apparatus (SCBA)	MSA Firehawk	Used for CBRN: chemical, biological, radiological, and nuclear exposures. Fit test required. Can be used for concentrations greater than the IDLH. Limited time use depending on air tank capacity.

[a]Information from Mine Safety Appliances web site, *www.msa.com*. Follow more detailed manufacturers' specifications and limitations. All respirators require training and medical surveillance.

Respirators can be used improperly and/or can be damaged to the extent that they do not provide the needed protection. OSHA and NIOSH have developed standards for using respirators,[15] including fit testing (to ensure that the device does not leak excessively), periodic inspections (to ensure that the equipment works properly), specified use applications (to ensure that the equipment is used for the correct job), training (to ensure that it is used properly), and record keeping (to ensure that the program is operating efficiently). All industrial users of respirators are legally bound to understand and fulfill these OSHA requirements.

Ventilation

For environmental control of airborne toxic material the most common method of choice is ventilation, for the following reasons:

- Ventilation can quickly remove dangerous concentrations of flammable and toxic materials.
- Ventilation can be highly localized, reducing the quantity of air moved and the equipment size.
- Ventilation equipment is readily available and can be easily installed.
- Ventilation equipment can be added to an existing facility.

The major disadvantage of ventilation is the operating cost. Substantial electrical energy may be needed to drive the potentially large fans, and the cost to heat or cool the large quantities of fresh air can be large. These operating costs need to be considered when evaluating alternatives.

Ventilation is based on two principles: (1) dilute the contaminant below the target concentration, and (2) remove the contaminant before workers are exposed.

Ventilation systems are composed of fans and ducts. The fans produce a small pressure drop (less than 0.1 psi) that moves the air. The best system is a negative pressure system, with the fans located at the exhaust end of the system, pulling air out. This ensures that leaks in the system draw air in from the workplace rather than expel contaminated air from the ducts into the workplace. This is shown in Figure 3-4.

There are two types of ventilation techniques: local and dilution ventilation.

[15]*NIOSH Respirator Selection Logic,* DHHS-NIOSH Publication 2005-100 (Washington, DC: US Department of Health and Human Services, 2004).

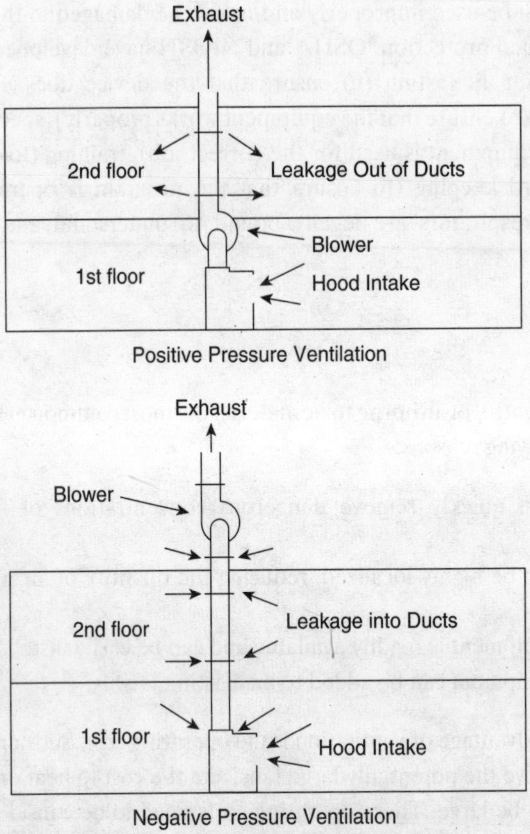

Figure 3-4 The difference between a positive and a negative pressure ventilation system. The negative pressure system ensures that contaminants do not leak into workplace environments.

Local Ventilation

The most common example of local ventilation is the hood. A hood is a device that either completely encloses the source of contaminant and/or moves the air in such a fashion as to carry the contaminant to an exhaust device. There are several types of hoods:

- An *enclosed hood* completely contains the source of contaminant.
- An *exterior hood* continuously draws contaminants into an exhaust from some distance away.
- A *receiving hood* is an exterior hood that uses the discharge motion of the contaminant for collection.
- A *push-pull hood* uses a stream of air from a supply to push contaminants toward an exhaust system.

The most common example of an enclosed hood is the laboratory hood. A standard laboratory utility hood is shown in Figure 3-5. Fresh air is drawn through the window area of the hood and is removed out the top through a duct. The airflow profiles within the hood are highly dependent on the location of the window sash. It is important to keep the sash open a few inches, minimally, to ensure adequate fresh air. Likewise, the sash should never be fully opened because contaminants might escape. The baffle which may be present at the rear of the hood ensures that contaminants are removed from the working surface and the rear lower corner.

Another type of laboratory hood is the bypass hood, shown in Figure 3-6. For this design bypass air is supplied through a grille at the top of the hood. This ensures the availability of fresh air to sweep out contaminants in the hood. The bypass air supply is reduced as the hood sash is opened.

The advantages of enclosed hoods are that they

- Completely eliminate exposure to workers
- Require minimal airflow
- Provide a containment device in the event of fire or explosion, and
- Provide a shield to the worker by means of a sliding door on the hood

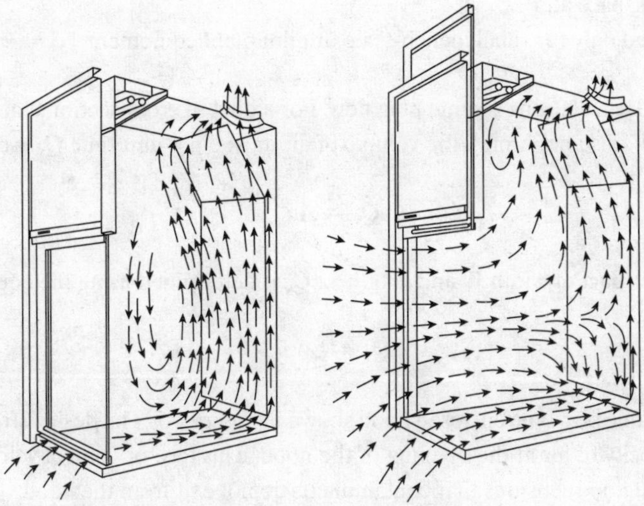

Figure 3-5 Standard utility laboratory hood. Airflow patterns and control velocity are dependent on sash height. Source: N. Irving Sax, *Dangerous Properties of Industrial Materials,* 4th ed. (New York: Van Nostrand Reinhold, 1975), p. 74.

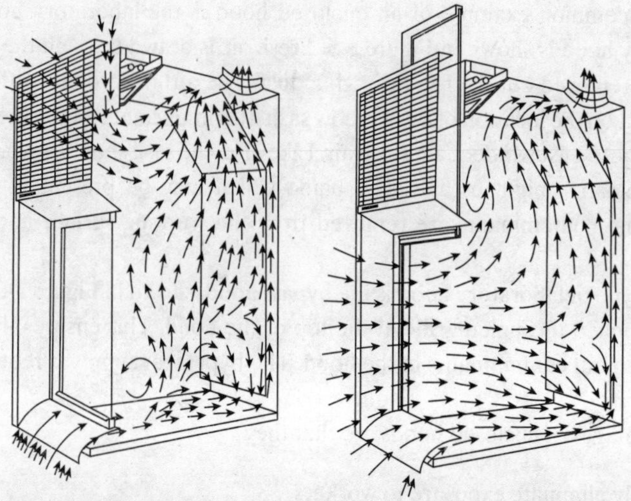

Figure 3-6 Standard bypass laboratory hood. The bypass air is controlled by the height of the sash. Source: N. Irving Sax, *Dangerous Properties of Industrial Materials,* 4th ed. (New York: Van Nostrand Reinhold, 1975), p. 75.

The disadvantages of hoods are that they

- Limit workspace and
- Can be used only for small, bench-scale or pilot plant equipment

Most hood calculations assume plug flow. For a duct of cross-sectional area A and average air velocity $\overline{u}$ (distance/time), the volume of air moved per unit time Q_v is computed from

$$Q_v = A\overline{u}. \tag{3-25}$$

For a rectangular duct of width W and length L, Q_v is determined using the equation

$$Q_v = LW\overline{u}. \tag{3-26}$$

Consider the simple box-type enclosed hood shown in Figure 3-7. The design strategy is to provide a fixed velocity of air at the opening of the hood. This face or control velocity (referring to the face of the hood) ensures that contaminants do not exit from the hood.

The required control velocity depends on the toxicity of the material, the depth of the hood, and the evolution rate of the contaminant. Shallower hoods need higher control velocities to prevent contaminants from exiting the front. However, experience has shown that higher velocities can lead to the formation of a turbulent eddy from the bottom of the sash;

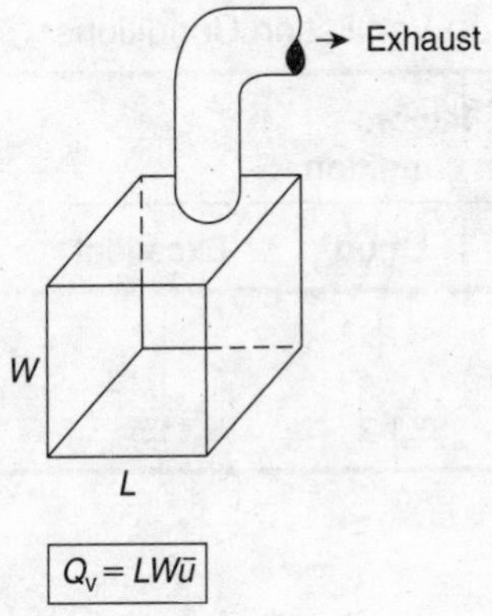

Q_v = Volumetric Flow Rate, Volume/Time
L = Length
W = Width
$\bar{u}$ = Required Control Velocity

Figure 3-7 Determining the total volumetric airflow rate for a box-type hood. For general operation a control velocity of between 80 and 120 feet per minute (fpm) is desired.

backflow of contaminated air is possible. For general operation a control velocity between 80 and 120 feet per minute (fpm) is suggested.

Instruments are available for measuring the airflow velocity at specific points of the hood window opening. Testing is an OSHA requirement.

The airflow velocity is a function of the sash height and the blower speed. Arrows are frequently used to indicate the proper sash height to ensure a specified face velocity.

Design equations are available for a wide variety of hood and duct shapes.[16]

Other types of local ventilation methods include "elephant trunks" and free-hanging canopies and plenums. The elephant trunk is simply a flexible vent duct that is positioned near a source of contaminant. It is most frequently used for loading and unloading toxic materials from drums and vessels. Free-hanging canopies and plenums can be either fixed in position or attached to a flexible duct to enable movement. These methods will most likely expose workers to toxicants, but in diluted amounts.

Dilution Ventilation

If the contaminant cannot be placed in a hood and must be used in an open area or room, dilution ventilation is necessary. Unlike hood ventilation, where the airflow prevents worker exposure, dilution ventilation always exposes the worker but in amounts diluted by fresh air. Dilution ventilation always requires more airflow than local ventilation; operating expenses can be substantial.

[16] *Industrial Ventilation: A Manual of Recommended Practice,* 27th ed. (Cincinnati, OH: American Conference of Governmental Industrial Hygienists, 2010).

Table 3-15 Nonideal Mixing Factor *k* for Various Dilution Ventilation Conditions[a]

Vapor concentration (ppm)	Dust concentration (mppcf)	Mixing factor: Ventilation condition			
		Poor	Average	Good	Excellent
over 500	50	1/7	1/4	1/3	1/2
101–500	20	1/8	1/5	1/4	1/3
0–100	5	1/11	1/8	1/7	1/6

[a]Sax, *Dangerous Properties*, p. 29. The values reported here are the *reciprocal* of Sax's values.

Equations 3-9, 3-12, and 3-14 are used to compute the ventilation rates required. Table 3-15 lists values for *k*, the nonideal mixing factor used with these equations.

For exposures to multiple sources the dilution air requirement is computed for each individual source. The total dilution requirement is the sum of the individual dilution requirements.

The following restrictions should be considered before implementing dilution ventilation:

- The contaminant must not be highly toxic.
- The contaminant must be evolved at a uniform rate.
- Workers must remain a suitable distance from the source to ensure proper dilution of the contaminant.
- Scrubbing systems must not be required to treat the air before exhaust into the environment.

Example 3-10

Xylene is used as a solvent in paint. A certain painting operation evaporates an estimated 3 gal of xylene in an 8-hr shift. The ventilation quality is rated as average. Determine the quantity of dilution ventilation air required to maintain the xylene concentration below 100 ppm, the TLV-TWA. Also, compute the air required if the operation is carried out in an enclosed hood with an opening of 50 ft^2 and a face velocity of 100 ft/min. The temperature is 77°F and the pressure is 1 atm. The specific gravity of the xylene is 0.864, and its molecular weight is 106.

Solution

The evaporation rate of xylene is

$$Q_m = \left(\frac{3 \text{ gal}}{8 \text{ hr}}\right)\left(\frac{1 \text{ hr}}{60 \text{ min}}\right)\left(\frac{0.1337 \text{ ft}^3}{1 \text{ gal}}\right)\left(\frac{62.4 \text{ lb}_m}{\text{ft}^3}\right)(0.864)$$

$$= 0.0450 \text{ lb}_m/\text{min}.$$

From Table 3-12, for average ventilation and a vapor concentration of 100 ppm, $k = 1/8 = 0.125$. With Equation 3-9, we solve for Q_v:

$$Q_v = \frac{Q_m R_g T}{k C_{ppm} P M} \times 10^6$$

$$= \frac{(0.0450\ \text{lb}_m/\text{min})(0.7302\ \text{ft}^3\ \text{atm/lb-mol°R})(537°\text{R})}{(0.125)(100\ \text{ppm})(1\ \text{atm})(106\ \text{lb}_m/\text{lb-mol})} \times 10^6$$

$$= 13{,}300\ \text{ft}^3/\text{min required dilution air.}$$

For a hood with an open area of 50 ft², using Equation 3-25 and assuming a required control velocity of 100 fpm, we get

$$Q_v = A\bar{u} = (50\ \text{ft}^2)(100\ \text{ft/min}) = 5000\ \text{ft}^3/\text{min}.$$

The hood requires significantly less airflow than dilution ventilation and prevents worker exposure completely.

On-Line Resources

The National Institute for Occupational Safety and Health (NIOSH), *www.cdc.gov/niosh*.

U.S. Code of Federal Regulations, *www.gpoaccess.gov*.

U.S. Department of Homeland Security (DHS), *www.dhs.gov*.

U.S. Occupational Safety and Health Administration (OSHA), *www.osha.gov*.

Suggested Reading

Industrial Hygiene

Roger L. Brauer, *Safety and Health for Engineers*, 2nd ed. (NY: Wiley Interscience, 2005).

Richard J. Lewis, ed. *Sax's Dangerous Properties of Industrial Materials*, 11th ed. (Hoboken, NJ: John Wiley, 2005).

Barbara A. Plog and Patricia J. Quinlan, *Fundamentals of Industrial Hygiene*, 5th ed. (Itasca, IL: National Safety Council, 2001).

Vernon E. Rose and Barbara Cohrssen, *Patty's Industrial Hygiene*, 6th ed. (Hoboken, NJ: John Wiley, 2011).

Security

Center for Chemical Process Safety (CCPS), *Guidelines for Managing and Analyzing the Security Vulnerabilities of Fixed Chemical Sites* (New York: American Institute of Chemical Engineers, 2002).

David A. Moore, "Security," *Perry's Chemical Engineers' Handbook*, 8th ed., Don W. Green and Robert H. Perry, eds. (New York: McGraw-Hill, 2008), pp. 23–104 to 23–109.

Ventilation

Industrial Ventilation: A Manual of Recommended Practice, 27th ed. (Cincinnati, OH: American Conference of Governmental Industrial Hygienists, 2010).

Problems

3-1. Determine (a) whether the following chemicals are covered under the PSM regulation (29 CFR 1910.119) and (b) their threshold quantities: acrolein, hydrogen chloride, phosgene, propane, ethylene oxide, and methanol.

3-2. Determine (a) whether the following chemicals are covered under the PSM regulation and (b) their threshold quantities: ammonia (anhydrous), hydrogen selenide, formaldehyde, methane, and ethanol.

3-3. Determine whether the following chemicals (a) are covered under the RMP (40 CFR 68.130) and (b) are listed as toxic or flammable. If they are listed, (c) what are their threshold quantities? The chemicals are acrolein, hydrogen chloride, phosgene, propane, ethylene oxide, and methanol.

3-4. Determine whether the following chemicals (a) are covered under the RMP and (b) are listed as toxic or flammable. If they are listed, (c) what are their threshold quantities? The chemicals are ammonia (anhydrous), hydrogen selenide, formaldehyde, methane, and ethanol.

3-5. In reviewing the results of Problems 3-1 to 3-4, describe why the threshold quantities are lower for the PSM-regulated chemicals than for the RMP-regulated chemicals.

3-6. Review the details of the RMP (40 CFR 68), and describe the three program categories that are used for consequence modeling.

3-7. Review the details of the RMP (40 CFR 68), and describe the endpoint parameters for consequence analyses for the worst-case scenarios.

3-8. Review the details of the RMP (40 CFR 68), and describe the endpoint parameters for consequence analyses for the alternative case scenarios.

3-9. Review the RMP (40 CFR 68) to determine the conditions that need to be used for dispersion modeling for the worst-case scenarios.

3-10. Review the RMP (40 CFR 68) to determine the conditions that need to be used for dispersion modeling for the alternative case scenarios.

3-11. Describe several typical alternative case scenarios for an RMP study.

3-12. A process plant inventories the following chemicals: vinyl chloride, methyl ethyl ketone, ethylene oxide, styrene, and cyclohexane. Determine the hazards associated with these chemicals. What additional information might you request to perform an appropriate assessment of the risk associated with these chemicals?

3-13. The TLV-TWA for a substance is 150 ppm. A worker begins a work shift at 8 AM and completes the shift at 5 PM. A one-hour lunch break is included between 12 noon and 1 PM, when it can be assumed that no exposure to the chemical occurs.

The data were taken in the work area at the times indicated. Has the worker exceeded the TLV specification?

Time	Concentration (ppm)
8:10 AM	110
9:05 AM	130
10:07 AM	143
11:20 AM	162
12:12 PM	142
1:17 PM	157
2:03 PM	159
3:13 PM	165
4:01 PM	153
5:00 PM	130

3-14. Air contains 4 ppm of carbon tetrachloride and 25 ppm of 1,1-dichloroethane. Compute the mixture TLV, and determine whether this value has been exceeded.

3-15. A substance has a TLV-TWA of 200 ppm, a TLV-STEL of 250 ppm, and a TLV-C of 300 ppm. The data in the following table were taken in a work area:

Time	Concentration (ppm)
8:01 AM	185
9:17 AM	240
10:05 AM	270
11:22 AM	230
12:08 PM	190
1:06 PM	150
2:05 PM	170
3:09 PM	165
4:00 PM	160
5:05 PM	130

A worker on an 8-hour shift is exposed to this toxic vapor. Is the exposure within compliance? If not, what are the violations? Assume that the worker is at lunch between the hours of 12 noon to 1 PM and is not exposed to the chemical during that time.

Problems 3-16 through 3-19 apply to toluene and benzene. The following data are available for these materials:

	Benzene (C_6H_6)	Toluene (C_7H_8)
Molecular weight	78.11	92.13
Specific gravity	0.8794	0.866
TLV (ppm)	0.5	20

Saturation vapor pressures:

$$\ln(P^{sat}) = A - \frac{B}{C + T},$$

where P^{sat} is the saturation vapor pressure in mm Hg, T is the temperature in K, and A, B, and C are the constants, given by the following:

	A	B	C
Benzene	15.9008	2788.51	−52.36
Toluene	16.0137	3096.52	−53.67

3-16. Compute the concentration (in ppm) of the saturated vapor with air above a solution of pure toluene. Compute the concentration (in ppm) of the equilibrium vapor with air above a solution of 50 mol % toluene and benzene. The temperature is 80°F and the total pressure is 1 atm.

3-17. Compute the density of pure air and the density of air contaminated with 100 ppm benzene. Do the densities of these two gases differ enough to ensure a higher concentration on floors and other low spots? The temperature is 70°F and the pressure is 1 atm.

3-18. Equations 3-12 and 3-14 represent the evaporation of a pure liquid. Modify these equations to represent the evaporation of a mixture of ideal miscible liquids.

3-19. Benzene and toluene form an ideal liquid mixture. A mixture composed of 50 mol % benzene is used in a chemical plant. The temperature is 80°F, and the pressure is 1 atm.

a. Determine the mixture TLV.

b. Determine the evaporation rate per unit area for this mixture.

c. A drum with a 2-in-diameter bung is used to contain the mixture. Determine the ventilation rate required to maintain the vapor concentration below the TLV. The ventilation quality within the vicinity of this operation is average.

3-20. A laboratory hood has an opening with a length of 4 ft and a height of 3 ft. The hood depth is 18 in. This hood will be used for an operation involving trichloroethylene (TCE) (TLV-TWA: 10 ppm). The TCE will be used in liquid form at room temperature. Determine an appropriate control velocity for this hood, and calculate the total airflow rate.

3-21. Normal air contains about 21% oxygen by volume. The human body is sensitive to reductions in oxygen concentration; concentrations below 19.5% are dangerous, and concentrations below 16% can cause distress. Respiratory equipment without self-contained air supplies must never be used in atmospheres below 19.5% oxygen.

A storage tank of 1000 ft^3 capacity must be cleaned before reuse. Proper procedures must be used to ensure that the oxygen concentration of the air within the tank is adequate.

Compute the cubic feet of additional nitrogen at 77°F and 1 atm that will reduce the oxygen concentration within the tank to (a) 19.5% and (b) 16%. Oxygen concentrations within tanks and enclosures can be reduced significantly by small amounts of inert elements!

3-22. It is desired to operate the hood of Problem 3-20 so that the vapor concentration in the hood plenum is below the lower explosion limit of 12.5% by volume. Estimate the minimum control velocity required to achieve this objective. The amount of TCE evaporated within the hood is 5.3 lb per hour. The molecular weight of TCE is 131.4. The temperature is 70°F and the pressure is 1 atm.

3-23. Spill containment should be provided when transporting chemicals in a laboratory.

A 2-liter bottle of tetrahydrofuran (THF) (C_4H_8O) must be transported from a laboratory storage cabinet to a hood. If an accident occurs and the container is broken, the THF will form an evaporating pool, resulting in a vapor concentration within the lab.

Consider two accident scenarios:

a. The THF is transferred without any containment. Assume that upon breakage of the container a pool of 1-cm depth is formed. Estimate the vapor concentration in the laboratory in ppm.

b. The THF is transferred using a tray with dimensions of 15 cm × 15 cm. If the container breaks, a pool will form completely within the container. Estimate the vapor concentration in the laboratory in ppm.

c. Compare the two values. Based on the equations, how does the vapor concentration scale with the area of the pool, that is, linear, quadratic, etc.? What recommendation can you make with respect to the size of the tray?

Assume that the temperature is 25°C and the pressure is 1 atm. Also assume a ventilation rate of 0.5 m^3/s in the laboratory.

For THF the following properties are available:

Molecular weight:	72.12
Vapor pressure:	114 mm Hg
Liquid density:	888 kg/m^3
TLV-TWA:	50 ppm

3-24. A worker splash-fills 400 liters of tetrahydrofuran (THF) (C_4H_8O) over a 5-min period into a reactor vessel of 1500 liters total volume. The filling is done through a manway of 0.5 m diameter. The local ventilation rate is 0.5 m^3/s, the ambient pressure is 1 atm, and the temperature is 25°C.

Estimate the local concentration of the THF, in ppm. What statement can you make regarding the worker's exposure to THF?

Physical property data for THF:

Molecular weight:	72.12
Vapor pressure:	114 mm Hg
Liquid density:	888 kg/m^3
TLV-TWA:	50 ppm

3-25. A benzene chlorination plant is located within a structure that is 60 ft wide, 200 ft long, and 30 ft high. For chemical processing inside buildings, a standard ventilation rate is 1.0 ft^3/min of ventilation per square foot of floor area.

The temperature is 70°F and the pressure is 1 atm.

a. What is the overall ventilation rate required for this structure?

b. If 100 lb of benzene spills and forms a 0.1-inch-deep pool on the flat concrete floor, what is the evaporation rate for the benzene?

c. What concentration can be expected within the building due to this spill, assuming the ventilation rate of part a?

Data:

Benzene: C_6H_6

Benzene liquid specific gravity: 0.8794

3-26. An open vessel of 1 m in diameter and 2 m tall is being splash-filled with ethyl acetate ($C_4H_8O_2$) liquid. The vessel takes 30 min to fill. The local ventilation rate is 0.50 m^3/s.

a. Estimate the local concentration (in ppm) of ethyl acetate. Compare to the TLV.

b. Estimate the local concentration (in ppm) if the vessel is covered with a flat metal sheet and the filling is done through a 5-cm-diameter hole. Compare to the TLV.

c. Which filling method do you recommend and why?

For both cases T = 25°C and the ambient pressure is 1 atm. The specific gravity of the ethyl acetate is 0.90.

3-27. Equations 3-12 and 3-14 can be applied to nonenclosed exposures by using an effective ventilation rate. The effective ventilation rate for outside exposures has been estimated at 3000 ft^3/min.[17]

A worker is standing near an open passageway of a tank containing 2-butoxyethanol (molecular weight = 118). The passageway area is 7 ft^2. Estimate the concentration (in ppm) of the vapor near the passageway opening. The vapor pressure of the 2-butoxyethanol is 0.6 mm Hg.

3-28. Fifty-five-gallon drums are being filled with 2-butoxyethanol. The drums are being splash-filled at the rate of 30 drums per hour. The bung opening through which the drums are being filled has an area of 8 cm^2. Estimate the ambient vapor concentration if the ventilation rate is 3000 ft^3/min. The vapor pressure of 2-butoxyethanol is 0.6 mm Hg under these conditions.

3-29. Equation 3-6 in the text provides a mass balance for the evolution of a volatile material in an enclosure:

$$V\frac{dC}{dt} = Q_m - kQ_vC.$$

[17]Matthieson, "Estimating Chemical Exposure," p. 33.

Integration of the above equation from an initial concentration C_o to any concentration C results in the following equation:

$$\frac{Q_m/V - C/\tau}{Q_m/V - C_o/\tau} = e^{-t/\tau},$$

where

t is the time,
C_o is the initial concentration of the volatile, and
τ is a time constant with units of time.

a. Integrate Equation 3-6 to derive the above expression.
b. Determine an expression for the time constant τ.
c. For the Michigan Tech Unit Operations Lab, the total volume of the lab is 74, 300 ft^3 with a floor area of 4,800 ft^2. If nitrogen gas is escaping at the rate of 4800 ft^3/min and the nonideal mixing factor k has a value of 0.1, determine the value of the time constant, in minutes.
d. Since the time constant represents the time required for the concentration to change 67% of its total change, make a statement about the magnitude of the results of part b.

3-30. Use the equation provided in Problem 3-29 to work this problem.

Toluene is evaporating from a drumming operation at the rate of 0.1 lb_m/min with a ventilation rate of 1000 ft^3/min. The facility has a floor area of 1000 ft^2 and a ceiling height of 10 ft. The temperature is 77°F and the pressure is 1 atm. Assume a nonideal mixing factor k of 0.5.

a. What is the steady-state concentration of toluene, in ppm?
b. If the ventilation rate is increased to 1500 ft^3/min, what is the new steady-state concentration, in ppm?
c. How long does it take for the concentration to change to 63.2% of the total change? 98.2% of the total change? Comment on the importance of using dynamic concentrations as opposed to steady-state values.

3-31. The 8-hr time-weighted average of a group of workers is 3.5 ppm of 2-ethoxyethanol, 3.4 ppm of 2-ethoxyethyl acetate, and 10.2 ppm of 2-butoxyethanol. Have the workers been overexposed?

Chemical	MW	TLV	Effect
2-Ethoxyethanol	90.12	5	Reproductive
2-Ethoxyethyl acetate	132.16	5	Reproductive
2-Butoxyethanol	118.17	20	Blood

3-32. Noise in an area measures 90 dBA for 2 hr a day, 97 dBA for 2 hr a day, and for the remaining 4 hr there are alternate noise levels of 95 dBA for 10 min and of 80 dBA for 10 min. Does this exposure exceed the permissible limit?

3-33. A storage vessel containing carbon tetrachloride (CCl_4) is contained within a diked area with dimensions of 10 m × 10 m. The storage tank is in a horizontal bullet configuration with legs to raise the vessel well above the dike floor. The temperature of the liquid is 35°C and the ambient pressure is 1 atm.

a. What is the evaporation rate if the floor of the dike is completely covered with carbon tetrachloride? What minimum spill rate (in kg/s) from the storage vessel is necessary to keep the floor of the dike covered with liquid?

b. If one of the accident scenarios for this vessel results in a leak with a discharge rate of 1 kg/s, estimate the carbon tetrachloride vapor concentration near the vessel (in ppm), assuming an effective ventilation rate for the outdoors of 3000 ft^3/min.

CHAPTER 4

Source Models

Most accidents in chemical plants result in spills of toxic, flammable, and explosive materials.

Source models are an important part of the consequence modeling procedure shown in Figure 4-1. Figure 4-1 also identifies the particular chapters in this book that are related to the topic shown. More details are provided elsewhere.[1] Accidents begin with an incident, which usually results in the loss of containment of material from the process. The material has hazardous properties, which might include toxic properties and energy content. Typical incidents might include the rupture or break of a pipeline, a hole in a tank or pipe, runaway reaction, or fire external to the vessel. Once the incident is known, source models are selected to describe how materials are discharged from the process. The source model provides a description of the rate of discharge, the total quantity discharged (or total time of discharge), and the state of the discharge (that is, solid, liquid, vapor, or a combination). A dispersion model is subsequently used to describe how the material is transported downwind and dispersed to some concentration levels. For flammable releases fire and explosion models convert the source model information on the release into energy hazard potentials, such as thermal radiation and explosion overpressures. Effect models convert these incident-specific results into effects on people (injury or death) and structures. Environmental impacts could also be considered, but we do not do so here. Additional refinement is provided by mitigation factors, such as water sprays, foam systems, and sheltering or evacuation, which tend to reduce the magnitude of potential effects in real incidents.

4-1 Introduction to Source Models

Source models are constructed from fundamental or empirical equations representing the physicochemical processes occurring during the release of materials. For a reasonably complex

[1] Center for Chemical Process Safety (CCPS), *Guidelines for Consequence Analysis of Chemical Releases* (New York: American Institute of Chemical Engineers, 1999).

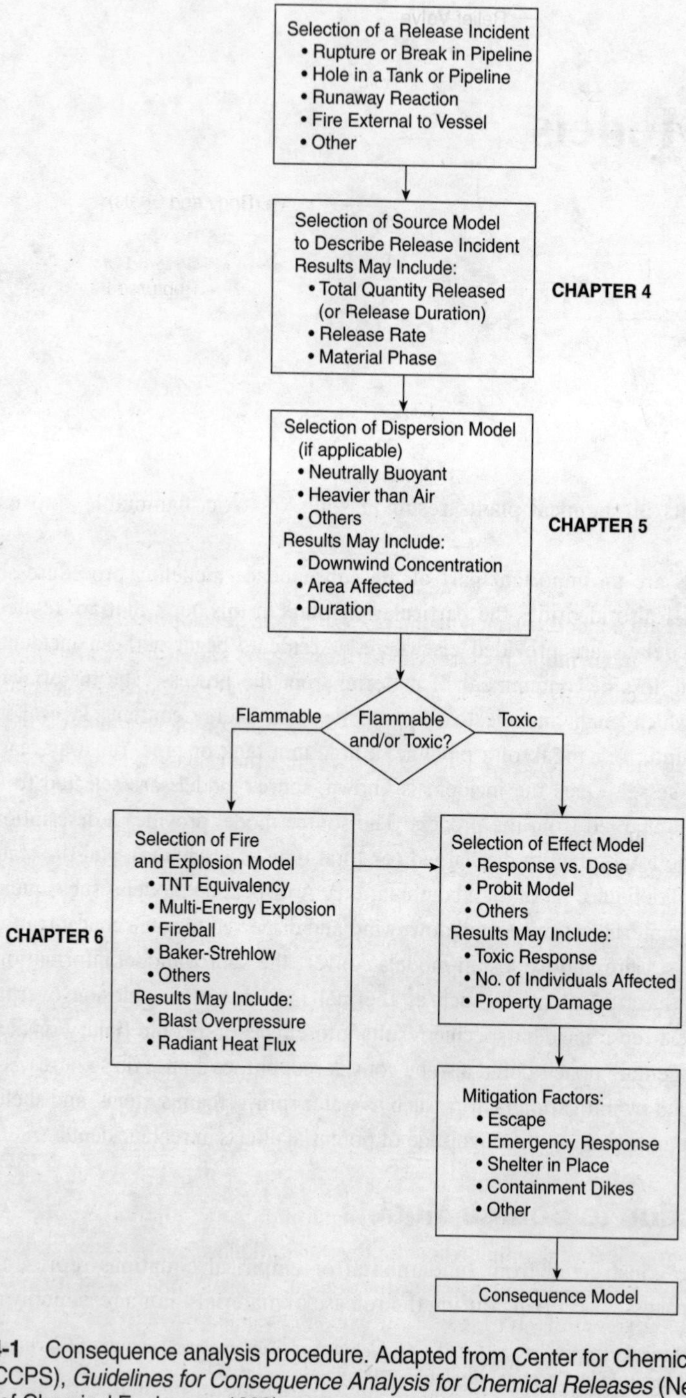

Figure 4-1 Consequence analysis procedure. Adapted from Center for Chemical Process Safety (CCPS), *Guidelines for Consequence Analysis for Chemical Releases* (New York: American Institute of Chemical Engineers, 1999).

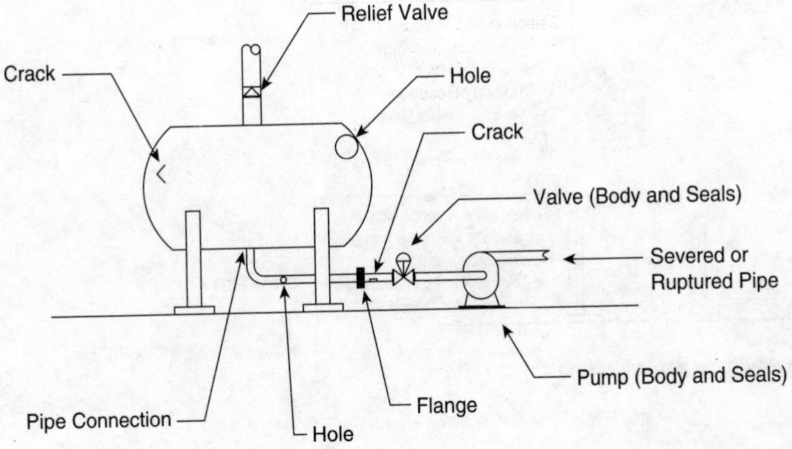

Figure 4-2 Various types of limited aperture releases.

plant many source models are needed to describe the release. Some development and modification of the original models is normally required to fit the specific situation. Frequently the results are only estimates because the physical properties of the materials are not adequately characterized or because the physical processes themselves are not completely understood. If uncertainty exists, the parameters should be selected to maximize the release rate and quantity. This ensures that a design is conservative.

Release mechanisms are classified into wide and limited aperture releases. In the wide aperture case a large hole develops in the process unit, releasing a substantial amount of material in a short time. An excellent example is the overpressuring and explosion of a storage tank. For the limited aperture case material is released at a slow enough rate that upstream conditions are not immediately affected; the assumption of constant upstream pressure is frequently valid.

Limited aperture releases are conceptualized in Figure 4-2. For these releases material is ejected from holes and cracks in tanks and pipes, leaks in flanges, valves, and pumps, and severed or ruptured pipes. Relief systems, designed to prevent the overpressuring of tanks and process vessels, are also potential sources of released material.

Figure 4-3 shows how the physical state of the material affects the release mechanism. For gases or vapors stored in a tank, a leak results in a jet of gas or vapor. For liquids a leak below the liquid level in the tank results in a stream of escaping liquid. If the liquid is stored under pressure above its atmospheric boiling point, a leak below the liquid level will result in a stream of liquid flashing partially into vapor. Small liquid droplets or aerosols might also form from the flashing stream, with the possibility of transport away from the leak by wind currents. A leak in the vapor space above the liquid can result in either a vapor stream or a two-phase stream composed of vapor and liquid, depending on the physical properties of the material.

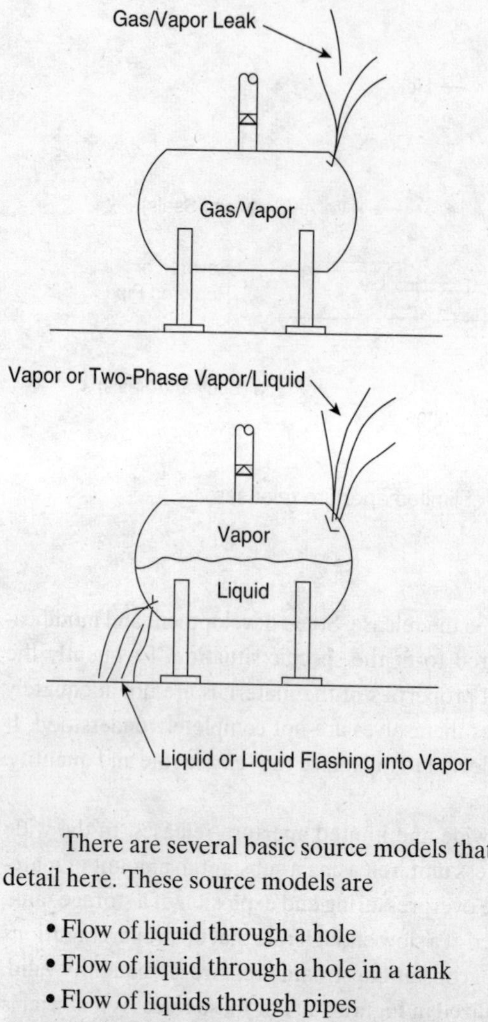

Figure 4-3 Vapor and liquid are ejected from process units in either single- or two-phase states.

There are several basic source models that are used repeatedly and will be developed in detail here. These source models are

- Flow of liquid through a hole
- Flow of liquid through a hole in a tank
- Flow of liquids through pipes
- Flow of gases or vapor through holes
- Flow of gases or vapor through pipes
- Flashing liquids
- Liquid pool evaporation or boiling

Other source models, specific to certain materials, are introduced in subsequent chapters.

4-2 Flow of Liquid through a Hole

A mechanical energy balance describes the various energy forms associated with flowing fluids:

$$\int \frac{dP}{\rho} + \Delta\left(\frac{\bar{u}^2}{2\alpha g_c}\right) + \frac{g}{g_c}\Delta z + F = -\frac{W_s}{\dot{m}}, \tag{4-1}$$

where

P is the pressure (force/area),
ρ is the fluid density (mass/volume),
$\bar{u}$ is the average instantaneous velocity of the fluid (length/time),
g_c is the gravitational constant (length mass/force time^2),
α is the unitless velocity profile correction factor with the following values:
$\alpha = 0.5$ for laminar flow, $\alpha = 1.0$ for plug flow, and $\alpha \rightarrow 1.0$ for turbulent flow,
g is the acceleration due to gravity (length/time^2),
z is the height above datum (length),
F is the net frictional loss term (length force/mass),
W_s is the shaft work (force length), and
$\dot{m}$ is the mass flow rate (mass/time).

The Δ function represents the final minus the initial state.

For incompressible liquids the density is constant, and

$$\int \frac{dP}{\rho} = \frac{\Delta P}{\rho}. \tag{4-2}$$

Consider a process unit that develops a small hole, as shown in Figure 4-4. The pressure of the liquid contained within the process unit is converted to kinetic energy as the fluid escapes through the leak. Frictional forces between the moving liquid and the wall of the leak convert some of the kinetic energy of the liquid into thermal energy, resulting in a reduced velocity.

For this limited aperture release, assume a constant gauge pressure P_g within the process unit. The external pressure is atmospheric; so $\Delta P = P_g$. The shaft work is zero, and the velocity of the fluid within the process unit is assumed negligible. The change in elevation of the fluid during the discharge through the hole is also negligible; so $\Delta z = 0$. The frictional losses in the leak are approximated by a constant discharge coefficient C_1, defined as

$$-\frac{\Delta P}{\rho} - F = C_1^2\left(-\frac{\Delta P}{\rho}\right). \tag{4-3}$$

The modifications are substituted into the mechanical energy balance (Equation 4-1) to determine $\bar{u}$, the average discharge velocity from the leak:

$$\bar{u} = C_1\sqrt{\alpha}\sqrt{\frac{2g_c P_g}{\rho}}. \tag{4-4}$$

A new discharge coefficient C_o is defined as

$$C_o = C_1\sqrt{\alpha}. \tag{4-5}$$

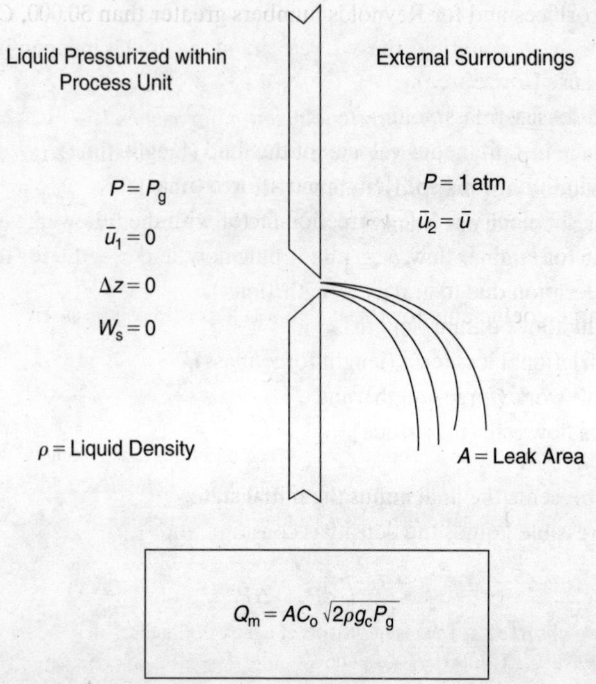

Figure 4-4 Liquid escaping through a hole in a process unit. The energy of the liquid resulting from its pressure in the vessel is converted to kinetic energy, with some frictional flow losses in the hole.

The resulting equation for the velocity of fluid exiting the leak is

$$\bar{u} = C_o\sqrt{\frac{2g_c P_g}{\rho}}. \tag{4-6}$$

The mass flow rate Q_m resulting from a hole of area A is given by

$$Q_m = \rho\bar{u}A = AC_o\sqrt{2\rho g_c P_g}. \tag{4-7}$$

The total mass of liquid spilled depends on the total time that the leak is active.

The discharge coefficient C_o is a complicated function of the Reynolds number of the fluid escaping through the leak and the diameter of the hole. The following guidelines are suggested:[2]

[2]Sam Mannan, ed., *Lees' Loss Prevention in the Process Industries,* 3rd ed. (Amsterdam: Elsevier, 2005), p. 15/7.

- For sharp-edged orifices and for Reynolds numbers greater than 30,000, C_o approaches the value 0.61. For these conditions the exit velocity of the fluid is independent of the size of the hole.
- For a well-rounded nozzle the discharge coefficient approaches 1.
- For short sections of pipe attached to a vessel (with a length-diameter ratio not less than 3), the discharge coefficient is approximately 0.81.
- When the discharge coefficient is unknown or uncertain, use a value of 1.0 to maximize the computed flows.

More details on discharge coefficients for these types of liquid discharges are provided elsewhere.[3]

Example 4-1

At 1 PM the plant operator notices a drop in pressure in a pipeline transporting benzene. The pressure is immediately restored to 100 psig. At 2:30 PM a 1/4-in-diameter leak is found in the pipeline and immediately repaired. Estimate the total amount of benzene spilled. The specific gravity of benzene is 0.8794.

Solution

The drop in pressure observed at 1 PM is indicative of a leak in the pipeline. The leak is assumed to be active between 1 PM and 2:30 PM, a total of 90 minutes. The area of the hole is

$$A = \frac{\pi d^2}{4} = \frac{(3.14)(0.25\text{ in})^2(1\text{ ft}^2/144\text{ in}^2)}{4}$$

$$= 3.41 \times 10^{-4}\text{ ft}^2.$$

The density of the benzene is

$$\rho = (0.8794)(62.4\text{ lb}_\text{m}/\text{ft}^3) = 54.9\text{ lb}_\text{m}/\text{ft}^3.$$

The leak mass flow rate is given by Equation 4-7. A discharge coefficient of 0.61 is assumed for this orifice-type leak:

$$Q_\text{m} = AC_\text{o}\sqrt{2\rho g_\text{c} P_\text{g}}$$

$$= (3.41 \times 10^{-4}\text{ ft}^2)(0.61)\sqrt{(2)\left(54.9\frac{\text{lb}_\text{m}}{\text{ft}^3}\right)\left(32.17\frac{\text{ft lb}_\text{m}}{\text{lb}_\text{f}\text{ s}^2}\right)\left(100\frac{\text{lb}_\text{f}}{\text{in}^2}\right)\left(144\frac{\text{in}^2}{\text{ft}^2}\right)}$$

$$= 1.48\text{ lb}_\text{m}/\text{s}.$$

The total quantity of benzene spilled is

$$(1.48\text{ lb}_\text{m}/\text{s})(90\text{ min})(60\text{ s/min}) = 7990\text{ lb}_\text{m} = 1090\text{ gal}.$$

[3] Robert H. Perry and Don W. Green, *Perry's Chemical Engineers Handbook*, 8th ed. (New York: McGraw-Hill, 2008), pp. 8–59.

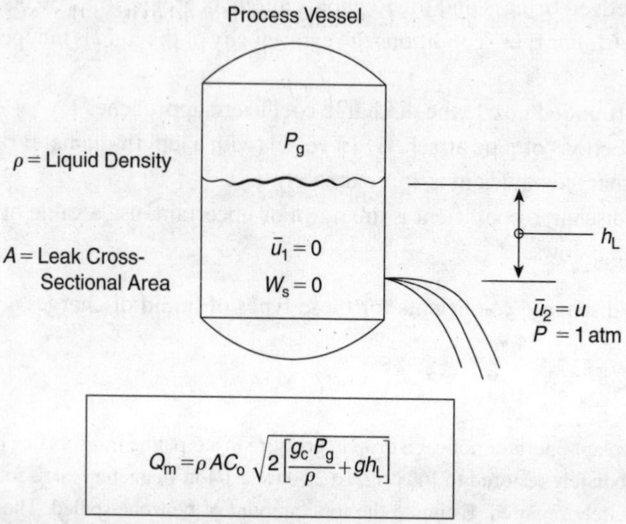

Figure 4-5 An orifice-type leak in a process vessel. The energy resulting from the pressure of the fluid height above the leak is converted to kinetic energy as the fluid exits through the hole. Some energy is lost because of frictional fluid flow.

4-3 Flow of Liquid through a Hole in a Tank

A storage tank is shown in Figure 4-5. A hole develops at a height h_L below the fluid level. The flow of liquid through this hole is represented by the mechanical energy balance (Equation 4-1) and the incompressible assumption, as shown in Equation 4-2.

The gauge pressure on the tank is P_g, and the external gauge pressure is atmospheric, or 0. The shaft work W_s is zero, and the velocity of the fluid in the tank is zero.

A dimensionless discharge coefficient C_1 is defined as

$$-\frac{\Delta P}{\rho} - \frac{g}{g_c}\Delta z - F = C_1^2\left(-\frac{\Delta P}{\rho} - \frac{g}{g_c}\Delta z\right). \tag{4-8}$$

The mechanical energy balance (Equation 4-1) is solved for $\bar{u}$, the average instantaneous discharge velocity from the leak:

$$\bar{u} = C_1\sqrt{\alpha}\sqrt{2\left(\frac{g_c P_g}{\rho} + g h_L\right)}, \tag{4-9}$$

where h_L is the liquid height above the leak. A new discharge coefficient C_o is defined as

$$C_o = C_1\sqrt{\alpha}. \tag{4-10}$$

The resulting equation for the instantaneous velocity of fluid exiting the leak is

$$\bar{u} = C_o \sqrt{2\left(\frac{g_c P_g}{\rho} + g h_L\right)}. \tag{4-11}$$

The instantaneous mass flow rate Q_m resulting from a hole of area A is given by

$$\boxed{Q_m = \rho \bar{u} A = \rho A C_o \sqrt{2\left(\frac{g_c P_g}{\rho} + g h_L\right)}.} \tag{4-12}$$

As the tank empties, the liquid height decreases and the velocity and mass flow rate decrease.

Assume that the gauge pressure P_g on the surface of the liquid is constant. This would occur if the vessel was padded with an inert gas to prevent explosion or was vented to the atmosphere. For a tank of constant cross-sectional area A_t, the total mass of liquid in the tank above the leak is

$$m = \rho A_t h_L. \tag{4-13}$$

The rate of change of mass within the tank is

$$\frac{dm}{dt} = -Q_m, \tag{4-14}$$

where Q_m is given by Equation 4-12. By substituting Equations 4-12 and 4-13 into Equation 4-14 and by assuming constant tank cross-section and liquid density, we can obtain a differential equation representing the change in the fluid height:

$$\frac{dh_L}{dt} = -\frac{C_o A}{A_t}\sqrt{2\left(\frac{g_c P_g}{\rho} + g h_L\right)}. \tag{4-15}$$

Equation 4-15 is rearranged and integrated from an initial height h_L^o to any height h_L:

$$\int_{h_L^o}^{h_L} \frac{dh_L}{\sqrt{\dfrac{2 g_c P_g}{\rho} + 2 g h_L}} = -\frac{C_o A}{A_t}\int_0^t dt. \tag{4-16}$$

This equation is integrated to

$$\frac{1}{g}\sqrt{\frac{2 g_c P_g}{\rho} + 2 g h_L} - \frac{1}{g}\sqrt{\frac{2 g_c P_g}{\rho} + 2 g h_L^o} = -\frac{C_o A}{A_t} t. \tag{4-17}$$

Solving for h_L, the liquid level height in the tank, yields

$$h_L = h_L^o - \frac{C_o A}{A_t}\sqrt{\frac{2g_c P_g}{\rho} + 2gh_L^o}\; t + \frac{g}{2}\left(\frac{C_o A}{A_t} t\right)^2. \tag{4-18}$$

Equation 4-18 is substituted into Equation 4-12 to obtain the mass discharge rate at any time t:

$$Q_m = \rho C_o A \sqrt{2\left(\frac{g_c P_g}{\rho} + gh_L^o\right)} - \frac{\rho g C_o^2 A^2}{A_t} t. \tag{4-19}$$

The first term on the right-hand side of Equation 4-19 is the initial mass discharge rate at $h_L = h_L^o$.

The time t_e for the vessel to empty to the level of the leak is found by solving Equation 4-18 for t after setting $h_L = 0$:

$$t_e = \frac{1}{C_o g}\left(\frac{A_t}{A}\right)\left[\sqrt{2\left(\frac{g_c P_g}{\rho} + gh_L^o\right)} - \sqrt{\frac{2g_c P_g}{\rho}}\right]. \tag{4-20}$$

If the vessel is at atmospheric pressure, $P_g = 0$ and Equation 4-20 reduces to

$$t_e = \frac{1}{C_o g}\left(\frac{A_t}{A}\right)\sqrt{2gh_L^o}. \tag{4-21}$$

Example 4-2

A cylindrical tank 20 ft high and 8 ft in diameter is used to store benzene. The tank is padded with nitrogen to a constant regulated pressure of 1 atm gauge to prevent explosion. The liquid level within the tank is presently at 17 ft. A 1-in puncture occurs in the tank 5 ft off the ground because of the careless driving of a forklift truck. Estimate (a) the gallons of benzene spilled, (b) the time required for the benzene to leak out, and (c) the maximum mass flow rate of benzene through the leak. The specific gravity of benzene at these conditions is 0.8794.

Solution

The density of the benzene is

$$\rho = (0.8794)(62.4\ \text{lb}_m/\text{ft}^3)$$
$$= 54.9\ \text{lb}_m/\text{ft}^3.$$

The area of the tank is

$$A_t = \frac{\pi d^2}{4} = \frac{(3.14)(8\text{ ft})^2}{4} = 50.2\text{ ft}^2.$$

The area of the leak is

$$A = \frac{(3.14)(1\text{ in})^2(1\text{ ft}^2/144\text{ in}^2)}{4} = 5.45 \times 10^{-3}\text{ ft}^2.$$

The gauge pressure is

$$P_g = (1\text{ atm})(14.7\text{ lb}_f/\text{in}^2)(144\text{ in}^2/\text{ft}^2) = 2.12 \times 10^3\text{ lb}_f/\text{ft}^2.$$

a. The volume of benzene above the leak is

$$V = A_t h_L^o = (50.2\text{ ft}^2)(17\text{ ft} - 5\text{ ft})(7.48\text{ gal/ft}^3) = 4506\text{ gal}.$$

This is the total benzene that will leak out.

b. The length of time for the benzene to leak out is given by Equation 4-20:

$$t_e = \frac{1}{C_o g}\left(\frac{A_t}{A}\right)\left[\sqrt{2\left(\frac{g_c P_g}{\rho} + g h_L^o\right)} - \sqrt{\frac{2 g_c P_g}{\rho}}\right]$$

$$= \frac{1}{(0.61)(32.17\text{ ft/s}^2)}\left(\frac{50.2\text{ ft}^2}{5.45 \times 10^{-3}\text{ ft}^2}\right)$$

$$\times \left\{\left[\frac{(2)(32.17\text{ ft-lb}_m/\text{ lb}_f\text{-s}^2)(2.12 \times 10^3\text{ lb}_f/\text{ft}^2)}{54.9\text{ lb}_m/\text{ft}^3}\right.\right.$$

$$\left.\left. + (2)(32.17\text{ ft/s}^2)(12\text{ ft})\right]^{1/2} - \sqrt{2484\text{ ft}^2/\text{s}^2}\right\}$$

$$= (469\text{ s}^2/\text{ft})(7.22\text{ ft/s}) = 3386\text{ s} = 56.4\text{ min}.$$

This appears to be more than adequate time to stop the leak or to invoke an emergency procedure to reduce the impact of the leak. However, the maximum discharge occurs when the hole is first opened.

c. The maximum discharge occurs at $t = 0$ at a liquid level of 17.0 ft. Equation 4-19 is used to compute the mass flow rate:

$$Q_m = \rho A C_o \sqrt{2\left(\frac{g_c P_g}{\rho} + g h_L^o\right)}$$

$$= (54.9\text{ lb}_m/\text{ft}^3)(5.45 \times 10^{-3}\text{ ft}^2)(0.61)\sqrt{3.26 \times 10^3\text{ ft}^2/\text{s}^2}$$

$$= 10.4\text{ lb}_m/\text{s}.$$

A general equation to represent the draining time for any vessel of any geometry is developed as follows. Assume that the head space above the liquid is at atmospheric pressure; then combining Equations 4-12 and 4-14, we get

$$\frac{dm}{dt} = \rho \frac{dV}{dt} = -\rho A C_o \sqrt{2gh_L}. \tag{4-22}$$

By rearranging and integrating, we obtain

$$-\frac{1}{AC_o\sqrt{2g}} \int_{V_1}^{V_2} \frac{dV}{\sqrt{h_L}} = \int_0^t dt, \tag{4-23}$$

which results in the general equation for the draining time for any vessel:

$$\boxed{t = \frac{1}{AC_o\sqrt{2g}} \int_{V_1}^{V_2} \frac{dV}{\sqrt{h_L}}.} \tag{4-24}$$

Equation 4-24 does not assume that the hole is at the bottom of the vessel.

For a vessel with the shape of a vertical cylinder, we have

$$dV = \frac{\pi D^2}{4} dh_L. \tag{4-25}$$

By substituting into Equation 4-24, we obtain

$$t = \frac{\pi D^2}{4AC_o\sqrt{2g}} \int \frac{dh_L}{\sqrt{h_L}}. \tag{4-26}$$

If the hole is at the bottom of the vessel, then Equation 4-26 is integrated from $h = 0$ to $h = h_o$. Equation 4-26 then provides the emptying time for the vessel:

$$t_e = \frac{\pi D^2/4}{AC_o} \sqrt{\frac{2h_L^o}{g}} = \frac{1}{C_o g}\left(\frac{\pi D^2/4}{A}\right)\sqrt{2gh_L^o}, \tag{4-27}$$

which is the same result as Equation 4-21.

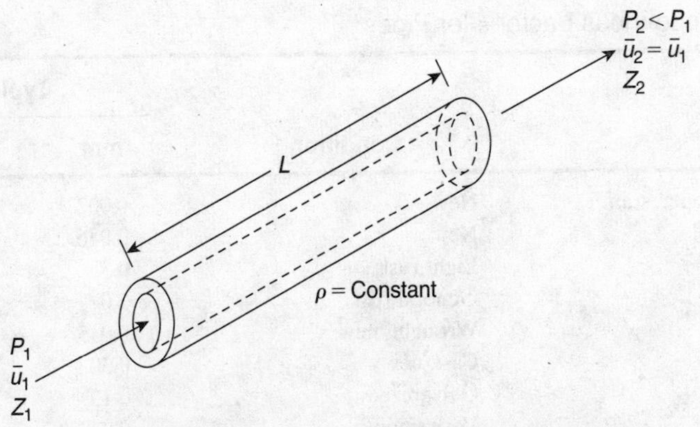

Figure 4-6 Liquid flowing through a pipe. The frictional flow losses between the fluid and the pipe wall result in a pressure drop across the pipe length. Kinetic energy changes are frequently negligible.

4-4 Flow of Liquids through Pipes

A pipe transporting liquid is shown in Figure 4-6. A pressure gradient across the pipe is the driving force for the movement of liquid. Frictional forces between the liquid and the wall of the pipe convert kinetic energy into thermal energy. This results in a decrease in the liquid pressure.

Flow of incompressible liquids through pipes is described by the mechanical energy balance (Equation 4-1) combined with the incompressible fluid assumption (Equation 4-2). The net result is

$$\frac{\Delta P}{\rho} + \frac{\Delta \bar{u}^2}{2\alpha g_c} + \frac{g}{g_c}\Delta z + F = -\frac{W_s}{\dot{m}}. \tag{4-28}$$

The frictional loss term F in Equation 4-28 represents the loss of mechanical energy resulting from friction and includes losses resulting from flow through lengths of pipe; fittings such as valves, elbows, orifices; and pipe entrances and exits. For each frictional device a loss term of the following form is used:

$$F = K_f\left(\frac{u^2}{2g_c}\right), \tag{4-29}$$

where

K_f is the excess head loss due to the pipe or pipe fitting (dimensionless) and
u is the fluid velocity (length/time).

Table 4-1 Roughness Factor ε for Pipes[a]

Pipe material	Condition	Typical ε mm	Typical ε inch
Drawn brass, copper, stainless	New	0.002	0.00008
Commercial steel	New	0.046	0.0018
	Light rust	0.3	0.015
	General rust	2.0	0.08
Iron	Wrought, new	0.045	0.0018
	Cast, new	0.30	0.025
	Galvanized	0.15	0.006
Concrete	Very smooth	0.04	0.0016
	Wood floated, brushed	0.3	0.012
	Rough, visible form marks	2.0	0.08
Glass or plastic	Drawn tubing	0.002[c]	0.0008[c]
Rubber	Smooth tubing	0.01	0.004
	Wire reinforced	1.0	0.04
Fiberglass[b]		0.005	0.0002

[a]Ron Darby, "Fluid Flow," *Albright's Chemical Engineering Handbook*, Lyle F. Albright, ed. (Boca Raton, FL: CRC Press, 2009), p. 421.

[b]William D. Stringfellow, ed., *Fiberglass Pipe Handbook* (Washington, DC: Society of the Plastics Industry, Inc., 1989).

[c]Generally considered smooth pipe with ε = 0.

For fluids flowing through pipes the excess head loss term K_f is given by

$$K_f = \frac{4fL}{d}, \tag{4-30}$$

where

f is the Fanning friction factor (unitless),
L is the flow path length (length), and
d is the flow path diameter (length).

The Fanning friction factor f is a function of the Reynolds number Re and the roughness of the pipe ε. Table 4-1 provides values of ε for various types of clean pipe. Figure 4-7 is a plot of the Fanning friction factor versus Reynolds number with the pipe roughness, ε/d, as a parameter.

For laminar flow the Fanning friction factor is given by

$$f = \frac{16}{Re}. \tag{4-31}$$

For turbulent flow the data shown in Figure 4-7 are represented by the Colebrook equation:

$$\frac{1}{\sqrt{f}} = -4\log\left(\frac{1}{3.7}\frac{\varepsilon}{d} + \frac{1.255}{Re\sqrt{f}}\right). \tag{4-32}$$

An alternative form of Equation 4-32, useful for determining the Reynolds number from the friction factor f, is

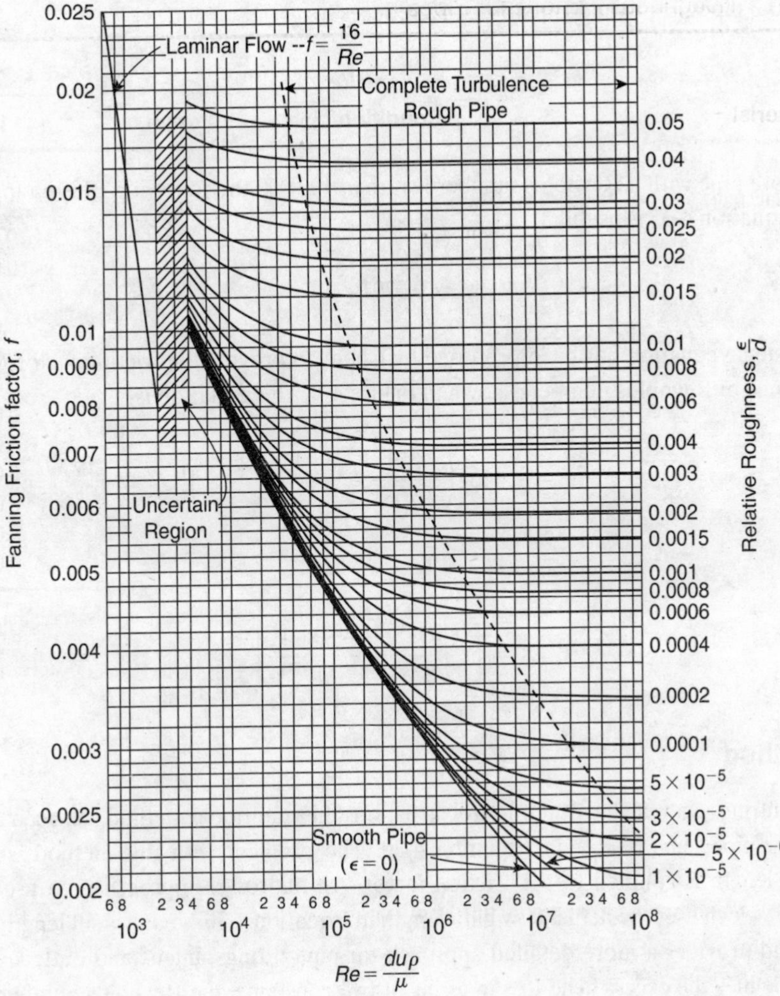

Figure 4-7 Plot of Fanning friction factor f versus Reynolds number. Source: Octave Levenspiel, *Engineering Flow and Heat Exchange* (New York: Plenum Press, 1984), p. 20. Reprinted by permission.

$$\frac{1}{Re} = \frac{\sqrt{f}}{1.255}\left(10^{-0.25/\sqrt{f}} - \frac{1}{3.7}\frac{\varepsilon}{d}\right). \tag{4-33}$$

For fully developed turbulent flow in rough pipes, f is independent of the Reynolds number, as shown by the nearly constant friction factors at high Reynolds number in Figure 4-7. For this case Equation 4-33 is simplified to

$$\frac{1}{\sqrt{f}} = 4\log\left(3.7\frac{d}{\varepsilon}\right). \tag{4-34}$$

For smooth pipes, $\varepsilon = 0$ and Equation 4-32 reduces to

$$\frac{1}{\sqrt{f}} = 4 \log \frac{Re\sqrt{f}}{1.255}. \tag{4-35}$$

For smooth pipe with a Reynolds number less than 100,000 the following Blasius approximation to Equation 4-35 is useful:

$$f = 0.079 Re^{-1/4}. \tag{4-36}$$

A single equation has been proposed by Chen[4] to provide the friction factor f over the entire range of Reynolds numbers shown in Figure 4-7. This equation is

$$\frac{1}{\sqrt{f}} = -4 \log\left(\frac{\varepsilon/d}{3.7065} - \frac{5.0452 \log A}{Re}\right), \tag{4-37}$$

where

$$A = \left[\frac{(\varepsilon/d)^{1.1098}}{2.8257} + \frac{5.8506}{Re^{0.8981}}\right].$$

2-K Method

For pipe fittings, valves, and other flow obstructions the traditional method has been to use an equivalent pipe length L_{equiv} in Equation 4-30. The problem with this method is that the specified length is coupled to the friction factor. An improved approach is to use the 2-K method,[5,6] which uses the actual flow path length in Equation 4-30 – equivalent lengths are not used – and provides a more detailed approach for pipe fittings, inlets, and outlets. The 2-K method defines the excess head loss in terms of two constants, the Reynolds number and the pipe internal diameter:

$$K_{\text{f}} = \frac{K_1}{Re} + K_\infty\left(1 + \frac{1}{ID_{\text{inches}}}\right), \tag{4-38}$$

where

K_{f} is the excess head loss (dimensionless),
K_1 and K_∞ are constants (dimensionless),

[4] N. H. Chen, *Industrial Engineering and Chemistry Fundamentals* (1979), 18: 296.
[5] W. B. Hooper, *Chemical Engineering* (Aug. 24, 1981), pp. 96–100.
[6] W. B. Hooper, *Chemical Engineering* (Nov. 7, 1988), pp. 89–92.

Table 4-2 2-K Constants for Loss Coefficients in Fittings and Valves[a]

Fittings	Description of fitting	K_1	K_∞
Elbows			
90°	Standard ($r/D = 1$), threaded	800	0.40
	Standard ($r/D = 1$), flanged/welded	800	0.25
	Long radius ($r/D = 1.5$), all types	800	0.20
	Mitered ($r/D = 1.5$): 1 weld (90°)	1000	1.15
	2 welds (45°)	800	0.35
	3 welds (30°)	800	0.30
	4 welds (22.5°)	800	0.27
	5 welds (18°)	800	0.25
45°	Standard ($r/D = 1$), all types	500	0.20
	Long radius ($r/D = 1.5$)	500	0.15
	Mitered, 1 weld (45°)	500	0.25
	Mitered, 2 welds (22.5°)	500	0.15
180°	Standard ($r/D = 1$), threaded	1000	0.60
	Standard ($r/D = 1$), flanged/welded	1000	0.35
	Long radius ($r/D = 1.5$), all types	1000	0.30
Tees			
Used as elbows	Standard, threaded	500	0.70
	Long radius, threaded	800	0.40
	Standard, flanged/welded	800	0.80
	Stub-in branch	1000	1.00
Run-through	Threaded	200	0.10
	Flanged/welded	150	0.50
	Stub-in branch	100	0.00
Valves			
Gate, ball or plug	Full line size, $\beta = 1.0$	300	0.10
	Reduced trim, $\beta = 0.9$	500	0.15
	Reduced trim, $\beta = 0.8$	1000	0.25
Globe	Standard	1500	4.00
	Angle or Y-type	1000	2.00
Diaphragm	Dam type	1000	2.00
Butterfly		800	0.25
Check	Lift	2000	10.0
	Swing	1500	1.50
	Tilting disk	1000	0.50

[a]William B. Hooper, *Chemical Engineering* (Aug. 24, 1981), p. 97.

Re is the Reynolds number (dimensionless), and

ID_{inches} is the internal diameter of the flow path (inches).

Table 4-2 contains a list of K values for use in Equation 4-38 for various types of fittings and valves.

For pipe entrances and exits Equation 4-38 is modified to account for the change in kinetic energy:

$$K_f = \frac{K_1}{Re} + K_\infty. \tag{4-39}$$

For pipe entrances, $K_1 = 160$ and $K_\infty = 0.50$ for a normal entrance. For a Borda-type pipe connection to a tank where the pipe sticks up into the bottom of the tank a short distance, $K_\infty = 1.0$. For pipe exits, $K_1 = 0$ and $K_\infty = 1.0$. The K factors for the entrance and exit effects account for the changes in kinetic energy through these piping changes, so no additional kinetic energy terms in the mechanical energy balance must be considered. For high Reynolds numbers (that is, $Re > 10{,}000$) the first term in Equation 4-39 is negligible and $K_f = K_\infty$. For low Reynolds numbers (that is, $Re < 50$) the first term dominates and $K_f = K_1/Re$.

Equations are also available for orifices[7] and for changes in pipe sizes.[8]

The 2-K method also represents liquid discharge through holes. From the 2-K method an expression for the discharge coefficient for liquid discharge through a hole can be determined. The result is

$$C_o = \frac{1}{\sqrt{1 + \sum K_f}}, \tag{4-40}$$

where ΣK_f is the sum of all excess head loss terms, including entrances, exits, pipe lengths, and fittings, provided by Equations 4-30, 4-38, and 4-39. For a simple hole in a tank with no pipe connections or fittings the friction is caused only by the entrance and exit effects of the hole. For Reynolds numbers greater than 10,000, $K_f = 0.5$ for the entrance and $K_f = 1.0$ for the exit. Thus $\Sigma K_f = 1.5$, and from Equation 4-40, $C_o = 0.63$, which nearly matches the suggested value of 0.61.

The solution procedure to determine the mass flow rate of discharged material from a piping system is as follows:

1. Given: the length, diameter, and type of pipe; pressures and elevation changes across the piping system; work input or output to the fluid resulting from pumps, turbines, etc.; number and type of fittings in the pipe; properties of the fluid, including density and viscosity.
2. Specify the initial point (point 1) and the final point (point 2). This must be done carefully because the individual terms in Equation 4-28 are highly dependent on this specification.
3. Determine the pressures and elevations at points 1 and 2. Determine the initial fluid velocity at point 1.

[7] W. B. Hooper, *Chemical Engineering* (Aug. 24, 1981), pp. 96–100.
[8] W. B. Hooper, *Chemical Engineering* (Nov. 7, 1988), pp. 89–92.

4. Guess a value for the velocity at point 2. If fully developed turbulent flow is expected, then this is not required.
5. Determine the friction factor for the pipe using Equations 4-31 through 4-37.
6. Determine the excess head loss terms for the pipe (using Equation 4-30), for the fittings (using Equation 4-38), and for any entrance and exit effects (using Equation 4-39). Sum the head loss terms, and compute the net frictional loss term using Equation 4-29. Use the velocity at point 2.
7. Compute values for all the terms in Equation 4-28, and substitute into the equation. If the sum of all the terms in Equation 4-28 is zero, then the computation is completed. If not, go back to step 4 and repeat the calculation.
8. Determine the mass flow rate using the equation $\dot{m} = \rho \bar{u} A$.

If fully developed turbulent flow is expected, the solution is direct. Substitute the known terms into Equation 4-28, leaving the velocity at point 2 as a variable. Solve for the velocity directly.

Example 4-3

Water contaminated with small amounts of hazardous waste is gravity-drained out of a large storage tank through a straight, new commercial steel pipe, 100 mm ID (internal diameter). The pipe is 100 m long with a gate valve near the tank. The entire pipe assembly is mostly horizontal. If the liquid level in the tank is 5.8 m above the pipe outlet, and the pipe is accidently severed 33 m from the tank, compute the flow rate of material escaping from the pipe.

Solution

The draining operation is shown in Figure 4-8. Assuming negligible kinetic energy changes, no pressure changes, and no shaft work, the mechanical energy balance (Equation 4-28) applied between points 1 and 2 reduces to

$$\frac{g}{g_c}\Delta z + F = 0.$$

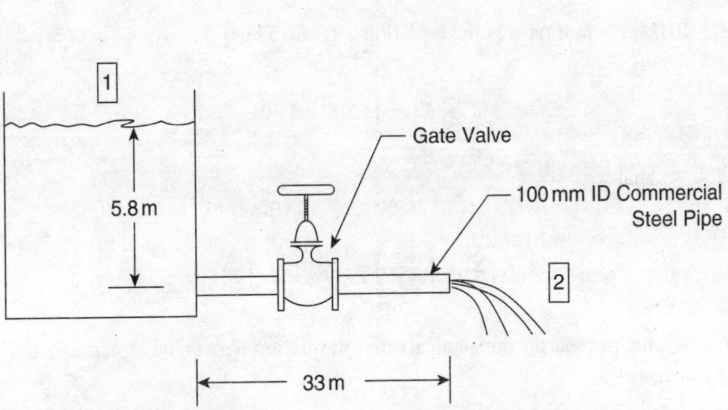

Figure 4-8 Draining geometry for Example 4-3.

For water

$$\mu = 1.0 \times 10^{-3}\ \text{kg/m s},$$

$$\rho = 1000\ \text{kg/m}^3.$$

The K factors for the entrance and exit effects are determined using Equation 4-39. The K factor for the gate valve is found in Table 4-2, and the K factor for the pipe length is given by Equation 4-30. For the pipe entrance,

$$K_f = \frac{160}{Re} + 0.50.$$

For the gate valve,

$$K_f = \frac{300}{Re} + 0.10.$$

For the pipe exit,

$$K_f = 1.0.$$

For the pipe length,

$$K_f = \frac{4fL}{d} = \frac{4f(33\ \text{m})}{(0.10\ \text{m})} = 1320f.$$

Summing the K factors gives

$$\sum K_f = \frac{460}{Re} + 1320f + 1.60.$$

For $Re > 10{,}000$ the first term in the equation is small. Thus

$$\sum K_f \approx 1320f + 1.60,$$

and it follows that

$$F = \sum K_f\left(\frac{\bar{u}^2}{2g_c}\right) = (660f + 0.80)\bar{u}^2.$$

The gravitational term in the mechanical energy equation is given by

$$\frac{g}{g_c}\Delta z = \left(\frac{9.8\ \text{m/s}^2}{1\ \text{kg m/s}^2/\text{N}}\right)(0 - 5.8\ \text{m}) = -56.8\ \text{Nm/kg} = -56.8\ \text{J/kg}.$$

Because there is no pressure change and no pump or shaft work, the mechanical energy balance (Equation 2-28) reduces to

$$\frac{\bar{u}_2^2}{2g_c} + \frac{g}{g_c}\Delta z + F = 0.$$

Solving for the exit velocity and substituting for the height change gives

$$\bar{u}_2^2 = -2g_c\left(\frac{g}{g_c}\Delta z + F\right) = -2g_c(-56.8 + F).$$

The Reynolds number is given by

$$Re = \frac{d\bar{u}\rho}{\mu} = \frac{(0.1\text{ m})(\bar{u})(1000\text{ kg/m}^3)}{1.0 \times 10^{-3}\text{ kg/m s}} = 1.0 \times 10^5\bar{u}.$$

For new commercial steel pipe, from Table 4-1, $\varepsilon = 0.0046$ mm and

$$\frac{\varepsilon}{d} = \frac{0.046\text{ mm}}{100\text{ mm}} = 0.00046.$$

Because the friction factor f and the frictional loss term F are functions of the Reynolds number and velocity, the solution is found by trial and error. The trial and error solution is shown in the following table:

Guessed $\bar{u}$ (m/s)	*Re*	*f*	*F*	Calculated $\bar{u}$ (m/s)
3.00	300,000	0.00451	34.09	6.75
3.50	350,000	0.00446	46.00	4.66
3.66	366,000	0.00444	50.18	3.66

Thus the velocity of the liquid discharging from the pipe is 3.66 m/s. The table also shows that the friction factor f changes little with the Reynolds number. Thus we can approximate it using Equation 4-34 for fully developed turbulent flow in rough pipes. Equation 4-34 produces a friction factor value of 0.0041. Then

$$F = (660f + 0.80)\bar{u}_2^2 = 3.51\bar{u}_2^2.$$

By substituting and solving, we obtain

$$\bar{u}_2^2 = -2g_c(-56.8 + 3.51\bar{u}_2^2)$$

$$= 113.6 - 7.02\bar{u}_2^2,$$

$$\bar{u}_2 = 3.76\text{ m/s}.$$

This result is close to the more exact trial and error solution.

The cross-sectional area of the pipe is

$$A = \frac{\pi d^2}{4} = \frac{(3.14)(0.1\text{ m})^2}{4} = 0.00785\text{ m}^2.$$

The mass flow rate is given by

$$Q_m = \rho \bar{u} A = (1000\text{ kg/m}^3)(3.66\text{ m/s})(0.00785\text{ m}^2) = 28.8\text{ kg/s}.$$

This represents a significant flow rate. Assuming a 15-min emergency response period to stop the release, a total of 26,000 kg of hazardous waste will be spilled. In addition to the material released by the flow, the liquid contained within the pipe between the valve and the rupture will also spill. An alternative system must be designed to limit the release. This could include a reduction in the emergency response period, replacement of the pipe by one with a smaller diameter, or modification of the piping system to include additional control valves to stop the flow.

4-5 Flow of Gases or Vapors through Holes

For flowing liquids the kinetic energy changes are frequently negligible and the physical properties (particularly the density) are constant. For flowing gases and vapors these assumptions are valid only for small pressure changes ($P_1/P_2 < 2$) and low velocities (<0.3 times the speed of sound in gas). Energy contained within the gas or vapor as a result of its pressure is converted into kinetic energy as the gas or vapor escapes and expands through the hole. The density, pressure, and temperature change as the gas or vapor exits through the leak.

Gas and vapor discharges are classified into throttling and free expansion releases. For throttling releases the gas issues through a small crack with large frictional losses; little of the energy inherent to the gas pressure is converted to kinetic energy. For free expansion releases most of the pressure energy is converted to kinetic energy; the assumption of isentropic behavior is usually valid.

Source models for throttling releases require detailed information on the physical structure of the leak; they are not considered here. Free expansion release source models require only the diameter of the leak.

A free expansion leak is shown in Figure 4-9. The mechanical energy balance (Equation 4-1) describes the flow of compressible gases and vapors. Assuming negligible potential energy changes and no shaft work results in a reduced form of the mechanical energy balance describing compressible flow through holes:

$$\int \frac{dP}{\rho} + \Delta\left(\frac{\bar{u}^2}{2\alpha g_c}\right) + F = 0. \quad (4\text{-}41)$$

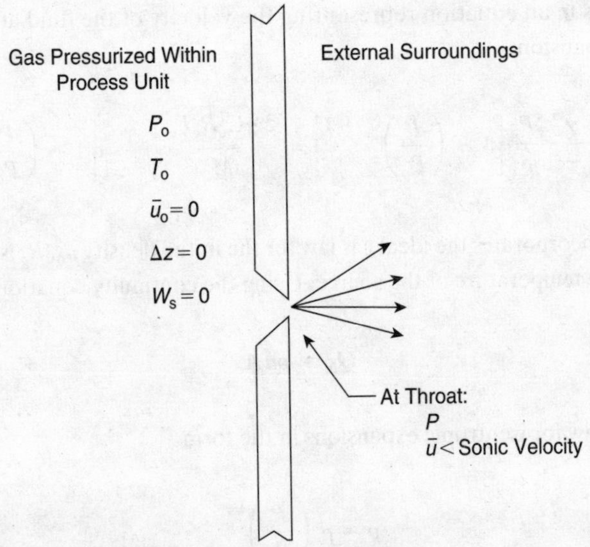

Figure 4-9 A free expansion gas leak. The gas expands isentropically through the hole. The gas properties (P, T) and velocity change during the expansion.

A discharge coefficient C_1 is defined in a similar fashion to the coefficient defined in Section 4-2:

$$-\int \frac{dP}{\rho} - F = C_1^2\left(-\int \frac{dP}{\rho}\right). \tag{4-42}$$

Equation 4-42 is combined with Equation 4-41 and integrated between any two convenient points. An initial point (denoted by subscript "o") is selected where the velocity is zero and the pressure is P_o. The integration is carried to any arbitrary final point (denoted without a subscript). The result is

$$C_1^2 \int_{P_o}^{P} \frac{dP}{\rho} + \frac{\bar{u}^2}{2\alpha g_c} = 0. \tag{4-43}$$

For any ideal gas undergoing an isentropic expansion,

$$Pv^\gamma = \frac{P}{\rho^\gamma} = \text{constant}, \tag{4-44}$$

where γ is the ratio of the heat capacities, $\gamma = C_p/C_v$. Substituting Equation 4-44 into Equation 4-43, defining a new discharge coefficient C_o identical to that in Equation 4-5, and integrating results in an equation representing the velocity of the fluid at any point during the isentropic expansion:

$$\bar{u}^2 = 2g_c C_o^2 \frac{\gamma}{\gamma - 1} \frac{P_o}{\rho_o} \left[1 - \left(\frac{P}{P_o} \right)^{(\gamma-1)/\gamma} \right] = \frac{2g_c C_o^2 R_g T_o}{M} \frac{\gamma}{\gamma - 1} \left[1 - \left(\frac{P}{P_o} \right)^{(\gamma-1)/\gamma} \right]. \tag{4-45}$$

The second form incorporates the ideal gas law for the initial density ρ_o. R_g is the ideal gas constant, and T_o is the temperature of the source. Using the continuity equation

$$Q_m = \rho \bar{u} A \tag{4-46}$$

and the ideal gas law for isentropic expansions in the form

$$\rho = \rho_o \left(\frac{P}{P_o} \right)^{1/\gamma} \tag{4-47}$$

results in an expression for the mass flow rate:

$$Q_m = C_o A P_o \sqrt{\frac{2g_c M}{R_g T_o} \frac{\gamma}{\gamma - 1} \left[\left(\frac{P}{P_o} \right)^{2/\gamma} - \left(\frac{P}{P_o} \right)^{(\gamma+1)/\gamma} \right]}. \tag{4-48}$$

Equation 4-48 describes the mass flow rate at any point during the isentropic expansion.

For many safety studies the maximum flow rate of vapor through the hole is required. This is determined by differentiating Equation 4-48 with respect to P/P_o and setting the derivative equal to zero. The result is solved for the pressure ratio resulting in the maximum flow:

$$\frac{P_{choked}}{P_o} = \left(\frac{2}{\gamma + 1} \right)^{\gamma/(\gamma-1)}. \tag{4-49}$$

The choked pressure P_{choked} is the maximum downstream pressure resulting in maximum flow through the hole or pipe. For downstream pressures *less* than P_{choked} the following statements are valid: (1) The velocity of the fluid at the throat of the leak is the velocity of sound at the prevailing conditions, and (2) the velocity and mass flow rate cannot be increased further by reducing the downstream pressure; they are independent of the downstream conditions. This type of flow is called *choked, critical,* or *sonic flow* and is illustrated in Figure 4-10.

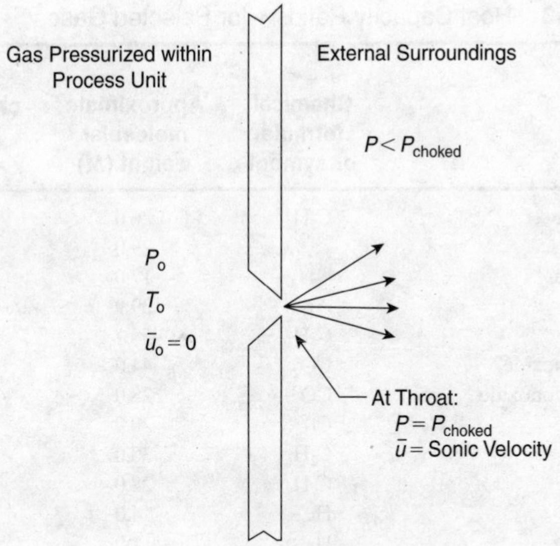

Figure 4-10 Choked flow of gas through a hole. The gas velocity is sonic at the throat. The mass flow rate is independent of the downstream pressure.

An interesting feature of Equation 4-49 is that for ideal gases the choked pressure is a function only of the heat capacity ratio γ. Thus:

Gas	γ	P_{choked}
Monotonic	$\cong$1.67	$0.487P_o$
Diatomic and air	$\cong$1.40	$0.528P_o$
Triatomic	$\cong$1.32	$0.542P_o$

For an air leak to atmospheric conditions (P_{choked} = 14.7 psia), if the upstream pressure is greater than 14.7/0.528 = 27.8 psia, or 13.1 psig, the flow will be choked and maximized through the leak. Conditions leading to choked flow are common in the process industries.

The maximum flow is determined by substituting Equation 4-49 into Equation 4-48:

$$(Q_m)_{\text{choked}} = C_o A P_o \sqrt{\frac{\gamma g_c M}{R_g T_o}\left(\frac{2}{\gamma+1}\right)^{(\gamma+1)/(\gamma-1)}}, \tag{4-50}$$

where

M is the molecular weight of the escaping vapor or gas,
T_o is the temperature of the source, and
R_g is the ideal gas constant.

Table 4-3 Heat Capacity Ratios γ for Selected Gases[a]

Gas	Chemical formula or symbol	Approximate molecular weight (M)	Heat capacity ratio $\gamma = C_p/C_v$
Acetylene	C_2H_2	26.0	1.30
Air	–	29.0	1.40
Ammonia	NH_3	17.0	1.32
Argon	Ar	39.9	1.67
Butane	C_4H_{10}	58.1	1.11
Carbon dioxide	CO_2	44.0	1.30
Carbon monoxide	CO	28.0	1.40
Chlorine	Cl_2	70.9	1.33
Ethane	C_2H_6	30.0	1.22
Ethylene	C_2H_4	28.0	1.22
Helium	He	4.0	1.66
Hydrogen	H_2	2.0	1.41
Hydrogen chloride	HCl	36.5	1.41
Hydrogen sulfide	H_2S	34.1	1.30
Methane	CH_4	16.0	1.32
Methyl chloride	CH_3Cl	50.5	1.20
Natural gas	–	19.5	1.27
Nitric oxide	NO	30.0	1.40
Nitrogen	N_2	28.0	1.41
Nitrous oxide	N_2O	44.0	1.31
Oxygen	O_2	32.0	1.40
Propane	C_3H_8	44.1	1.15
Propene (propylene)	C_3H_6	42.1	1.14
Sulfur dioxide	SO_2	64.1	1.26

[a]Crane Co., *Flow of Fluids Through Valves, Fittings, and Pipes,* Technical Paper 410 (New York: Crane Co., 2009), *www.flowoffluids.com.*

For sharp-edged orifices with Reynolds numbers greater than 30,000 (and not choked), a constant discharge coefficient C_o of 0.61 is indicated. However, for choked flows the discharge coefficient increases as the downstream pressure decreases.[9] For these flows and for situations where C_o is uncertain, a conservative value of 1.0 is recommended.

Values for the heat capacity ratio γ for a variety of gases are provided in Table 4-3.

[9]Robert H. Perry and Cecil H. Chilton, *Chemical Engineers Handbook,* 7th ed. (New York: McGraw-Hill, 1997), pp. 10–16.

Example 4-4

A 0.1-in hole forms in a tank containing nitrogen at 200 psig and 80°F. Determine the mass flow rate through this leak.

Solution

From Table 4-3, for nitrogen $\gamma = 1.41$. Then from Equation 4-49

$$\frac{P_{\text{choked}}}{P_{\text{o}}} = \left(\frac{2}{\gamma+1}\right)^{\gamma/(\gamma-1)} = \left(\frac{2}{2.41}\right)^{1.41/0.41} = 0.527.$$

Thus

$$P_{\text{choked}} = 0.527(200 + 14.7) \text{ psia} = 113.1 \text{ psia}.$$

An external pressure less than 113.1 psia will result in choked flow through the leak. Because the external pressure is atmospheric in this case, choked flow is expected and Equation 4-50 applies. The area of the hole is

$$A = \frac{\pi d^2}{4} = \frac{(3.14)(0.1 \text{ in})^2(1 \text{ ft}^2/144 \text{ in}^2)}{4} = 5.45 \times 10^{-5} \text{ ft}^2.$$

The discharge coefficient C_{o} is assumed to be 1.0. Also,

$$P_{\text{o}} = 200 + 14.7 = 214.7 \text{ psia},$$

$$T_{\text{o}} = 80 + 460 = 540\text{°R},$$

$$\left(\frac{2}{\gamma+1}\right)^{(\gamma+1)/(\gamma-1)} = \left(\frac{2}{2.41}\right)^{2.41/0.41} = 0.829^{5.87} = 0.347.$$

Then, using Equation 4-50,

$$(Q_{\text{m}})_{\text{choked}} = C_{\text{o}} A P_{\text{o}} \sqrt{\frac{\gamma g_{\text{c}} M}{R_{\text{g}} T_{\text{o}}}\left(\frac{2}{\gamma+1}\right)^{(\gamma+1)/(\gamma-1)}}$$

$$= (1.0)(5.45 \times 10^{-5} \text{ ft}^2)(214.7 \text{ lb}_{\text{f}}/\text{in}^2)(144 \text{ in}^2/\text{ft}^2)$$

$$\times \sqrt{\frac{(1.4)(32.17 \text{ ft lb}_{\text{m}}/\text{lb}_{\text{f}}\text{ s}^2)(28 \text{ lb}_{\text{m}}/\text{lb-mol})}{(1545 \text{ ft lb}_{\text{f}}/\text{lb-mol°R})(540\text{°R})}(0.347)}$$

$$= 1.685 \text{ lb}_{\text{f}} \sqrt{5.24 \times 10^{-4} \text{ lb}_{\text{m}}^2/\text{lb}_{\text{f}}^2 \text{ s}^2}$$

$$\boxed{(Q_{\text{m}})_{\text{choked}} = 3.86 \times 10^{-2} \text{ lb}_{\text{m}}/\text{s}.}$$

4-6 Flow of Gases or Vapors through Pipes

Vapor flow through pipes is modeled using two special cases: adiabatic and isothermal behavior. The adiabatic case corresponds to rapid vapor flow through an insulated pipe. The isothermal case corresponds to flow through an uninsulated pipe maintained at a constant temperature; an underwater pipeline is an excellent example. Real vapor flows behave somewhere between the adiabatic and isothermal cases. Unfortunately, the real case must be modeled numerically and no generalized and useful equations are available.

For both the isothermal and adiabatic cases it is convenient to define a Mach (Ma) number as the ratio of the gas velocity to the velocity of sound in the gas at the prevailing conditions:

$$\text{Ma} = \frac{\bar{u}}{a}, \tag{4-51}$$

where a is the velocity of sound. The velocity of sound is determined using the thermodynamic relationship

$$a = \sqrt{g_c \left(\frac{\partial P}{\partial \rho} \right)_S}, \tag{4-52}$$

which for an ideal gas is equivalent to

$$a = \sqrt{\gamma g_c R_g T / M}, \tag{4-53}$$

which demonstrates that for ideal gases the sonic velocity is a function of temperature only. For air at 20°C the velocity of sound is 344 m/s (1129 ft/s).

Adiabatic Flows

An adiabatic pipe containing a flowing vapor is shown in Figure 4-11. For this particular case the outlet velocity is less than the sonic velocity. The flow is driven by a pressure gradient across the pipe. As the gas flows through the pipe, it expands because of a decrease in pressure. This expansion leads to an increase in velocity and an increase in the kinetic energy of the gas. The kinetic energy is extracted from the thermal energy of the gas; a decrease in temperature occurs. However, frictional forces are present between the gas and the pipe wall. These frictional forces increase the temperature of the gas. Depending on the magnitude of the kinetic and frictional energy terms, either an increase or a decrease in the gas temperature is possible.

The mechanical energy balance (Equation 4-1) also applies to adiabatic flows. For this case it is more conveniently written in the form

$$\frac{dP}{\rho} + \frac{\bar{u}\,d\bar{u}}{\alpha g_c} + \frac{g}{g_c} dz + dF = -\frac{\delta W_s}{m}. \tag{4-54}$$

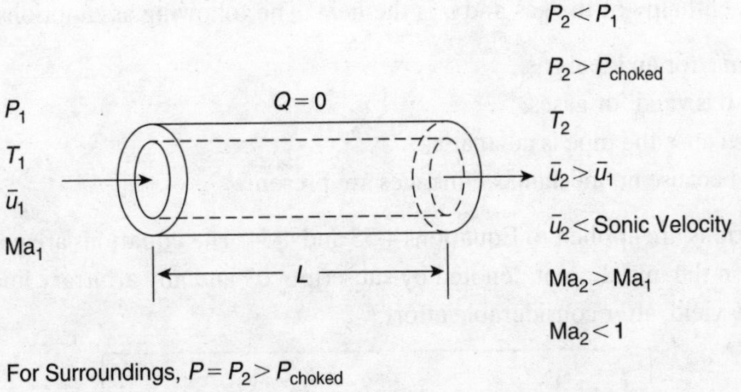

Figure 4-11 Adiabatic nonchoked flow of gas through a pipe. The gas temperature might increase or decrease, depending on the magnitude of the frictional losses.

The following assumptions are valid for this case:

$$\frac{g}{g_c} dz \approx 0$$

is valid for gases. Assuming a straight pipe without any valves or fittings, Equations 4-29 and 4-30 can be combined and then differentiated to result in

$$dF = \frac{2f\,\bar{u}^2\,dL}{g_c d}.$$

Because no mechanical linkages are present,

$$\delta W_s = 0.$$

An important part of the frictional loss term is the assumption of a constant Fanning friction factor f across the length of the pipe. This assumption is valid only at high Reynolds numbers.

A total energy balance is useful for describing the temperature changes within the flowing gas. For this open steady flow process the total energy balance is given by

$$dh + \frac{\bar{u}d\bar{u}}{\alpha g_c} + \frac{g}{g_c} dz = \delta q - \frac{\delta W_s}{m}, \tag{4-55}$$

where h is the enthalpy of the gas and q is the heat. The following assumptions are invoked:

$dh = C_p\,dT$ for an ideal gas,
$g/g_c\,dz \approx 0$ is valid for gases,
$\delta q = 0$ because the pipe is adiabatic,
$\delta W_s = 0$ because no mechanical linkages are present.

These assumptions are applied to Equations 4-55 and 4-54. The equations are combined, integrated (between the initial point denoted by subscript "o" and any arbitrary final point), and manipulated to yield, after considerable effort,[10]

$$\frac{T_2}{T_1} = \frac{Y_1}{Y_2}, \quad \text{where } Y_i = 1 + \frac{\gamma - 1}{2}\text{Ma}_i^2, \tag{4-56}$$

$$\frac{P_2}{P_1} = \frac{\text{Ma}_1}{\text{Ma}_2}\sqrt{\frac{Y_1}{Y_2}}, \tag{4-57}$$

$$\frac{\rho_2}{\rho_1} = \frac{\text{Ma}_1}{\text{Ma}_2}\sqrt{\frac{Y_2}{Y_1}}, \tag{4-58}$$

$$G = \rho\bar{u} = \text{Ma}_1 P_1\sqrt{\frac{\gamma g_c M}{R_g T_1}} = \text{Ma}_2 P_2\sqrt{\frac{\gamma g_c M}{R_g T_2}}, \tag{4-59}$$

where G is the mass flux with units of mass/(area-time) and

$$\underbrace{\frac{\gamma + 1}{2}\ln\left(\frac{\text{Ma}_2^2 Y_1}{\text{Ma}_1^2 Y_2}\right)}_{\text{kinetic energy}} - \underbrace{\left(\frac{1}{\text{Ma}_1^2} - \frac{1}{\text{Ma}_2^2}\right)}_{\text{compressibility}} + \underbrace{\gamma\left(\frac{4fL}{d}\right)}_{\text{pipe friction}} = 0. \tag{4-60}$$

Equation 4-60 relates the Mach numbers to the frictional losses in the pipe. The various energy contributions are identified. The compressibility term accounts for the change in velocity resulting from the expansion of the gas.

Equations 4-59 and 4-60 are converted to a more convenient and useful form by replacing the Mach numbers with temperatures and pressures, using Equations 4-56 through 4-58:

$$\frac{\gamma + 1}{\gamma}\ln\frac{P_1 T_2}{P_2 T_1} - \frac{\gamma - 1}{2\gamma}\left(\frac{P_1^2 T_2^2 - P_2^2 T_1^2}{T_2 - T_1}\right)\left(\frac{1}{P_1^2 T_2} - \frac{1}{P_2^2 T_1}\right) + \frac{4fL}{d} = 0, \tag{4-61}$$

$$G = \sqrt{\frac{2g_c M}{R_g}\frac{\gamma}{\gamma - 1}\frac{T_2 - T_1}{(T_1/P_1)^2 - (T_2/P_2)^2}}. \tag{4-62}$$

[10] Octave Levenspiel, *Engineering Flow and Heat Exchange,* 2nd ed. (New York: Springer, 1998), p. 43.

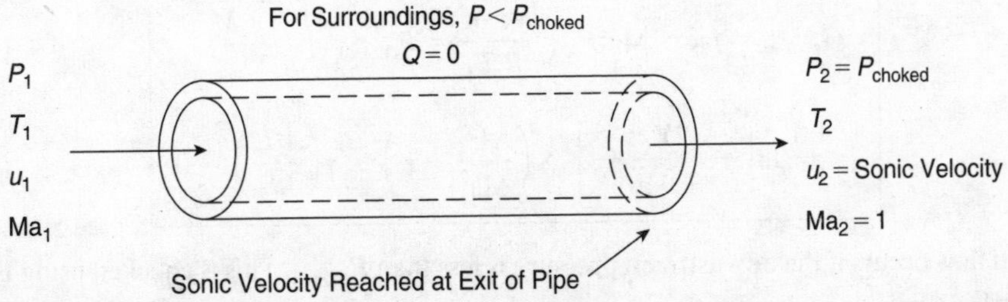

Figure 4-12 Adiabatic choked flow of gas through a pipe. The maximum velocity is reached at the end of the pipe.

For most problems the pipe length (L), inside diameter (d), upstream temperature (T_1) and pressure (P_1), and downstream pressure (P_2) are known. To compute the mass flux G, the procedure is as follows:

1. Determine pipe roughness ε from Table 4-1. Compute ε/d.
2. Determine the Fanning friction factor f from Equation 4-34. This assumes fully developed turbulent flow at high Reynolds numbers. This assumption can be checked later but is normally valid.
3. Determine T_2 from Equation 4-61.
4. Compute the total mass flux G from Equation 4-62.

For long pipes or for large pressure differences across the pipe the velocity of the gas can approach the sonic velocity. This case is shown in Figure 4-12. When the sonic velocity is reached, the gas flow is called choked. The gas reaches the sonic velocity at the end of the pipe. If the upstream pressure is increased or if the downstream pressure is decreased, the gas velocity at the end of the pipe remains constant at the sonic velocity. If the downstream pressure is decreased below the choked pressure P_{choked}, the flow through the pipe remains choked and constant, independent of the downstream pressure. The pressure at the end of the pipe will remain at P_{choked} even if this pressure is greater than the ambient pressure. The gas exiting the pipe makes an abrupt change from P_{choked} to the ambient pressure. For choked flow Equations 4-56 through 4-60 are simplified by setting $\text{Ma}_2 = 1.0$. The results are

$$\frac{T_{\text{choked}}}{T_1} = \frac{2Y_1}{\gamma + 1}, \tag{4-63}$$

$$\frac{P_{\text{choked}}}{P_1} = \text{Ma}_1\sqrt{\frac{2Y_1}{\gamma + 1}}, \tag{4-64}$$

$$\frac{\rho_{\text{choked}}}{\rho_1} = \text{Ma}_1\sqrt{\frac{\gamma + 1}{2Y_1}}, \tag{4-65}$$

$$G_{\text{choked}} = \rho\bar{u} = \text{Ma}_1 P_1 \sqrt{\frac{\gamma g_c M}{R_g T_1}} = P_{\text{choked}} \sqrt{\frac{\gamma g_c M}{R_g T_{\text{choked}}}}, \tag{4-66}$$

$$\frac{\gamma + 1}{2} \ln\left[\frac{2Y_1}{(\gamma + 1)\text{Ma}_1^2}\right] - \left(\frac{1}{\text{Ma}_1^2} - 1\right) + \gamma\left(\frac{4fL}{d}\right) = 0. \tag{4-67}$$

Choked flow occurs if the downstream pressure is less than P_{choked}. This is checked using Equation 4-64.

For most problems involving choked adiabatic flows the pipe length (L), inside diameter (d), and upstream pressure (P_1) and temperature (T_1) are known. To compute the mass flux G, the procedure is as follows:

1. Determine the Fanning friction factor f using Equation 4-34. This assumes fully developed turbulent flow at high Reynolds numbers. This assumption can be checked later but is normally valid.
2. Determine Ma_1 from Equation 4-67.
3. Determine the mass flux G_{choked} from Equation 4-66.
4. Determine P_{choked} from Equation 4-64 to confirm operation at choked conditions.

Equations 4-63 through 4-67 for adiabatic pipe flow can be modified to use the 2-K method discussed previously by substituting ΣK_f for $4fL/d$.

The procedure can be simplified by defining a gas expansion factor Y_g. For ideal gas flow the mass flow for both sonic and nonsonic conditions is represented by the Darcy formula:[11]

$$G = \frac{\dot{m}}{A} = Y_g \sqrt{\frac{2g_c\rho_1(P_1 - P_2)}{\sum K_f}}, \tag{4-68}$$

where

G is the mass flux (mass/area-time),
$\dot{m}$ is the mass flow rate of gas (mass/time),
A is the area of the discharge (length^2),
Y_g is a gas expansion factor (unitless),
g_c is the gravitational constant (force/mass-acceleration),
ρ_1 is the upstream gas density (mass/volume),
P_1 is the upstream gas pressure (force/area),
P_2 is the downstream gas pressure (force/area), and
ΣK_f are the excess head loss terms, including pipe entrances and exits, pipe lengths, and fittings (unitless).

[11] Crane Co., *Flow of Fluids.*

The excess head loss terms ΣK_f are found using the 2-K method presented earlier in section 4-4. For most accidental discharges of gases the flow is fully developed turbulent flow. This means that for pipes the friction factor is independent of the Reynolds number and that for fittings $K_f = K_\infty$ and the solution is direct.

The gas expansion factor Y_g in Equation 4-68 depends only on the heat capacity ratio of the gas γ and the frictional elements in the flow path ΣK_f. An equation for the gas expansion factor for choked flow is obtained by equating Equation 4-68 to Equation 4-59 and solving for Y_g. The result is

$$Y_g = \mathrm{Ma}_1\sqrt{\frac{\gamma \Sigma K_f}{2}\left(\frac{P_1}{P_1 - P_2}\right)}, \qquad (4\text{-}69)$$

where Ma_1 is the upstream Mach number.

The procedure to determine the gas expansion factor is as follows. First, the upstream Mach number Ma_1 is determined using Equation 4-67. ΣK_f must be substituted for $4fL/d$ to include the effects of pipes and fittings. The solution is obtained by trial and error, by guessing values of the upstream Mach number and determining whether the guessed value meets the equation objectives. This can be easily done using a spreadsheet.

The next step in the procedure is to determine the sonic pressure ratio. This is found from Equation 4-64. If the actual ratio is greater than the ratio from Equation 4-64, then the flow is sonic or choked and the pressure drop predicted by Equation 4-64 is used to continue the calculation. If less than the ratio from Equation 4-64, then the flow is not sonic and the actual pressure drop ratio is used.

Finally, the expansion factor Y_g is calculated from Equation 4-69.

The calculation to determine the expansion factor can be completed once γ and the frictional loss terms ΣK_f are specified. This computation can be done once and for all with the results shown in Figures 4-13 and 4-14. As shown in Figure 4-13, the pressure ratio $(P_1 - P_2)/P_1$ is a weak function of the heat capacity ratio γ. The expansion factor Y_g has little dependence on γ, with the value of Y_g varying by less than 1% from the value at $\gamma = 1.4$ over the range from $\gamma = 1.2$ to $\gamma = 1.67$. Figure 4-14 shows the expansion factor for $\gamma = 1.4$.

The functional results of Figures 4-13 and 4-14 can be fitted using an equation of the form $\ln Y_g = A(\ln K_f)^3 + B(\ln K_f)^2 + C(\ln K_f) + D$, where A, B, C, and D are constants. The results are shown in Table 4-4 and are valid for the K_f ranges indicated, within 1%.

The procedure to determine the adiabatic mass flow rate through a pipe or hole is as follows:

1. Given: γ based on the type of gas; pipe length, diameter, and type; pipe entrances and exits; total number and type of fittings; total pressure drop; upstream gas density.
2. Assume fully developed turbulent flow to determine the friction factor for the pipe and the excess head loss terms for the fittings and pipe entrances and exits. The Reynolds number can be calculated at the completion of the calculation to check this assumption. Sum the individual excess head loss terms to get ΣK_f.

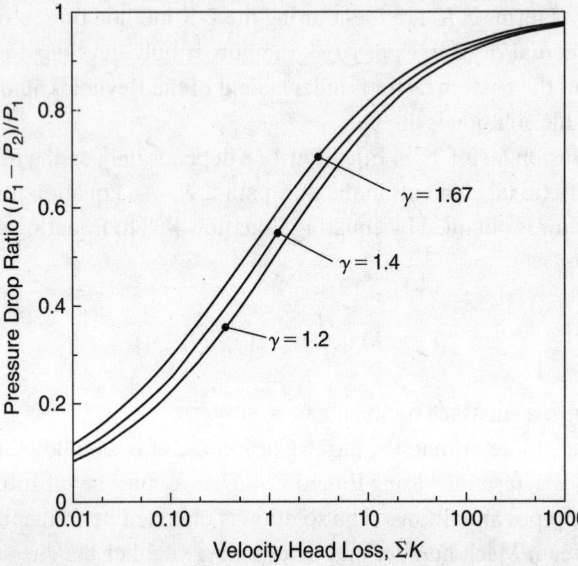

Figure 4-13 Pressure drop ratio as a function of the excess velocity head pipe losses for adiabatic flow. (Reprinted from *J. Loss Prevention in the Proc. Ind.*, Vol. 18, J. M. Keith and D. A. Crowl, "Estimating Sonic Gas Flow Rates in Pipelines," pp. 55–62, 2005, with permission from Elsevier.)

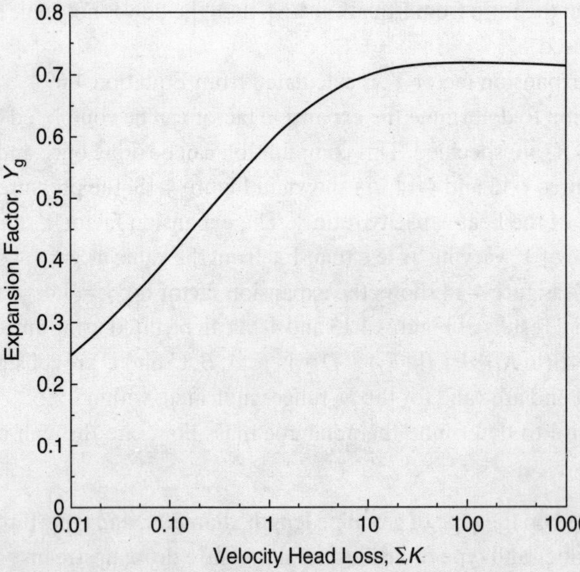

Figure 4-14 Gas expansion factor as a function of the excess velocity head pipe losses for adiabatic flow. The results are a weak function of heat capacity, but the difference is less than can be shown on this figure. (Reprinted from *J. Loss Prevention in the Proc. Ind.*, Vol. 18, J. M. Keith and D. A. Crowl, "Estimating Sonic Gas Flow Rates in Pipelines," pp. 55–62, 2005, with permission from Elsevier.)

Table 4-4 Correlations for the Expansion Factor Y_g and the Sonic Pressure Drop Ratio $(P_1 - P_2)/P_1$ as a Function of the Pipe Loss ΣK for Adiabatic Flow Conditions[a]

Function value[b]	A	B	C	D	Range of validity, K
Expansion factor Y_g	0.00129	−0.0216	0.116	−0.528	0.2–1000
Sonic pressure drop ratio $\gamma = 1.2$	0.943	0.00727	1.12	–	0.01–1000
Sonic pressure drop ratio $\gamma = 1.4$	0.965	0.00461	0.944	–	0.2–1000
Sonic pressure drop ratio $\gamma = 1.67$	0.989	0.00178	0.767	–	0.01–1000

[a] J. Keith and D. A. Crowl, "Estimating Sonic Gas Flow Rates in Pipelines," *J. Loss Prevention in the Proc. Ind.* (2005), 18: 55–62.

[b] The equations used to fit the functions are of the form $\ln Y = A(\ln K)^3 + B(\ln K)^2 + C(\ln K) + D$ for the expansion factor and $\{(P_1 - P_2)/P_1\}^{-1} = A + B(\ln K)^2 + C / K^{0.5}$ for the pressure drop ratio.

3. Calculate $(P_1 - P_2)/P_1$ from the specified pressure drop. Check this value against Figure 4-13 to determine whether the flow is sonic. All areas above the curves in Figure 4-13 represent sonic flow. Determine the sonic choking pressure P_2 by using Figure 4-13 directly, interpolating a value from the table, or using the equations provided in Table 4-4.
4. Determine the expansion factor from Figure 4-14. Either read the value off of the figure, interpolate it from the table, or use the equation provided in Table 4-4.
5. Calculate the mass flow rate using Equation 4-68. Use the sonic choking pressure determined in step 3 in this expression.

This method is applicable to gas discharges through piping systems and holes.

Isothermal Flows

Isothermal flow of gas in a pipe with friction is shown in Figure 4-15. For this case the gas velocity is assumed to be well below the sonic velocity of the gas. A pressure gradient across

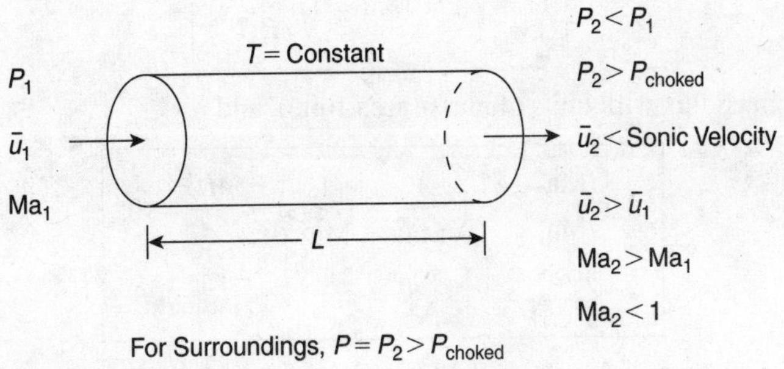

Figure 4-15 Isothermal nonchoked flow of gas through a pipe.

the pipe provides the driving force for the gas transport. As the gas expands through the pressure gradient, the velocity must increase to maintain the same mass flow rate. The pressure at the end of the pipe is equal to the pressure of the surroundings. The temperature is constant across the entire pipe length.

Isothermal flow is represented by the mechanical energy balance in the form shown in Equation 4-54. The following assumptions are valid for this case:

$$\frac{g}{g_c} dz \approx 0$$

is valid for gases, and, by combining Equations 4-29 and 4-30 and differentiating,

$$dF = \frac{2f\bar{u}^2 dL}{g_c d},$$

assuming constant f, and

$$\delta W_s = 0$$

because no mechanical linkages are present. A total energy balance is not required because the temperature is constant.

By applying the assumptions to Equation 4-54 and manipulating them considerably, we obtain[12]

$$T_2 = T_1, \tag{4-70}$$

$$\frac{P_2}{P_1} = \frac{\text{Ma}_1}{\text{Ma}_2}, \tag{4-71}$$

$$\frac{\rho_2}{\rho_1} = \frac{\text{Ma}_1}{\text{Ma}_2}, \tag{4-72}$$

$$G = \rho\bar{u} = \text{Ma}_1 P_1 \sqrt{\frac{\gamma g_c M}{R_g T}}, \tag{4-73}$$

where G is the mass flux with units of mass/(area-time), and

$$\underbrace{2\ln\frac{\text{Ma}_2}{\text{Ma}_1}}_{\text{kinetic energy}} - \underbrace{\frac{1}{\gamma}\left(\frac{1}{\text{Ma}_1^2} - \frac{1}{\text{Ma}_2^2}\right)}_{\text{compressibility}} + \underbrace{\frac{4fL}{d}}_{\text{pipe friction}} = 0. \tag{4-74}$$

The various energy terms in Equation 4-74 have been identified.

[12] Levenspiel, *Engineering Flow and Heat Exchange*, 2nd ed. (1998), p. 46.

A more convenient form of Equation 4-74 is in terms of pressure instead of Mach numbers. This form is achieved by using Equations 4-70 through 4-72. The result is

$$2 \ln \frac{P_1}{P_2} - \frac{g_c M}{G^2 R_g T}(P_1^2 - P_2^2) + \frac{4fL}{d} = 0. \tag{4-75}$$

A typical problem is to determine the mass flux G given the pipe length (L), inside diameter (d), and upstream and downstream pressures (P_1 and P_2). The procedure is as follows:

1. Determine the Fanning friction factor f using Equation 4-34. This assumes fully developed turbulent flow at high Reynolds numbers. This assumption can be checked later but is usually valid.
2. Compute the mass flux G from Equation 4-75.

Levenspiel[13] showed that the maximum velocity possible during the isothermal flow of gas in a pipe is not the sonic velocity, as in the adiabatic case. In terms of the Mach number the maximum velocity is

$$\mathrm{Ma}_{\text{choked}} = \frac{1}{\sqrt{\gamma}}. \tag{4-76}$$

This result is shown by starting with the mechanical energy balance and rearranging it into the following form:

$$-\frac{dP}{dL} = \frac{2fG^2}{g_c \rho d}\left[\frac{1}{1 - (\bar{u}^2 \rho / g_c P)}\right] = \frac{2fG^2}{g_c \rho d}\left(\frac{1}{1 - \gamma \mathrm{Ma}^2}\right). \tag{4-77}$$

The quantity $-(dP/dL) \rightarrow \infty$ when $\mathrm{Ma} \rightarrow 1/\sqrt{\gamma}$. Thus for choked flow in an isothermal pipe, as shown in Figure 4-16, the following equations apply:

$$T_{\text{choked}} = T_1, \tag{4-78}$$

$$\frac{P_{\text{choked}}}{P_1} = \mathrm{Ma}_1 \sqrt{\gamma}, \tag{4-79}$$

$$\frac{\rho_{\text{choked}}}{\rho_1} = \mathrm{Ma}_1 \sqrt{\gamma}, \tag{4-80}$$

$$\frac{\bar{u}_{\text{choked}}}{\bar{u}_1} = \frac{1}{\mathrm{Ma}_1 \sqrt{\gamma}}, \tag{4-81}$$

$$G_{\text{choked}} = \rho \bar{u} = \rho_1 \bar{u}_1 = \mathrm{Ma}_1 P_1 \sqrt{\frac{\gamma g_c M}{R_g T}} = P_{\text{choked}} \sqrt{\frac{g_c M}{R_g T}}, \tag{4-82}$$

[13]Levenspiel, *Engineering Flow and Heat Exchange,* 2nd ed. (1998) p. 46.

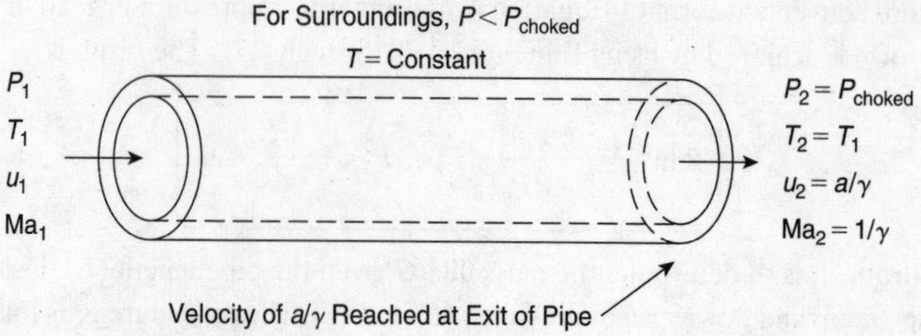

Figure 4-16 Isothermal choked flow of gas through a pipe. The maximum velocity is reached at the end of the pipe.

where G_{choked} is the mass flux with units of mass/(area-time), and

$$\ln\left(\frac{1}{\gamma \mathrm{Ma}_1^2}\right) - \left(\frac{1}{\gamma \mathrm{Ma}_1^2} - 1\right) + \frac{4fL}{d} = 0. \tag{4-83}$$

For most typical problems the pipe length (L), inside diameter (d), upstream pressure (P_1), and temperature (T) are known. The mass flux G is determined using the following procedure:

1. Determine the Fanning friction factor using Equation 4-34. This assumes fully developed turbulent flow at high Reynolds numbers. This assumption can be checked later but is usually valid.
2. Determine Ma_1 from Equation 4-83.
3. Determine the mass flux G from Equation 4-82.

The direct method using Equations 4-68 and 4-69 can also be applied to isothermal flows. Table 4-5 provides the equations for the expansion factor and the pressure drop ratio. Figures 4-17 and 4-18 are plots of these functions. The procedure is identical to the procedure for adiabatic flows.

Keith and Crowl[14] found that for both the adiabatic and isothermal cases the expansion factor Y_g exhibited a maximum value. For isothermal flows this maximum was the same for all values of the heat capacity ratio γ and occurred at a velocity head loss of 56.3 with a maximum expansion factor of 0.7248. For adiabatic flows the maximum value of the expansion factor is a function of the heat capacity ratio γ. For $\gamma = 1.4$ the expansion factor has a maximum value of 0.7182 at a velocity head loss of 90.0.

For both the adiabatic and isothermal flow cases the expansion factor approaches an asymptote as the velocity head loss becomes large – the asymptote is the same for both cases.

[14]Keith and Crowl, "Estimating Sonic Gas Flow Rates."

This asymptote is $1/\sqrt{2} = 0.7071$ for both the adiabatic and isothermal flow cases. Comparison of detailed calculations with the asymptotic solution show that for velocity head loss values of 100 and 500 the difference between the detailed and asymptotic solution is 2.2% and 0.2%, respectively.

The asymptotic solution can be inserted into Equation 4-68 to result in the following simplified equation for the mass flow:

$$G = \frac{\dot{m}}{A} = \sqrt{\frac{g_c \rho_1 P_1}{\Sigma K}}. \tag{4-84}$$

Table 4-5 Correlations for the Expansion Factor Y_g and the Sonic Pressure Drop Ratio $(P_1 - P_2)/P_1$ as a Function of the Pipe Loss ΣK for Isothermal Flow Conditions[a]

Function value[b]	A	B	C	D	Range of validity, K
Expansion factor Y_g	0.00130	−0.0216	0.111	−0.502	0.2–1000
Sonic pressure drop ratio, all γ	0.911	0.0118	1.38	–	0.01–1000

[a]Keith and Crowl, "Estimating Sonic Gas Flow Rates."
[b]The equations used to fit the functions are of the form $\ln Y_g = A(\ln K)^3 + B(\ln K)^2 + C(\ln K) + D$ for the expansion factor and $\{(P_1 - P_2)/P_1\}^{-1} = A + B(\ln K)^2 + C / K^{0.5}$ for the pressure drop ratio.

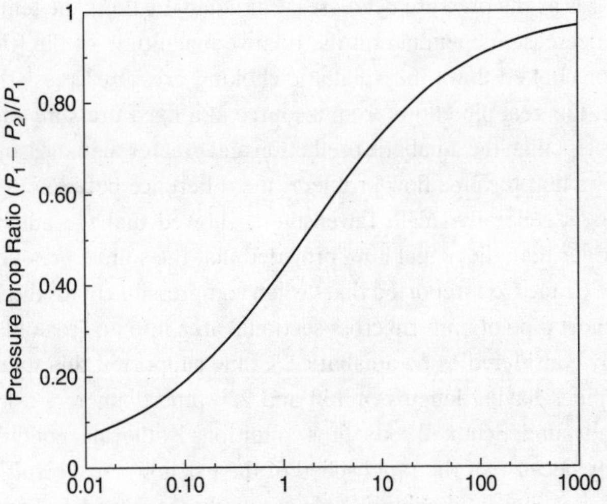

Figure 4-17 Pressure drop ratio as a function of the excess velocity head pipe losses for isothermal flow. The results are independent of the heat capacity ratio. Reprinted from *J. Loss Prevention in the Proc. Ind.*, Vol. 18, J. M. Keith and D. A. Crowl, "Estimating Sonic Gas Flow Rates in Pipelines," pp. 55–62, 2005, with permission from Elsevier.

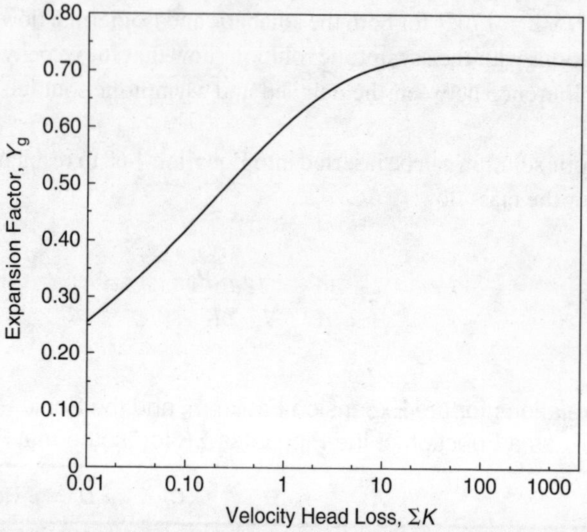

Figure 4-18 Gas expansion factor as a function of the excess velocity head pipe losses for isothermal flow. The results are independent of the heat capacity ratio. Reprinted from *J. Loss Prevention in the Proc. Ind.*, Vol. 18, J. M. Keith and D. A. Crowl, "Estimating Sonic Gas Flow Rates in Pipelines," pp. 55–62, 2005, with permission from Elsevier.

For gas releases through pipes the issue of whether the release occurs adiabatically or isothermally is important. For both cases the velocity of the gas increases because of the expansion of the gas as the pressure decreases. For adiabatic flows the temperature of the gas may increase or decrease, depending on the relative magnitude of the frictional and kinetic energy terms. For choked flows the adiabatic choking pressure is less than the isothermal choking pressure. For real pipe flows from a source at a fixed pressure and temperature, the actual flow rate is less than the adiabatic prediction and greater than the isothermal prediction. Example 4-5 shows that for pipe flow problems the difference between the adiabatic and the isothermal results is generally small. Levenspiel[15] showed that the adiabatic model always predicts a flow larger than the actual flow, provided that the source pressure and temperature are the same. The Crane Co.[16] reported that "when compressible fluids discharge from the end of a reasonably short pipe of uniform cross-sectional area into an area of larger cross section, the flow is usually considered to be adiabatic." Crane supported this statement with experimental data on pipes having lengths of 130 and 220 pipe diameters discharging air to the atmosphere. Finally, under choked sonic flow conditions isothermal conditions are difficult to achieve practically because of the rapid speed of the gas flow. As a result, the adiabatic flow model is the model of choice for compressible gas discharges through pipes.

[15]Levenspiel, *Engineering Flow and Heat Exchange,* 2nd ed. (1998), p. 45.
[16]Crane Co., *Flow of Fluids.*

Example 4-5

The vapor space above liquid ethylene oxide (EO) in storage tanks must be purged of oxygen and then padded with 81-psig nitrogen to prevent explosion. The nitrogen in a particular facility is supplied from a 200-psig source. It is regulated to 81 psig and supplied to the storage vessel through 33 ft of new commercial steel pipe with an internal diameter of 1.049 in.

In the event of a failure of the nitrogen regulator, the vessel will be exposed to the full 200-psig pressure from the nitrogen source. This will exceed the pressure rating of the storage vessel. To prevent rupture of the storage vessel, it must be equipped with a relief device to vent this nitrogen. Determine the required minimum mass flow rate of nitrogen through the relief device to prevent the pressure from rising within the tank in the event of a regulator failure.

Determine the mass flow rate assuming (a) an orifice with a throat diameter equal to the pipe diameter, (b) an adiabatic pipe, and (c) an isothermal pipe. Decide which result most closely corresponds to the real situation. Which mass flow rate should be used?

Solution

a. The maximum flow rate through the orifice occurs under choked conditions. The area of the pipe is

$$A = \frac{\pi d^2}{4} = \frac{(3.14)(1.049\ \text{in})^2(1\ \text{ft}^2/144\ \text{in}^2)}{4}$$

$$= 6.00 \times 10^{-3}\ \text{ft}^2.$$

The absolute pressure of the nitrogen source is

$$P_o = 200 + 14.7 = 214.7\ \text{psia} = 3.09 \times 10^4\ \text{lb}_f/\text{ft}^2.$$

The choked pressure from Equation 4-49 is, for a diatomic gas,

$$P_{\text{choked}} = (0.528)(214.7\ \text{psia}) = 113.4\ \text{psia}$$

$$= 1.63 \times 10^4\ \text{lb}_f/\text{ft}^2.$$

Choked flow can be expected because the system is venting to atmospheric conditions. Equation 4-50 provides the maximum mass flow rate. For nitrogen, $\gamma = 1.4$ and

$$\left(\frac{2}{\gamma + 1}\right)^{(\gamma+1)/(\gamma-1)} = \left(\frac{2}{2.4}\right)^{2.4/0.4} = 0.335.$$

The molecular weight of nitrogen is 28 lb_m/lb-mol. Without any additional information, assume a unit discharge coefficient $C_o = 1.0$. Thus

$$Q_m = (1.0)(6.00 \times 10^{-3}\ \text{ft}^2)(3.09 \times 10^4\ \text{lb}_f/\text{ft}^2) \times \sqrt{\frac{(1.4)(32.17\ \text{ft lb}_m/\text{lb}_f\,\text{s}^2)(28\ \text{lb}_m/\text{lb-mol})}{(1545\ \text{ft lb}_f/\text{lb-mol}^\circ\text{R})(540^\circ\text{R})}(0.335)}$$

$$= (185\ \text{lb}_f)\sqrt{5.06 \times 10^{-4}\ \text{lb}_m^2/\text{lb}_f^2\,\text{s}^2}$$

$$\boxed{Q_m = 4.16\ \text{lb}_m/\text{s}.}$$

b. Assume adiabatic choked flow conditions. For commercial steel pipe, from Table 4-1, $\varepsilon = 0.046$ mm. The diameter of the pipe in millimeters is (1.049 in) (25.4 mm/in) = 26.6 mm. Thus

$$\frac{\varepsilon}{d} = \frac{0.046\text{ mm}}{26.6\text{ mm}} = 0.00173.$$

From Equation 4-34

$$\frac{1}{\sqrt{f}} = 4\log\left(3.7\frac{d}{\varepsilon}\right)$$
$$= 4\log(3.7/0.00173) = 13.32,$$
$$\sqrt{f} = 0.0751,$$
$$f = 0.00564.$$

For nitrogen, $\gamma = 1.4$.

The upstream Mach number is determined from Equation 4-67:

$$\frac{\gamma+1}{2}\ln\left[\frac{2Y_1}{(\gamma+1)\text{Ma}_1^2}\right] - \left(\frac{1}{\text{Ma}_1^2} - 1\right) + \gamma\left(\frac{4fL}{d}\right) = 0,$$

with Y_1 given by Equation 4-56. Substituting the numbers provided gives

$$\frac{1.4+1}{2}\ln\left[\frac{2+(1.4-1)\text{Ma}^2}{(1.4+1)\text{Ma}^2}\right] - \left(\frac{1}{\text{Ma}^2} - 1\right) + 1.4\left[\frac{(4)(0.00564)(33\text{ ft})}{(1.049\text{ in})(1\text{ ft}/12\text{ in})}\right] = 0,$$

$$1.2\ln\left(\frac{2+0.4\text{Ma}^2}{2.4\text{Ma}^2}\right) - \left(\frac{1}{\text{Ma}^2} - 1\right) + 11.92 = 0.$$

This equation is solved by trial and error or a solver program or spreadsheet for the value of Ma. The results are tabulated as follows:

Guessed Ma	Value of left-hand side of equation
0.20	−8.43
0.25	0.043

This last guessed Mach number gives a result close to zero. Then from Equation 4-56

$$Y_1 = 1 + \frac{\gamma-1}{2}\text{Ma}^2 = 1 + \frac{1.4-1}{2}(0.25)^2 = 1.012,$$

and from Equations 4-63 and 4-64

$$\frac{T_{\text{choked}}}{T_1} = \frac{2Y_1}{\gamma+1} = \frac{2(1.012)}{1.4+1} = 0.843,$$

$$T_{\text{choked}} = (0.843)(80+460)^\circ\text{R} = 455^\circ\text{R},$$

$$\frac{P_{\text{choked}}}{P_1} = \text{Ma}\sqrt{\frac{2Y_1}{\gamma + 1}} = (0.25)\sqrt{0.843} = 0.230,$$

$$P_{\text{choked}} = (0.230)(214.7 \text{ psia}) = 49.4 \text{ psia} = 7.11 \times 10^3 \text{ lb}_f/\text{ft}^2.$$

The pipe outlet pressure must be less than 49.4 psia to ensure choked flow. The mass flux is computed using Equation 4-66:

$$G_{\text{choked}} = P_{\text{choked}}\sqrt{\frac{\gamma g_c M}{R_g T_{\text{choked}}}}$$

$$= (7.11 \times 10^3 \text{ lb}_f/\text{ft}^2)\sqrt{\frac{(1.4)(32.17 \text{ ft lb}_m/\text{lb}_f \text{s}^2)(28 \text{ lb}_m/\text{lb-mol})}{(1545 \text{ ft lb}_f/\text{lb-mol}°\text{R})(455°\text{R})}}$$

$$= 7.11 \times 10^3 \text{ lb}_f/\text{ft}^2\sqrt{1.79 \times 10^{-3} \text{ lb}_m^2/\text{lb}_f^2 \text{s}^2} = 301 \text{ lb}_m/\text{ft}^2 \text{ s},$$

$$Q_m = GA = (301 \text{ lb}_m/\text{ft}^2\text{s})(6.00 \times 10^{-3} \text{ ft}^2)$$

$$\boxed{= 1.81 \text{ lb}_m/\text{s}.}$$

The simplified procedure with a direct solution can also be used. The excess head loss resulting from the pipe length is given by Equation 4-30. The friction factor f has already been determined:

$$K_f = \frac{4fL}{d} = \frac{(4)(0.00564)(10.1 \text{ m})}{(1.049 \text{ in})(0.0254 \text{ m/in})} = 8.56.$$

For this solution only the pipe friction will be considered and the exit effects will be ignored. The first consideration is whether the flow is sonic. The sonic pressure ratio is given in Figure 4-13 (or the equations in Table 4-4). For $\gamma = 1.4$ and $K_f = 8.56$

$$\frac{P_1 - P_2}{P_1} = 0.770 \Rightarrow P_2 = 49.4 \text{ psia}.$$

It follows that the flow is sonic because the downstream pressure is less than 49.4 psia. From Figure 4-14 (or Table 4-4) the gas expansion factor $Y_g = 0.69$. The gas density under the upstream conditions is

$$\rho_1 = \frac{P_1 M}{R_g T} = \frac{(214.7 \text{ psia})(28 \text{ lb}_m/\text{lb-mol})}{(10.731 \text{ psia ft}^3/\text{lb-mol}°\text{R})(540°\text{R})} = 1.037 \text{ lb}_m/\text{ft}^3.$$

By substituting this value into Equation 4-68 and using the choking pressure determined for P_2, we obtain

$$\dot{m} = Y_g A\sqrt{\frac{2g_c\rho_1(P_1 - P_2)}{\sum K_f}},$$

$$= (0.69)(6.00 \times 10^{-3} \text{ ft}^2)\sqrt{\frac{(2)\left(32.17\frac{\text{ft lb}_m}{\text{lb}_f \text{ s}^2}\right)\left(1.037\frac{\text{lb}_m}{\text{ft}^3}\right)(214.7 - 49.4)\left(\frac{\text{lb}_f}{\text{in}^2}\right)\left(144\frac{\text{in}^2}{\text{ft}^2}\right)}{8.56}}$$

$$\boxed{= 1.78 \text{ lb}_m/\text{s}.}$$

This result is essentially identical to the previous result, although with a lot less effort.

c. For the isothermal case the upstream Mach number is given by Equation 4-83. Substituting the numbers provided, we obtain

$$\ln\left(\frac{1}{1.4\text{Ma}^2}\right) - \left(\frac{1}{1.4\text{Ma}^2} - 1\right) + 8.52 = 0.$$

The solution is found by trial and error:

Guessed Ma	Value of left-hand side of equation
0.25	0.526
0.24	−0.362
0.245	0.097
0.244	0.005 ← Final result

The choked pressure is, from Equation 4-79,

$$P_{\text{choked}} = P_1\text{Ma}_1\sqrt{\gamma} = (214.7\ \text{lb}_f/\text{in}^2)(0.244)\sqrt{1.4} = 62.0\ \text{psia} = 8.93 \times 10^3\ \text{lb}_f/\text{ft}^2.$$

The mass flow rate is computed using Equation 4-82:

$$G_{\text{choked}} = P_{\text{choked}}\sqrt{\frac{g_c M}{R_g T}} = 8.93 \times 10^3\ \text{lb}_f/\text{ft}^2 \times \sqrt{\frac{(32.17\ \text{ft lb}_m/\text{lb}_f\ \text{s}^2)(28\ \text{lb}_m/\text{lb-mol})}{(1545\ \text{ft lb}_f/\text{lb-mol}^\circ\text{R})(540^\circ\text{R})}}$$

$$= 8.93 \times 10^3\ \text{lb}_f/\text{ft}^2\sqrt{1.08 \times 10^{-3}\ \text{lb}_m^2/\text{lb}_f^2\ \text{s}^2} = 293\ \text{lb}_m/\text{ft}^2\ \text{s},$$

$$Q_m = G_{\text{choked}}A = (293\ \text{lb}_m/\text{ft}^2\ \text{s})(6.00 \times 10^{-3}\ \text{ft}^2)$$

$$\boxed{= 1.76\ \text{lb}_m/\text{s}.}$$

Using the simplified, direct solution, from Table 4-5 or Figure 4-15,

$$\frac{P_1 - P_2}{P_1} = 0.70 \Rightarrow P_2 = 64.4\ \text{psia}.$$

And it follows that the flow is sonic. From Table 4-5 or Figure 4-16, $Y_g = 0.70$. Substituting into Equation 4-68, remembering to use the choking pressure above, gives $\dot{m} = 1.74\ \text{lb}_m/\text{sec}$. This is close to the more detailed method.

The results are summarized in the following table:

Case	P_{choked} (psia)	Q_m (lb_m/s)
Orifice	113.4	4.16
Adiabatic pipe	49.4	1.81
Isothermal pipe	62.0	1.76

A standard procedure for these types of problems is to represent the discharge through the pipe as an orifice. The results show that this approach results in a large result for this case. The orifice method always produces a larger value than the adiabatic pipe method, ensuring a conservative safety design. The orifice calculation, however, is easier to apply, requiring only the pipe diameter and the upstream supply pressure and temperature. The configurational details of the piping are not required, as in the adiabatic and isothermal pipe methods.

Also note that the computed choked pressures differ for each case, with a substantial difference between the orifice and the adiabatic/isothermal cases. A choking design based on an orifice calculation might not be choked in reality because of high downstream pressures.

Finally, note that the adiabatic and isothermal pipe methods produce results that are reasonably close. For most real situations the heat transfer characteristics cannot be easily determined. Thus the adiabatic pipe method is the method of choice; it will always produce the larger number for a conservative safety design.

4-7 Flashing Liquids

Liquids stored under pressure above their normal boiling point temperature present substantial problems because of flashing. If the tank, pipe, or other containment device develops a leak, the liquid will partially flash into vapor, sometimes explosively.

Flashing occurs so rapidly that the process is assumed to be adiabatic. The excess energy contained in the superheated liquid vaporizes the liquid and lowers the temperature to the new boiling point. If m is the mass of original liquid, C_p the heat capacity of the liquid (energy/mass deg), T_o the temperature of the liquid before depressurization, and T_b the depressurized boiling point of the liquid, then the excess energy contained in the superheated liquid is given by

$$Q = mC_p(T_o - T_b). \tag{4-85}$$

This energy vaporizes the liquid. If ΔH_v is the heat of vaporization of the liquid, the mass of liquid vaporized m_v is given by

$$m_v = \frac{Q}{\Delta H_v} = \frac{mC_p(T_o - T_b)}{\Delta H_v}. \tag{4-86}$$

The fraction of the liquid vaporized is

$$\boxed{f_v = \frac{m_v}{m} = \frac{C_p(T_o - T_b)}{\Delta H_v}.} \tag{4-87}$$

Equation 4-87 assumes constant physical properties over the temperature range T_o to T_b. A more general expression without this assumption is derived as follows.

The change in liquid mass m resulting from a change in temperature T is given by

$$dm = \frac{mC_p}{\Delta H_v} dT. \tag{4-88}$$

Equation 4-88 is integrated between the initial temperature T_o (with liquid mass m) and the final boiling point temperature T_b (with liquid mass $m - m_v$):

$$\int_m^{m-m_v} \frac{dm}{m} = \int_{T_o}^{T_b} \frac{C_p}{\Delta H_v} dT, \tag{4-89}$$

$$\ln\left(\frac{m - m_v}{m}\right) = -\frac{\overline{C_p}(T_o - T_b)}{\overline{\Delta H_v}}, \tag{4-90}$$

where $\overline{C_p}$ and $\overline{\Delta H_v}$ are the mean heat capacity and the mean latent heat of vaporization, respectively, over the temperature range T_o to T_b. Solving for the fraction of the liquid vaporized, $f_v = m_v/m$, we obtain

$$f_v = 1 - \exp[-\overline{C_p}(T_o - T_b)/\overline{\Delta H_v}]. \tag{4-91}$$

Example 4-6

One lb_m of saturated liquid water is contained in a vessel at 350°F. The vessel ruptures and the pressure is reduced to 1 atm. Compute the fraction of material vaporized using (a) the steam tables, (b) Equation 4-87, and (c) Equation 4-91.

Solution

a. The initial state is saturated liquid water at $T_o = 350°F$. From the steam tables

$$P = 134.6 \text{ psia},$$
$$H = 321.6 \text{ Btu/lb}_m.$$

The final temperature is the boiling point at 1 atm, or 212°F. At this temperature and under saturated conditions

$$H_{vapor} = 1150.4 \text{ Btu/lb}_m,$$
$$H_{liquid} = 180.07 \text{ Btu/lb}_m.$$

Because the process occurs adiabatically, $H_{final} = H_{initial}$ and the fraction of vapor (or quality) is computed from

$$H_{final} = H_{liquid} + f_v(H_{vapor} - H_{liquid}),$$

$$321.6 = 180.07 + f_v(1150.4 - 180.07),$$

$$\boxed{f_v = 0.1459.}$$

That is, 14.59% of the mass of the original liquid is vaporized.

b. For liquid water at 212°F

$C_p = 1.01\ \text{Btu/lb}_m\ °\text{F}$,
$\Delta H_v = 970.3\ \text{Btu/lb}_m$.

From Equation 4-87

$$f_v = \frac{C_p(T_o - T_b)}{\Delta H_v} = \frac{(1.01\ \text{Btu/lb}_m\ °\text{F})(350 - 212)°\text{F}}{970.3\ \text{Btu/lb}_m},$$

$$\boxed{f_v = 0.1436.}$$

c. The mean properties for liquid water between T_o and T_b are

$\overline{C_p} = 1.04\ \text{Btu/lb}_m\ °\text{F}$,
$\overline{\Delta H_v} = 920.7\ \text{Btu/lb}_m$.

Substituting into Equation 4-91 gives

$$\begin{aligned} f_v &= 1 - \exp[-\overline{C_p}(T_o - T_b)/\overline{\Delta H_v}] \\ &= 1 - \exp[-(1.04\ \text{Btu/lb}_m\ °\text{F})(350 - 212)°\text{F}/(920.7\ \text{Btu/lb}_m)] \\ &= 1 - 0.8557 \end{aligned}$$

$$\boxed{f_v = 0.1443.}$$

Both expressions work about as well compared to the actual value from the steam table.

For flashing liquids composed of many miscible substances, the flash calculation is complicated considerably, because the more volatile components flash preferentially. Procedures are available to solve this problem.[17]

Flashing liquids escaping through holes and pipes require special consideration because two-phase flow conditions may be present. Several special cases need consideration.[18] If the fluid path length of the release is short (through a hole in a thin-walled container), nonequilibrium conditions exist, and the liquid does not have time to flash within the hole; the fluid flashes external to the hole. The equations describing incompressible fluid flow through holes apply (see Section 4-2).

[17] J. M. Smith and H. C. Van Ness, *Introduction to Chemical Engineering Thermodynamics,* 6th ed. (New York: McGraw-Hill, 2000).

[18] Hans K. Fauske, "Flashing Flows or: Some Practical Guidelines for Emergency Releases," *Plant/Operations Progress* (July 1985), p. 133.

If the fluid path length through the release is greater than 10 cm (through a pipe or thick-walled container), equilibrium flashing conditions are achieved and the flow is choked. A good approximation is to assume a choked pressure equal to the saturation vapor pressure of the flashing liquid. The result will be valid only for liquids stored at a pressure higher than the saturation vapor pressure. With this assumption the mass flow rate is given by

$$\boxed{Q_m = AC_o\sqrt{2\rho_f g_c(P - P^{sat})},} \tag{4-92}$$

where

A is the area of the release,
C_o is the discharge coefficient (unitless),
ρ_f is the density of the liquid (mass/volume),
P is the pressure within the tank, and
P^{sat} is the saturation vapor pressure of the flashing liquid at ambient temperature.

Example 4-7

Liquid ammonia is stored in a tank at 24°C and a pressure of 1.4×10^6 Pa. A pipe of diameter 0.0945 m breaks off a short distance from the vessel (the tank), allowing the flashing ammonia to escape. The saturation vapor pressure of liquid ammonia at this temperature is 0.968×10^6 Pa, and its density is 603 kg/m^3. Determine the mass flow rate through the leak. Equilibrium flashing conditions can be assumed.

Solution

Equation 4-92 applies for the case of equilibrium flashing conditions. Assume a discharge coefficient of 0.61. Then

$$Q_m = AC_o\sqrt{2\rho_f g_c(P - P^{sat})}$$
$$= (0.61)\frac{(3.14)(0.0945\text{ m})^2}{4}$$
$$\times \sqrt{2(603\text{ kg/m}^3)[1(\text{kg m/s}^2)/\text{N}](1.4 \times 10^6 - 0.968 \times 10^6)(\text{N/m}^2)}$$

$$\boxed{Q_m = 97.6\text{ kg/s}.}$$

For liquids stored at their saturation vapor pressure, $P = P^{sat}$, Equation 4-92 is no longer valid. A much more detailed approach is required. Consider a fluid that is initially quiescent and is accelerated through the leak. Assume that kinetic energy is dominant and that potential energy effects are negligible. Then, from a mechanical energy balance (Equation 4-1), and realizing that the specific volume (with units of volume/mass) $v = 1/\rho$, we can write

$$-\int_1^2 v\,dP = \frac{\bar{u}_2^2}{2g_c}. \tag{4-93}$$

A mass velocity G with units of mass/(area-time) is defined by

$$G = \rho\bar{u} = \frac{\bar{u}}{v}. \tag{4-94}$$

Combining Equation 4-94 with Equation 4-93 and assuming that the mass velocity is constant results in

$$-\int_1^2 v\,dP = \frac{\bar{u}_2^2}{2g_c} = \frac{G^2 v_2^2}{2g_c}. \tag{4-95}$$

Solving for the mass velocity G and assuming that point 2 can be defined at any point along the flow path, we obtain

$$G = \frac{\sqrt{-2g_c \int v\,dP}}{v}. \tag{4-96}$$

Equation 4-96 contains a maximum, at which choked flow occurs. Under choked flow conditions, $dG/dP = 0$. Differentiating Equation 4-96 and setting the result equal to zero gives

$$\frac{dG}{dP} = 0 = -\frac{(dv/dP)}{v^2}\sqrt{-2g_c \int v\,dP} - \frac{g_c}{\sqrt{-2g_c \int v\,dP}} \tag{4-97}$$

$$0 = -\frac{G(dv/dP)}{v} - \frac{g_c}{vG}. \tag{4-98}$$

Solving Equation 4-98 for G, we obtain

$$\boxed{G = \frac{Q_m}{A} = \sqrt{-\frac{g_c}{(dv/dP)}}.} \tag{4-99}$$

The two-phase specific volume is given by

$$v = v_{fg} f_v + v_f, \tag{4-100}$$

where

v_{fg} is the difference in specific volume between vapor and liquid,
v_f is the liquid specific volume, and
f_v is the mass fraction of vapor.

Differentiating Equation 4-100 with respect to pressure gives

$$\frac{dv}{dP} = v_{fg}\frac{df_v}{dP}. \tag{4-101}$$

But, from Equation 4-87,

$$df_v = -\frac{C_p}{\Delta H_v}dT, \tag{4-102}$$

and from the Clausius-Clapyron equation, at saturation

$$\frac{dP}{dT} = \frac{\Delta H_v}{T v_{fg}}. \tag{4-103}$$

Substituting Equations 4-103 and 4-102 into Equation 4-101 yields

$$\frac{dv}{dP} = -\frac{v_{fg}^2}{\Delta H_v^2}TC_p. \tag{4-104}$$

The mass flow rate is determined by combining Equation 4-104 with Equation 4-99:

$$\boxed{Q_m = \frac{\Delta H_v A}{v_{fg}}\sqrt{\frac{g_c}{TC_p}}}. \tag{4-105}$$

Note that the temperature T in Equation 4-105 is the absolute temperature from the Clausius-Clapyron equation and is not associated with the heat capacity.

Small droplets of liquid also form in a jet of flashing vapor. These aerosol droplets are readily entrained by the wind and transported away from the release site. The assumption that the quantity of droplets formed is equal to the amount of material flashed is frequently made.[19]

Example 4-8

Propylene is stored at 25°C in a tank at its saturation pressure. A 1-cm-diameter hole develops in the tank. Estimate the mass flow rate through the hole under these conditions for propylene:

$\Delta H_v = 3.34 \times 10^5$ J/kg,
$v_{fg} = 0.042$ m^3/kg,
$P^{sat} = 1.15 \times 10^6$ Pa,
$C_p = 2.18 \times 10^3$ J/kg K.

[19]Trevor A. Kletz, "Unconfined Vapor Cloud Explosions," in *Eleventh Loss Prevention Symposium* (New York: American Institute of Chemical Engineers, 1977).

Solution

Equation 4-105 applies to this case. The area of the leak is

$$A = \frac{\pi d^2}{4} = \frac{(3.14)(1 \times 10^{-2}\ \text{m})^2}{4} = 7.85 \times 10^{-5}\ \text{m}^2.$$

Using Equation 4-105, we obtain

$$Q_\text{m} = \frac{\Delta H_\text{v} A}{v_\text{fg}} \sqrt{\frac{g_\text{c}}{TC_\text{p}}}$$

$$= (3.34 \times 10^5\ \text{J/kg})(1\ \text{N m/J}) \frac{(7.85 \times 10^{-5}\ \text{m}^2)}{(0.042\ \text{m}^3/\text{kg})}$$

$$\times \sqrt{\frac{1.0(\text{kg m/s}^2)/\text{N}}{(2.18 \times 10^3\ \text{J/kg K})(298\ \text{K})(1\ \text{N m/J})}}$$

$$\boxed{Q_\text{m} = 0.774\ \text{kg/s.}}$$

4-8 Liquid Pool Evaporation or Boiling

The case for evaporation of a volatile from a pool of liquid has already been considered in Chapter 3. The total mass flow rate from the evaporating pool is given by Equation 3-12:

$$\boxed{Q_\text{m} = \frac{MKAP^\text{sat}}{R_\text{g} T_\text{L}}}, \tag{3-12}$$

where

Q_m is the mass vaporization rate (mass/time),
M is the molecular weight of the pure material,
K is the mass transfer coefficient (length/time),
A is the area of exposure,
P^sat is the saturation vapor pressure of the liquid,
R_g is the ideal gas constant, and
T_L is the temperature of the liquid.

For liquids boiling from a pool the boiling rate is limited by the heat transfer from the surroundings to the liquid in the pool. Heat is transferred (1) from the ground by conduction, (2) from the air by conduction and convection, and (3) by radiation from the sun and/or adjacent sources such as a fire.

The initial stage of boiling is usually controlled by the heat transfer from the ground. This is especially true for a spill of liquid with a normal boiling point below ambient temperature or ground temperature. The heat transfer from the ground is modeled with a simple one-dimensional heat conduction equation, given by

$$q_g = \frac{k_s(T_g - T)}{(\pi \alpha_s t)^{1/2}}, \tag{4-106}$$

where

q_g is the heat flux from the ground (energy/area-time),
k_s is the thermal conductivity of the soil (energy/length-time-degree),
T_g is the temperature of the soil (degree),
T is the temperature of the liquid pool (degree),
α_s is the thermal diffusivity of the soil (area/time), and
t is the time after spill (time).

Equation 4-106 is not considered conservative.

The rate of boiling is determined by assuming that all the heat is used to boil the liquid. Thus

$$Q_m = \frac{q_g A}{\Delta H_v}, \tag{4-107}$$

where

Q_m is the mass boiling rate (mass/time),
q_g is the heat transfer for the pool from the ground, determined by Equation 4-106 (energy/area-time),
A is the area of the pool (area), and
ΔH_v is the heat of vaporization of the liquid in the pool (energy/mass).

At later times, solar heat fluxes and convective heat transfer from the atmosphere become important. For a spill onto an insulated dike floor these fluxes may be the only energy contributions. This approach seems to work adequately for liquefied natural gas (LNG) and perhaps for ethane and ethylene. The higher hydrocarbons (C_3 and above) require a more detailed heat transfer mechanism. This model also neglects possible water freezing effects in the ground, which can significantly alter the heat transfer behavior. More details on boiling pools are provided elsewhere.[20]

4-9 Realistic and Worst-Case Releases

Table 4-6 lists a number of realistic and worst-case releases. The realistic releases represent the incident outcomes with a high probability of occurring. Thus, rather than assuming that an entire storage vessel fails catastrophically, it is more realistic to assume that a high probability exists that the release will occur from the disconnection of the largest pipe connected to the tank.

The worst-case releases are those that assume almost catastrophic failure of the process, resulting in near instantaneous release of the entire process inventory or release over a short period of time.

[20]CCPS, *Guidelines for Consequence Analysis of Chemical Releases* (1999).

Table 4-6 Guidelines for Selection of Process Incidents

Incident characteristic	Guideline
Realistic release incidents[a]	
Process pipes	Rupture of the largest diameter process pipe as follows: For diameters smaller than 2 in, assume a full bore rupture. For diameters 2–4 in, assume rupture equal to that of a 2-inch-diameter pipe. For diameters greater than 4 in, assume rupture area equal to 20% of the pipe cross-sectional area.
Hoses	Assume full bore rupture.
Pressure relief devices relieving directly to the atmosphere	Use calculated total release rate at set pressure. Refer to pressure relief calculation. All material released is assumed to be airborne.
Vessels	Assume a rupture based on the largest diameter process pipe attached to the vessel. Use the pipe criteria.
Other	Incidents can be established based on the plant's experience, or the incidents can be developed from the outcome of a review or derived from hazard analysis studies.
Worst-case incidents[b]	
Quantity	Assume release of the largest quantity of substance handled on-site in a single process vessel at any time. To estimate the release rate, assume the entire quantity is released within 10 min.
Wind speed / stability	Assume F stability, 1.5 m/s wind speed, unless meteorological data indicate otherwise.
Ambient temperature / humidity	Assume the highest daily maximum temperature and average humidity.
Height of release	Assume that the release occurs at ground level.
Topography	Assume urban or rural topography, as appropriate.
Temperature of release substance	Consider liquids to be released at the highest daily maximum temperature, based on data for the previous three years, or at process temperature, whichever is higher. Assume that gases liquefied by refrigeration at atmospheric pressure are released at their boiling points.

[a] *Dow's Chemical Exposure Index Guide* (New York: American Institute of Chemical Engineers, 1994).
[b] US EPA, *RMP Offsite Consequence Analysis Guidance* (Washington, DC: US Environmental Protection Agency, 1996).

The selection of the release case depends on the requirements of the consequence study. If an internal company study is being completed to determine the actual consequences of plant releases, then the realistic cases would be selected. However, if a study is being completed to meet the requirements of the EPA Risk Management Plan, then the worst-case releases must be used.

4-10 Conservative Analysis

All models, including consequence models, have uncertainties. These uncertainties arise because of (1) an incomplete understanding of the geometry of the release (that is, the hole size), (2) unknown or poorly characterized physical properties, (3) a poor understanding of the chemical or release process, and (4) unknown or poorly understood mixture behavior, to name a few.

Uncertainties that arise during the consequence modeling procedure are treated by assigning conservative values to some of these unknowns. By doing so, a *conservative estimate* of the consequence is obtained, defining the limits of the design envelope. This ensures that the resulting engineering design to mitigate or remove the hazard is *overdesigned*. Every effort, however, should be made to achieve a result consistent with the demands of the problem.

For any particular modeling study several receptors might be present that require different decisions for conservative design. For example, dispersion modeling based on a ground-level release will maximize the consequence for the surrounding community but will not maximize the consequence for plant workers at the top of a process structure.

To illustrate conservative modeling, consider a problem requiring an estimate of the gas discharge rate from a hole in a storage tank. This discharge rate is used to estimate the downwind concentrations of the gas, with the intent of estimating the toxicological impact. The discharge rate depends on a number of parameters, including (1) the hole area, (2) the pressure within and outside the tank, (3) the physical properties of the gas, and (4) the temperature of the gas, to name a few.

The reality of the situation is that the maximum discharge rate of gas occurs when the leak first occurs, with the discharge rate decreasing as a function of time as the pressure within the tank decreases. The complete dynamic solution to this problem is difficult, requiring a mass discharge model cross-coupled to a material balance on the contents of the tank. An equation of state (perhaps nonideal) is required to determine the tank pressure given the total mass. Complicated temperature effects are also possible. A modeling effort of this detail is not necessarily required to estimate the consequence.

A much simpler procedure is to calculate the mass discharge rate at the instant the leak occurs, assuming a fixed temperature and pressure within the tank equal to the initial temperature and pressure. The actual discharge rate at later times will always be less, and the downwind concentrations will always be less. In this fashion a conservative result is ensured.

For the hole area a possible decision is to consider the area of the largest pipe connected to the tank, because pipe disconnections are a frequent source of tank leaks. Again, this maximizes the consequence and ensures a conservative result. This procedure is continued until all the model parameters are specified.

Unfortunately, this procedure can result in a consequence that is many times larger than the actual, leading to a potential overdesign of the mitigation procedures or safety systems. This occurs, in particular, if several decisions are made during the analysis, with each decision producing a maximum result. For this reason, consequence analysis should be approached with intelligence, tempered with a good dose of reality and common sense.

Suggested Reading

Consequence Modeling

Center for Chemical Process Safety (CCPS), *Guidelines for Consequence Analysis of Chemical Releases* (New York: American Institute of Chemical Engineers, 1999).

Center for Chemical Process Safety (CCPS), *Guidelines for Chemical Process Quantitative Risk Analysis* (New York: American Institute of Chemical Engineers, 2000).

Flow of Liquid through Holes

Sam Mannan, ed., *Lees' Loss Prevention in the Process Industries,* 3rd ed. (London: Butterworths, 2005), p. 15/6.

Flow of Liquid through Pipes

Octave Levenspiel, *Engineering Flow and Heat Exchange*, 2nd ed. (New York: Springer, 1998), ch. 2.

Warren L. McCabe, Julian C. Smith, and Peter Harriott, *Unit Operations of Chemical Engineering,* 7th ed. (New York: McGraw-Hill, 2004), ch. 5.

Flow of Vapor through Holes

Mannan, *Loss Prevention,* p. 15/10.

Levenspiel, *Engineering Flow and Heat Exchange*, 2nd ed. (1998), pp. 48–51.

Flow of Vapor through Pipes

Jason Keith and Daniel A. Crowl, "Estimating Sonic Gas Flow Rates in Pipelines," *J. Loss Prev. Proc. Ind.* (2005), 18: 55–62.

Levenspiel, *Engineering Flow and Heat Exchange,* 2nd ed. (1998), Ch. 3.

Flashing Liquids

Steven R. Hanna and Peter J. Drivas, *Guidelines for Use of Vapor Dispersion Models,* 2nd ed. (New York: American Institute of Chemical Engineers, 1996), pp. 24–32.

Mannan, *Loss Prevention,* p. 15/11.

Liquid Pool Evaporation and Boiling

Hanna and Drivas, *Guidelines,* pp. 31, 39.

Problems

4-1. A 0.20-in hole develops in a pipeline containing toluene. The pressure in the pipeline at the point of the leak is 100 psig. Determine the leakage rate. The specific gravity of toluene is 0.866.

4-2. A 100-ft-long horizontal pipeline transporting benzene develops a leak 43 ft from the high-pressure end. The diameter of the leak is estimated to be 0.1 in. At the time, the upstream pressure in the pipeline is 50 psig and the downstream pressure is 40 psig. Estimate the mass flow rate of benzene through the leak. The specific gravity of benzene is 0.8794.

4-3. The TLV-TWA for hydrogen sulfide gas is 10 ppm. Hydrogen sulfide gas is stored in a tank at 100 psig and 80°F. Estimate the diameter of a hole in the tank leading to a local hydrogen sulfide concentration equal to the TLV. The local ventilation rate is 2000 ft^3/min and is deemed average. The ambient pressure is 1 atm.

4-4. A storage tank is 10 m high. At a particular time the liquid level is 5 m high within the tank. The tank is pressurized with nitrogen to 0.1 bar gauge to prevent a flammable atmosphere within the tank. The liquid in the tank has a density of 490 kg/m^3.

a. If a 10-mm hole forms 3 m above the ground, what is the initial mass discharge rate of liquid (in kg/s)?

b. Estimate the distance from the tank the stream of liquid will hit the ground. Determine whether this stream will be contained by a 1-m-high dike located 1 m from the tank wall.

Hint: For a freely falling body the time to reach the ground is given by

$$t = \sqrt{\frac{2h}{g}},$$

where t is the time, h is the initial height above the ground, and g is the acceleration due to gravity.

4-5. Use a mechanical energy balance to show that the pump work required to pump a liquid through a pipe from one tank to another is given by

$$W_s = -\frac{2fL\dot{m}^3}{g_c d\rho^2 A^2} = -\frac{32fL\dot{m}^3}{\pi^2 g_c d^5 \rho^2},$$

where W_s is the work input to the pump, f is the Fanning friction factor, L is the length of the pipe, $\dot{m}$ is the mass flow rate, d is the diameter of the pipe, ρ is the density of the liquid, and A is the cross-sectional area of the pipe. Be sure to list clearly your assumptions!

4-6. A tank containing liquid chlorine is used by a local water treatment plant. The plant uses chlorine gas which is supplied from the top of the tank through a 3-mm-ID pipe. If the pipe supplying the gas breaks, estimate the chlorine concentration (in ppm) in the vicinity of the leak. Assume a ventilation rate of 30 m^3/min and "good" ventilation. Comment on the result and how that might change your operation.

Additional information on Cl_2:

Molecular weight:	70.9
Saturation vapor pressure of liquid chlorine at 298K:	6.8 atm

4-7. Calculate the number of liters per year of liquid that can be transported through the following pipe sizes, assuming a constant liquid velocity of 1 m/s:

a. 3 cm internal diameter.

b. 5 cm internal diameter.

c. 25 cm internal diameter.

d. 50 cm internal diameter.

Comment on the magnitude of the result and the necessity for large pipe sizes in a chemical plant.

4-8. Calculate the number of kilograms per year of ideal gas that can be transported through the following pipe sizes, assuming a gas velocity of 3 m/s, a pressure of 689 kPa gauge, a temperature of 25°C, and a molecular weight of 44:

a. 3 cm internal diameter.

b. 5 cm internal diameter.

c. 25 cm internal diameter.

d. 50 cm internal diameter.

Comment on the magnitude of the result and the necessity for large pipe sizes in a chemical plant.

4-9. Large storage tanks need a breather vent (technically called a conservation vent) to allow air to move into and out of the tank as a result of temperature and pressure changes and a change in the tank liquid level. Unfortunately, these vents also allow volatile materials to escape, resulting in potential worker exposures.

An expression that can be used to estimate the volatile emission rate in a storage tank resulting from a single change in temperature is given by

$$m = \frac{MP^{\text{sat}}V_{\text{o}}}{R_{\text{g}}T_{\text{L}}}\left(\frac{T_{\text{H}}}{T_{\text{L}}} - 1\right),$$

where m is the total mass of volatile released, M is the molecular weight of the volatile, P^{sat} is the saturation vapor pressure of the liquid, V_{o} is the vapor volume of the tank, R_{g} is the ideal gas constant, T_{L} is the initial low absolute temperature, and T_{H} is the final absolute temperature.

A storage tank is 15 m in diameter and 10 m tall. It is currently half full of toluene ($M = 92$, $P^{\text{sat}} = 36.4$ mm Hg). If the temperature changes from 4°C to 30°C over a period of 12 hr,

a. Derive the equation for m.

b. Estimate the rate of emission of toluene (in kg/s).

c. If a worker is standing near the vent, estimate the concentration (in ppm) of toluene in the air. Use an average temperature and an effective ventilation rate of 3000 ft^3/min. Is the worker overexposed?

4-10. A 3-cm (internal diameter) pipe has broken off of a 1-ton pig (or tank) of nitrogen. Estimate the maximum mass flow rate (in kg/s) of the gas if the initial pressure in the tank is 800 kPa gauge. The temperature is 25°C, and the ambient pressure is 1 atm.

4-11. Estimate the vaporization rate resulting from heating from the ground at 10 s after the instantaneous spill of 1500 m^3 of liquefied natural gas (LNG) into a rectangular concrete dike of dimensions 7 m by 10 m. You will need the following data:

Thermal diffusivity of soil: 4.16×10^{-7} m^2/s
Thermal conductivity of soil: 0.92 W/ m K
Temperature of liquid pool: 109 K
Temperature of soil: 293 K
Heat of vaporization of pool: 498 kJ/kg at 109 K

4-12. The strip chart in Figure 4-19 displays the history of a leak in a storage tank. No other pumping or filling operations occur during this time. The tank is 10 m high and 10 m in diameter, and it contains a liquid with a specific gravity of 0.9.

a. When did the leak start, and about how long did it last?
b. At what height is the leak?
c. What is the total quantity (in kg) leaked?

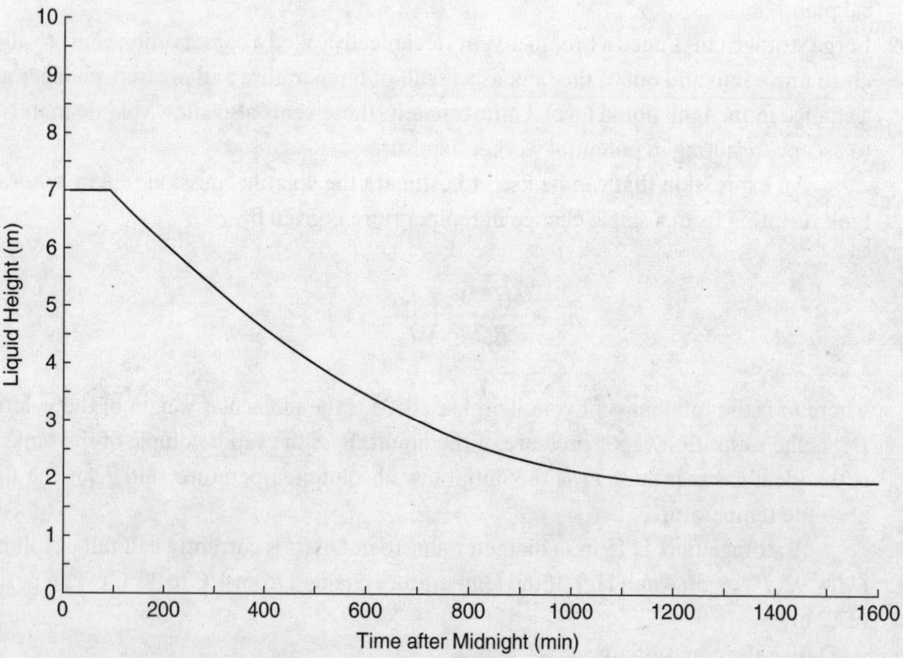

Figure 4-19 Strip chart data for Problem 4-12.

d. Estimate the maximum discharge rate of the fluid (in kg/s).

e. Estimate the leak hole diameter (in cm).

4-13. A typical automobile tire has a gas volume of about 10 liters. If a tire is inflated with air to 3 atm gauge, and the temperature is 30°C, what size hole, in mm, is required to deflate the tire to 1 atm absolute in 1 minute? Assume that the initial gas discharge rate when the hole is first formed is constant during the entire deflation process and that the tire volume is unchanged.

4-14. Water is pumped through a 1-in schedule 40 pipe (internal diameter = 1.049 in) at 400 gal/hr. If the pressure at one point in the pipe is 103 psig and a small leak develops 22 ft downstream, compute the fluid pressure at the leak. The pipe section is horizontal and without fittings or valves. For water at these conditions the viscosity is 1.0 centipoise and the density is 62.4 lb_m/ft^3. Assume new, commercial steel pipe.

4-15. A tank with a drain pipe is shown in Figure 4-20. The tank contains crude oil, and there is concern that the drain pipe might shear off below the tank, allowing the tank contents to leak out.

a. If the drain pipe shears 2 meters below the tank, and the oil level is 7 m at the time, estimate the initial mass flow rate of material out of the drain pipe.

b. If the pipe shears off at the tank bottom, leaving a 50-mm hole, estimate the initial mass flow rate.

The crude oil has a density of 928 kg/m^3 and a viscosity of 0.004 kg/m s.

4-16. A 10-m-diameter round tank sits on the ground within a 20-m-square diked area. The tank contains a hazardous material dissolved in mostly water. The tank is vented to the atmosphere.

A leak occurred in the tank because a 0.1-m-diameter pipe located 1 m above the bottom of the tank was accidentally disconnected. By the time the liquid flow was stopped, the liquid level in the diked area had reached a height of 0.79 m.

a. Estimate the total amount of liquid spilled (in m^3 and in kg).

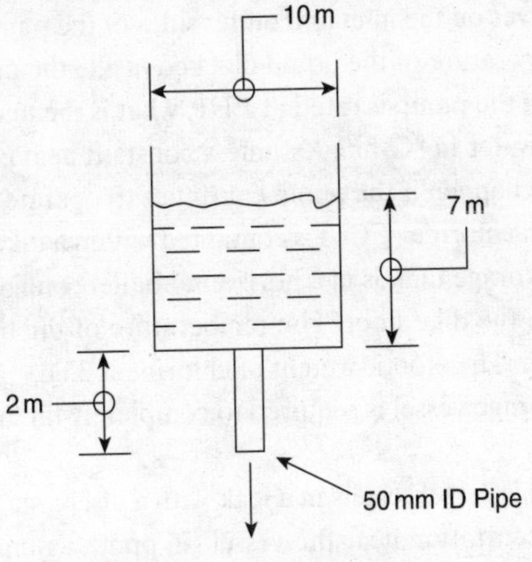

Figure 4-20 Tank draining process for Problem 4-15.

b. If the liquid level in the tank at the end of the spill was 8.5 m above the tank bottom, estimate the length of time for the leak.

c. What was the original liquid level in the tank?

4-17. Show that for a spherical storage vessel containing liquid at an initial height h_o the time for the liquid to drain from a hole in the bottom of the sphere is given by

$$t = \frac{\sqrt{2}\pi(h_o)^{3/2}\left(D - \frac{3}{5}h_o\right)}{3AC_o\sqrt{g}},$$

where D is the inside diameter of the sphere, A is the area of the hole, C_o is the discharge coefficient, and g is the acceleration due to gravity.

4-18. Liquid chlorine is supplied to a process from a regulated pressure source at 20 barg through 300 m of horizontal new commercial steel pipe of actual inside diameter of 0.02 m. The ambient pressure is 1 atm and the ambient temperature is 30°C.

a. If the pipe breaks off at the regulated source, estimate the flow rate through the leak, in kg/s.

b. If the pipe breaks off at the end of the 300-m length, estimate the flow in kg/s.

For chlorine, the following properties are available at these conditions:

Density:	1380 kg/m^3
Viscosity:	0.328×10^{-3} Pa-s

4-19. A 31.5% hydrochloric acid solution is pumped from one storage tank to another. The power input to the pump is 2 kW and is 50% efficient. The pipe is plastic PVC pipe with an internal diameter of 50 mm. At a certain time the liquid level in the first tank is 4.1 m above the pipe outlet. Because of an accident, the pipe is severed between the pump and the second tank, at a point 2.1 m below the pipe outlet of the first tank. This point is 27 m in equivalent pipe length from the first tank. Compute the flow rate (in kg/s) from the leak. The viscosity of the solution is 1.8×10^{-3} kg/m s, and the density is 1600 kg/m^3.

4-20. Pumps can be blocked in by closing valves on the inlet and outlet sides of the pump. This can lead to a rapid increase in the temperature of the liquid blocked inside the pump.

A pump contains 4 kg of water. If the pump is rated at 1 HP, what is the maximum temperature increase expected in the water in °C/hr? Assume a constant heat capacity for the water of 1 kcal/kg°C. What will happen if the pump continues to operate?

4-21. A storage vessel containing carbon tetrachloride (CCl_4) is contained within a diked area with dimensions of 10 m × 10 m. The storage tank is in a horizontal bullet configuration with legs to raise the vessel well above the dike floor. The temperature of the liquid is 35°C, and the ambient pressure is 1 atm. The atomic weight of chlorine is 35.4.

a. What spill rate (in kg/s) from the storage vessel is required to completely fill the floor of the dike with liquid?

b. If one of the accident scenarios for this vessel results in a leak with a discharge rate of 1 kg/s, estimate the CCl_4 vapor concentration near the vessel (in ppm), assuming an effective ventilation rate for the outdoors of 3000 ft^3/min.

4-22. Gasoline tank trucks typically have four separate chambers so that they can transport several different gasoline grades. The front and rear chambers are usually the largest. A drain valve is found in the very bottom of the chamber for both filling and draining. Draining is typically done by gravity alone. The drain valve is connected by a metal rod to a vent valve at the top of the chamber – this ensures that the vent valve is open when the chamber is being either filled or drained.

Gasoline tank trucks cannot withstand much pressure or vacuum – the pressure in the vapor space must be kept as close as possible to atmospheric at all times.

During normal operations, the chamber must not have a pressure higher than 4500 Pa above ambient or lower than 1500 Pa below ambient, which is well below the pressure rating of the chamber of 20,000 Pa above ambient for pressure and 10,000 Pa below ambient for vacuum.

When the chamber is filled with gasoline, the liquid height is 1.86 m above the bottom of the chamber.

The plant has asked us to evaluate several potential scenarios for a truck with a rear chamber volume of 11,860 liters. The total amount of gasoline that this chamber can hold is 11,400 liters, providing enough vapor space for liquid expansion.

The gasoline has a specific gravity of 0.75 and the ambient temperature is 25°C and 1 atm.

a. The plant is concerned about implosion of the tank truck due to a plugging of the vent system during gasoline unloading. If the chamber is filled with 11,400 liters of gasoline, how much liquid must be drained out to reach a pressure of 1500 Pa below ambient? How much must be drained to reach 10,000 Pa below ambient? Assume the initial pressure above the liquid is 1 atm.

b. The plant is also concerned about overpressurizing the chamber during tank filling. Beginning with a completely empty chamber at 1 atm, how much liquid must be added to increase the pressure to 4500 Pa above ambient? 20,000 Pa?

c. The drain at the bottom of the chamber connects to a 100-mm-ID pipe and then to a 100-mm-ID hose. If the chamber is filled with gasoline and the pipe connection at the bottom of the chamber breaks off, leaving a 100-mm hole, what is the initial discharge rate (kg/s) of the gasoline?

d. An 8-m-long hose (100 mm ID) is now connected to the bottom of the chamber and feeds gasoline to an underground storage tank. The underground storage tank connection is 1 m below the bottom of the chamber. If the hose becomes disconnected from the storage tank, estimate the gas flow (kg/s) for this scenario. In this case, assume a constant friction factor for the hose of 0.005.

4-23. The morning inspection of the tank farm finds a leak in the turpentine tank. The leak is repaired. An investigation finds that the leak was 0.1 in in diameter and 7 ft above the tank bottom. Records show that the turpentine level in the tank was 17.3 ft before the leak occurred and 13.0 ft after the leak was repaired. The tank diameter is 15 ft. Determine (a) the total amount of turpentine spilled, (b) the maximum spill rate, and (c) the total time the leak was active. The density of turpentine at these conditions is 55 lb/ft^3.

4-24. A home hot water heater contains 40 gal of water. Because of a failure of the heat control, heat is continuously applied to the water in the tank, increasing the temperature and pressure. Unfortunately, the relief valve is clogged and the pressure rises past the maximum pressure of the vessel. At 250 psig the tank ruptures. Estimate the quantity of water flashed.

4-25. Compute the pressure in the pipe at the location shown in Figure 4-21. The flow rate through the pipe is 10,000 L/hr. The pipe is new commercial steel pipe with an internal diameter of 50 mm. The liquid in the pipe is crude oil with a density of 928 kg/m^3 and a viscosity of 0.004 kg/m s. The tank is vented to the atmosphere.

4-26. A storage tank contains water contaminated with a small quantity of a soluble hazardous waste material. The tank is 3 m in diameter and 6 m high. At the current time the liquid height is within 1 m of the top of the tank.

a. If a 3-cm (internal diameter) feed pipe at the bottom of the tank breaks off, how much liquid (in m^3) is spilled if an emergency response procedure requires 30 min to stop the flow?

b. What is the final liquid level (in m)?

c. What is the maximum spill rate of liquid (in kg/s)?

Assume that the tank is vented.

4-27. Steam is supplied to the heating coils of a reactor vessel at 125 psig, saturated. The coils are 0.5-in schedule 80 pipe (internal diameter = 0.546 in). The steam is supplied from a main header through similar pipe with an equivalent length of 53 ft. The heating coils consist of 20 ft of the pipe wound in a coil within the reactor.

If the heating coil pipe shears accidentally, the reactor vessel will be exposed to the full 125-psig pressure of the steam, exceeding the vessel's pressure rating. As a result, the

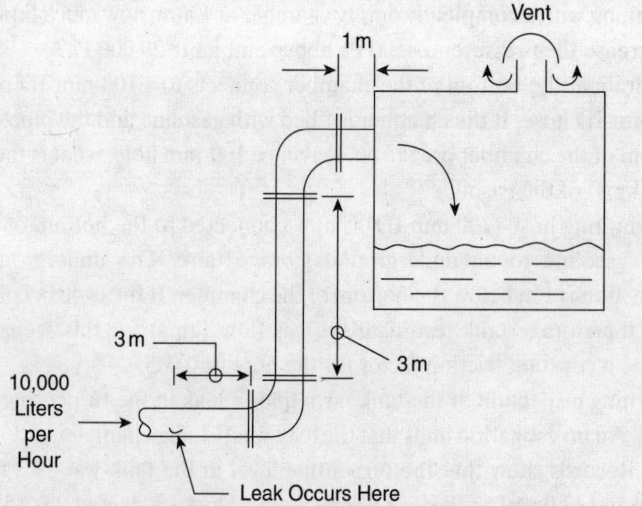

Figure 4-21 Process configuration for Problem 4-25.

reactor must be equipped with a relief system to discharge the steam in the event of a coil shear. Compute the maximum mass flow rate of steam from the sheared coils using two approaches:

a. Assuming the leak in the coil is represented by an orifice.

b. Assuming adiabatic flow through the pipe.

4-28. Calculate the mass flux (kg/m² s) for the following tank leaks given that the storage pressure is equal to the vapor pressure at 25°C:

Toxic material	Pressure (Pa)	Heat of vaporization (J/kg)	v_{fg} (m³/kg)	Heat capacity (J/kg K)
a. Propane	0.95×10^6	3.33×10^5	0.048	2.23×10^3
b. Ammonia	1×10^6	1.17×10^6	0.127	4.49×10^3
c. Methyl chloride	0.56×10^6	3.75×10^5	0.077	1.5×10^3
d. Sulfur dioxide	0.39×10^6	3.56×10^5	0.09	1.36×10^3

4-29. In Example 4-5 the maximum flow through the nitrogen line was determined in order to size the relief device.

An important concept in process safety is *inherent safety.* This means that the process is designed in such a fashion as to prevent hazards from resulting in an accident.

Suppose that the reactor of Example 4-5 is equipped with a relief device capable of relieving nitrogen from the reactor vessel at the rate of 0.5 lb_m/s. This is not enough to prevent overpressuring of the reactor in the event of a regulator failure. One inherently safer design method is to install an orifice in the nitrogen supply line to limit the flow of nitrogen.

a. Calculate the orifice diameter required to reduce the flow from the nitrogen line to 0.5 lb_m/s.

b. What new safety or operational problems might arise as a result of installing the orifice?

4-30. a. Show that for any pump the maximum liquid discharge velocity is given by

$$u = \sqrt[3]{\frac{2g_c W_s}{\rho A}},$$

where u is the maximum liquid discharge velocity, W_s is the pump shaft work, ρ is the density of the liquid, and A is the pump outlet discharge area. Make sure you list your assumptions in your solution.

b. A 1-kW pump discharges water through a 50-mm (internal diameter) pump outlet. What is the maximum velocity of the liquid from this pump? What is the maximum discharge rate (in kg/s)?

4-31. One accident mitigation procedure is called emergency material transfer, in which the material is transported away from the accident site before it becomes involved. We plan on mitigating a crude oil tank fire scenario by pumping the tank empty in 1 hr total time.

The crude oil storage tank is 30 m in diameter, and the crude oil is typically at a level of 9 m.

The transfer will be accomplished by pumping the crude oil through a 200-mm (internal diameter) new commercial steel pipe to another tank 40 m in diameter and 10 m high. The pipeline represents 50 m of equivalent pipe.

a. Estimate the minimum pump size (in HP) required to pump the entire tank empty in 1 hr. Assume a pump efficiency of 80%.

b. If a 100-HP pump (80% efficient) is available, how long will it take to empty the tank?

c. What conclusions can be drawn about the viability of this approach?

The density of the crude oil is 928 kg/m^3 with a viscosity of 0.004 kg/m s.

CHAPTER 5

Toxic Release and Dispersion Models

During an accident, process equipment can release toxic materials quickly and in significant enough quantities to spread in dangerous clouds throughout a plant site and the local community. A few examples are explosive rupture of a process vessel as a result of excessive pressure caused by a runaway reaction, rupture of a pipeline containing toxic materials at high pressure, rupture of a tank containing toxic material stored above its atmospheric boiling point, and rupture of a train or truck transportation tank following an accident.

Serious accidents (such as Bhopal) emphasize the importance of planning for emergencies and of designing plants to minimize the occurrence and consequences of a toxic release. Toxic release models are routinely used to estimate the effects of a release on the plant and community environments.

An excellent safety program strives to identify problems before they occur. Chemical engineers must understand all aspects of toxic release to prevent the existence of release situations and to reduce the impact of a release if one occurs. This requires a toxic release model.

Toxic release and dispersion models are an important part of the consequence modeling procedure shown in Figure 4-1. The toxic release model represents the first three steps in the consequence modeling procedure. These steps are

1. Identifying the release incident (what process situations can lead to a release? This was described in Sections 4-9 and 4-10)
2. Developing a source model to describe how materials are released and the rate of release (this was detailed in Chapter 4)
3. Estimating the downwind concentrations of the toxic material using a dispersion model (once the downwind concentrations are known, several criteria are available to estimate the impact or effect, as discussed in Section 5-4)

Various options are available, based on the predictions of the toxic release model, for example, (1) developing an emergency response plan with the surrounding community, (2) developing engineering modifications to eliminate the source of the release, (3) enclosing the potential release and adding appropriate vent scrubbers or other vapor removal equipment, (4) reducing inventories of hazardous materials to reduce the quantity released, and (5) adding area monitors to detect incipient leaks and providing block valves and engineering controls to eliminate hazardous levels of spills and leaks. These options are discussed in more detail in Section 5-6 on release mitigation.

5-1 Parameters Affecting Dispersion

Dispersion models describe the airborne transport of toxic materials away from the accident site and into the plant and community. After a release the airborne toxic material is carried away by the wind in a characteristic plume, as shown in Figure 5-1, or a puff, as shown in Figure 5-2. The maximum concentration of toxic material occurs at the release point (which may not be at ground level). Concentrations downwind are less, because of turbulent mixing and dispersion of the toxic substance with air.

A wide variety of parameters affect atmospheric dispersion of toxic materials:

- Wind speed
- Atmospheric stability
- Ground conditions (buildings, water, trees)
- Height of the release above ground level
- Momentum and buoyancy of the initial material released

As the wind speed increases, the plume in Figure 5-1 becomes longer and narrower; the substance is carried downwind faster but is diluted faster by a larger quantity of air.

Atmospheric stability relates to vertical mixing of the air. During the day, the air temperature decreases rapidly with height, encouraging vertical motions. At night the temperature decrease is less, resulting in less vertical motion. Temperature profiles for day and night situations are shown in Figure 5-3. Sometimes an inversion occurs. During an inversion, the temperature increases with height, resulting in minimal vertical motion. This most often occurs at night because the ground cools rapidly as a result of thermal radiation.

Atmospheric stability is classified according to three stability classes: unstable, neutral, and stable. For unstable atmospheric conditions the sun heats the ground faster than the heat can be removed so that the air temperature near the ground is higher than the air temperature at higher elevations, as might be observed in the early morning hours. This results in instable stability because air of lower density is below air of greater density. This influence of buoyancy enhances atmospheric mechanical turbulence. For neutral stability the air above the ground warms and the wind speed increases, reducing the effect of solar energy input, or insolation. The air temperature difference does not influence atmospheric mechanical turbulence. For stable atmospheric conditions the sun cannot heat the ground as fast as the ground cools; therefore

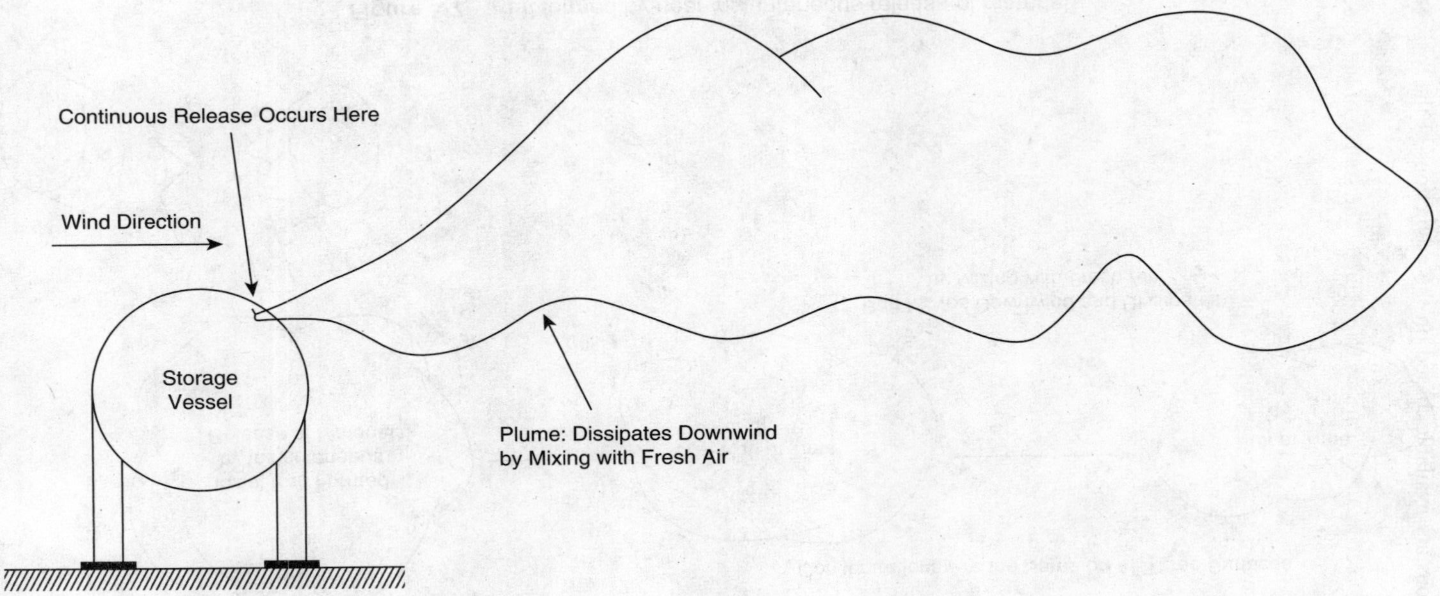

Figure 5-1 Characteristic plume formed by a continuous release of material.

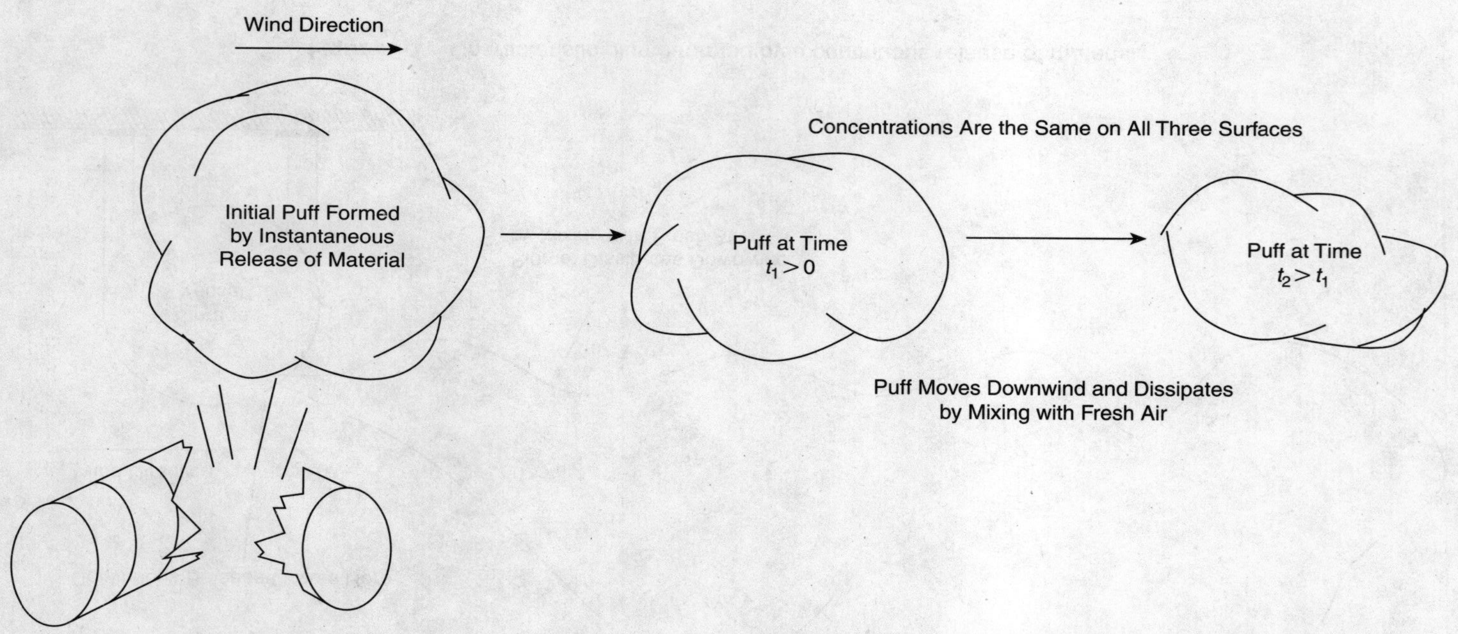

Figure 5-2 Puff formed by near instantaneous release of material.

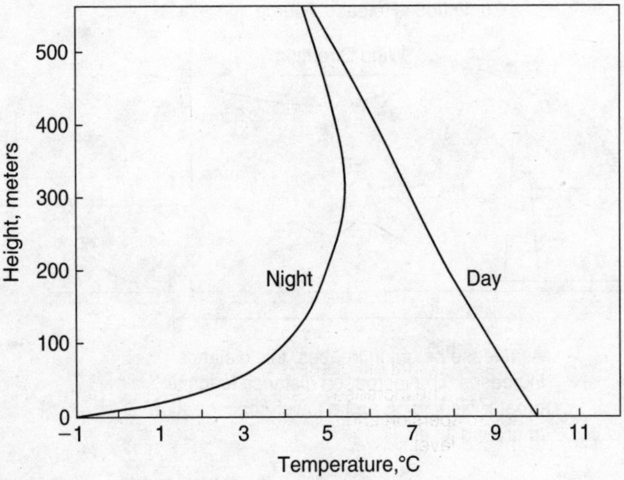

Figure 5-3 Air temperature as a function of altitude for day and night conditions. The temperature gradient affects the vertical air motion. Adapted from D. Bruce Turner, *Workbook of Atmospheric Dispersion Estimates* (Cincinnati: US Department of Health, Education, and Welfare, 1970), p. 1.

the temperature near the ground is lower than the air temperature at higher elevations. This condition is stable because the air of higher density is below air of lower density. The influence of buoyancy suppresses mechanical turbulence.

Ground conditions affect the mechanical mixing at the surface and the wind profile with height. Trees and buildings increase mixing, whereas lakes and open areas decrease it. Figure 5-4 shows the change in wind speed versus height for a variety of surface conditions.

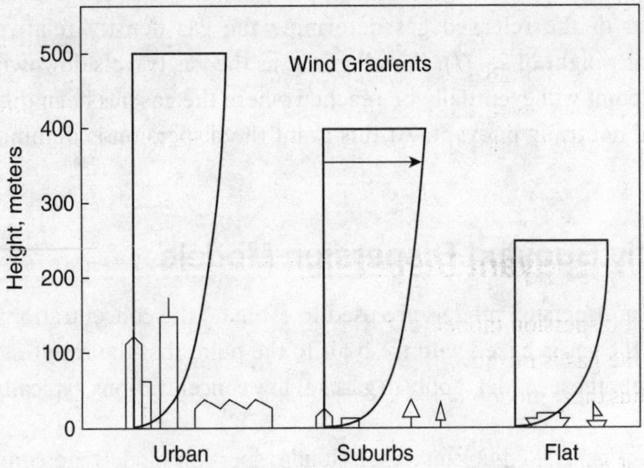

Figure 5-4 Effect of ground conditions on vertical wind gradient. Adapted from D. Bruce Turner, *Workbook of Atmospheric Dispersion Estimates* (Cincinnati: US Department of Health, Education, and Welfare, 1970), p. 2.

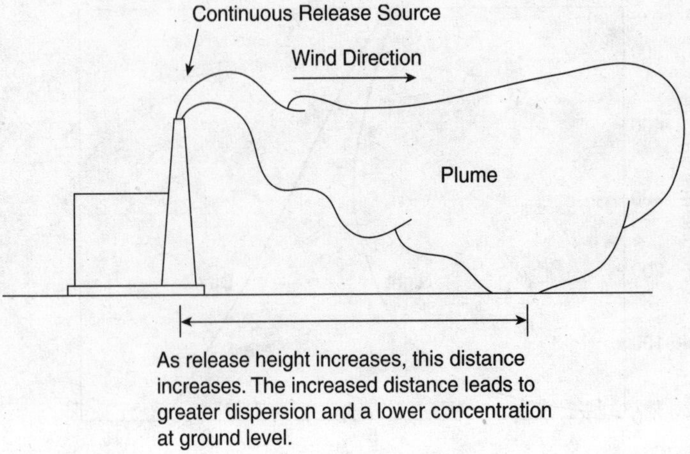
Continuous Release Source
Wind Direction
Plume
As release height increases, this distance increases. The increased distance leads to greater dispersion and a lower concentration at ground level.

Figure 5-5 Increased release height decreases the ground concentration.

The release height significantly affects ground-level concentrations. As the release height increases, ground-level concentrations are reduced because the plume must disperse a greater distance vertically. This is shown in Figure 5-5.

The buoyancy and momentum of the material released change the effective height of the release. Figure 5-6 demonstrates these effects. The momentum of a high-velocity jet will carry the gas higher than the point of release, resulting in a much higher effective release height. If the gas has a density less than air, the released gas will initially be positively buoyant and will lift upward. If the gas has a density greater than air, then the released gas will initially be negatively buoyant and will slump toward the ground. The temperature and molecular weight of the released gas determine the gas density relative to that of air (with a molecular weight of 28.97). For all gases, as the gas travels downwind and is mixed with fresh air, a point will eventually be reached where the gas has been diluted adequately to be considered neutrally buoyant. At this point the dispersion is dominated by ambient turbulence.

5-2 Neutrally Buoyant Dispersion Models

Neutrally buoyant dispersion models are used to estimate the concentrations downwind of a release in which the gas is mixed with fresh air to the point that the resulting mixture is neutrally buoyant. Thus these models apply to gases at low concentrations, typically in the parts per million range.

Two types of neutrally buoyant vapor cloud dispersion models are commonly used: the plume and the puff models. The plume model describes the steady-state concentration of material released from a continuous source. The puff model describes the temporal concentration of

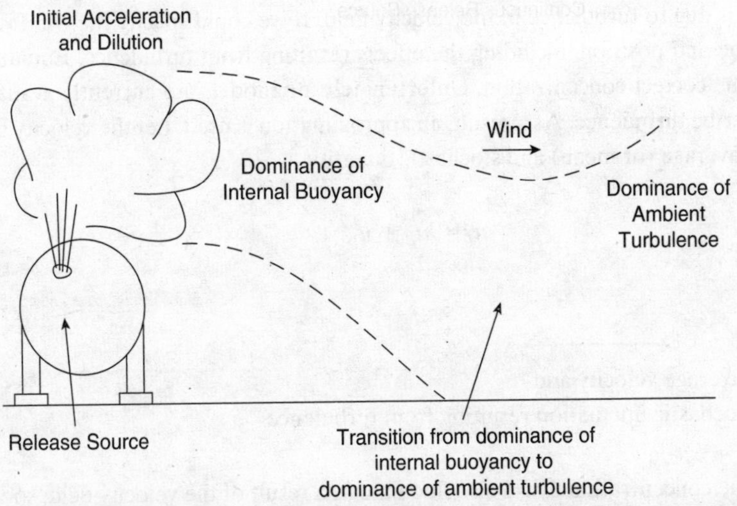

Figure 5-6 The initial acceleration and buoyancy of the released material affect the plume character. The dispersion models discussed in this chapter represent only ambient turbulence. Adapted from Steven R. Hanna and Peter J. Drivas, *Guidelines for Use of Vapor Cloud Dispersion Models* (New York: American Institute of Chemical Engineers, 1987), p. 6.

material from a single release of a fixed amount of material. The distinction between the two models is shown graphically in Figures 5-1 and 5-2. For the plume model a typical example is the continuous release of gases from a smokestack. A steady-state plume is formed downwind from the smokestack. For the puff model a typical example is the sudden release of a fixed amount of material because of the rupture of a storage vessel. A large vapor cloud is formed that moves away from the rupture point.

The puff model can be used to describe a plume; a plume is simply the release of continuous puffs. However, if steady-state plume information is all that is required, the plume model is recommended because it is easier to use. For studies involving dynamic plumes (for instance, the effect on a plume of a change in wind direction), the puff model must be used.

Consider the instantaneous release of a fixed mass of material, Q_m^*, into an infinite expanse of air (a ground surface will be added later). The coordinate system is fixed at the source. Assuming no reaction or molecular diffusion, the concentration C of material resulting from this release is given by the advection equation

$$\frac{\partial C}{\partial t} + \frac{\partial}{\partial x_j}(u_j C) = 0, \tag{5-1}$$

where u_j is the velocity of the air and the subscript j represents the summation over all coordinate directions x, y, and z. If the velocity u_j in Equation 5-1 is set equal to the average wind velocity and the equation is solved, we would find that the material disperses much faster than predicted. This is due to turbulence in the velocity field. If we could specify the wind velocity exactly with time and position, including the effects resulting from turbulence, Equation 5-1 would predict the correct concentration. Unfortunately, no models are currently available to adequately describe turbulence. As a result, an approximation is used. Let the velocity be represented by an average (or mean) and stochastic quantity

$$u_j = \langle u_j \rangle + u'_j, \tag{5-2}$$

where

$\langle u_j \rangle$ is the average velocity and
u'_j is the stochastic fluctuation resulting from turbulence.

It follows that the concentration C will also fluctuate as a result of the velocity field; so

$$C = \langle C \rangle + C', \tag{5-3}$$

where

$\langle C \rangle$ is the mean concentration and
C' is the stochastic fluctuation.

Because the fluctuations in both C and u_j are around the average or mean values, it follows that

$$\langle u'_j \rangle = 0,$$
$$\langle C' \rangle = 0. \tag{5-4}$$

Substituting Equations 5-2 and 5-3 into Equation 5-1 and averaging the result over time yields

$$\frac{\partial \langle C \rangle}{\partial t} + \frac{\partial}{\partial x_j}(\langle u_j \rangle \langle C \rangle) + \frac{\partial}{\partial x_j}\langle u'_j C' \rangle = 0. \tag{5-5}$$

The terms $\langle u_j \rangle C'$ and $u'_j \langle C \rangle$ are zero when averaged ($\langle \langle u_j \rangle C' \rangle = \langle u_j \rangle \langle C' \rangle = 0$), but the turbulent flux term $\langle u'_j C' \rangle$ is not necessarily zero and remains in the equation.

An additional equation is required to describe the turbulent flux. The usual approach is to define an eddy diffusivity K_j (with units of area/time) such that

$$\langle u'_j C' \rangle = -K_j \frac{\partial \langle C \rangle}{\partial x_j}. \tag{5-6}$$

Substituting Equation 5-6 into Equation 5-5 yields

$$\frac{\partial\langle C\rangle}{\partial t}+\frac{\partial}{\partial x_j}(\langle u_j\rangle\langle C\rangle)=\frac{\partial}{\partial x_j}\left(K_j\frac{\partial\langle C\rangle}{\partial x_j}\right). \tag{5-7}$$

If the atmosphere is assumed to be incompressible, then

$$\frac{\partial\langle u_j\rangle}{\partial x_j}=0, \tag{5-8}$$

and Equation 5-7 becomes

$$\boxed{\frac{\partial\langle C\rangle}{\partial t}+\langle u_j\rangle\frac{\partial\langle C\rangle}{\partial x_j}=\frac{\partial}{\partial x_j}\left(K_j\frac{\partial\langle C\rangle}{\partial x_j}\right).} \tag{5-9}$$

Equation 5-9 together with appropriate boundary and initial conditions forms the fundamental basis for dispersion modeling. This equation will be solved for a variety of cases.

The coordinate system used for the dispersion models is shown in Figures 5-7 and 5-8. The x axis is the centerline directly downwind from the release point and is rotated for different wind directions. The y axis is the distance off the centerline, and the z axis is the elevation

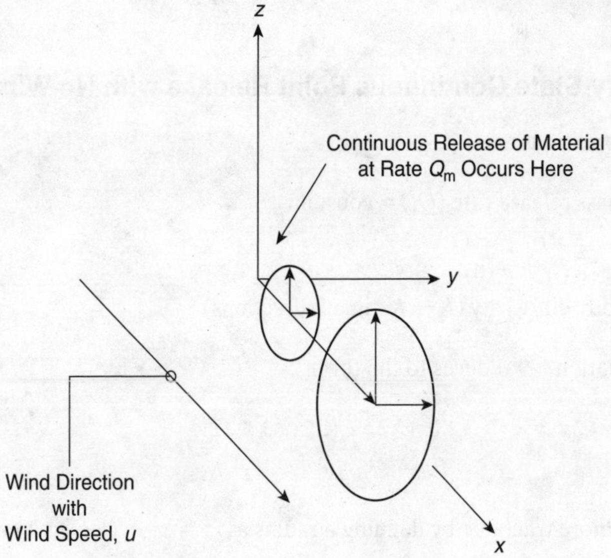

Figure 5-7 Steady-state continuous point source release with wind. Note the coordinate system: x is downwind direction, y is off-wind direction, and z is vertical direction.

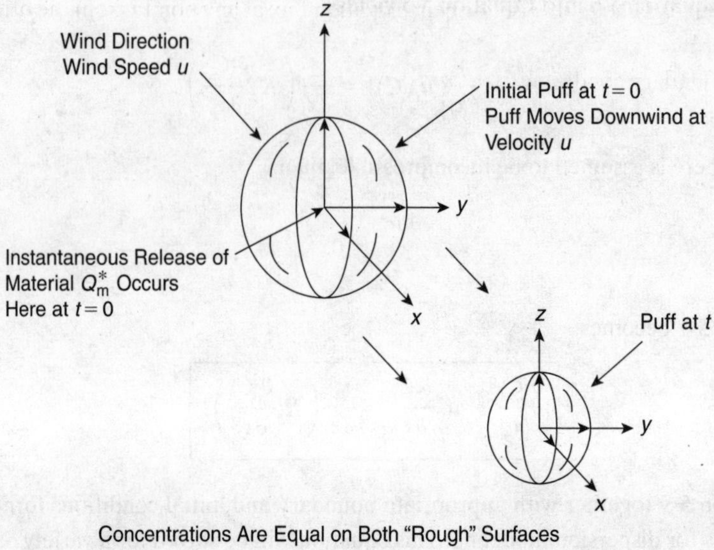

Figure 5-8 Puff with wind. After the initial instantaneous release, the puff moves with the wind.

above the release point. The point $(x, y, z) = (0, 0, 0)$ is at the release point. The coordinates $(x, y, 0)$ are level with the release point, and the coordinates $(x, 0, 0)$ are along the centerline, or x axis.

Case 1: Steady-State Continuous Point Release with No Wind

The applicable conditions are

- Constant mass release rate (Q_m = constant)
- No wind ($\langle u_j \rangle = 0$)
- Steady state ($\partial \langle C \rangle / \partial t = 0$)
- Constant eddy diffusivity ($K_j = K^*$ in all directions)

For this case Equation 5-9 reduces to the form

$$\frac{\partial^2 \langle C \rangle}{\partial x^2} + \frac{\partial^2 \langle C \rangle}{\partial y^2} + \frac{\partial^2 \langle C \rangle}{\partial z^2} = 0. \qquad (5\text{-}10)$$

Equation 5-10 is more tractable by defining a radius as $r^2 = x^2 + y^2 + z^2$. Transforming Equation 5-10 in terms of r yields

$$\frac{d}{dr}\left(r^2 \frac{d\langle C \rangle}{dr} \right) = 0. \qquad (5\text{-}11)$$

For a continuous steady-state release the concentration flux at any point r from the origin must equal the release rate Q_m (with units of mass/time). This is represented mathematically by the following flux boundary condition:

$$-4\pi r^2 K^* \frac{d\langle C\rangle}{dr} = Q_m. \tag{5-12}$$

The remaining boundary condition is

$$\text{As } r \to \infty, \qquad \langle C\rangle \to 0. \tag{5-13}$$

Equation 5-12 is separated and integrated between any point r and $r = \infty$:

$$\int_{\langle C\rangle}^{0} d\langle C\rangle = -\frac{Q_m}{4\pi K^*}\int_{r}^{\infty} \frac{dr}{r^2}. \tag{5-14}$$

Solving Equation 5-14 for $\langle C\rangle$ yields

$$\langle C\rangle(r) = \frac{Q_m}{4\pi K^* r}. \tag{5-15}$$

It is easy to verify by substitution that Equation 5-15 is also a solution to Equation 5-11 and thus a solution to this case. Equation 5-15 is transformed to rectangular coordinates to yield

$$\langle C\rangle(x, y, z) = \frac{Q_m}{4\pi K^* \sqrt{x^2 + y^2 + z^2}}. \tag{5-16}$$

Case 2: Puff with No Wind

The applicable conditions are

- Puff release, that is, instantaneous release of a fixed mass of material Q_m^* (with units of mass)
- No wind ($\langle u_j\rangle = 0$)
- Constant eddy diffusivity ($K_j = K^*$ in all directions)

Equation 5-9 reduces for this case to

$$\frac{1}{K^*}\frac{\partial\langle C\rangle}{\partial t} = \frac{\partial^2\langle C\rangle}{\partial x^2} + \frac{\partial^2\langle C\rangle}{\partial y^2} + \frac{\partial^2\langle C\rangle}{\partial z^2}. \tag{5-17}$$

The initial condition required to solve Equation 5-17 is

$$\langle C\rangle (x, y, z, t) = 0 \quad \text{at } t = 0. \tag{5-18}$$

The solution to Equation 5-17 in spherical coordinates[1] is

$$\langle C\rangle(r, t) = \frac{Q_m^*}{8(\pi K^* t)^{3/2}} \exp\left(-\frac{r^2}{4K^* t}\right), \tag{5-19}$$

and in rectangular coordinates it is

$$\langle C\rangle(x, y, z, t) = \frac{Q_m^*}{8(\pi K^* t)^{3/2}} \exp\left[-\frac{(x^2 + y^2 + z^2)}{4K^* t}\right]. \tag{5-20}$$

Case 3: Non-Steady-State Continuous Point Release with No Wind

The applicable conditions are

- constant mass release rate (Q_m = constant),
- no wind ($\langle u_j\rangle = 0$), and
- constant eddy diffusivity ($K_j = K^*$ in all directions).

For this case Equation 5-9 reduces to Equation 5-17 with the initial condition expressed by Equation 5-18 and the boundary condition expressed by Equation 5-13. The solution is found by integrating the instantaneous solution (Equation 5-19 or 5-20) with respect to time. The result in spherical coordinates[2] is

$$\langle C\rangle(r, t) = \frac{Q_m}{4\pi K^* r} \operatorname{erfc}\left(\frac{r}{2\sqrt{K^* t}}\right), \tag{5-21}$$

and in rectangular coordinates it is

$$\langle C\rangle(x, y, z, t) = \frac{Q_m}{4\pi K^* \sqrt{x^2 + y^2 + z^2}} \operatorname{erfc}\left(\frac{\sqrt{x^2 + y^2 + z^2}}{2\sqrt{K^* t}}\right). \tag{5-22}$$

As $t \to \infty$, Equations 5-21 and 5-22 reduce to the corresponding steady-state solutions (Equations 5-15 and 5-16).

[1] H. S. Carslaw and J. C. Jaeger, *Conduction of Heat in Solids* (London: Oxford University Press, 1959), p. 256.

[2] Carslaw and Jaeger, *Conduction of Heat*, p. 261.

Case 4: Steady-State Continuous Point Source Release with Wind

This case is shown in Figure 5-7. The applicable conditions are

- continuous release (Q_m = constant),
- wind blowing in x direction only ($\langle u_j \rangle = \langle u_x \rangle = u$ = constant), and
- constant eddy diffusivity ($K_j = K^*$ in all directions).

For this case Equation 5-9 reduces to

$$\frac{u}{K^*}\frac{\partial\langle C\rangle}{\partial x} = \frac{\partial^2\langle C\rangle}{\partial x^2} + \frac{\partial^2\langle C\rangle}{\partial y^2} + \frac{\partial^2\langle C\rangle}{\partial z^2}. \tag{5-23}$$

Equation 5-23 is solved together with boundary conditions expressed by Equations 5-12 and 5-13. The solution for the average concentration at any point[3] is

$$\langle C\rangle(x, y, z) = \frac{Q_m}{4\pi K^*\sqrt{x^2 + y^2 + z^2}}\exp\left[-\frac{u}{2K^*}\left(\sqrt{x^2 + y^2 + z^2} - x\right)\right]. \tag{5-24}$$

If a slender plume is assumed (the plume is long and slender and is not far removed from the x axis), that is,

$$y^2 + z^2 \ll x^2, \tag{5-25}$$

then by using $\sqrt{1 + a} \approx 1 + a/2$, Equation 5-24 is simplified to

$$\langle C\rangle(x, y, z) = \frac{Q_m}{4\pi K^* x}\exp\left[-\frac{u}{4K^* x}(y^2 + z^2)\right]. \tag{5-26}$$

Along the centerline of this plume, $y = z = 0$, and

$$\langle C\rangle(x) = \frac{Q_m}{4\pi K^* x}. \tag{5-27}$$

Case 5: Puff with No Wind and Eddy Diffusivity Is a Function of Direction

This case is the same as case 2 but with eddy diffusivity a function of direction. The applicable conditions are

- puff release (Q_m^* = constant),
- no wind ($\langle u_j \rangle = 0$), and
- each coordinate direction has a different but constant eddy diffusivity (K_x, K_y, and K_z).

[3]Carslaw and Jaeger, *Conduction of Heat,* p. 267.

Equation 5-9 reduces to the following equation for this case:

$$\frac{\partial\langle C\rangle}{\partial t} = K_x\frac{\partial^2\langle C\rangle}{\partial x^2} + K_y\frac{\partial^2\langle C\rangle}{\partial y^2} + K_z\frac{\partial^2\langle C\rangle}{\partial z^2}. \tag{5-28}$$

The solution is[4]

$$\langle C\rangle(x, y, z, t) = \frac{Q_m^*}{8(\pi t)^{3/2}\sqrt{K_xK_yK_z}}\exp\left[-\frac{1}{4t}\left(\frac{x^2}{K_x} + \frac{y^2}{K_y} + \frac{z^2}{K_z}\right)\right]. \tag{5-29}$$

Case 6: Steady-State Continuous Point Source Release with Wind and Eddy Diffusivity Is a Function of Direction

This case is the same as case 4 but with eddy diffusivity a function of direction. The applicable conditions are

- continuous release (Q_m = constant),
- steady state ($\partial\langle C\rangle/\partial t = 0$),
- wind blowing in x direction only ($\langle u_j\rangle = \langle u_x\rangle = u$ = constant),
- each coordinate direction has a different but constant eddy diffusivity (K_x, K_y, and K_z), and
- slender plume approximation (Equation 5-25).

Equation 5-9 reduces to

$$u\frac{\partial\langle C\rangle}{\partial x} = K_x\frac{\partial^2\langle C\rangle}{\partial x^2} + K_y\frac{\partial^2\langle C\rangle}{\partial y^2} + K_z\frac{\partial^2\langle C\rangle}{\partial z^2}. \tag{5-30}$$

The solution is[5]

$$\langle C\rangle(x, y, z) = \frac{Q_m}{4\pi x\sqrt{K_xK_y}}\exp\left[-\frac{u}{4x}\left(\frac{y^2}{K_y} + \frac{z^2}{K_z}\right)\right]. \tag{5-31}$$

Along the centerline of this plume, $y = z = 0$, and the average concentration is given by

$$\langle C\rangle(x) = \frac{Q_m}{4\pi x\sqrt{K_yK_z}}. \tag{5-32}$$

Case 7: Puff with Wind

This case is the same as case 5 but with wind. Figure 5-8 shows the geometry. The applicable conditions are

- puff release (Q_m^* = constant),
- wind blowing in x direction only ($\langle u_j\rangle = \langle u_x\rangle = u$ = constant), and
- each coordinate direction has a different but constant eddy diffusivity (K_x, K_y, and K_z).

[4] Frank P. Lees, *Loss Prevention in the Process Industries,* 2nd ed. (London: Butterworths, 1996), p. 15/106.

[5] Lees, *Loss Prevention,* p. 15/107.

The solution to this problem is found by a simple transformation of coordinates. The solution to case 5 represents a puff fixed around the release point. If the puff moves with the wind along the x axis, the solution to this case is found by replacing the existing coordinate x by a new coordinate system, $x - ut$, that moves with the wind velocity. The variable t is the time since the release of the puff, and u is the wind velocity. The solution is simply Equation 5-29, transformed into this new coordinate system:

$$\langle C\rangle(x, y, z, t) = \frac{Q_m^*}{8(\pi t)^{3/2}\sqrt{K_x K_y K_z}} \exp\left\{-\frac{1}{4t}\left[\frac{(x-ut)^2}{K_x} + \frac{y^2}{K_y} + \frac{z^2}{K_z}\right]\right\}. \tag{5-33}$$

Case 8: Puff with No Wind and with Source on Ground

This case is the same as case 5 but with the source on the ground. The ground represents an impervious boundary. As a result, the concentration is twice the concentration in case 5. The solution is 2 times Equation 5-29:

$$\langle C\rangle(x, y, z, t) = \frac{Q_m^*}{4(\pi t)^{3/2}\sqrt{K_x K_y K_z}} \exp\left[-\frac{1}{4t}\left(\frac{x^2}{K_x} + \frac{y^2}{K_y} + \frac{z^2}{K_z}\right)\right]. \tag{5-34}$$

Case 9: Steady-State Plume with Source on Ground

This case is the same as case 6 but with the release source on the ground, as shown in Figure 5-9. The ground represents an impervious boundary. As a result, the concentration is twice the concentration in case 6. The solution is 2 times Equation 5-31:

$$\langle C\rangle(x, y, z) = \frac{Q_m}{2\pi x\sqrt{K_x K_y}} \exp\left[-\frac{u}{4x}\left(\frac{y^2}{K_y} + \frac{z^2}{K_z}\right)\right]. \tag{5-35}$$

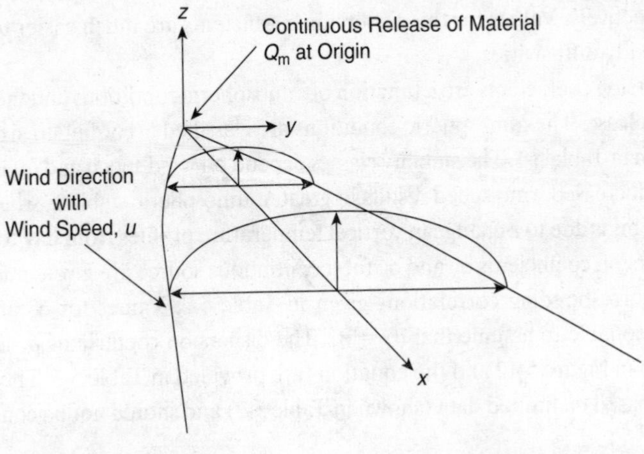

Figure 5-9 Steady-state plume with source at ground level. The concentration is twice the concentration of a plume without the ground.

Case 10: Continuous Steady-State Source with Source at Height H_r above the Ground

For this case the ground acts as an impervious boundary at a distance H from the source. The solution is[6]

$$\langle C\rangle(x, y, z) = \frac{Q_m}{4\pi x\sqrt{K_y K_z}} \exp\left(-\frac{uy^2}{4K_y x}\right)$$
$$\times \left\{\exp\left[-\frac{u}{4K_z x}(z - H_r)^2\right] + \exp\left[-\frac{u}{4K_z x}(z + H_r)^2\right]\right\}. \qquad (5\text{-}36)$$

If $H_r = 0$, Equation 5-36 reduces to Equation 5-35 for a source on the ground.

Pasquill-Gifford Model

Cases 1 through 10 all depend on the specification of a value for the eddy diffusivity K_j. In general, K_j changes with position, time, wind velocity, and prevailing weather conditions. Although the eddy diffusivity approach is useful theoretically, it is not convenient experimentally and does not provide a useful framework for correlation.

Sutton[7] solved this difficulty by proposing the following definition for a *dispersion coefficient:*

$$\sigma_x^2 = \frac{1}{2}\langle C\rangle^2 (ut)^{2-n}, \qquad (5\text{-}37)$$

with similiar expressions given for σ_y and σ_z. The dispersion coefficients σ_x, σ_y, and σ_z represent the standard deviations of the concentration in the downwind, crosswind, and vertical (x, y, z) directions, respectively. Values for the dispersion coefficients are much easier to obtain experimentally than eddy diffusivities.

The dispersion coefficients are a function of atmospheric conditions and the distance downwind from the release. The atmospheric conditions are classified according to six different stability classes, shown in Table 5-1. The stability classes depend on wind speed and quantity of sunlight. During the day, increased wind speed results in greater atmospheric stability, whereas at night the reverse is true. This is due to a change in vertical temperature profiles from day to night.

The dispersion coefficients σ_y and σ_z for a continuous source are given in Figures 5-10 and 5-11, with the corresponding correlations given in Table 5-2. Values for σ_x are not provided because it is reasonable to assume that $\sigma_x = \sigma_y$. The dispersion coefficients σ_y and σ_z for a puff release are given in Figure 5-12 and the equations are provided in Table 5-3. The puff dispersion coefficients are based on limited data (shown in Table 5-2) and should not be considered precise.

[6]Lees, *Loss Prevention,* p. 15/107.
[7]O. G. Sutton, *Micrometeorology* (New York: McGraw-Hill, 1953), p. 286.

Table 5-1 Atmospheric Stability Classes for Use with the Pasquill-Gifford Dispersion Model [a,b]

Surface wind speed (m/s)	Daytime insolation[c]			Nighttime conditions[d]	
	Strong	Moderate	Slight	Thin overcast or >4/8 low cloud	≤3/8 cloudiness
<2	A	A–B	B	F[e]	F[e]
2–3	A–B	B	C	E	F
3–4	B	B–C	C	D[f]	E
4–6	C	C–D	D[f]	D[f]	D[f]
>6	C	D[f]	D[f]	D[f]	D[f]

Stability classes:

A, extremely unstable
B, moderately unstable
C, slightly unstable
D, neutrally stable
E, slightly stable
F, moderately stable

[a]F. A. Gifford, "Use of Routine Meteorological Observations for Estimating Atmospheric Dispersion," *Nuclear Safety* (1961), 2(4): 47.

[b]F. A. Gifford, "Turbulent Diffusion-Typing Schemes: A Review," *Nuclear Safety* (1976), 17(1): 68.

[c]Strong insolation corresponds to a sunny midday in midsummer in England. Slight insolation corresponds to similar conditions in midwinter.

[d]Night refers to the period 1 hr before sunset and 1 hr after dawn.

[e]These values are filled in to complete the table.

[f]The neutral category D should be used, regardless of wind speed, for overcast conditions during day or night and for any sky conditions during the hour before or after sunset or sunrise, respectively.

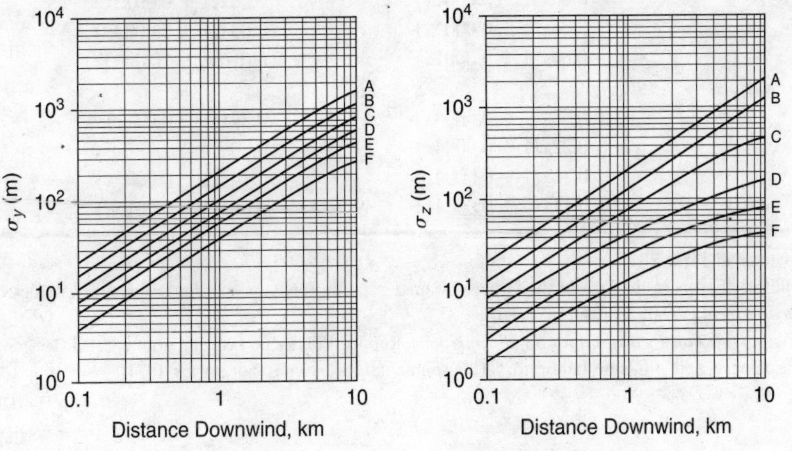

Figure 5-10 Dispersion coefficients for Pasquill-Gifford plume model for rural releases.

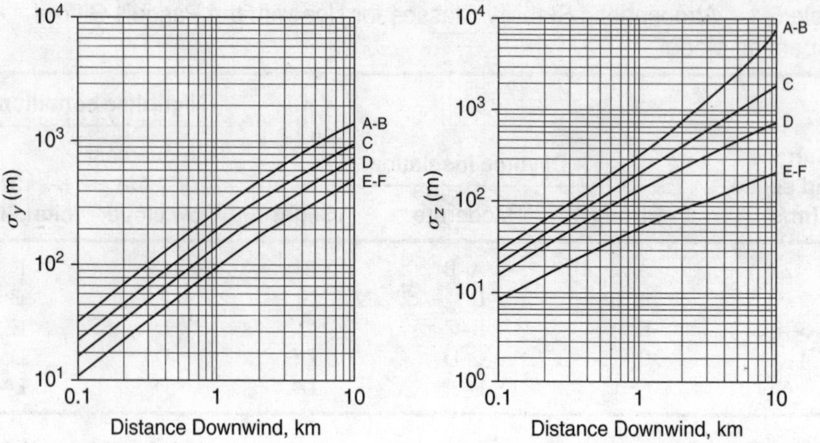

Figure 5-11 Dispersion coefficients for Pasquill-Gifford plume model for urban releases.

Table 5-2 Recommended Equations for Pasquill-Gifford Dispersion Coefficients for Plume Dispersion[a,b] (the downwind distance x has units of meters)

Pasquill-Gifford stability class	σ_y (m)	σ_z (m)
Rural conditions		
A	$0.22x(1 + 0.0001x)^{-1/2}$	$0.20x$
B	$0.16x(1 + 0.0001x)^{-1/2}$	$0.12x$
C	$0.11x(1 + 0.0001x)^{-1/2}$	$0.08x(1 + 0.0002x)^{-1/2}$
D	$0.08x(1 + 0.0001x)^{-1/2}$	$0.06x(1 + 0.0015x)^{-1/2}$
E	$0.06x(1 + 0.0001x)^{-1/2}$	$0.03x(1 + 0.0003x)^{-1}$
F	$0.04x(1 + 0.0001x)^{-1/2}$	$0.016x(1 + 0.0003x)^{-1}$
Urban conditions		
A–B	$0.32x(1 + 0.0004x)^{-1/2}$	$0.24x(1 + 0.001x)^{+1/2}$
C	$0.22x(1 + 0.0004x)^{-1/2}$	$0.20x$
D	$0.16x(1 + 0.0004x)^{-1/2}$	$0.14x(1 + 0.0003x)^{-1/2}$
E–F	$0.11x(1 + 0.0004x)^{-1/2}$	$0.08x(1 + 0.0015x)^{-1/2}$

A–F are defined in Table 5-1.

[a]R. F. Griffiths, "Errors in the Use of the Briggs Parameterization for Atmospheric Dispersion Coefficients," *Atmospheric Environment* (1994), 28(17): 2861–2865.

[b]G. A. Briggs, *Diffusion Estimation for Small Emissions,* Report ATDL-106 (Washington, DC: Air Resources, Atmospheric Turbulence, and Diffusion Laboratory, Environmental Research Laboratories, 1974).

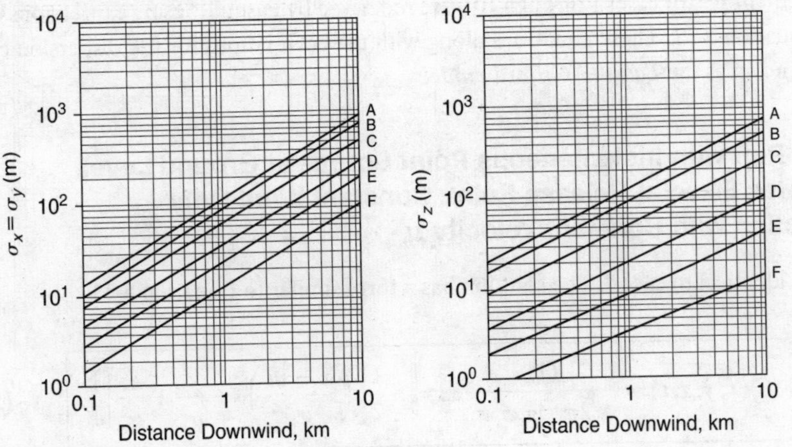

Figure 5-12 Dispersion coefficients for Pasquill-Gifford puff model.

Table 5-3 Recommended Equations for Pasquill-Gifford Dispersion Coefficients for Puff Dispersion[a,b] (the downwind distance x has units of meters)

Pasquill-Gifford stability class	σ_y (m) or σ_x (m)	σ_z (m)
A	$0.18x^{0.92}$	$0.60x^{0.75}$
B	$0.14x^{0.92}$	$0.53x^{0.73}$
C	$0.10x^{0.92}$	$0.34x^{0.71}$
D	$0.06x^{0.92}$	$0.15x^{0.70}$
E	$0.04x^{0.92}$	$0.10x^{0.65}$
F	$0.02x^{0.89}$	$0.05x^{0.61}$

A–F are defined in Table 5-1.
[a]R. F. Griffiths, "Errors in the Use of the Briggs Parameterization for Atmospheric Dispersion Coefficients," *Atmospheric Environment* (1994), 28(17): 2861–2865.
[b]G. A. Briggs, *Diffusion Estimation for Small Emissions,* Report ATDL-106 (Washington, DC: Air Resources, Atmospheric Turbulence, and Diffusion Laboratory, Environmental Research Laboratories, 1974).

The equations for cases 1 through 10 were rederived by Pasquill[8] using expressions of the form of Equation 5-37. These equations along with the correlations for the dispersion coefficients are known as the *Pasquill-Gifford model.*

Case 11: Puff with Instantaneous Point Source at Ground Level, Coordinates Fixed at Release Point, Constant Wind Only in *x* Direction with Constant Velocity *u*

This case is identical to case 7. The solution has a form similar to Equation 5-33:

$$\langle C\rangle(x,y,z,t) = \frac{Q_m^*}{\sqrt{2}\pi^{3/2}\sigma_x\sigma_y\sigma_z}\exp\left\{-\frac{1}{2}\left[\left(\frac{x-ut}{\sigma_x}\right)^2 + \frac{y^2}{\sigma_y^2} + \frac{z^2}{\sigma_z^2}\right]\right\}. \tag{5-38}$$

The ground-level concentration is given at $z = 0$:

$$\langle C\rangle(x,y,0,t) = \frac{Q_m^*}{\sqrt{2}\pi^{3/2}\sigma_x\sigma_y\sigma_z}\exp\left\{-\frac{1}{2}\left[\left(\frac{x-ut}{\sigma_x}\right)^2 + \frac{y^2}{\sigma_y^2}\right]\right\}. \tag{5-39}$$

The ground-level concentration along the x axis is given at $y = z = 0$:

$$\langle C\rangle(x,0,0,t) = \frac{Q_m^*}{\sqrt{2}\pi^{3/2}\sigma_x\sigma_y\sigma_z}\exp\left[-\frac{1}{2}\left(\frac{x-ut}{\sigma_x}\right)^2\right]. \tag{5-40}$$

The center of the cloud is found at coordinates $(ut, 0, 0)$. The concentration at the center of this moving cloud is given by

$$\langle C\rangle(ut,0,0,t) = \frac{Q_m^*}{\sqrt{2}\pi^{3/2}\sigma_x\sigma_y\sigma_z}. \tag{5-41}$$

The total integrated dose D_{tid} received by an individual standing at fixed coordinates (x, y, z) is the time integral of the concentration:

$$D_{tid}(x,y,z) = \int_0^\infty \langle C\rangle(x,y,z,t)\,dt. \tag{5-42}$$

[8]F. Pasquill, *Atmospheric Diffusion* (London: Van Nostrand, 1962).

The total integrated dose at ground level is found by integrating Equation 5-39 according to Equation 5-42. The result is

$$D_{\text{tid}}(x, y, 0) = \frac{Q_{\text{m}}^*}{\pi \sigma_y \sigma_z u} \exp\left(-\frac{1}{2}\frac{y^2}{\sigma_y^2}\right). \tag{5-43}$$

The total integrated dose along the x axis on the ground is

$$D_{\text{tid}}(x, 0, 0) = \frac{Q_{\text{m}}^*}{\pi \sigma_y \sigma_z u}. \tag{5-44}$$

Frequently the cloud boundary defined by a fixed concentration is required. The line connecting points of equal concentration around the cloud boundary is called an isopleth. For a specified concentration $\langle C \rangle^*$ the isopleths at ground level are determined by dividing the equation for the centerline concentration (Equation 5-40) by the equation for the general ground-level concentration (Equation 5-39). This equation is solved directly for y:

$$y = \sigma_y \sqrt{2 \ln\left(\frac{\langle C \rangle(x, 0, 0, t)}{\langle C \rangle(x, y, 0, t)}\right)}. \tag{5-45}$$

The procedure is

1. Specify $\langle C \rangle^*$, u, and t.
2. Determine the concentrations $\langle C \rangle(x, 0, 0, t)$ along the x axis using Equation 5-40. Define the boundary of the cloud along the x axis.
3. Set $\langle C \rangle(x, y, 0, t) = \langle C \rangle^*$ in Equation 5-45, and determine the values of y at each centerline point determined in step 2.

The procedure is repeated for each value of t required.

Case 12: Plume with Continuous Steady-State Source at Ground Level and Wind Moving in *x* Direction at Constant Velocity *u*

This case is identical to case 9. The solution has a form similar to Equation 5-35:

$$\langle C \rangle(x, y, z) = \frac{Q_{\text{m}}}{\pi \sigma_y \sigma_z u} \exp\left[-\frac{1}{2}\left(\frac{y^2}{\sigma_y^2} + \frac{z^2}{\sigma_z^2}\right)\right]. \tag{5-46}$$

The ground-level concentration is given at $z = 0$:

$$\langle C\rangle(x, y, 0) = \frac{Q_m}{\pi\sigma_y\sigma_z u}\exp\left[-\frac{1}{2}\left(\frac{y}{\sigma_y}\right)^2\right]. \tag{5-47}$$

The concentration along the centerline of the plume directly downwind is given at $y = z = 0$:

$$\langle C\rangle(x, 0, 0) = \frac{Q_m}{\pi\sigma_y\sigma_z u}. \tag{5-48}$$

The isopleths are found using a procedure identical to the isopleth procedure used for case 11.

For continuous ground-level releases the maximum concentration occurs at the release point.

Case 13: Plume with Continuous Steady-State Source at Height H_r above Ground Level and Wind Moving in *x* Direction at Constant Velocity *u*

This case is identical to case 10. The solution has a form similar to Equation 5-36:

$$\langle C\rangle(x, y, z) = \frac{Q_m}{2\pi\sigma_y\sigma_z u}\exp\left[-\frac{1}{2}\left(\frac{y}{\sigma_y}\right)^2\right] \times \left\{\exp\left[-\frac{1}{2}\left(\frac{z - H_r}{\sigma_z}\right)^2\right] + \exp\left[-\frac{1}{2}\left(\frac{z + H_r}{\sigma_z}\right)^2\right]\right\}. \tag{5-49}$$

The ground-level concentration is found by setting $z = 0$:

$$\langle C\rangle(x, y, 0) = \frac{Q_m}{\pi\sigma_y\sigma_z u}\exp\left[-\frac{1}{2}\left(\frac{y}{\sigma_y}\right)^2 - \frac{1}{2}\left(\frac{H_r}{\sigma_z}\right)^2\right]. \tag{5-50}$$

The ground-level centerline concentrations are found by setting $y = z = 0$:

$$\langle C\rangle(x, 0, 0) = \frac{Q_m}{\pi\sigma_y\sigma_z u}\exp\left[-\frac{1}{2}\left(\frac{H_r}{\sigma_z}\right)^2\right]. \tag{5-51}$$

The maximum ground-level concentration along the *x* axis $\langle C\rangle_{max}$ is found using

$$\langle C\rangle_{max} = \frac{2Q_m}{e\pi u H_r^2}\left(\frac{\sigma_z}{\sigma_y}\right). \tag{5-52}$$

The distance downwind at which the maximum ground-level concentration occurs is found from

$$\sigma_z = \frac{H_r}{\sqrt{2}}. \tag{5-53}$$

The procedure for finding the maximum concentration and the downwind distance is to use Equation 5-53 to determine the distance, followed by using Equation 5-52 to determine the maximum concentration.

Case 14: Puff with Instantaneous Point Source at Height H_r above Ground Level and a Coordinate System on the Ground That Moves with the Puff

For this case the center of the puff is found at $x = ut$. The average concentration is given by

$$\langle C\rangle(x, y, z, t) = \frac{Q_m^*}{(2\pi)^{3/2}\sigma_x\sigma_y\sigma_z}\exp\left[-\frac{1}{2}\left(\frac{y}{\sigma_y}\right)^2\right] \times \left\{\exp\left[-\frac{1}{2}\left(\frac{z-H_r}{\sigma_z}\right)^2\right] + \exp\left[-\frac{1}{2}\left(\frac{z+H_r}{\sigma_z}\right)^2\right]\right\}. \tag{5-54}$$

The time dependence is achieved through the dispersion coefficients, because their values change as the puff moves downwind from the release point. If wind is absent ($u = 0$), Equation 5-54 does not predict the correct result.

At ground level, $z = 0$, and the concentration is computed using

$$\langle C\rangle(x, y, 0, t) = \frac{Q_m^*}{\sqrt{2}\pi^{3/2}\sigma_x\sigma_y\sigma_z}\exp\left[-\frac{1}{2}\left(\frac{y}{\sigma_y}\right)^2 - \frac{1}{2}\left(\frac{H_r}{\sigma_z}\right)^2\right]. \tag{5-55}$$

The concentration along the ground at the centerline is given at $y = z = 0$:

$$\langle C\rangle(x, 0, 0, t) = \frac{Q_m^*}{\sqrt{2}\pi^{3/2}\sigma_x\sigma_y\sigma_z}\exp\left[-\frac{1}{2}\left(\frac{H_r}{\sigma_z}\right)^2\right]. \tag{5-56}$$

The total integrated dose at ground level is found by applying Equation 5-42 to Equation 5-55. The result is

$$D_{\text{tid}}(x, y, 0) = \frac{Q_m^*}{\pi\sigma_y\sigma_z u}\exp\left[-\frac{1}{2}\left(\frac{y}{\sigma_y}\right)^2 - \frac{1}{2}\left(\frac{H_r}{\sigma_z}\right)^2\right]. \tag{5-57}$$

Case 15: Puff with Instantaneous Point Source at Height H_r above Ground Level and a Coordinate System Fixed on the Ground at the Release Point

For this case the result is obtained using a transformation of coordinates similar to the transformation used for case 7. The result is

$$\langle C\rangle(x, y, z, t) = \begin{array}{l}\text{[Puff equations with moving coordinate} \\ \text{system (Equations 5-54 through 5-56)]} \\ \times \exp\left[-\frac{1}{2}\left(\frac{x - ut}{\sigma_x}\right)^2\right],\end{array} \tag{5-58}$$

where t is the time since the release of the puff.

Worst-Case Conditions

For a plume the highest concentration is always found at the release point. If the release occurs above ground level, then the highest concentration on the ground is found at a point downwind from the release.

For a puff the maximum concentration is always found at the puff center. For a release above ground level the puff center will move parallel to the ground and the maximum concentration on the ground will occur directly below the puff center. For a puff isopleth the isopleth is close to circular as it moves downwind. The diameter of the isopleth increases initially as the puff travels downwind, reaches a maximum, and then decreases in diameter.

If weather conditions are not known or are not specified, then certain assumptions can be made to result in a worst-case result; that is, the highest concentration is estimated. The weather conditions in the Pasquill-Gifford dispersion equations are included by means of the dispersion coefficients and the wind speed. By examining the Pasquill-Gifford dispersion equations for estimating the concentrations, it is readily evident that the dispersion coefficients and wind speed are in the denominator. Thus the maximum concentration is estimated by selecting the weather conditions and wind speed that result in the smallest values of the dispersion coefficients and the wind speed. By inspecting Figures 5-10 through 5-12, we can see that the smallest dispersion coefficients occur with F stability. Clearly, the wind speed cannot be zero, so a finite value must be selected. The EPA[9] suggests that F stability can exist with wind speeds as low as 1.5 m/s. Some risk analysts use a wind speed of 2 m/s. The assumptions used in the calculation must be clearly stated.

Limitations to Pasquill-Gifford Dispersion Modeling

Pasquill-Gifford or Gaussian dispersion applies only to neutrally buoyant dispersion of gases in which the turbulent mixing is the dominant feature of the dispersion. It is typically valid only for a distance of 0.1–10 km from the release point.

[9]EPA, *RMP Offsite Consequence Analysis Guidance* (Washington, DC: US Environmental Protection Agency, 1996).

The concentrations predicted by the Gaussian models are time averages. Thus it is possible for instantaneous local concentrations to exceed the average values predicted – this might be important for emergency response. The models presented here assume a 10-minute time average. Actual instantaneous concentrations may vary by as much as a factor of 2 from the concentrations computed using Gaussian models.

5-3 Dense Gas Dispersion

A dense gas is defined as any gas whose density is greater than the density of the ambient air through which it is being dispersed. This result can be due to a gas with a molecular weight greater than that of air or a gas with a low temperature resulting from autorefrigeration during release or other processes.

Following a typical puff release, a cloud having similar vertical and horizontal dimensions (near the source) may form. The dense cloud slumps toward the ground under the influence of gravity, increasing its diameter and reducing its height. Considerable initial dilution occurs because of the gravity-driven intrusion of the cloud into the ambient air. Subsequently the cloud height increases because of further entrainment of air across both the vertical and the horizontal interfaces. After sufficient dilution occurs, normal atmospheric turbulence predominates over gravitational forces and typical Gaussian dispersion characteristics are exhibited.

The Britter and McQuaid[10] model was developed by performing a dimensional analysis and correlating existing data on dense cloud dispersion. The model is best suited for instantaneous or continuous ground-level releases of dense gases. The release is assumed to occur at ambient temperature and without aerosol or liquid droplet formation. Atmospheric stability was found to have little effect on the results and is not a part of the model. Most of the data came from dispersion tests in remote rural areas on mostly flat terrain. Thus the results are not applicable to areas where terrain effects are significant.

The model requires a specification of the initial cloud volume, the initial plume volume flux, the duration of release, and the initial gas density. Also required are the wind speed at a height of 10 m, the distance downwind, and the ambient gas density.

The first step is to determine whether the dense gas model is applicable. The initial cloud buoyancy is defined as

$$g_o = g(\rho_o - \rho_a)/\rho_a, \tag{5-59}$$

where

g_o is the initial buoyancy factor (length/time^2),
g is the acceleration due to gravity (length/time^2),
ρ_o is the initial density of released material (mass/volume), and
ρ_a is the density of ambient air (mass/volume).

[10] R. E. Britter and J. McQuaid, *Workbook on the Dispersion of Dense Gases* (Sheffield, United Kingdom: Health and Safety Executive, 1988).

A characteristic source dimension, dependent on the type of release, can also be defined. For continuous releases

$$D_c = \left(\frac{q_o}{u}\right)^{1/2}, \tag{5-60}$$

where

D_c is the characteristic source dimension for continuous releases of dense gases (length),
q_o is the initial plume volume flux for dense gas dispersion (volume/time), and
u is the wind speed at 10 m elevation (length/time).

For instantaneous releases the characteristic source dimension is defined as

$$D_i = V_o^{1/3}, \tag{5-61}$$

where

D_i is the characteristic source dimension for instantaneous releases of dense gases (length) and
V_o is the initial volume of released dense gas material (length^3).

The criteria for a sufficiently dense cloud to require a dense cloud representation are, for continuous releases,

$$\left(\frac{g_o q_o}{u^3 D_c}\right)^{1/3} \geq 0.15 \tag{5-62}$$

and, for instantaneous releases,

$$\frac{\sqrt{g_o V_o}}{u D_i} \geq 0.20. \tag{5-63}$$

If these criteria are satisfied, then Figures 5-13 and 5-14 are used to estimate the downwind concentrations. Tables 5-4 and 5-5 provide equations for the correlations in these figures.

The criterion for determining whether the release is continuous or instantaneous is calculated using the following group:

$$\frac{u R_d}{x}, \tag{5-64}$$

where

R_d is the release duration (time) and
x is the downwind distance in dimensional space (length).

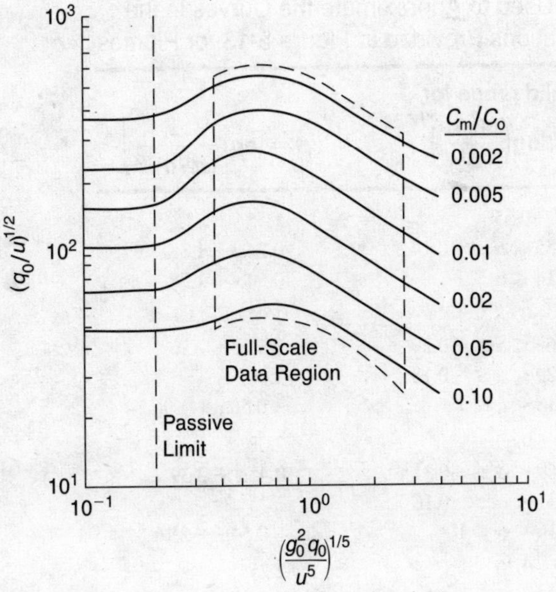

Figure 5-13 Britter-McQuaid dimensional correlation for dispersion of dense gas plumes.

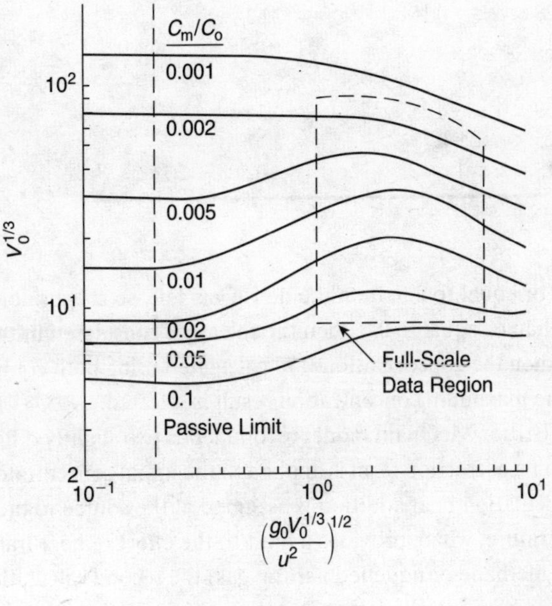

Figure 5-14 Britter-McQuaid dimensional correlation for dispersion of dense gas puffs.

Table 5-4 Equations Used to Approximate the Curves in the Britter-McQuaid Correlations Provided in Figure 5-13 for Plumes

Concentration ratio (C_m/C_o)	Valid range for $\alpha = \log\left(\frac{g_o^2 q_o}{u^5}\right)^{1/5}$	$\beta = \log\left[\frac{x}{(q_o/u)^{1/2}}\right]$
0.1	$\alpha \le -0.55$	1.75
	$-0.55 < \alpha \le -0.14$	$0.24\alpha + 1.88$
	$-0.14 < \alpha \le 1$	$0.50\alpha + 1.78$
0.05	$\alpha \le -0.68$	1.92
	$-0.68 < \alpha \le -0.29$	$0.36\alpha + 2.16$
	$-0.29 < \alpha \le -0.18$	2.06
	$-0.18 < \alpha \le 1$	$-0.56\alpha + 1.96$
0.02	$\alpha \le -0.69$	2.08
	$-0.69 < \alpha \le -0.31$	$0.45\alpha + 2.39$
	$-0.31 < \alpha \le -0.16$	2.25
	$-0.16 < \alpha \le 1$	$-0.54\alpha + 2.16$
0.01	$\alpha \le -0.70$	2.25
	$-0.70 < \alpha \le -0.29$	$0.49\alpha + 2.59$
	$-0.29 < \alpha \le -0.20$	2.45
	$-0.20 < \alpha \le 1$	$-0.52\alpha + 2.35$
0.005	$\alpha \le -0.67$	2.40
	$-0.67 < \alpha \le -0.28$	$0.59\alpha + 2.80$
	$-0.28 < \alpha \le -0.15$	2.63
	$-0.15 < \alpha \le 1$	$-0.49\alpha + 2.56$
0.002	$\alpha \le -0.69$	2.6
	$-0.69 < \alpha \le -0.25$	$0.39\alpha + 2.87$
	$-0.25 < \alpha \le -0.13$	2.77
	$-0.13 < \alpha \le 1$	$-0.50\alpha + 2.71$

If this group has a value greater than or equal to 2.5, then the dense gas release is considered continuous. If the group value is less than or equal to 0.6, then the release is considered instantaneous. If the value lies in-between, then the concentrations are calculated using both continuous and instantaneous models and the maximum concentration result is selected.

For nonisothermal releases the Britter-McQuaid model recommends two slightly different calculations. For the first calculation a correction term is applied to the initial concentratoin (see Example 5-3). For the second calculation heat addition is assumed at the source to bring the source material to ambient temperature, which provides a limit to the effect of heat transfer. For gases lighter than air (such as methane or liquefied natural gas) the second calculation might be meaningless. If the difference between the two calculations is small, then the nonisothermal effects are assumed negligible. If the two calculations are within a factor of 2, then the calculation providing the maximum, or most pessimistic, concentration is used. If the

Table 5-5 Equations Used to Approximate the Curves in the Britter-McQuaid Correlations Provided in Figure 5-14 for Puffs

Concentration ratio (C_m/C_o)	Valid range for $\alpha = \log\left(\frac{g_o V_o^{1/3}}{u^2}\right)^{1/2}$	$\beta = \log\left(\frac{x}{V_o^{1/3}}\right)$
0.1	$\alpha \leq -0.44$	0.70
	$-0.44 < \alpha \leq 0.43$	$0.26\alpha + 0.81$
	$0.43 < \alpha \leq 1$	0.93
0.05	$\alpha \leq -0.56$	0.85
	$-0.56 < \alpha \leq 0.31$	$0.26\alpha + 1.0$
	$0.31 < \alpha \leq 1.0$	$-0.12\alpha + 1.12$
0.02	$\alpha \leq -0.66$	0.95
	$-0.66 < \alpha \leq 0.32$	$0.36\alpha + 1.19$
	$0.32 < \alpha \leq 1$	$-0.26\alpha + 1.38$
0.01	$\alpha \leq -0.71$	1.15
	$-0.71 < \alpha \leq 0.37$	$0.34\alpha + 1.39$
	$0.37 < \alpha \leq 1$	$-0.38\alpha + 1.66$
0.005	$\alpha \leq -0.52$	1.48
	$-0.52 < \alpha \leq 0.24$	$0.26\alpha + 1.62$
	$0.24 < \alpha \leq 1$	$0.30\alpha + 1.75$
0.002	$\alpha \leq 0.27$	1.83
	$0.27 < \alpha \leq 1$	$-0.32\alpha + 1.92$
0.001	$\alpha \leq -0.10$	2.075
	$-0.10 < \alpha \leq 1$	$-0.27\alpha + 2.05$

difference is very large (greater than a factor of 2), then the maximum, or most pessimistic, concentration is selected, but further investigation using more detailed methods (such as a computer code) may be worthwhile.

The Britter-McQuaid model is a dimensional analysis technique, based on a correlation developed from experimental data. However, the model is based only on data from flat rural terrain and is applicable only to these types of releases. The model is also unable to account for the effects of parameters such as release height, ground roughness, and wind speed profiles.

Example 5-1

On an overcast day a stack with an effective height of 60 m is releasing sulfur dioxide at the rate of 80 g/s. The wind speed is 6 m/s. The stack is located in a rural area. Determine

a. The mean concentration of SO_2 on the ground 500 m downwind.

b. The mean concentration on the ground 500 m downwind and 50 m crosswind.

c. The location and value of the maximum mean concentration on ground level directly downwind.

Solution

a. This is a continuous release. The ground concentration directly downwind is given by Equation 5-51:

$$\langle C\rangle(x,0,0)=\frac{Q_m}{\pi\sigma_y\sigma_z u}\exp\left[-\frac{1}{2}\left(\frac{H_r}{\sigma_z}\right)^2\right]. \tag{5-51}$$

From Table 5-1 the stability class is D.

The dispersion coefficients are obtained from either Figure 5-11 or Table 5-2. Using Table 5-2:

$$\sigma_y = 0.08x(1+0.0001x)^{-1/2}$$
$$= (0.08)(500\text{ m})[1+(0.0001)(500\text{ m})]^{-1/2} = 39.0\text{ m},$$
$$\sigma_z = 0.06x(1+0.0015x)^{-1/2}$$
$$= (0.06)(500\text{ m})[1+(0.0015)(500\text{ m})]^{-1/2} = 22.7\text{ m}.$$

Substituting into Equation 5-51, we obtain

$$\langle C\rangle(500\text{ m},0,0)=\frac{80\text{ g/s}}{(3.14)(39.0\text{ m})(22.7\text{ m})(6\text{ m/s})}\exp\left[-\frac{1}{2}\left(\frac{60\text{ m}}{22.7\text{ m}}\right)^2\right]$$
$$= 1.45\times10^{-4}\text{ g/m}^3.$$

b. The mean concentration 50 m crosswind is found by using Equation 5-50 and by setting $y = 50$. The results from part a are applied directly:

$$\langle C\rangle(500\text{ m},50\text{ m},0) = \langle C\rangle(500\text{ m},0,0)\exp\left[-\frac{1}{2}\left(\frac{y}{\sigma_y}\right)^2\right]$$
$$= (1.45\times10^{-4}\text{ g/m}^3)\exp\left[-\frac{1}{2}\left(\frac{50\text{ m}}{39\text{ m}}\right)^2\right]$$
$$= 6.37\times10^{-5}\text{ g/m}^3.$$

c. The location of the maximum concentration is found from Equation 5-53:

$$\sigma_z=\frac{H_r}{\sqrt{2}}=\frac{60\text{ m}}{\sqrt{2}}=42.4\text{ m}.$$

From Figure 5-10 for D stability, σ_z has this value at about 1200 m downwind. From Figure 5-10 or Table 5-2, $\sigma_y = 88$ m. The maximum concentration is determined using Equation 5-52:

$$\langle C\rangle_{\max}=\frac{2Q_m}{e\pi uH_r^2}\left(\frac{\sigma_z}{\sigma_y}\right)$$
$$=\frac{(2)(80\text{ g/s})}{(2.72)(3.14)(6\text{ m/s})(60\text{ m})^2}\left(\frac{42.4\text{ m}}{88\text{ m}}\right)$$
$$= 4.18\times10^{-4}\text{ g/m}^3. \tag{5-52}$$

Example 5-2

Chlorine is used in a particular chemical process. A source model study indicates that for a particular accident scenario 1.0 kg of chlorine will be released instantaneously. The release will occur at ground level. A residential area is 500 m away from the chlorine source. Determine

a. The time required for the center of the cloud to reach the residential area. Assume a wind speed of 2 m/s.

b. The maximum concentration of chlorine in the residential area. Compare this with an ERPG-1 for chlorine of 1.0 ppm. What stability conditions and wind speed produce the maximum concentration?

c. Determine the distance the cloud must travel to disperse the cloud to a maximum concentration below the ERPG-1. Use the conditions of part b.

d. Determine the size of the cloud, based on the ERPG-1, at a point 5 km directly downwind on the ground. Assume the conditions of part b.

Assume in all cases that the chlorine cloud released is neutrally buoyant (which might not be a valid assumption).

Solution

a. For a distance of 500 m and a wind speed of 2 m/s, the time required for the center of the cloud to reach the residential area is

$$t = \frac{x}{u} = \frac{500 \text{ m}}{2 \text{ m/s}} = 250 \text{ s} = 4.2 \text{ min.}$$

This leaves very little time for emergency warning.

b. The maximum concentration occurs at the center of the cloud directly downwind from the release. The concentration is given by Equation 5-41:

$$\langle C \rangle (ut, 0, 0, t) = \frac{Q_m^*}{\sqrt{2}\pi^{3/2}\sigma_x\sigma_y\sigma_z}. \tag{5-41}$$

The stability conditions are selected to maximize $\langle C \rangle$ in Equation 5-41. This requires dispersion coefficients of minimum value. From Figure 5-12 the lowest value of either dispersion coefficient occurs with F stability conditions. This is for nighttime conditions with thin to light overcast and a wind speed less than 3 m/s. The maximum concentration in the puff also occurs at the closest point to the release in the residential area. This occurs at a distance of 500 m. Thus

$$\sigma_x = \sigma_y = 0.02x^{0.89} = (0.02)(500 \text{ m})^{0.89} = 5.0 \text{ m},$$

$$\sigma_z = 0.05x^{0.61} = (0.05)(500 \text{ m})^{0.61} = 2.2 \text{ m}.$$

From Equation 5-41

$$\langle C \rangle = \frac{1.0 \text{ kg}}{\sqrt{2}(3.14)^{3/2}(5.0 \text{ m})^2(2.2 \text{ m})} = 2.31 \times 10^{-3} \text{ kg/m}^3 = 2310 \text{ mg/m}^3.$$

This is converted to ppm using Equation 2-6. Assuming a pressure of 1 atm and a temperature of 298 K, the concentration in ppm is 798 ppm. This is much higher than the ERPG-1 of 1.0 ppm. Any individuals within the immediate residential area and any personnel within the plant will be excessively exposed if they are outside and downwind from the source.

c. From Table 2-7 the ERPG-1 of 1.0 ppm is 3.0 mg/m³ or 3.0×10^{-6} kg/m³. The concentration at the center of the cloud is given by Equation 5-41. Substituting the known values, we obtain

$$3.0 \times 10^{-6} \text{ kg/m}^3 = \frac{1.0 \text{ kg}}{\sqrt{2}(3.14)^{3/2}\sigma_y^2\sigma_z},$$

$$\sigma_y^2\sigma_z = 4.24 \times 10^4 \text{ m}^3.$$

The distance downwind is solved using the equations provided in Table 5-3. Thus for F stability

$$\sigma_y^2\sigma_z = (0.02x^{0.89})^2(0.05x^{0.61}) = 4.24 \times 10^4 \text{ m}^3.$$

Solving for x by trial and error results in $x = 8.0$ km downwind.

d. The downwind centerline concentration is given by Equation 5-40:

$$\langle C \rangle(x, 0, 0, t) = \frac{Q_m^*}{\sqrt{2}\pi^{3/2}\sigma_x\sigma_y\sigma_z} \exp\left[-\frac{1}{2}\left(\frac{x - ut}{\sigma_x}\right)^2\right]. \tag{5-40}$$

The time required for the center of the plume to arrive is

$$t = \frac{x}{u} = \frac{5000 \text{ m}}{2 \text{ m/s}} = 2500 \text{ s}.$$

At a downwind distance of $x = 5$ km $= 5000$ m and assuming F stability conditions, we calculate

$$\sigma_x = \sigma_y = 0.02x^{0.89} = 39.2 \text{ m},$$

$$\sigma_z = 0.05x^{0.61} = 9.0 \text{ m}.$$

Substituting the numbers provided gives

$$3.0 \times 10^{-6} \text{ kg/m}^3 = \frac{1.0 \text{ kg}}{\sqrt{2}\pi^{3/2}(39.2 \text{ m})^2(9.0 \text{ m})} \exp\left[-\frac{1}{2}\left(\frac{x - 5000}{39.2 \text{ m}}\right)^2\right],$$

where x has units of meters. The quantity $(x - 5000)$ represents the width of the plume. Solving for this quantity, we obtain

$$0.326 = \exp\left[-\frac{1}{2}\left(\frac{x - 5000}{39.2\text{ m}}\right)^2\right],$$

$$x - 5000 = 58.7$$

The cloud is $2 \times 58.7 = 109.4$ m wide at this point, based on the ERPG-1 concentration. At 2 m/s it will take approximately

$$\frac{109.4\text{ m}}{2\text{ m/s}} = 58.7\text{ s}$$

to pass.

An appropriate emergency procedure would be to alert residents to stay indoors with the windows closed and ventilation off until the cloud passes. An effort by the plant to reduce the quantity of chlorine released is also indicated.

Example 5-3[11]

Compute the distance downwind from the following liquefied natural gas (LNG) release to obtain a concentration equal to the lower flammability limit (LFL) of 5% vapor concentration by volume. Assume ambient conditions of 298 K and 1 atm. The following data are available:

Spill rate of liquid: 0.23 m^3/s,
Spill duration (R_d): 174 s,
Wind speed at 10 m above ground (u): 10.9 m/s,
LNG density: 425.6 kg/m^3,
LNG vapor density at boiling point of −162°C: 1.76 kg/m^3.

Solution

The volumetric discharge rate is given by

$$q_o = (0.23\text{ m}^3\text{/s})(425.6\text{ kg/m}^3)/1.76\text{ kg/m}^3 = 55.6\text{ m}^3\text{/s}.$$

The ambient air density is computed from the ideal gas law and gives a result of 1.22 kg/m^3. Thus from Equation 5-59:

$$g_o = g\left(\frac{\rho_o - \rho_a}{\rho_a}\right) = (9.8\text{ m/s}^2)\left(\frac{1.76 - 1.22}{1.22}\right) = 4.34\text{ m/s}^2.$$

[11]Britter and McQuaid, *Workbook on the Dispersion of Dense Gases.*

Step 1. Determine whether the release is considered continuous or instantaneous. For this case Equation 5-64 applies, and the quantity must be greater than 2.5 for a continuous release. Substituting the required numbers gives

$$\frac{uR_d}{x} = \frac{(10.9 \text{ m/s})(174 \text{ s})}{x} \geq 2.5,$$

and it follows that for a continuous release

$$x \leq 758 \text{ m}.$$

The final distance must be less than this.

Step 2. Determine whether a dense cloud model applies. For this case Equations 5-60 and 5-62 apply. Substituting the appropriate numbers gives

$$D_c = \left(\frac{q_o}{u}\right)^{1/2} = \left(\frac{55.6 \text{ m}^3/\text{s}}{10.9 \text{ m/s}}\right)^{1/2} = 2.26 \text{ m},$$

$$\left(\frac{g_o q_o}{u^3 D_c}\right)^{1/3} = \left[\frac{(4.29 \text{ m/s}^2)(55.6 \text{ m}^3/\text{s})}{(10.9 \text{ m/s})^3(2.26 \text{ m})}\right]^{1/3} = 0.44 \geq 0.15,$$

and it is clear that the dense cloud model applies.

Step 3. Adjust the concentration for a nonisothermal release. The Britter-McQuaid model provides an adjustment to the concentration to account for nonisothermal release of the vapor. If the original concentration is C^*, then the effective concentration is given by

$$C = \frac{C^*}{C^* + (1 - C^*)(T_a/T_o)},$$

where T_a is the ambient temperature and T_o is the source temperature, both in absolute temperature. For our required concentration of 0.05, the equation for C gives an effective concentration of 0.019.

Step 4. Compute the dimensionless groups for Figure 5-13:

$$\left(\frac{g_o^2 q_o}{u^5}\right)^{1/5} = \left[\frac{(4.34 \text{ m/s}^2)^2(55.6 \text{ m}^3/\text{s})}{(10.9 \text{ m/s})^5}\right]^{1/5} = 0.369$$

and

$$\left(\frac{q_o}{u}\right)^{1/2} = \left(\frac{55.6 \text{ m}^3/\text{s}}{10.9 \text{ m/s}}\right)^{1/2} = 2.26 \text{ m}.$$

Step 5. Apply Figure 5-13 to determine the downwind distance. The initial concentration of gas C_o is essentially pure LNG. Thus $C_o = 1.0$, and it follows that $C_m/C_o = 0.019$. From Figure 5-13,

$$\frac{x}{\left(\frac{q_o}{u}\right)^{1/2}} = 126,$$

and it follows that $x = (2.26 \text{ m})(126) = 285$ m. This compares to an experimentally determined distance of 200 m. This demonstrates that dense gas dispersion estimates can easily be off by a factor of 2.

5-4 Dense Gas Transition to Neutrally Buoyant Gas

As shown in Figure 5-15, as a dense gas moves downstream the concentration decreases. At the transition x_t it becomes a neutrally buoyant gas. In the dense gas region the downstream concentration is computed using the methods in Section 5-3. After the transition, the compositions are computed using the neutrally buoyant equations for ground-level releases; see cases 11 and 12 in Section 5-2 on neutrally buoyant dispersion models. As shown in Figure 5-15, these neutrally buoyant gas compositions are computed from a point that is upwind of the transition. The methods for determining the virtual distance x_v and the downwind compositions are described in this section.

Continuous Release Transition

To locate the transition point x_t for a continuous release, Equation 5-62 is modified to include the local properties.[12,13] The local properties are shown below:

$$\rho_x = \rho_0\left(\frac{C_x}{C_0}\right) + \rho_a\left(1 - \frac{C_x}{C_0}\right), \tag{5-65}$$

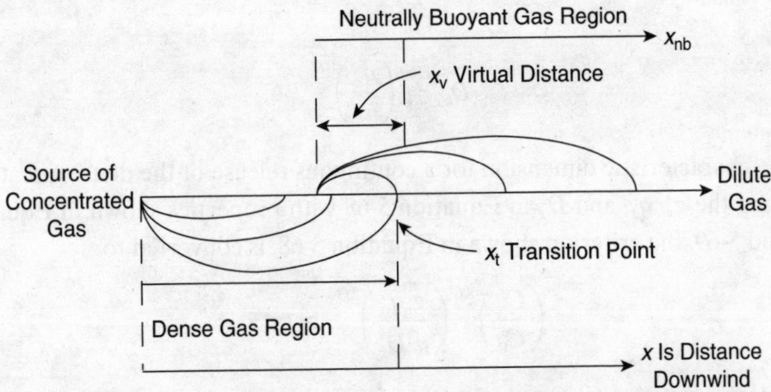

Figure 5-15 Sketch describing the transition from dense gas to neutrally buoyant gas.

[12]Hanna and Drivas, *Guidelines for Use of Vapor Cloud Dispersion Models.*

[13]J. A. Havens and T. O. Spicer, *Development of an Atmospheric Dispersion Model for Heavier than Air Gas Mixtures*, USCG Report CG D 22 85 (Washington, DC: United States Coast Guard Headquarters, 1985).

$$g_x = g\left(\frac{\rho_x - \rho_a}{\rho_a}\right) = g\left(\frac{C_x}{C_0}\right)\left(\frac{\rho_0 - \rho_a}{\rho_a}\right), \tag{5-66}$$

where

C_x is the concentration at x downwind from the source (mass/volume),
C_0 is the concentration at the source (mass/volume),
ρ_x is the density at x downwind from the source (mass/volume), and
g_x is the buoyancy factor at x (length/time^2).

Since the dense gas dispersions are based on the original volumes being diluted with entrained air, there is a simple material balance relationship between the concentrations and flows as shown in Equation 5-67:

$$q_x C_x = q_0 C_0, \tag{5-67}$$

where q_x is the plume volume flux at x (volume/time).

To determine the transition point, the criterion shown in Equation 5-62 is converted to local conditions as shown in Equation 5-68:

$$\left(\frac{g_x q_x}{u^3 D_{cx}}\right)^{1/3} \geq 0.15, \tag{5-68}$$

where

$$D_{cx} = \left(\frac{q_x}{u}\right)^{1/2} \tag{5-69}$$

and D_{cx} is the characteristic dimension for a continuous release of the dense gas at x (length). After replacing the g_x, q_x, and D_x in Equation 5-68 with properties shown in Equations 5-65, 5-66, 5-67, and 5-69, the criterion shown in Equation 5-68, is converted to

$$\left(\frac{C_x}{C_0}\right)^{1/6}\left(\frac{g_0 q_0}{u^3 D_c}\right)^{1/3} \geq 0.15. \tag{5-70}$$

The concentration ratio C_x/C_0 at the transition (dense to neutrally buoyant gas) is determined at the transition by converting the inequality in Equation 5-70 to an equality sign. The transition x_t is then determined using Figure 5-13; that is, it is determined at the value of the ordinate corresponding to the intersection of the known abscissa and C_x/C_0.

Continuous Release Downwind Concentration

If the concentration is desired in the dense gas region (see Figure 5-15), then the dense gas calculations are made using the methods shown in Section 5-3. If the concentration is desired in the neutrally buoyant region (at a distance downwind of the transition), the neutrally buoyant models are used for a ground-level release (see Section 5-2). The ground-level release is used because all heavy gas releases, even from stacks, slump to the ground.

As shown in Figure 5-15, the neutrally buoyant calculations are made from a position upwind from the transition, at a distance x_v (virtual distance) that gives the neutrally buoyant concentration the same as the dense gas concentration at the transition.

The virtual distance x_v is determined using Equation 5-71, where the concentration at the transition is C_x. In this equation, the only unknown is x_v which is in both dispersion coefficients taken from Table 5-2.

$$\sigma_y \sigma_z = \frac{q_0}{C_x \pi u} \tag{5-71}$$

The composition at any distance x from the source is subsequently computed using the neutrally buoyant equations for continuous ground-level releases as shown in case 12 (Section 5-2). But the downwind distance for the dispersion coefficients is x_{nb} as shown in Figure 5-15. Equation 5-72 shows the relationship between the various distances:

$$x_{nb} = x - x_t + x_v, \tag{5-72}$$

where

x is the distance from the source (length),
x_t is the distance from the source to the transition (length),
x_v is the virtual distance (length), and
x_{nb} is the distance used in the neutrally buoyant model to compute the concentration downwind of the transition.

Instantaneous Release Transition

The equation for the dense gas criterion for a puff model is derived using Equations 5-65, 5-66, and the material balance equation (Equation 5-73):

$$V_x C_x = V_0 C_0, \tag{5-73}$$

where V_x is the volume of gas at x (length^3).

The criterion for any location is

$$\frac{\sqrt{g_x V_x}}{u D_{xi}} \geq 0.20, \tag{5-74}$$

where

$$D_{xi} = (V_x)^{1/3} \tag{5-75}$$

and D_{xi} is the characteristic dimension for an instantaneous release of dense gas at x (length). After replacing the g_x, q_x, and D_{xi} in Equation 5-74 with properties shown in Equations 5-65, 5-66, 5-73, and 5-75, the criterion (Equation 5-74) is converted to Equation 5-76.

$$\left(\frac{C_x}{C_0}\right)^{1/3}\left(\frac{\sqrt{g_0 V_0}}{u V_0^{1/3}}\right) \geq 0.20. \tag{5-76}$$

The concentration ratio C_x/C_0 at the transition (dense to neutrally buoyant gas) is determined by converting the inequality in Equation 5-76 to an equality sign. The transition x_t is then determined with Figure 5-14.

Instantaneous Release Downwind Composition

The virtual distance x_v is determined using Equation 5-77 where the concentration at the transition is C_x. In this equation the only unknown is x_v, which is determined with x that gives the left-hand side equal to the right-hand side. The appropriate dispersion coefficients are taken from Table 5-3. The virtual distance x_v can then computed:

$$\sigma_x \sigma_y \sigma_z = \frac{V_0}{C_x \sqrt{2}\pi^{3/2}}. \tag{5-77}$$

The composition at any distance x from the source is computed with the neutrally buoyant equations for ground-level puff releases as shown in case 11 (Section 5-2). But the downwind distance in the dispersion coefficients is x_{nb} as shown in Figure 5-15. Equation 5-72 shows the relationship between the various distances.

Example 5-4

A gas is continuously released from a stack that is 25 m high. Determine the centerline concentration ($y = 0$) for this gas at a distance of 100 m from the source in a rural environment. The following conditions are specified:

Release rate: 100 g/s,
Molecular weight of gas: 50 g/g mole,
Temperature and pressure: 25°C and 1 atm,
Wind speed and weather conditions: 4 m/s and overcast day.

Solution

Step 1. Determine whether this gas is dense.

The density of the gas at the source is

$$\rho = \frac{P \times MW}{82.057 \times (Temp + 273)} = \frac{1 \times 50}{82.057 \times (25 + 273)} = 2.045 \times 10^{-3} \text{ g/cm}^3,$$

and the air density is 1.186×10^{-3} g/cm^3.

The volumetric discharge rate is given by

$$q_0 = \frac{(release\_rate)}{\rho \times 10^6} = \frac{100}{2.045 \times 10^{-3} \times 10^6} = 0.049 \text{ m}^3/\text{s},$$

and the initial buoyancy factor is

$$g_0 = g\left(\frac{\rho - \rho_a}{\rho_a}\right) = 9.8 \text{ m/s}^2 \left[\frac{2.045 \times 10^{-3} - 1.186 \times 10^{-3}}{1.186 \times 10^{-3}}\right] = 7.097 \text{ m/s}^2.$$

D_c is computed using Equation 5-60:

$$D_c = \left(\frac{q_0}{u}\right)^{1/2} = \left(\frac{0.049}{4}\right)^{1/2} = 0.1 \text{ m}$$

$$\left(\frac{g_0 q_0}{u^3 D_c}\right)^{1/3} = \left(\frac{7.097}{4^3 \times 0.1}\right)^{1/3} = 0.366 \text{ which is greater than } 0.15.$$

Therefore, this is a dense gas.

Step 2. Determine the point downwind where the gas goes from a dense to a neutrally buoyant gas. The concentration ratio at the transition is determined using Equation 5-70:

$$\left(\frac{C_x}{C_0}\right)^{1/6}\left(\frac{g_0 q_0}{u^3 D_c}\right)^{1/3} = 0.15$$

$$\left(\frac{C_x}{C_0}\right) = \left(\frac{0.15}{0.366}\right)^6 = 4.74 \times 10^{-3}.$$

The concentration at the transition is therefore

$$C = 4.74 \times 10^{-3} \times \rho = 4.7 \times 10^{-3} \times 2.045 \times 10^3 = 9.6 \text{ g/m}^3.$$

The transition point x_t is determined using Figure 5-13 in a three-step process: (1) compute the abscissa, (2) find the magnitude of the ordinate from Figure 5-13 that is at the intersection of the abscissa and the concentration ratio, and (3) use this magnitude of the ordinate to compute x_t.

$$\text{The abscissa is } \left(\frac{g_0^2 q_0}{u^5}\right)^{1/5} = 0.299.$$

The intersection of this abscissa and the concentration ratio corresponds to an ordinate in Figure 5-13 of 340. This is used to compute the x_t as shown below:

$$\frac{x_t}{(q_0/u)^{1/2}} = 340$$

$$x_t = 340 \times (0.049/4)^{1/2} = 37.6 \text{ m}.$$

This is the point downwind where the gas goes from dense to neutrally buoyant. Since the problem requests a composition at 100 m and it is downwind of the transition, the virtual distance is required.

Step 3. Determine the virtual distance using Equation 5-71.
In this problem the atmospheric stability class is D for the wind speed of 4 m/s, an overcast day, and a rural environment as noted in Table 5-1 and footnote 6. Therefore the dispersion coefficients are

$$\sigma_y = 0.08 \times x_v (1 + 0.0001 \times x_v)^{-1/2},$$

$$\sigma_z = 0.06 \times x_v (1 + 0.0015 \times x_v)^{-1/2},$$

and x_v is determined as shown below:

$$\sigma_y \sigma_z = \frac{q_0}{C_x \pi u}$$

$$0.08 \times x_v (1 + 0.0001 \times x_v)^{-1/2} \times 0.06 \times x_v (1 + 0.0015 \times x_v)^{-1/2} = \frac{0.049}{9.6 \times \pi \times 4}.$$

Therefore

$$x_v = 13.2 \text{ m}.$$

Step 4. Determine the composition at $x = 100$ m.
The composition downwind of the transition at 100 m is computed using Equation 5-48. The distance used to compute this composition is

$$x_{nb} = x - x_t - x_v$$

$$x_{nb} = x - x_t + x_v = 100 - 37.6 + 13.2 = 75.6 \text{ m}.$$

The result using Equation 5-71 is

$$0.08 \times x_{nb} (1 + 0.0001 \times x_{nb})^{-1/2} \times 0.06 \times x_{nb} (1 + 0.0015 \times x_{nb})^{-1/2} = \frac{0.049}{C \times \pi \times 4},$$

or

$$C = 0.31 \text{ g/m}^3.$$

In summary, the compositions at each location are:
At the source: $C = 2045 \text{ g/m}^3$.
At the transition (37.5 m): $C = 9.6 \text{ g/m}^3$.
At 100 m downstream from the source: $C = 0.31 \text{ g/m}^3$.

5-5 Toxic Effect Criteria

Once the dispersion calculations are completed, the question arises: What concentration is considered dangerous? Concentrations based on TLV-TWA values, discussed in Chapter 2, are overly conservative and are designed for worker exposures, not short-term exposures under emergency conditions.

One approach is to use the probit models developed in Chapter 2. These models are also capable of including the effects resulting from transient changes in toxic concentrations. Unfortunately, published correlations are available for only a few chemicals, and the data show wide variations from the correlations.

One simplified approach is to specify a toxic concentration criterion above which it is assumed that individuals exposed to this value will be in danger. This approach has led to many criteria promulgated by several government agencies and private associations. Some of these criteria and methods include

- Emergency response planning guidelines (ERPGs) for air contaminants issued by the American Industrial Hygiene Association (AIHA)
- IDLH levels established by NIOSH
- Emergency exposure guidance levels (EEGLs) and short-term public emergency guidance levels (SPEGLs) issued by the National Academy of Sciences/National Research Council
- TLVs established by the ACGIH, including short-term exposure limits (TLV-STELs) and ceiling concentrations (TLV-Cs)
- PELs promulgated by OSHA
- Toxicity dispersion (TXDS) methods used by the New Jersey Department of Environmental Protection
- Toxic endpoints promulgated by the EPA as part of the RMP

These criteria and methods are based on a combination of results from animal experiments, observations of long- and short-term human exposures, and expert judgment. The following paragraphs define these criteria and describe some of their features.

ERPGs are prepared by an industry task force and are published by the AIHA. Three concentration ranges are provided as a consequence of exposure to a specific substance:

1. ERPG-1 is the maximum airborne concentration below which it is believed nearly all individuals could be exposed for up to 1 hr without experiencing effects other than mild transient adverse health effects or perceiving a clearly defined objectionable odor.
2. ERPG-2 is the maximum airborne concentration below which it is believed nearly all individuals could be exposed for up to 1 hr without experiencing or developing irreversible or other serious health effects or symptoms that could impair their abilities to take protective action.
3. ERPG-3 is the maximum airborne concentration below which it is believed nearly all individuals could be exposed for up to 1 hr without experiencing or developing life-threatening health effects (similar to EEGLs).

ERPG data are shown in Table 5-6. To date, 47 ERPGs have been developed and are being reviewed, updated, and expanded by an AIHA peer review task force. Because of the comprehensive effort to develop acute toxicity values, ERPGs are becoming an acceptable industry/government norm.

Table 5-6 Emergency Response Planning Guidelines (ERPGs)[a] (all values are in ppm unless otherwise noted)

Chemical	ERPG-1	ERPG-2	ERPG-3
Acetaldehyde	10	200	1000
Acetic acid	5	35	250
Acetic anhydride	0.5	15	100
Acrolein	0.05	0.15	1.5
Acrylic acid	1.0	50	250
Acrylonitrile	10	35	75
Allyl chloride	3	40	300
Ammonia	25	150	750
Benzene	50	150	1000
Benzyl chloride	1	10	50
Beryllium	NA	25 μg/m^3	100 μg/m^3
Bromine	0.1	0.5	5
1,3-Butadiene	10	200	5000
n-Butyl acrylate	0.05	25	250
n-Butyl isocyanate	0.01	0.05	1
Carbon disulfide	1	50	500
Carbon monoxide	200	350	500
Carbon tetrachloride	20	100	750
Chlorine	1	3	20

Table 5-6 *(continued)*

Chemical	ERPG-1	ERPG-2	ERPG-3
Chlorine trifluoride	0.1	1	10
Chloroacetyl chloride	0.05	0.5	10
Chloroform	NA	50	5000
Chloropicrin	0.1	0.3	1.5
Chlorosulfonic acid	2 mg/m^3	10 mg/m^3	30 mg/m^3
Chlorotrifluoroethylene	20	100	300
Crotonaldehyde	0.2	1	3
Diborane	NA	1	3
1, 2-Dichloroethane	50	200	300
Diketene	1	5	20
Dimethylamine	0.6	100	350
Dimethyldichlorosilane	2	10	75
Dimethyl disulfide	0.01	50	250
Epichlorohydrin	5	20	100
Ethanol	1800	3300	NA
Ethyl chloroformate	ID	100	200
Ethylene oxide	NA	50	500
Florine	0.5	5	20
Formaldehyde	1	10	25
Formic acid	3	25	250
Gasoline	200	1000	4000
Hexachlorobutadiene	1	3	10
Hexafluoroacetone	NA	1	50
Hexafluoropropylene	10	50	500
Hydrogen chloride	3	20	150
Hydrogen cyanide	NA	10	25
Hydrogen fluoride	2	20	50
Hydrogen peroxide	10	50	100
Hydrogen sulfide	0.1	30	100
Isobutyronitrile	10	50	200
2-Isocyanatoethyl methacrylate	ID	0.1	1
Lithium hydride	25 μg/m^3	100 μg/m^3	500 μg/m^3
Methanol	200	1,000	5,000
Methyl chloride	NA	400	1000
Methylene diphenyl diisocynate	0.2 mg/m^3	2 mg/m^3	25 mg/m^3
Methyl isocyanate	0.025	0.25	1.5
Methyl mercaptan	0.005	25	100
Methyltrichlorosilane	0.5	3	15
Monomethylamine	10	100	500
Nitrogen dioxide	1	15	30
Perfluoroisobutylene	NA	0.1	0.3
Phenol	10	50	200

(continues)

Table 5-6 *(continued)*

Chemical	ERPG-1	ERPG-2	ERPG-3
Phosgene	NA	0.5	1.5
Phosphorus pentoxide	1 mg/m^3	10 mg/m^3	50 mg/m^3
Propylene oxide	50	250	750
Styrene	50	250	1,000
Sulfonic acid (oleum, sulfur trioxide, and sulfuric acid)	2 mg/m^3	10 mg/m^3	120 mg/m^3
Sulfur dioxide	0.3	3	15
Tetrafluoroethylene	200	1000	10,000
Titanium tetrachloride	5 mg/m^3	20 mg/m^3	100 mg/m^3
Toluene	50	300	1000
Trimethylamine	0.1	100	500
Uranium hexafluoride	5 mg/m^3	15 mg/m^3	30 mg/m^3
Vinyl acetate	5	75	500
Vinyl chloride	500	5000	20,000

Notes: NA = Not approprate
ID = Insufficient data
[a]AIHA, *Emergency Response Planning Guidelines and Workplace Environmental Exposure Levels* (Fairfax, VA: American Industrial Hygiene Association, 2010) and *www.aiha.org.*

NIOSH publishes IDLH concentrations to be used as acute toxicity measures for common industrial gases. An IDLH exposure condition is defined as a condition "that poses a threat of exposure to airborne contaminants when that exposure is likely to cause death or immediate or delayed permanent adverse health effects or prevent escape from such an environment."[14] IDLH values also take into consideration acute toxic reactions, such as severe eye irritation, that could prevent escape. The IDLH level is considered a maximum concentration above which only a highly reliable breathing apparatus providing maximum worker protection is permitted. If IDLH values are exceeded, all unprotected workers must leave the area immediately.

IDLH data are currently available for 380 materials. Because IDLH values were developed to protect healthy worker populations, they must be adjusted for sensitive populations, such as older, disabled, or ill populations. For flammable vapors the IDLH concentration is defined as one-tenth of the lower flammability limit (LFL) concentration. Also note that IDLH levels have not been peer-reviewed and that no substantive documentation for the values exists.

Since the 1940s, the National Research Council's Committee on Toxicology has submitted EEGLs for 44 chemicals of special concern to the Department of Defense. An EEGL is defined as a concentration of a gas, vapor, or aerosol that is judged acceptable and that allows exposed individuals to perform specific tasks during emergency conditions lasting from 1 to 24 hr. Exposure to concentrations at the EEGL may produce transient irritation or central nervous system effects but should not produce effects that are lasting or that would impair performance

[14]NIOSH, *NIOSH Pocket Guide to Chemical Hazards* (Washington, DC: US Department of Health and Human Services, 2005).

of a task. In addition to EEGLs, the National Research Council has developed SPEGLs, defined as acceptable concentrations for exposures of members of the general public. SPEGLs are generally set at 10–50% of the EEGL and are calculated to take account of the effects of exposure on sensitive heterogeneous populations. The advantages of using EEGLs and SPEGLs rather than IDLH values are (1) a SPEGL considers effects on sensitive populations, (2) EEGLs and SPEGLs are developed for several different exposure durations, and (3) the methods by which EEGLs and SPEGLs were developed are well documented in National Research Council publications. EEGL and SPEGL values are shown in Table 5-7.

Certain (ACGIH) criteria may be appropriate for use as benchmarks. The ACGIH threshold limit values— TLV-STELs and TLV-Cs— are designed to protect workers from acute effects resulting from exposure to chemicals; such effects include irritation and narcosis. These criteria are discussed in Chapter 2. These criteria can be used for toxic gas dispersion but typically produce a conservative result because they are designed for worker exposures.

The PELs are promulgated by OSHA and have force of law. These levels are similar to the ACGIH criteria for TLV-TWAs because they are also based on 8-hr time-weighted average exposures. OSHA-cited "acceptable ceiling concentrations," "excursion limits," or "action levels" may be appropriate for use as benchmarks.

The New Jersey Department of Environmental Protection uses the TXDS method of consequence analysis to estimate potentially catastrophic quantities of toxic substances, as required by the New Jersey Toxic Catastrophe Prevention Act (TCPA). An acute toxic concentration (ATC) is defined as the concentration of a gas or vapor of a toxic substance that will result in acute health effects in the affected population and 1 fatality out of 20 or less (5% or more) during a 1-hr exposure. ATC values, as proposed by the New Jersey Department of Environmental Protection, are estimated for 103 "extraordinarily hazardous substances" and are based on the lowest value of one of the following: (1) the lowest reported lethal concentration (LCLO) value for animal test data, (2) the median lethal concentration (LC50) value from animal test data multiplied by 0.1, or (3) the IDLH value.

The EPA has promulgated a set of toxic endpoints to be used for air dispersion modeling for toxic gas releases as part of the EPA RMP.[15] The toxic endpoint is, in order of preference, (1) the ERPG-2 or (2) the level of concern (LOC) promulgated by the Emergency Planning and Community Right-to-Know Act. The LOC is considered "the maximum concentration of an extremely hazardous substance in air that will not cause serious irreversible health effects in the general population when exposed to the substance for relatively short duration." Toxic endpoints are provided for 74 chemicals under the RMP rule and are shown in Table 5-8.

In general, the most directly relevant toxicologic criteria currently available, particularly for developing emergency response plans, are ERPGs, SPEGLs, and EEGLs. These were developed specifically to apply to general populations and to account for sensitive populations and scientific uncertainty in toxicologic data. For incidents involving substances for which no SPEGLs or EEGLs are available, IDLH levels provide alternative criteria. However, because

[15]EPA, *RMP Offsite Consequence Analysis Guidance* (Washington, DC: US Environmental Protection Agency, 1996).

Table 5-7 Emergency Exposure Guidance Levels (EEGLs) from the National Research Council (NRC) (all values are in ppm unless otherwise noted)

Compound	1-hr EEGL	24-hr EEGL	Source
Acetone	8500	1000	NRC I
Acrolein	0.05	0.01	NRC I
Aluminum oxide	15 mg/m^3	100	NRC IV
Ammonia	100		NRC VII
Arsine	1	0.1	NRC I
Benzene	50	2	NRC VI
Bromotrifluoromethane	25,000		NRC III
Carbon disulfide	50		NRC I
Carbon monoxide	400	50	NRC IV
Chlorine	3	0.5	NRC II
Chlorine trifluoride	1		NRC II
Chloroform	100	30	NRC I
Dichlorodifluoromethane	10,000	1000	NRC II
Dichlorofluoromethane	100	3	NRC II
Dichlorotetrafluoroethane	10,000	1000	NRC II
1,1-Dimethylhydrazine	0.24[a]	0.01[a]	NRC V
Ethanolamine	50	3	NRC II
Ethylene glycol	40	20	NRC IV
Ethylene oxide	20	1	NRC VI
Fluorine	7.5		NRC I
Hydrazine	0.12[a]	0.005[a]	NRC V
Hydrogen chloride	20/1[a]	20/1[a]	NRC VII
Hydrogen sulfide		10	NRC IV
Isopropyl alcohol	400	200	NRC II
Lithium bromide	15 mg/m^3	7 mg/m^3	NRC VII
Lithium chromate	100 μg/m^3	50 μg/m^3	NRC VIII
Mercury (vapor)		0.2 mg/m^3	NRC I
Methane		5000	NRC I
Methanol	200	10	NRC IV
Methylhydrazine	0.24[a]	0.01[a]	NRC V
Nitrogen dioxide	1[a]	0.04[a]	NRC IV
Nitrous oxide	10,000		NRC IV
Ozone	1	0.1	NRC I
Phosgene	0.2	0.02	NRC II
Sodium hydroxide	2 mg/m^3		NRC II
Sulfur dioxide	10	5	NRC II
Sulfuric acid	1 mg/m^3		NRC I
Toluene	200	100	NRC VII
Trichloroethylene	200 ppm	10 ppm	NRC VIII
Trichlorofluoromethane	1500	500	NRC II
Trichlorotrifluoroethane	1500	500	NRC II
Vinylidene chloride		10	NRC II
Xylene	200	100	NRC II

[a]SPEGL value.

Table 5-8 Toxic Endpoints Specified by the EPA Risk Management Plan[a]

Chemical name	Toxic endpoint (mg/L)
Gases	
Ammonia (anhydrous)	0.14
Arsine	0.0019
Boron trichloride	0.010
Boron trifluoride	0.028
Chlorine	0.0087
Chlorine dioxide	0.0028
Cyanogen chloride	0.030
Diborane	0.0011
Ethylene oxide	0.090
Fluorine	0.0039
Formaldehyde (anhydrous)	0.012
Hydrocyanic acid	0.011
Hydrogen chloride (anhydrous)	0.030
Hydrogen fluoride (anhydrous)	0.016
Hydrogen selenide	0.00066
Hydrogen sulfide	0.042
Methyl chloride	0.82
Methyl mercaptan	0.049
Nitric oxide	0.031
Phosgene	0.00081
Phosphine	0.0035
Sulfur dioxide (anhydrous)	0.0078
Sulfur tetrafluoride	0.0092
Liquids	
Acrolein	0.0011
Acrylonitrile	0.076
Acrylyl chloride	0.00090
Allyl alcohol	0.036
Allylamine	0.0032
Arsenuous trichloride	0.01
Boron trifluoride compound with methyl ether (1:1)	0.023
Bromine	0.0065
Carbon disulfide	0.16
Chloroform	0.49
Chloromethyl ether	0.00025
Chloromethyl methyl ether	0.0018
Crotonaldehyde	0.029
Liquids (*continued*)	
Cyclohexylamine	0.16
Dimethyldichlorosilane	0.026
1,1-Dimethylhydrazine	0.012
Epichlorohydrin	0.076
Ethylenediamine	0.49
Ethyleneimine	0.018
Furan	0.0012
Hydrazine	0.011
Iron, pentacarbonyl-	0.00044
Isobutyronitrile	0.14
Isopropyl chloroformate	0.10
Methacrylonitrile	0.0027
Methyl chloroformate	0.0019
Methyl hydrazine	0.0094
Methyl isocyanate	0.0012
Methyl thiocyanate	0.085
Methyltrichlorosilane	0.018
Nickel carbonyl	0.00067
Nitric acid (100%)	0.026
Peracetic acid	0.0045
Perchloromethylmercaptan	0.0076
Phosphorus oxychloride	0.0030
Phosphorus trichloride	0.028
Piperidine	0.022
Propionitrile	0.0037
Propyl chloroformate	0.010
Propyleneimine	0.12
Propylene oxide	0.59
Sulfur trioxide	0.010
Tetramethyllead	0.0040
Tetranitromethane	0.0040
Titanium tetrachloride	0.020
Toluene 2,4-diisocyanate	0.0070
Toluene 2,6-diisocyanate	0.0070
Toluene diisocyanate (unspecified)	0.0070
Trimethylchlorosilane	0.050
Vinyl acetate monomer	0.26

[a]EPA, *RMP Offsite Consequence Analysis Guidance* (Washington, DC: US Environmental Protection Agency, 1996).

Table 5-9 Recommended Hierarchy of Alternative Concentration Guidelines[a]

Primary guideline	Hierarchy of alternative guidelines	Source
ERPG-1		AIHA
	EEGL (30-min)	NRC
	IDLH	NIOSH
ERPG-2		AIHA
	EEGL (60 min)	NRC
	LOC	EPA/FEMA/DOT
	PEL-C	OSHA
	TLV-C	ACGIH
	5 × TLV-TWA	ACGIH
ERPG-3		AIHA
	PEL-STEL	OSHA
	TLV-STEL	ACGIH
	3 × TLV-TWA	ACGIH

AIHA: American Industrial Hygiene Association
NIOSH: National Institute for Occupational Safety and Health
NRC: National Research Council Committee on Toxicology
EPA: Environmental Protection Agency
FEMA: Federal Emergency Management Agency
DOT: US Department of Transportation
OSHA: US Occupational Safety and Health Administration
ACGIH: American Conference of Governmental Industrial Hygienists
[a]D. K. Craig, J. S. Davis, R. DeVore, D. J. Hansen, A. J. Petrocchi, and T. J. Powell, "Alternative Guideline Limits for Chemicals without Environmental Response Planning Guidelines," *AIHA Journal* (1995), 56.

IDLH levels were not developed to account for sensitive populations and because they were based on a maximum 30-min exposure period, the EPA suggests that the identification of an effect zone should be based on exposure levels of one-tenth the IDLH level. For example, the IDLH level for chlorine dioxide is 5 ppm. Effect zones resulting from the release of this gas are defined as any zone in which the concentration of chlorine dioxide is estimated to exceed 0.5 ppm. Of course, the approach is conservative and gives unrealistic results; a more realistic approach is to use a constant-dose assumption for releases less than 30 min using the IDLH level.

The use of TLV-STELs and ceiling limits may be most appropriate if the objective is to identify effect zones in which the primary concerns include more transient effects, such as sensory irritation or odor perception. In general, persons located outside the zone that is based on these limits can be assumed to be unaffected by the release.

Craig et al.[16] provided a hierarchy of alternative concentration guidelines in the event that ERPG data are not available. This hierarchy is shown in Table 5-9.

[16]D. K. Craig, J. S. Davis, R. DeVore, D. J. Hansen, A. J. Petrocchi, and T. J. Powell, "Alternative Guideline Limits for Chemicals without Environmental Response Planning Guidelines," *AIHA Journal* (1995), 56.

These methods may result in some inconsistencies because the different methods are based on different concepts. Good judgment should prevail.

5-6 Effect of Release Momentum and Buoyancy

Figure 5-6 indicates that the release characteristics of a puff or plume depend on the initial release momentum and buoyancy. The initial momentum and buoyancy change the effective height of release. A release that occurs at ground level but in an upward spouting jet of vaporizing liquid has a greater effective height than a release without a jet. Similarly, a release of vapor at a temperature higher than the ambient air temperature will rise because of buoyancy effects, increasing the effective height of the release.

Both effects are demonstrated by the traditional smokestack release shown in Figure 5-16. The material released from the smokestack contains momentum, based on its upward velocity within the stack pipe, and it is also buoyant, because its temperature is higher than the ambient temperature. Thus the material continues to rise after its release from the stack. The upward rise is slowed and eventually stopped as the released material cools and the momentum is dissipated.

For smokestack releases Turner[17] suggested using the empirical Holland formula to compute the additional height resulting from the buoyancy and momentum of the release:

$$\Delta H_r = \frac{\bar{u}_s d}{\bar{u}}\left[1.5 + 2.68 \times 10^{-3} P d\left(\frac{T_s - T_a}{T_s}\right)\right], \tag{5-65}$$

where

ΔH_r is the correction to the release height H_r,
$\bar{u}_s$ is the stack gas exit velocity (in m/s),

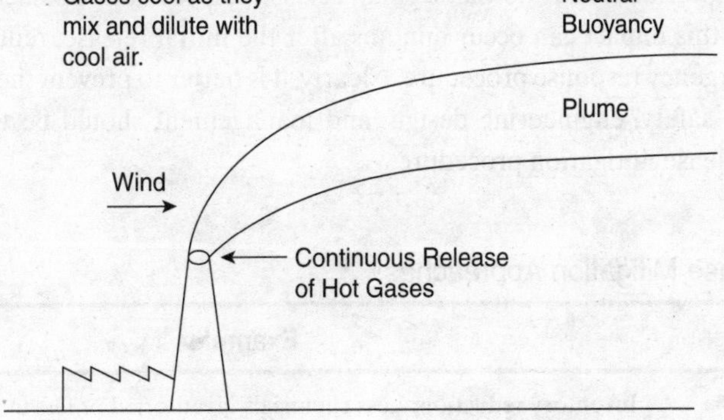

Figure 5-16 Smokestack plume demonstrating initial buoyant rise of hot gases.

[17] D. Bruce Turner, *Workbook of Atmospheric Dispersion Estimates* (Cincinnati: US Department of Health, Education, and Welfare, 1970), p. 31.

d is the inside stack diameter (in m),
$\bar{u}$ is the wind speed (in m/s),
P is the atmospheric pressure (in mb),
T_s is the stack gas temperature (in K), and
T_a is the air temperature (in K).

For heavier-than-air vapors, if the material is released above ground level, then the material will initially fall toward the ground until it disperses enough to reduce the cloud density.

5-7 Release Mitigation

The purpose of the toxic release model is to provide a tool for performing release mitigation. Release mitigation is defined as "lessening the risk of a release incident by acting on the source (at the point of release) either (1) in a preventive way by reducing the likelihood of an event that could generate a hazardous vapor cloud or (2) in a protective way by reducing the magnitude of the release and/or the exposure of local persons or property."[18]

The release mitigation procedure is part of the consequence modeling procedure shown in Figure 4-1. After selection of a release incident, a source model is used to determine either the release rate or the total quantity released. This is coupled to a dispersion model and subsequent models for fires or explosions. Finally, an effect model is used to estimate the impact of the release, which is a measure of the consequence.

Risk is composed of both consequence and probability. Thus an estimate of the consequences of a release provides only half the total risk assessment. It is possible that a particular release incident might have high consequences, leading to extensive plant mitigation efforts to reduce the consequence. However, if the probability is low, the effort might not be required. Both the consequence and the probability must be included to assess risk.

Table 5-10 contains a number of measures to mitigate a release. The example problems presented in this chapter demonstrate that a small release can result in significant downwind impact. In addition, this impact can occur minutes after the initial release, reducing the time available for an emergency response procedure. Clearly, it is better to prevent the release in the first place. Inherent safety, engineering design, and management should be the first issues considered in any release mitigation procedure.

Table 5-10 Release Mitigation Approaches[a]

Major area	Examples
Inherent safety	Inventory reduction: Less chemicals inventoried or less in process vessels Chemical substitution: Substitute a less hazardous chemical for one more hazardous Process attentuation: Use lower temperatures and pressures

Table 5-10 (*continued*)

Major area	Examples
Engineering design	Plant physical integrity: Use better seals or materials of construction Process integrity: Ensure proper operating conditions and material purity Process design features for emergency control: Emergency relief systems Spill containment: Dikes and spill vessels
Management	Operating policies and procedures Training for vapor release prevention and control Audits and inspections Equipment testing Maintenance program Management of modifications and changes to prevent new hazards Security
Early vapor detection and warning	Detection by sensors Detection by personnel
Countermeasures	Water sprays Water curtains Steam curtains Air curtains Deliberate ignition of explosive cloud Dilution Foams
Emergency response	On-site communications Emergency shutdown equipment and procedures Site evacuation Safe havens Personal protective equipment Medical treatment On-site emergency plans, procedures, training, and drills

[a]Richard W. Prugh and Robert W. Johnson, *Guidelines for Vapor Release Mitigation* (New York: American Institute of Chemical Engineers, 1988), p. 2.

Suggested Reading

Dispersion Modeling

Center for Chemical Process Safety (CCPS), *Guidelines for Consequence Analysis of Chemical Releases* (New York: American Institute of Chemical Engineers, 1999).

Guidelines for Vapor Cloud Dispersion Models, 2nd ed. (New York: American Institute of Chemical Engineers, 1996).

Steven Hanna, Seshu Dharmavaram, John Zhang, Ian Sykes, Henk Witlox, Shah Khajehnajafi, and Kay Koslan, "Comparison of Six Widely-Used Dense Gas Dispersion Models for Three Recent Chlorine Railcar Accidents," *Process Safety Progress* (Sept. 2008), 27(3): 248–259.

International Conference and Workshop on Modeling the Consequences of Accidental Releases of Hazardous Materials (New York: American Institute of Chemical Engineers, 1999).

S. Mannan, ed. *Lees' Loss Prevention in the Process Industries*, 3rd ed. (London: Butterworth-Heinemann, 2005).

J. McQuaid, "Trials on Dispersion of Heavy Gas Clouds," *Plant/Operations Progress* (Jan. 1985), 4(1): 58–61.

John H. Seinfeld, *Atmospheric Chemistry and Physics of Air Pollution* (New York: Wiley, 1986), ch. 12, 13, and 14.

D. Bruce Turner, *Workbook of Atmospheric Dispersion Estimates* (Cincinnati: US Department of Health, Education, and Welfare, 1970).

Release Mitigation

Keith Moodie, "The Use of Water Spray Barriers to Disperse Spills of Heavy Gases," *Plant/Operations Progress* (Oct. 1985), 4(4): 234–241.

Richard W. Prugh and Robert W. Johnson, *Guidelines for Vapor Release Mitigation* (New York: American Institute of Chemical Engineers, 1988).

Morshed A. Rana, Benjamin R. Cormier, Jaffee A. Suardin, Yingchun Zhang, and M. Sam Mannan, "Experimental Study of Effective Water Spray Curtain Application in Dispersing Liquefied Natural Gas Vapor Clouds," *Process Safety Progress* (2008), 27(4): 345–353.

Problems

5-1. Contaminated toluene is fed to a water wash system shown in Figure 5-17. The toluene is pumped from a 50-gal drum into a countercurrent centrifugal extractor. The extractor separates the water from the toluene by centrifugal force acting on the difference in densities. The contaminated toluene enters the extractor at the periphery and flows to the center. The water enters the center of the extractor and flows to the periphery. The washed toluene and contaminated water flow into 50-gal drums. Determine a number of release incidents for this equipment.

5-2. A burning dump emits an estimated 3 g/s of oxides of nitrogen. What is the average concentration of oxides of nitrogen from this source directly downwind at a distance of 3 km on an overcast night with a wind speed of 7 m/s? Assume that this dump is a point ground-level source.

5-3. A trash incinerator has an effective stack height of 100 m. On a sunny day with a 2 m/s wind the concentration of sulfur dioxide 200 m directly downwind is measured at 5.0×10^{-5} g/m^3. Estimate the mass release rate (in g/s) of sulfur dioxide from this stack. Also estimate the maximum sulfur dioxide concentration expected on the ground and its location downwind from the stack.

5-4. You have been suddenly enveloped by a plume of toxic material from a nearby chemical plant. Which way should you run with respect to the wind to minimize your exposure?

5-5. An air sampling station is located at an azimuth of 203° from a cement plant at a distance of 1500 m. The cement plant releases fine particulates (less than 15 μm diameter) at the

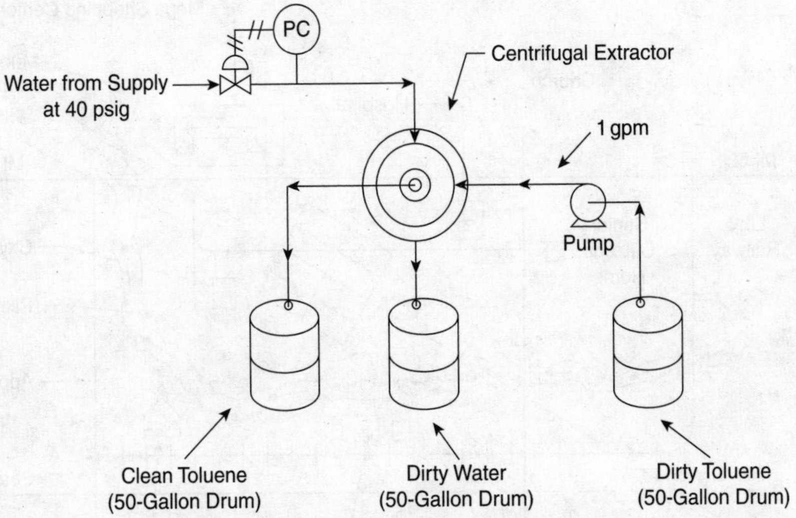

Figure 5-17 Toluene water wash process.

rate of 750 lb/hr from a 30-m stack. What is the concentration of particulates at the air sampling station when the wind is from 30° at 3 m/s on a clear day in the late fall at 4:00 PM?

5-6. A storage tank containing acrolein (ERPG-1 = 0.05 ppm) is located 1500 m from a residential area. Estimate the amount of acrolein that must be instantaneously released at ground level to produce a concentration at the boundary of the residential area equal to the ERPG-1.

5-7. Consider again Problem 5-6, but assume a continuous release at ground level. What is the release rate required to produce an average concentration at the boundary to the residential area equal to the ERPG-1?

5-8. The concentration of vinyl chloride 2 km downwind from a continuous release 25 m high is 1.6 mg/m^3. It is a sunny day, and the wind speed is 18 km/hr. Determine the average concentration 0.1 km perpendicular to the plume 2 km downwind.

5-9. An 800-lb tank of chlorine is stored at a water treatment plant. A study of the release scenarios indicates that the entire tank contents could be released as vapor in a period of 10 min. For chlorine gas, evacuation of the population must occur for areas where the vapor concentration exceeds the ERPG-1. Without any additional information, estimate the distance downwind that must be evacuated.

5-10. You have been appointed emergency coordinator for the community of Smallville, shown in figure 5-18.

ABC Chemical Company is shown on the map. They report the following chemicals and amounts: 100 lb of hydrogen chloride and 100 gal of sulfuric acid. You are required to develop an emergency plan for the community.

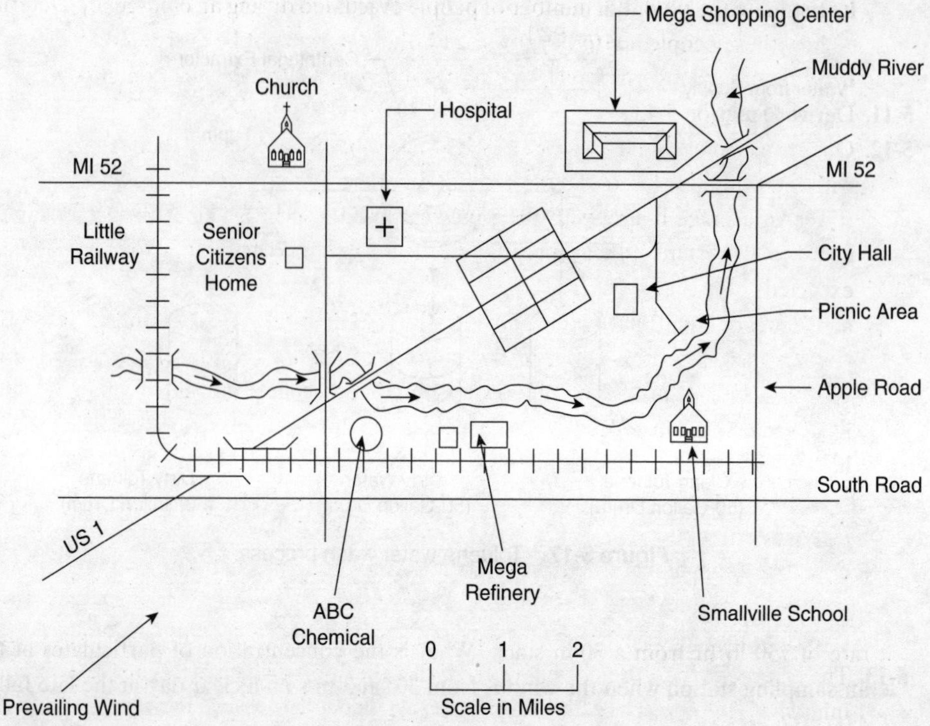

Figure 5-18 Map of Smallville.

a. Determine which chemical presents the greater hazard to the community.

b. Assuming all of the chemical is released during a 10-min period, determine the distance downwind that must be evacuated.

c. Identify locations that might be affected by a release incident at the plant or might contribute to the incident because of their proximity to the plant.

d. Determine transportation routes that will be used to transport hazardous materials into or out of the facility. Identify any high-risk intersections where accidents might occur.

e. Determine the vulnerable zone along the transportation routes identified in part d. Use a distance of 0.5 mi on either side of the route, unless a smaller distance is indicated by part b.

f. Identify any special concerns (schools, nursing homes, shopping centers, and the like) that appear in the transportation route vulnerable zone.

g. Determine evacuation routes for the areas surrounding the plant.

h. Determine alternative traffic routes around the potential hazard.

i. Determine the resources required to support the needs of parts g and h.

j. Identify the means required to warn the area, and describe the content of an example warning message that could be used in an emergency at the facility.

k. Estimate the potential number of people evacuated during an emergency. Determine how these people are to be moved and where they might be evacuated to.

l. What other concerns might be important during a chemical emergency?

5-11. Derive Equation 5-43.

5-12. One response to a short-term release is to warn people to stay in their homes or offices with the windows closed and the ventilation off.

An average house, with the windows closed, exchanges air with the surroundings equal to three times the volume of the house per hour (although wide variations are expected).

a. Derive an equation for the concentration of chemical vapor within the house based on a parameter, N_t, equal to the number of volume exchanges per hour. Assume well-mixed behavior for the air, an initial zero concentration of vapor within the house, and a constant external concentration during the exposure period.

b. A vapor cloud with a maximum concentration of 20 ppm is moving through a community. Determine the time before the vapor concentration within an average house reaches 10 ppm.

c. If the wind is blowing at 2 mph and the plant is 1 mi upwind from the community, what is the maximum time available to the plant personnel to stop or reduce the release to ensure that the concentrations within the homes do not exceed the 10 ppm value?

5-13. The emergency coordinator has decided that the appropriate emergency response to the immediate release of a toxic material is to alert people to stay in their homes, with doors and windows closed, until the cloud has passed. The coordinator has also indicated that homes 4000 m downwind must not be exposed to concentrations exceeding 0.10 mg/m^3 of this material for any longer than 2 min. Estimate the maximum instantaneous release of material (in kg) allowed for these specifications. Be sure to clearly state any assumptions about weather conditions, wind speed, etc.

5-14. Derive Equation 5-65.

5-15. A tank has ruptured and a pool of benzene has formed. The pool is approximately rectangular with dimensions of 20 ft by 30 ft. Estimate the evaporation rate and the distance affected downwind. Define the plume boundary using 10 ppm. It is an overcast day with a 9 mph wind. The temperature is 90°F.

5-16. Derive Equation 5-70.

5-17. Derive Equation 5-76.

5-18. Develop a spreadsheet to determine the isopleths for a puff at a specified time after the release of material.

The spreadsheet should contain specific cells for user input of the following quantities: time after release (s), wind speed (2 m/s), total release (kg), release height (m), molecular weight of released gas, ambient temperature (K), ambient pressure (atm), and isopleth concentration (ppm).

The spreadsheet output should include, at each point downwind, downwind location, both y and z dispersion coefficients, downwind centerline concentration, and isopleth distance off-center (+/−).

The spreadsheet output should also include a graph of the isopleth location.

For your spreadsheet construction, we suggest that you set up the cells to move with the puff center. Otherwise, you will need a large number of cells.

Use the spreadsheet for the following case:

Release mass: 0.5 kg

Release height: 0 m

Molecular weight of gas: 30

Ambient temperature: 298 K

Ambient pressure: 1 atm

Isopleth concentration: 1 ppm

Atmospheric stability: F

Run the spreadsheet for a number of different times, and plot the maximum puff width as a function of distance downwind from the release.

Answer the following questions:

a. At what distance downwind does the puff reach its maximum width?

b. At what distance and time does the puff dissipate?

c. Estimate the total area swept out by the puff from initial release to dissipation.

Your submitted work should include a description of your method of solution, a complete spreadsheet output at 2000 s after release, a plot of maximum puff width as a function of downwind distance, and the calculation of the total swept area.

5-19. A tank truck hauling liquid benzene (C_6H_6) has overturned on I-94 in Detroit and a pool of benzene 30 m in diameter has formed. The terrain is fairly flat. It is 1 PM on a clear, sunny day. The wind is blowing at 7 m/s. The ambient temperature is 30°C.

a. Estimate the evaporation rate of the benzene in kg/s.

b. Use a dispersion model to estimate the downwind distance, in meters, to the ERPG-1 concentration.

All physical properties required are contained within the textbook.

5-20. A fixed mass of toxic gas has been released almost instantaneously from a process unit. You have been asked to determine the percentage of fatalities expected 2000 m downwind from the release. Prepare a spreadsheet to calculate the concentration profile around the center of the puff 2000 m downwind from the release. Use the total release quantity as a parameter. Determine the percentage of fatalities at the 2000-m downwind location as a result of the passing puff. Vary the total release quantity to result in a range of fatalities from 0 to 100%. Record the results at enough points to provide an accurate plot of the percentage of fatalities versus quantity released. The release occurs at night with calm and clear conditions.

Change the concentration exponent value to 2.00 instead of 2.75 in the probit equation, and rerun your spreadsheet for a total release amount of 5 kg. How sensitive are the results to this exponent?

Hint: Assume that the puff shape and concentration profile remain essentially fixed as the puff passes.

Supplemental information:

Molecular weight of gas: 30

Temperature: 298 K

Pressure: 1 atm

Release height: 0

Wind speed: 2 m/s

Use a probit equation for fatalities of the form

$$Y = -17.1 + 1.69 \ln\left(\sum C^{2.75} T \right),$$

where Y is the probit variable, C is the concentration in ppm, and T is the time interval (min).

Your submitted work must include a single output of the spreadsheet for a total release of 5 kg, including the puff concentration profile and the percent fatalities; a plot of the concentration profile for the 5-kg case versus the distance in meters from the center of the puff; a plot of the percentage of fatalities versus total quantity released; a single output of the spreadsheet for a 5-kg release with a probit exponent of 2.00; and a complete discussion of your method and your results.

5-21. Use the Britter-McQuaid dense gas dispersion model to determine the distance to the 1% concentration for a release of chlorine gas. Assume that the release occurs over a duration of 500 s with a volumetric release rate of 1 m^3/s. The wind speed at 10 m height is 10 m/s. The boiling point for the chlorine is −34°C, and the density of the liquid at the boiling point is 1470 kg/m^3. Assume ambient conditions of 298 K and 1 atm.

5-22. You are developing emergency evacuation plans for the local community downwind of your plant. One scenario identified is the rupture of an ammonia pipeline. It is estimated that ammonia will release at the rate of 10 lb/s if this pipeline ruptures. You have decided that anyone exposed to more than 100 ppm of ammonia must be evacuated until repairs are made. What evacuation distance downwind will you recommend?

5-23. The EPA Risk Management Plan (RMP) defines a worst-case scenario as the catastrophic release of the entire process inventory in a 10-min period (assumed to be a continuous release). The dispersion calculations must be completed assuming F stability and 1.5 m/s wind speed. As part of the RMP rule, each facility must determine the downwind distance to a toxic endpoint. These results must be reported to the EPA and to the surrounding community.

a. A plant has a 100-lb tank of anhydrous hydrogen fluoride (molecular weight = 20). The toxic endpoint is specified in the RMP as 0.016 mg/L. Determine the distance downwind (in miles) to the toxic endpoint for an EPA worst-case release.

b. Comment on the viability of using a continuous release model for a 10-min release period.

c. One hundred pounds of HF is a small quantity. Many plants have much larger vessels on site. Comment on how a larger quantity would affect the downwind distance and how this might affect the public's perception of your facility. What does this imply about the size of chemical inventories for chemical plants?

5-24. Use a spreadsheet program to determine the location of a ground isopleth for a plume. The spreadsheet should have specific cell inputs for release rate (g/s), release height (m), spatial increment (m), wind speed (m/s), molecular weight of the released material, temperature (K), pressure (atm), and isopleth concentration (ppm).

The spreadsheet output should include, at each point downwind, both y and z dispersion coefficients (m), downwind centerline concentrations (ppm), and isopleth locations (m).

The spreadsheet should also have cells providing the downwind distance, the total area of the plume, and the maximum width of the plume, all based on the isopleth values.

Your submitted work should include a brief description of your method of solution, outputs from the spreadsheet, and plots of the isopleth locations.

Use the following two cases for computations, and assume worst-case stability conditions:

Case a: Release rate: 200 g/s
Release height: 0 m
Molecular weight: 100
Temperature: 298 K
Pressure: 1 atm
Isopleth concentration: 10 ppm

Case b: Same as above, but release height = 10 m. Compare the plume width, area, and downwind distance for each case. Comment on the difference between the two cases.

5-25. A tank containing hydrogen sulfide gas (molecular weight 34) has been overpressured and the relief device has been opened. In this case the relief device has a 3-cm diameter, and the flow through the relief is equivalent to the flow obtained through a 3-cm-diameter hole in the tank. In this case the flow of gas has been calculated to be 1.76 kg/s.

A cloud of material has formed downwind of the release. Determine the distance downwind that must be evacuated (in km). Assume that evacuation must occur in any location that exceeds the OSHA PEL. For this release the hydrogen sulfide in the tank is at a pressure of 1 MPa absolute and 25°C, the release occurs at ground level, and it is a clear night with a wind speed of 5.5 m/s.

CHAPTER 6

Fires and Explosions

Chemicals present a substantial hazard in the form of fires and explosions. The combustion of one gallon of toluene can destroy an ordinary chemistry laboratory in minutes; persons present may be killed. The potential consequences of fires and explosions in pilot plants and plant environments are even greater.

The three most common chemical plant accidents are fires, explosions, and toxic releases, in that order (see Chapter 1). Organic solvents are the most common source of fires and explosions in the chemical industry.

Chemical and hydrocarbon plant losses resulting from fires and explosions are substantial, with yearly property losses in the United States estimated at almost $300 million (1997 dollars).[1] Additional losses in life and business interruptions are also substantial. To prevent accidents resulting from fires and explosions, engineers must be familiar with

- The fire and explosion properties of materials,
- The nature of the fire and explosion process, and
- Procedures to reduce fire and explosion hazards.

In this chapter we cover the first two topics, emphasizing definitions and calculation methods for estimating the magnitude and consequences of fires and explosions. We discuss procedures to reduce fire and explosion hazards in Chapter 7.

6-1 The Fire Triangle

The essential elements for combustion are fuel, an oxidizer, and an ignition source. These elements are illustrated by the fire triangle, shown in Figure 6-1.

[1] *Large Property Damage Losses in the Hydrocarbon-Chemical Industry: A Thirty Year Review* (New York: J. H. Marsh & McLennan, 1998).

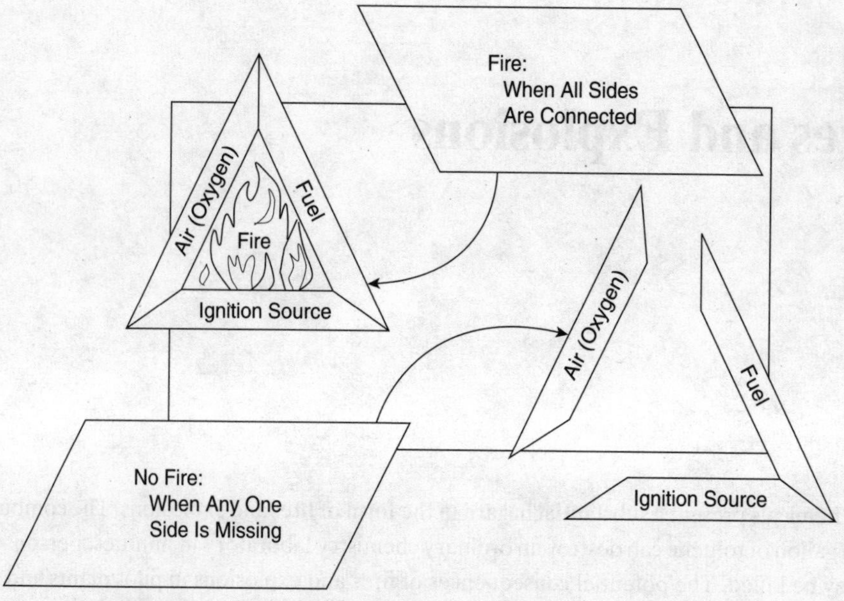

Figure 6-1 The fire triangle.

Fire, or burning, is the rapid exothermic oxidation of an ignited fuel. The fuel can be in solid, liquid, or vapor form, but vapor and liquid fuels are generally easier to ignite. The combustion always occurs in the vapor phase; liquids are volatized and solids are decomposed into vapor before combustion.

When fuel, oxidizer, and an ignition source are present at the necessary levels, burning will occur. This means a fire will *not* occur if (1) fuel is not present or is not present in sufficient quantities, (2) an oxidizer is not present or is not present in sufficient quantities, and (3) the ignition source is not energetic enough to initiate the fire.

Two common examples of the three components of the fire triangle are wood, air, and a match; and gasoline, air, and a spark. However, other, less obvious combinations of chemicals can lead to fires and explosions. Various fuels, oxidizers, and ignition sources common in the chemical industry are

Fuels

Liquids: gasoline, acetone, ether, pentane
Solids: plastics, wood dust, fibers, metal particles
Gases: acetylene, propane, carbon monoxide, hydrogen

Oxidizers

Gases: oxygen, fluorine, chlorine
Liquids: hydrogen peroxide, nitric acid, perchloric acid
Solids: metal peroxides, ammonium nitrite

Ignition sources

Sparks, flames, static electricity, heat

In the past the sole method for controlling fires and explosions was elimination of or reduction in ignition sources. Practical experience has shown that this is not robust enough – the ignition energies for most flammable materials are too low and ignition sources too plentiful. As a result, current practice is to prevent fires and explosions by continuing to eliminate ignition sources while focusing efforts strongly on preventing flammable mixtures.

6-2 Distinction between Fires and Explosions

The major distinction between fires and explosions is the rate of energy release. Fires release energy slowly, whereas explosions release energy rapidly, typically on the order of microseconds. Fires can also result from explosions, and explosions can result from fires.

A good example of how the energy release rate affects the consequences of an accident is a standard automobile tire. The compressed air within the tire contains energy. If the energy is released slowly through the nozzle, the tire is harmlessly deflated. If the tire ruptures suddenly and all the energy within the compressed tire releases rapidly, the result is a dangerous explosion.

6-3 Definitions

Some of the commonly used definitions related to fires and explosions are given in what follows. These definitions are discussed in greater detail in later sections.

Combustion or fire: Combustion or fire is a chemical reaction in which a substance combines with an oxidant and releases energy. Part of the energy released is used to sustain the reaction.

Ignition: Ignition of a flammable mixture may be caused by a flammable mixture coming in contact with a source of ignition with sufficient energy or the gas reaching a temperature high enough to cause the gas to autoignite.

Autoignition temperature (AIT): A fixed temperature above which adequate energy is available in the environment to provide an ignition source.

Flash point (FP): The flash point of a liquid is the lowest temperature at which it gives off enough vapor to form an ignitable mixture with air. At the flash point the vapor will burn but only briefly; inadequate vapor is produced to maintain combustion. The flash point generally increases with increasing pressure.

There are several different experimental methods used to determine flash points. Each method produces a somewhat different value. The two most commonly used methods are open cup and closed cup, depending on the physical configuration of the experimental equipment. The open-cup flash point is a few degrees higher than the closed-cup flash point.

Fire point: The fire point is the lowest temperature at which a vapor above a liquid will continue to burn once ignited; the fire point temperature is higher than the flash point.

Flammability limits: Vapor-air mixtures will ignite and burn only over a well-specified range of compositions. The mixture will not burn when the composition is lower than the lower flammable limit (LFL); the mixture is too lean for combustion. The mixture is also not combustible when the composition is too rich, that is, when it is above the upper flammable limit (UFL). A mixture is flammable only when the composition is between the LFL and the UFL. Commonly used units are volume percent fuel (percentage of fuel plus air).

Lower explosion limit (LEL) and upper explosion limit (UEL) are used interchangeably with LFL and UFL.

Explosion: An explosion is a rapid expansion of gases resulting in a rapidly moving pressure or shock wave. The expansion can be mechanical (by means of a sudden rupture of a pressurized vessel), or it can be the result of a rapid chemical reaction. Explosion damage is caused by the pressure or shock wave.

Mechanical explosion: An explosion resulting from the sudden failure of a vessel containing high-pressure nonreactive gas.

Deflagration: An explosion in which the reaction front moves at a speed less than the speed of sound in the unreacted medium.

Detonation: An explosion in which the reaction front moves at a speed greater than the speed of sound in the unreacted medium.

Confined explosion: An explosion occurring within a vessel or a building. These are most common and usually result in injury to the building inhabitants and extensive damage.

Unconfined explosion: Unconfined explosions occur in the open. This type of explosion is usually the result of a flammable gas release. The gas is dispersed and mixed with air until it comes in contact with an ignition source. Unconfined explosions are rarer than confined explosions because the explosive material is frequently diluted below the LFL by wind dispersion. These explosions are destructive because large quantities of gas and large areas are frequently involved.

Boiling-liquid expanding-vapor explosion (BLEVE): A BLEVE occurs if a vessel that contains a liquid at a temperature above its atmospheric pressure boiling point ruptures. The subsequent BLEVE is the explosive vaporization of a large fraction of the vessel contents, possibly followed by combustion or explosion of the vaporized cloud if it is combustible. This type of explosion occurs when an external fire heats the contents of a tank of volatile material. As the tank contents heat, the vapor pressure of the liquid within the tank increases and the tank's structural integrity is reduced because of the heating. If the tank ruptures, the hot liquid volatilizes explosively.

Dust explosion: This explosion results from the rapid combustion of fine solid particles. Many solid materials (including common metals such as iron and aluminum) become flammable when reduced to a fine powder.

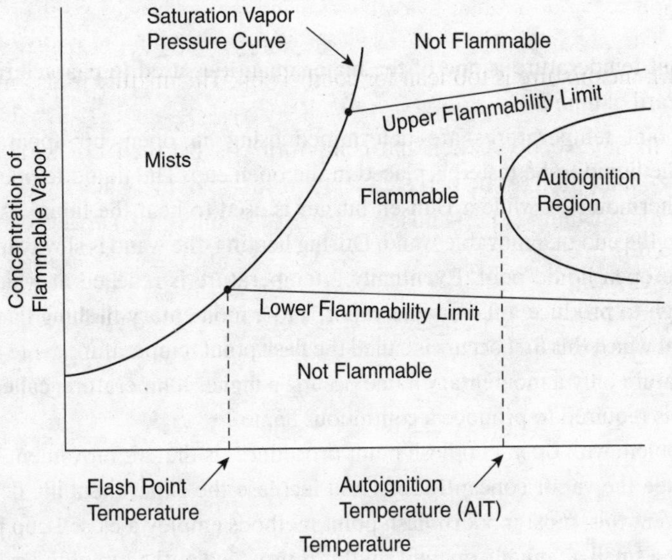

Figure 6-2 Relationships between various flammability properties.

Shock wave: An abrupt pressure wave moving through a gas. A shock wave in open air is followed by a strong wind; the combination of shock wave and wind is called a blast wave. The pressure increase in the shock wave is so rapid that the process is mostly adiabatic.

Overpressure: The pressure on an object as a result of an impacting shock wave.

Figure 6-2 is a plot of concentration versus temperature and shows how several of these definitions are related. The exponential curve in Figure 6-2 represents the saturation vapor pressure curve for the liquid material. Typically, the UFL increases and the LFL decreases with temperature. The LFL theoretically intersects the saturation vapor pressure curve at the flash point, although experimental data do not always agree with this. The autoignition temperature is actually the lowest temperature of an autoignition region. The behavior of the autoignition region and the flammability limits at higher temperatures are not known.

The flash point and flammability limits are not fundamental properties but are defined only by the specific experimental apparatus and procedure used.

6-4 Flammability Characteristics of Liquids and Vapors

Flammability characteristics of some important organic chemicals (liquids and gases) are provided in Appendix B.

Liquids

The flash point temperature is one of the major quantities used to characterize the fire and explosion hazard of liquids.

Flash point temperatures are determined using an open-cup apparatus, shown in Figure 6-3. The liquid to be tested is placed in the open cup. The liquid temperature is measured with a thermometer while a Bunsen burner is used to heat the liquid. A small flame is established on the end of a movable wand. During heating, the wand is slowly moved back and forth over the open liquid pool. Eventually a temperature is reached at which the liquid is volatile enough to produce a flammable vapor, and a momentary flashing flame occurs. The temperature at which this first occurs is called the flash point temperature. Note that at the flash point temperature only a momentary flame occurs; a higher temperature, called the fire point temperature, is required to produce a continuous flame.

The problem with open-cup flash point procedures is that air movements over the open cup may change the vapor concentrations and increase the experimentally determined flash point. To prevent this, most modern flash point methods employ a closed-cup procedure. For this apparatus a small, manually opened shutter is provided at the top of the cup. The liquid is

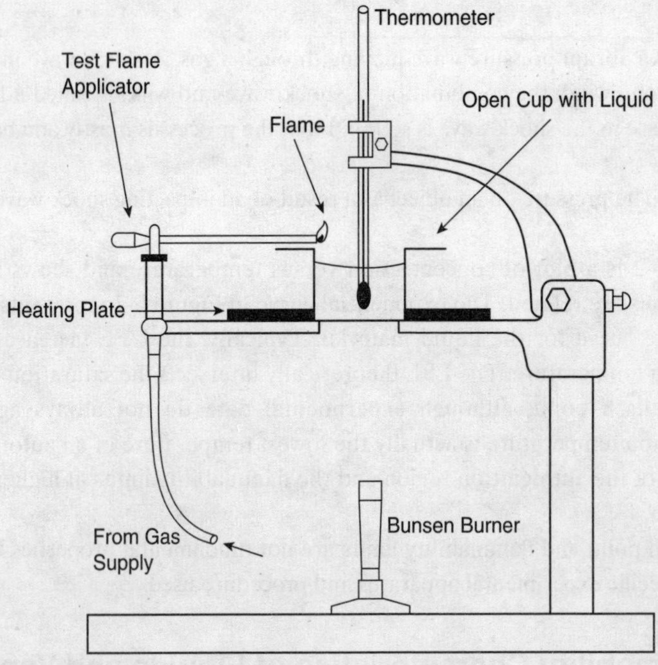

Figure 6-3 Cleveland open-cup flash point determination. The test flame applicator is moved back and forth horizontally over the liquid sample.

Table 6-1 Constants Used in Equation 6-1 for Predicting the Flash Point[a]

Chemical group	*a*	*b*	*c*
Hydrocarbons	225.1	537.6	2217
Alcohols	230.8	390.5	1780
Amines	222.4	416.6	1900
Acids	323.2	600.1	2970
Ethers	275.9	700.0	2879
Sulfur	238.0	577.9	2297
Esters	260.8	449.2	2217
Ketones	260.5	296.0	1908
Halogens	262.1	414.0	2154
Aldehydes	264.5	293.0	1970
Phosphorus-containing	201.7	416.1	1666
Nitrogen-containing	185.7	432.0	1645
Petroleum fractions	237.9	334.4	1807

[a]K. Satyanarayana and P. G. Rao, "Improved Equation to Estimate Flash Points of Organic Compounds," *Journal of Hazardous Materials* (1992), 32: 81–85.

placed in a preheated cup and allowed to sit for a fixed time period. The shutter is then opened and the liquid is exposed to the flame. Closed-cup methods typically result in lower flash points.

Satyanarayana and Rao[2] showed that the flash point temperatures for pure materials correlate well with the boiling point of the liquid. They were able to fit the flash point for over 1200 compounds with an error of less than 1% using the equation

$$T_f = a + \frac{b(c/T_b)^2 e^{-c/T_b}}{(1 - e^{-c/T_b})^2}, \tag{6-1}$$

where

T_f is the flash point temperature (K),
a, b, and c are constants provided in Table 6-1 (K), and
T_b is the boiling point temperature of the material (K).

Flash points can be estimated for multicomponent mixtures if only one component is flammable and if the flash point of the flammable component is known. In this case the flash point temperature is estimated by determining the temperature at which the vapor pressure of the flammable component in the mixture is equal to the pure component vapor pressure at its

[2]Satyanarayana and Rao, "Improved Equation to Estimate Flash Points of Organic Compounds."

flash point. Experimentally determined flash points are recommended for multicomponent mixtures with more than one flammable component.

Example 6-1

Methanol has a flash point of 54°F, and its vapor pressure at this temperature is 62 mm Hg. What is the flash point of a solution containing 75% methanol and 25% water by weight?

Solution

The mole fractions of each component are needed to apply Raoult's law. Assuming a basis of 100 lb of solution, we can construct the following:

	Pounds	Molecular weight	Moles	Mole fraction
Water	25	18	1.39	0.37
Methanol	75	32	2.34	0.63
			3.73	1.00

Raoult's law is used to compute the vapor pressure (P^{sat}) of pure methanol, based on the partial pressure required to flash:

$$p = xP^{sat}$$

$$P^{sat} = p/x = 62/0.63 = 98.4 \text{ mm Hg.}$$

Using a graph of the vapor pressure versus temperature, shown in Figure 6-4, the flash point of the solution is 20.5°C, or 68.9°F.

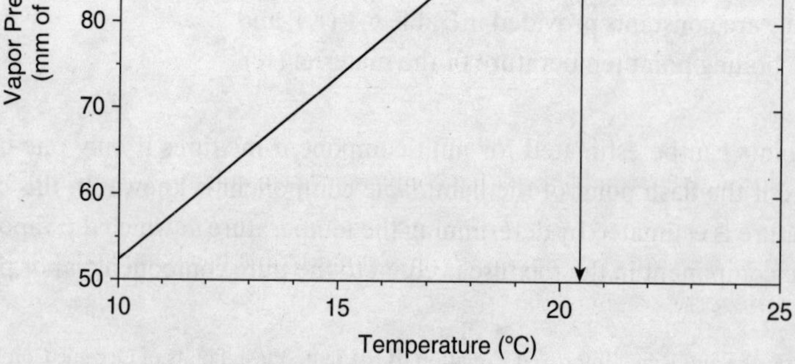

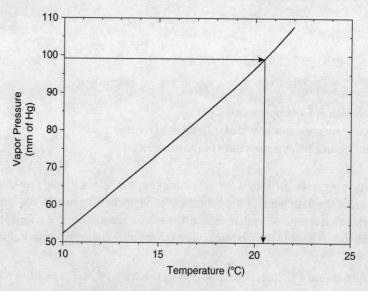

Figure 6-4 Saturation vapor pressure for methanol.

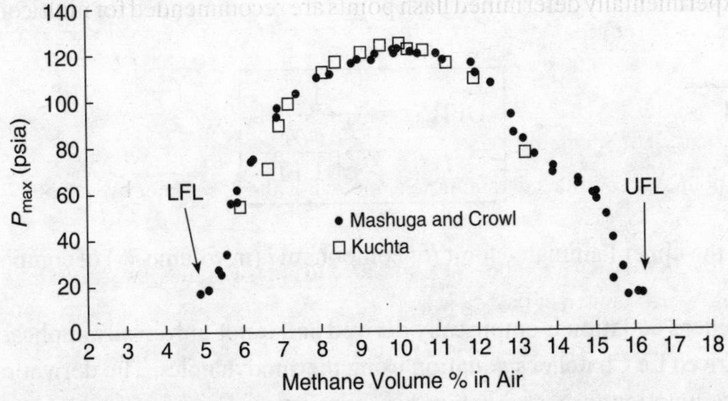

Figure 6-5 Maximum pressure for methane combustion in a 20-L sphere. The flammability limits are defined at 1 psig maximum pressure. Data from C. V. Mashuga and D. A. Crowl, "Application of the Flammability Diagram for Evaluation of Fire and Explosion Hazards of Flammable Vapors," *Process Safety Progress* (1998), 17(3): 176–183; and J. M. Kuchta, *Investigation of Fire and Explosion Accidents in the Chemical, Mining, and Fuel-Related Industries: A Manual*, US Bureau of Mines Report 680 (Washington, DC: US Bureau of Mines, 1985).

Gases and Vapors

Flammability limits for vapors are determined experimentally in a specially designed closed vessel apparatus (see Figure 6-15 on page 272). Vapor-air mixtures of known concentration are added and then ignited. The maximum explosion pressure is measured. This test is repeated with different concentrations to establish the range of flammability for the specific gas. Figure 6-5 shows the results for methane.

Vapor Mixtures

Frequently LFLs and UFLs for mixtures are needed. These mixture limits are computed using the Le Chatelier equation:[3]

$$\mathrm{LFL_{mix}} = \frac{1}{\sum_{i=1}^{n} \frac{y_i}{\mathrm{LFL}_i}}, \tag{6-2}$$

where

LFL_i is the lower flammable limit for component i (in volume %) of component i in fuel and air,

y_i is the mole fraction of component i on a combustible basis, and

n is the number of combustible species.

[3]H. Le Chatelier, "Estimation of Firedamp by Flammability Limits," *Ann. Mines* (1891), ser. 8, 19: 388–395.

Similarly,

$$\text{UFL}_{\text{mix}} = \frac{1}{\sum_{i=1}^{n} \frac{y_i}{\text{UFL}_i}}, \tag{6-3}$$

where UFL_i is the upper flammable limit for component i (in volume %) of component i in fuel and air.

Le Chatelier's equation is empirically derived and is not universally applicable. Mashuga and Crowl[4] derived Le Chatelier's equation using thermodynamics. The derivation shows that the following assumptions are inherent in this equation:

- The product heat capacities are constant.
- The number of moles of gas is constant.
- The combustion kinetics of the pure species is independent and unchanged by the presence of other combustible species.
- The adiabatic temperature rise at the flammability limit is the same for all species.

These assumptions were found to be reasonably valid at the LFL and less so at the UFL.

Proper usage of Le Chatelier's rule requires flammability limit data at the same temperature and pressure. Also, flammability data reported in the literature may be from disparate sources, with wide variability in the data. Combining data from these disparate sources may cause unsatisfactory results, which may not be obvious to the user.

Example 6-2

What are the LFL and UFL of a gas mixture composed of 0.8% hexane, 2.0% methane, and 0.5% ethylene by volume?

Solution

The mole fractions on a fuel-only basis are calculated in the following table. The LFL and UFL data are obtained from Appendix B.

	Volume %	Mole fraction on combustible basis	LFL_i (vol. %)	UFL_i (vol. %)
Hexane	0.8	0.24	1.2	7.5
Methane	2.0	0.61	5.0	15
Ethylene	0.5	0.15	2.7	36.0
Total combustibles	3.3			
Air	96.7			

[4] C. V. Mashuga and D. A. Crowl, "Derivation of Le Chatelier's Mixing Rule for Flammable Limits," *Process Safety Progress* (2000), 19(2): 112–117.

Equation 6-2 is used to determine the LFL of the mixture:

$$\mathrm{LFL_{mix}} = \frac{1}{\sum_{i=1}^{n} \frac{y_i}{\mathrm{LFL}_i}}$$

$$= \frac{1}{\frac{0.24}{1.2} + \frac{0.61}{5.0} + \frac{0.15}{2.7}}$$

$$= 1/0.378 = 2.65 \text{ by volume total combustibles.}$$

Equation 6-3 is used to determine the UFL of the mixture:

$$\mathrm{UFL_{mix}} = \frac{1}{\sum_{i=1}^{n} \frac{y_i}{\mathrm{UFL}_i}}$$

$$= \frac{1}{\frac{0.24}{7.5} + \frac{0.61}{15} + \frac{0.15}{36.0}}$$

$$= 13.0 \text{ by volume total combustibles.}$$

Because the mixture contains 3.3% total combustibles, it is flammable.

Flammability Limit Dependence on Temperature

In general, the flammability range increases with temperature.[5] The following empirically derived equations are available for vapors:

$$\mathrm{LFL}_T = \mathrm{LFL}_{25} - \frac{0.75}{\Delta H_c}(T - 25), \quad (6\text{-}4)$$

$$\mathrm{UFL}_T = \mathrm{UFL}_{25} + \frac{0.75}{\Delta H_c}(T - 25), \quad (6\text{-}5)$$

where

ΔH_c is the net heat of combustion (kcal/mole) and
T is the temperature (°C).

Equations (6-4) and (6-5) are very approximate and only work for a very limited number of hydrocarbons over a limited temperature range. The 0.75 is actually 100 C_p.

[5]M. G. Zabetakis, S. Lambiris, and G. S. Scott, "Flame Temperatures of Limit Mixtures," in *Seventh Symposium on Combustion* (London: Butterworths, 1959), p. 484.

Flammability Limit Dependence on Pressure

Pressure has little effect on the LFL except at very low pressures (<50 mm Hg absolute), where flames do not propagate.

The UFL increases significantly as the pressure is increased, broadening the flammability range. An empirical expression for the UFL for vapors as a function of pressure is available:[6]

$$\boxed{\mathrm{UFL}_P = \mathrm{UFL} + 20.6(\log P + 1),} \tag{6-6}$$

where

P is the pressure (megapascals absolute) and
UFL is the upper flammable limit (volume % of fuel plus air at 1 atm).

Example 6-3

If the UFL for a substance is 11.0% by volume at 0.0 MPa gauge, what is the UFL at 6.2 MPa gauge?

Solution

The absolute pressure is $P = 6.2 + 0.101 = 6.301$ MPa. The UFL is determined using Equation 6-6:

$$\begin{aligned}\mathrm{UFL}_P &= \mathrm{UFL} + 20.6(\log P + 1)\\ &= 11.0 + 20.6(\log 6.301 + 1)\\ &= 48 \text{ vol. \% fuel in air.}\end{aligned}$$

Estimating Flammability Limits

For some situations it may be necessary to estimate the flammability limits without experimental data. Flammability limits are easily measured; experimental determination is always recommended.

Jones[7] found that for many hydrocarbon vapors the LFL and the UFL are a function of the stoichiometric concentration (C_{st}) of fuel:

$$\boxed{\mathrm{LFL} = 0.55C_{st},} \tag{6-7}$$

$$\boxed{\mathrm{UFL} = 3.50C_{st},} \tag{6-8}$$

where C_{st} is volume % fuel in fuel plus air.

The stoichiometric concentration for most organic compounds is determined using the general combustion reaction

$$C_mH_xO_y + zO_2 \rightarrow mCO_2 + \frac{x}{2}H_2O. \tag{6-9}$$

[6] M. G. Zabetakis, "Fire and Explosion Hazards at Temperature and Pressure Extremes," *AICHE Inst. Chem. Engr. Symp.*, ser. 2, *Chem. Engr. Extreme Cond. Proc. Symp.* (1965), pp. 99–104.

[7] G. W. Jones, "Inflammation Limits and Their Practical Application in Hazardous Industrial Operations," *Chem. Rev.* (1938), 22(1): 1–26.

It follows from the stoichiometry that

$$z = m + \frac{x}{4} - \frac{y}{2},$$

where z has units of moles O_2/mole fuel.

Additional stoichiometric and unit changes are required to determine C_{st} as a function of z:

$$C_{st} = \frac{\text{moles fuel}}{\text{moles fuel} + \text{moles air}} \times 100$$

$$= \frac{100}{1 + \left(\frac{\text{moles air}}{\text{moles fuel}}\right)}$$

$$= \frac{100}{1 + \left(\frac{1}{0.21}\right)\left(\frac{\text{moles } O_2}{\text{moles fuel}}\right)}$$

$$= \frac{100}{1 + \left(\frac{z}{0.21}\right)}.$$

Substituting z and applying Equations 6-7 and 6-8 yields

$$\boxed{\text{LFL} = \frac{0.55(100)}{4.76m + 1.19x - 2.38y + 1},} \tag{6-10}$$

$$\boxed{\text{UFL} = \frac{3.50(100)}{4.76m + 1.19x - 2.38y + 1}.} \tag{6-11}$$

Another method[8,9] correlates the flammability limits as a function of the heat of combustion of the fuel. A good fit was obtained for 123 organic materials containing carbon, hydrogen, oxygen, nitrogen, and sulfur. The resulting correlations are

$$\text{LFL} = \frac{-3.42}{\Delta H_c} + 0.569\Delta H_c + 0.0538\Delta H_c^2 + 1.80, \tag{6-12}$$

$$\text{UFL} = 6.30\Delta H_c + 0.567\Delta H_c^2 + 23.5, \tag{6-13}$$

[8] T. Suzuki, "Empirical Relationship Between Lower Flammability Limits and Standard Enthalpies of Combustion of Organic Compounds," *Fire and Materials* (1994), 18: 333–336.

[9] T. Suzuki and K. Koide, "Correlation between Upper Flammability Limits and Thermochemical Properties of Organic Compounds," *Fire and Materials* (1994), 18: 393–397.

where

LFL and UFL are the lower and upper flammable limits (volume % fuel in air), respectively, and

ΔH_c is the heat of combustion for the fuel (in 10^3 kJ/mol).

Equation 6-13 is applicable only over the UFL range of 4.9–23%. If the heat of combustion is provided in kcal/mol, it can be converted to kJ/mol by multiplying by 4.184.

The prediction capability of Equations 6-6 through 6-13 is only modest at best. For hydrogen the predictions are poor. For methane and the higher hydrocarbons the results are improved. Thus these methods should be used only for a quick initial estimate and should not replace actual experimental data.

Example 6-4

Estimate the LFL and the UFL for hexane, and compare the calculated limits to the actual values determined experimentally.

Solution

The stoichiometry is

$$C_6H_{14} + zO_2 \rightarrow mCO_2 + \frac{x}{2}H_2O,$$

and z, m, x, and y are found by balancing this chemical reaction using the definitions in Equation 6-9:

$m = 6,$

$x = 14,$

$y = 0.$

The LFL and the UFL are determined by using Equations 6-10 and 6-11:

$$\text{LFL} = 0.55(100)/[4.76(6) + 1.19(14) + 1]$$

$$= 1.19 \text{ vol. \% versus } 1.2 \text{ vol. \% actual},$$

$$\text{UFL} = 3.5(100)/[4.76(6) + 1.19(14) + 1]$$

$$= 7.57 \text{ vol. \% versus } 7.5 \text{ vol. \% actual}.$$

Flammability limits, in general, are defined in air. As you will see later, flammable limits in pure oxygen are frequently useful for designing systems to prevent fires and explosions. Combustion in pure oxygen also exhibits a lower oxygen limit (LOL) and an upper oxygen limit (UOL), just like the LFL and UFL in air. These flammable limits have units of percent fuel in oxygen. Table 6-2 presents flammability data for a variety of fuels in pure oxygen.

Table 6-2 Flammability Limits in Pure Oxygen[a]

Compound	Formula	Limits of flammability in pure oxygen	
		Lower (LOL)	Upper (UOL)
Hydrogen	H_2	4.0	94
Deuterium	D_2	5.0	95
Carbon monoxide[b]	CO	15.5	94
Ammonia	NH_3	15.0	79
Methane	CH_4	5.1	61
Ethane	C_2H_6	3.0	66
Ethylene	C_2H_4	3.0	80
Propylene	C_3H_6	2.1	53
Cyclopropane	C_3H_6	2.5	60
Diethyl ether	$C_4H_{10}O$	2.0	82
Divinyl ether	C_4H_6O	1.8	85

[a]Data from B. Lewis and G. von Elbe, *Combustion, Flames, and Explosions of Gases* (New York: Harcourt Brace Jovanovich, 1987).
[b]The limits are insensitive to p_{H_2O} above a few mm Hg.

In general, for most common hydrocarbons the LOL is close to the LFL.

Hansen and Crowl[10] derived an empirical equation for the UOL based on drawing lines along the flammable boundaries. They found that a good estimate of the UOL can be found from

$$UOL = \frac{UFL[100 - C_{UOL}(100 - UFL_O)]}{UFL_O + UFL(1 - C_{UOL})}, \tag{6-14}$$

where

UOL is the upper oxygen limit (vol. % fuel in oxygen),
UFL is the upper flammable limit (vol. % fuel in air),
UFL_O is the oxygen concentration at the upper flammable limit (vol. % oxygen in air), and
C_{UOL} is a fitting constant.

This equation only requires UFL data. Hansen and Crowl found a good fit of Equation 6-14 for a number of fuels using $C_{UOL} = -1.87$.

[10] Travis J. Hansen and Daniel A. Crowl, "Estimation of the Flammable Zone Boundaries for Flammable Gases," *Process Safety Progress* (June 2010), 29: 3.

Example 6-5

Estimate the UOL for methane using Equation 6-14.

Solution

From Appendix B, the UFL for methane is 15.0 vol. % fuel in air, so UFL = 15%. If we select a basis of 100 moles of gas mixture, then 15 moles are methane and the remaining 85 moles are air. Of the 85 moles of air, (0.21)(85) = 17.85 moles of oxygen. Thus, UFL_O = 17.85%. Substituting into Equation 6-14:

$$UOL = \frac{UFL[100 - C_{UOL}(100 - UFL_O)]}{UFL_O + UFL(1 - C_{UOL})} = \frac{(15\%)[100 + 1.87(100 - 17.85\%)]}{17.85\% + (15\%)(1 + 1.87)} = 62.4\%.$$

This compares to the experimental value of 61% shown in Table 6-3.

6-5 Limiting Oxygen Concentration and Inerting

The LFL is based on fuel in air. However, oxygen is the key ingredient and there is a minimum oxygen concentration required to propagate a flame. This is an especially useful result, because explosions and fires can be prevented by reducing the oxygen concentration regardless of the concentration of the fuel. This concept is the basis for a common procedure called inerting (see Chapter 7).

Below the limiting oxygen concentration (LOC) the reaction cannot generate enough energy to heat the entire mixture of gases (including the inert gases) to the extent required for the self-propagation of the flame.

The LOC has also been called the minimum oxygen concentration (MOC), the maximum safe oxygen concentration (MSOC), and other names.

Table 6-3 contains LOC values for a number of materials. The LOC depends on the inert gas species.

The LOC has units of percentage of moles of oxygen in total moles. If experimental data are not available, the LOC is estimated using the stoichiometry of the combustion reaction and the LFL. This procedure works for many hydrocarbons.

Example 6-6

Estimate the LOC for butane (C_4H_{10}).

Solution

The stoichiometry for this reaction is

$$C_4H_{10} + 6.5O_2 \rightarrow 4CO_2 + 5H_2O.$$

The LFL for butane (from Appendix B) is 1.8% by volume. From the stoichiometry

$$LOC = \left(\frac{\text{moles fuel}}{\text{total moles}}\right)\left(\frac{\text{moles } O_2}{\text{moles fuel}}\right) = LFL\left(\frac{\text{moles } O_2}{\text{moles fuel}}\right).$$

Table 6-3 Limiting Oxygen Concentrations (LOCs) (volume percent oxygen concentration above which combustion can occur)[a]

Gas or vapor	N_2/Air	CO_2/Air	Gas or vapor	N_2/Air	CO_2/Air
Methane	12	14.5	Kerosene	10 (150°C)	13 (150°C)
Ethane	11	13.5	JP-1 fuel	10.5 (150°C)	14 (150°C)
Propane	11.5	14.5	JP-3 fuel	12	14.5
n-Butane	12	14.5	JP-4 fuel	11.5	14.5
Isobutane	12	15	Natural gas	12	14.5
n-Pentane	12	14.5	*n*-Butyl chloride	14	–
Isopentane	12	14.5		12 (100°C)	–
n-Hexane	12	14.5	Methylene chloride	19 (30°C)	–
n-Heptane	11.5	14.5		17 (100°C)	–
Ethylene	10	11.5	Ethylene dichloride	13	–
Propylene	11.5	14		11.5 (100°C)	–
1-Butene	11.5	14	Methyl chloroform	14	–
Isobutylene	12	15	Trichloroethylene	9 (100°C)	–
Butadiene	10.5	13	Acetone	11.5	14
3-Methyl-1-butene	11.5	14	*t*-butanol	NA	16.5 (150°C)
Benzene	11.4	14	Carbon disulfide	5	7.5
Toluene	9.5	–	Carbon monoxide	5.5	5.5
Styrene	9.0	–	Ethanol	10.5	13
Ethylbenzene	9.0	–	2-Ethyl butanol	9.5 (150°C)	–
Vinyltoluene	9.0	–	Ethyl ether	10.5	13
Diethylbenzene	8.5	–	Hydrogen	5	5.2
Cyclopropane	11.5	14	Hydrogen sulfide	7.5	11.5
Gasoline			Isobutyl formate	12.5	15
(73/100)	12	15	Methanol	10	12
(100/130)	12	15	Methyl acetate	11	13.5
(115/145)	12	14.5			

[a]Data from NFPA 68, *Venting of Deflagrations* (Quincy, MA: National Fire Protection Association, 1994).

By substitution, we obtain

$$\text{LOC} = \left(1.8 \frac{\text{moles fuel}}{\text{total moles}}\right)\left(\frac{6.5 \text{ moles } O_2}{1.0 \text{ moles fuel}}\right)$$

$$= 11.7 \text{ vol. \% } O_2.$$

The combustion of butane is preventable by adding nitrogen, carbon dioxide, or even water vapor until the oxygen concentration is below 11.7%. The addition of water, however, is not recommended because any condition that condenses water would move the oxygen concentration back into the flammable region.

Example 6-6 shows that the LOC can be estimated using the equation

$$LOC = z\ (LFL). \tag{6-15}$$

Equation 6-15 does not produce very good results.

Hansen and Crowl[11] found that a better estimate of the LOC is given by

$$LOC = \left(\frac{LFL - C_{LOC}UFL}{1 - C_{LOC}}\right)\left(\frac{UFL_o}{UFL}\right), \tag{6-16}$$

where

LOC is the limiting oxygen concentration (percent oxygen),
LFL is the lower flammable limit (percent fuel in air),
UFL is the upper flammable limit (percent fuel in air),
UFL_O is the oxygen concentration at the upper flammable limit (vol% oxygen in air), and
C_{LOC} is a fitting constant.

Data analysis of numerous experimental values found that $C_{LOC} = -1.11$ gave a good fit for many hydrocarbons.

Example 6-7

Estimate the LOC for butane using Equation 6-16. Compare to the results of Example 6-6.

Solution

From Appendix B for butane, LFL = 1.8%, UFL = 8.5%. The oxygen concentration at the upper flammable limit is

$$UFL_o = (0.21)(100 - 8.5) = 19.21\% \text{ oxygen.}$$

Substituting into Equation 6-16,

$$LOC = \left(\frac{LFL - C_{LOC}UFL}{1 - C_{LOC}}\right)\left(\frac{UFL_o}{UFL}\right) = \left[\frac{1.8\% + (1.11)(8.5\%)}{1 + 1.11}\right]\left(\frac{19.21\%}{8.5\%}\right) = 12.0\%.$$

This compares to the experimental value of 12% shown in Table 6-3. Equation 6-15 produces a value of 11.7%, which is lower than the experimental value.

6-6 Flammability Diagram

A general way to represent the flammability of a gas or vapor is by the triangle diagram shown in Figure 6-6. Concentrations of fuel, oxygen, and inert material (in volume or mole %) are plotted on the three axes. Each apex of the triangle represents either 100% fuel, oxygen, or

[11] Hansen and Crowl, "Estimation of the Flammable Zone Boundaries."

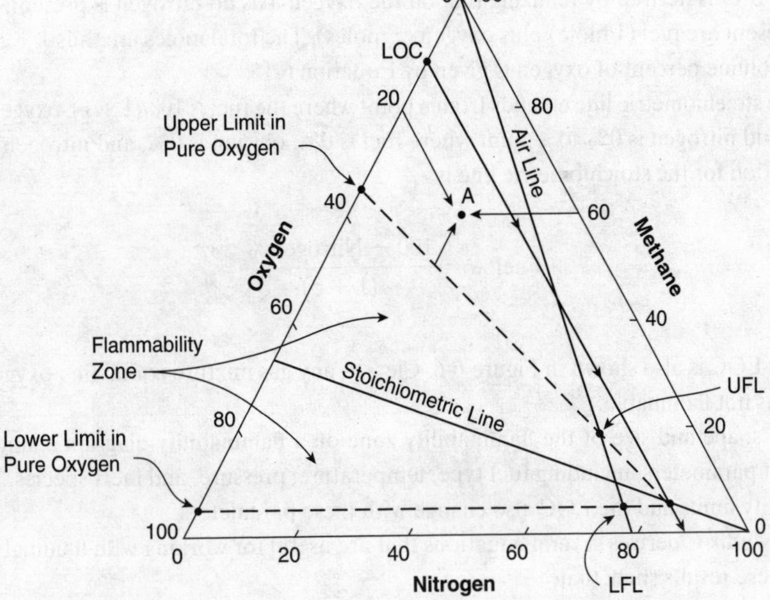

Figure 6-6 Flammability diagram for methane at an initial temperature and pressure of 25°C and 1 atm. Source: C. V. Mashuga and D. A. Crowl, "Application of the Flammability Diagram," 176–183.

nitrogen. The tick marks on the scales show the direction in which the scale moves across the figure. Thus point A represents a mixture composed of 60% methane, 20% oxygen, and 20% nitrogen. The zone enclosed by the dashed line represents all mixtures that are flammable. Because point A lies outside the flammable zone, a mixture of this composition is not flammable.

The air line represents all possible combinations of fuel plus air. The air line extends from the point where fuel is 0%, oxygen is 21%, and nitrogen is 79% to the point where fuel is 100%, oxygen is 0%, and nitrogen is 0%. The equation for this line is

$$\text{Fuel\%} = -\left(\frac{100}{79}\right) \times \text{nitrogen\%} + 100. \tag{6-17}$$

The stoichiometric line represents all stoichiometric combinations of fuel plus oxygen. The combustion reaction can be written in the form

$$\text{Fuel} + zO_2 \rightarrow \text{combustion products}, \tag{6-18}$$

where z is the stoichiometric coefficient for oxygen. The intersection of the stoichiometric line with the oxygen axis (in volume % oxygen) is given by

$$100\left(\frac{z}{1+z}\right). \tag{6-19}$$

Equation 6-19 is derived by realizing that on the oxygen axis no nitrogen is present. Thus the moles present are fuel (1 mole) plus oxygen (z moles). The total moles are thus $1 + z$, and the mole or volume percent of oxygen is given by Equation 6-15.

The stoichiometric line extends from a point where the fuel is $100/(1 + z)$, oxygen is $100z/(1 + z)$, and nitrogen is 0% to a point where fuel is 0%, oxygen is 0%, and nitrogen is 100%. The equation for the stoichiometric line is

$$\text{Fuel}\% = \frac{100 - \text{Nitrogen}\%}{(1 + z)}. \qquad (6\text{-}20)$$

The LOC is also shown in Figure 6-6. Clearly, any gas mixture containing oxygen below the LOC is not flammable.

The shape and size of the flammability zone on a flammability diagram change with a number of parameters, including fuel type, temperature, pressure, and inert species. Thus the flammability limits and the LOC also change with these parameters.

Appendix C derives several equations that are useful for working with flammability diagrams. These results show that:

1. If two gas mixtures R and S are combined, the resulting mixture composition lies on a line connecting the points R and S on the flammability diagram. The location of the final mixture on the straight line depends on the relative moles in the mixtures combined: If mixture S has more moles, the final mixture point will lie closer to point S. This is identical to the lever rule used for phase diagrams.
2. If a mixture R is continuously diluted with mixture S, the mixture composition follows along the straight line between points R and S on the flammability diagram. As the dilution continues, the mixture composition moves closer and closer to point S. Eventually, at infinite dilution the mixture composition is at point S.
3. For systems having composition points that fall on a straight line passing through an apex corresponding to one pure component, the other two components are present in a fixed ratio along the entire line length.
4. The LOC can be estimated by reading the oxygen concentration at the intersection of the stoichiometric line and a horizontal line drawn through the LFL (see Appendix C). This is equivalent to the equation

$$\text{LOC} = z(\text{LFL}). \qquad (6\text{-}15)$$

These results are useful for tracking the gas composition during a process operation to determine whether a flammable mixture exists during the procedure. For example, consider a storage vessel containing pure methane whose inside walls must be inspected as part of its periodic maintenance procedure. For this operation the methane must be removed from the vessel and replaced by air for the inspection workers to breathe. The first step in the procedure is to depressurize the vessel to atmospheric pressure. At this point the vessel contains 100% methane, represented by point A in Figure 6-7. If the vessel is opened and air is allowed to enter, the composition of gas within the vessel will follow the air line in Figure 6-7 until the vessel gas composition eventually reaches point B, pure air. Note that at some point in this operation the gas composition passes through the flammability zone. If an ignition source of sufficient strength were present, then a fire or explosion would result.

The procedure is reversed for placing the vessel back into service. In this case the procedure begins at point B in Figure 6-7, with the vessel containing air. If the vessel is closed and methane is pumped in, then the gas composition inside the vessel will follow the air line and finish at point A. Again, the mixture is flammable as the gas composition moves through the flammability zone.

An inerting procedure can be used to avoid the flammability zone for both cases. This is discussed in more detail in Chapter 7.

The determination of a complete flammability diagram requires several hundred tests using a specific testing apparatus (see Figure 6-15 on page 272). Diagrams with experimental data for methane, ethylene, and hydrogen are shown in Figures 6-8 to 6-10, respectively. Data in the center region of the flammability zone are not available because the maximum pressure

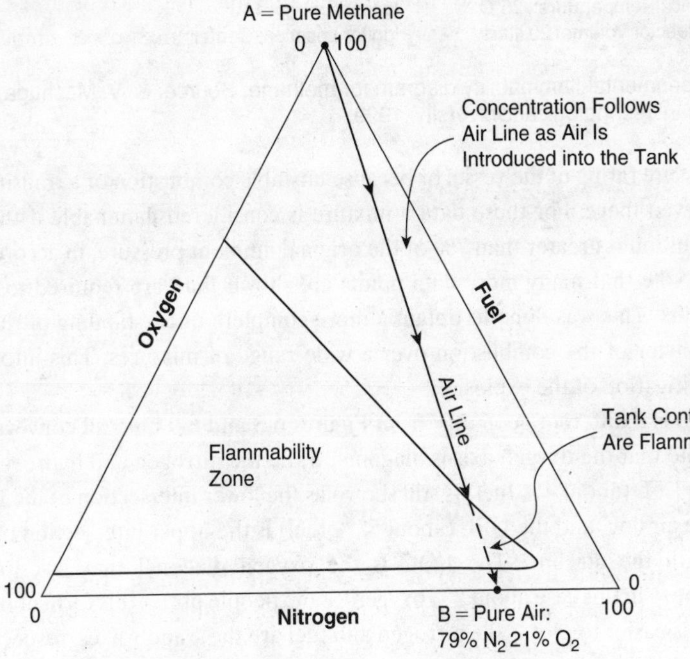

Figure 6-7 The gas concentration during an operation to remove a vessel from service.

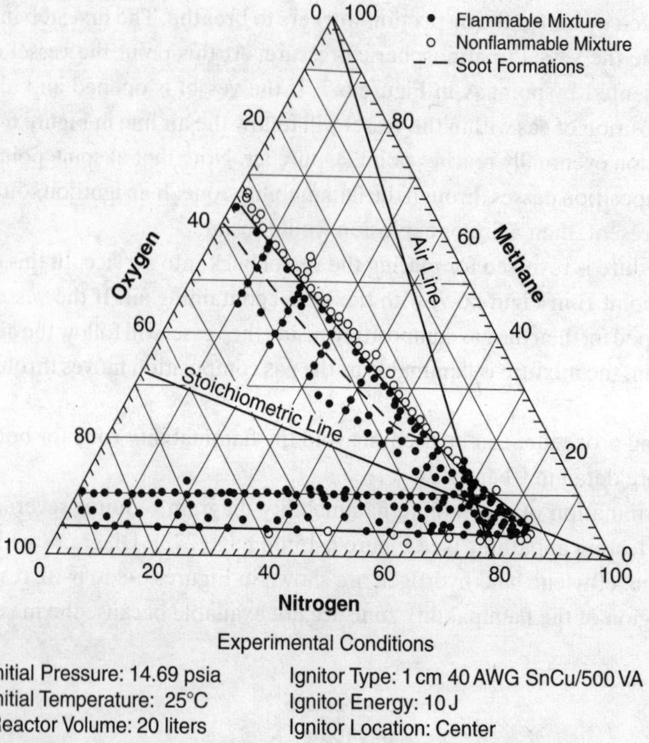

Figure 6-8 Experimental flammability diagram for methane. Source: C. V. Mashuga, Ph.D. dissertation, Michigan Technological University, 1999.

exceeds the pressure rating of the vessel or because unstable combustion or a transition to detonation is observed there. For these data a mixture is considered flammable if the pressure increase after ignition is greater than 7% of the original ambient pressure, in accordance with ASTM E918.[12] Note that many more data points are shown than are required to define the flammability limits. This was done to obtain a more complete understanding of the pressure versus time behavior of the combustion over a wide range of mixtures. This information is important for mitigation of the explosion.

Figure 6-10 is a different geometry from Figures 6-8 and 6-9 but still conveys the same information. Note that the oxygen axis is diagonal, while the nitrogen and hydrogen axes are rectangular. The LFL (about 4% fuel) is still shown as the lower intersection of the flammability zone with the air line, and the UFL (about 75% fuel) is the upper intersection of the flammaility zone with the air line. The LOC is the oxygen diagonal that just touches the flammability zone – in this case about 5% oxygen. Some people prefer this form of the triangle diagram since it is easier to plot – the nitrogen and fuel are the *x* and *y* axes, respectively.

[12] ASTM E918-83, *Standard Practice for Determining Limits of Flammability of Chemicals at Elevated Temperature and Pressure* (W. Conshocken, PA: ASTM, 2005).

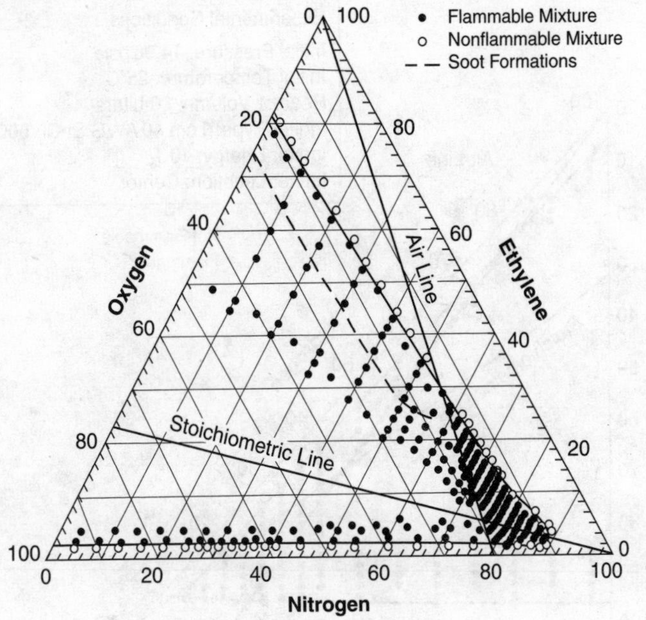

Figure 6-9 Experimental flammability diagram for ethylene. Source: C. V. Mashuga, Ph.D. dissertation, Michigan Technological University, 1999.

A number of important features are shown in Figures 6-8 to 6-10. First, the size of the flammability zone increases from methane to ethylene to hydrogen – the UFL is correspondingly higher. Second, the combustion of the methane and ethylene produces copious amounts of soot in the upper fuel-rich parts of the flammability zone. There is no soot with hydrogen because there is no carbon. Finally, the lower boundary of the flammability zone is mostly horizontal and can be approximated by the LFL.

For most flammable materials, detailed experimental data of the type shown in Figures 6-8 to 6-10 are unavailable. Several methods have been developed to approximate the flammability zone:

Method 1 (Figure 6-11): Given the flammability limits in air, the LOC, and flammability limits in pure oxygen, the procedure is as follows:

1. Draw flammability limits in air as points on the air line.
2. Draw flammability limits in pure oxygen as points on the oxygen scale.

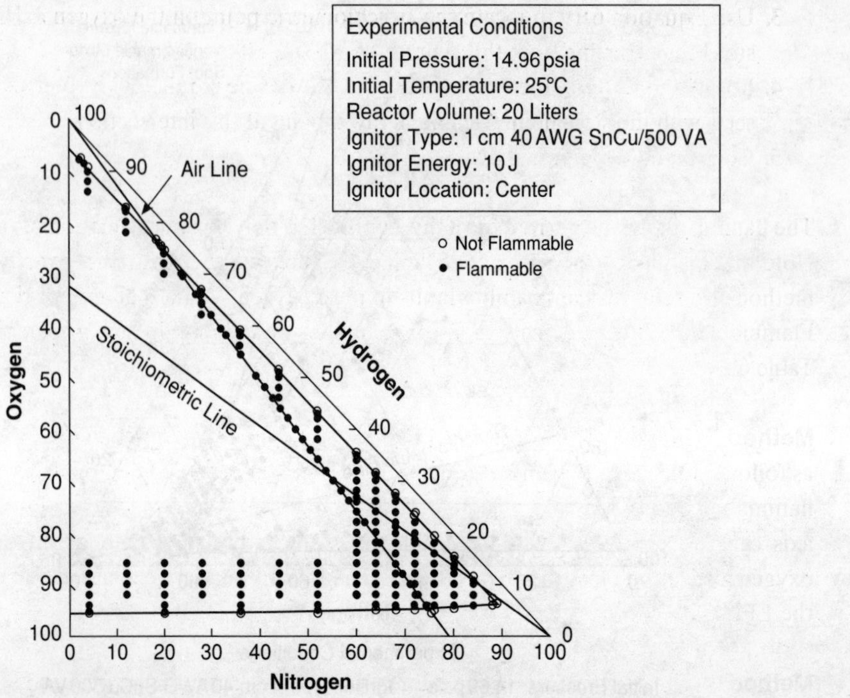

Figure 6-10 Experimental flammability diagram for hydrogen. This is a different geometry but still conveys the same information. (Source: Y. D. Jo and D. A. Crowl, Michigan Technological University, 2006.)

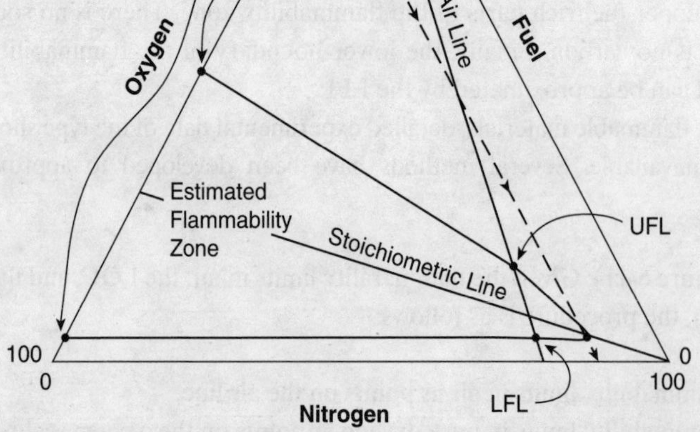

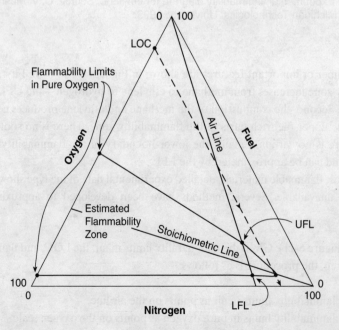

Figure 6-11 Method 1 for the approximation of the flammability zone.

3. Use Equation 6-19 to locate the stoichiometric point on the oxygen axis, and draw the stoichiometric line from this point to the 100% nitrogen apex.
4. Locate the LOC on the oxygen axis, and draw a line parallel to the fuel axis until it intersects with the stoichiometric line. Draw a point at this intersection.
5. Connect all the points shown.

The flammability zone derived from this approach is only an approximation of the actual zone. Note that the lines defining the zone limits in Figures 6-8 to 6-10 are not exactly straight. This method also requires flammability limits in pure oxygen – data that are not readily available. Flammability limits in pure oxygen for a number of common hydrocarbons are provided in Table 6-2.

Method 2 (Figure 6-12): Given the flammability limits in air and the LOC, the procedure is as follows: Use steps 1, 3, and 4 from method 1. In this case only the points at the nose of the flammability zone can be connected. The flammability zone from the air line to the oxygen axis cannot be detailed without additional data, although it extends all the way to the oxygen axis and typically expands in size. The lower boundary can also be approximated by the LFL.

Method 3 (Figure 6-13): Given the flammability limits in air, the procedure is as follows: Use steps 1 and 3 from method 1. Estimate the LOC using Equation 6-15 or 6-16. This is only an estimate, and usually (but not always) provides a conservative LOC.

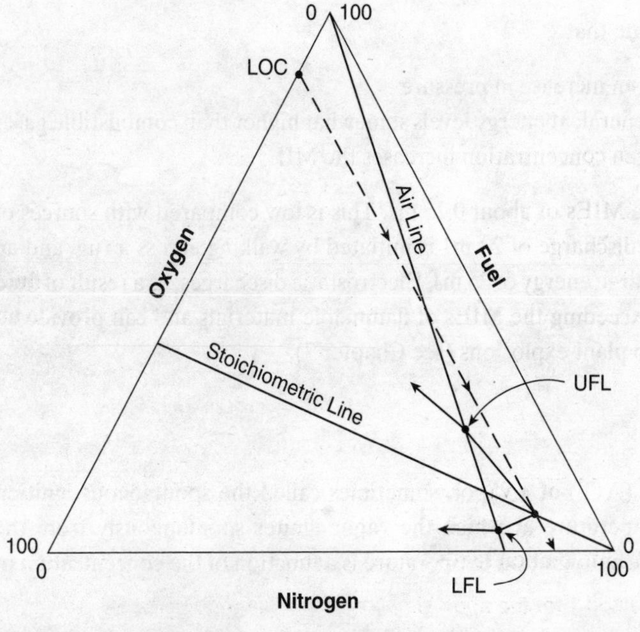

Figure 6-12 Method 2 for the approximation of the flammability zone. Only the area to the right of the air line can be determined.

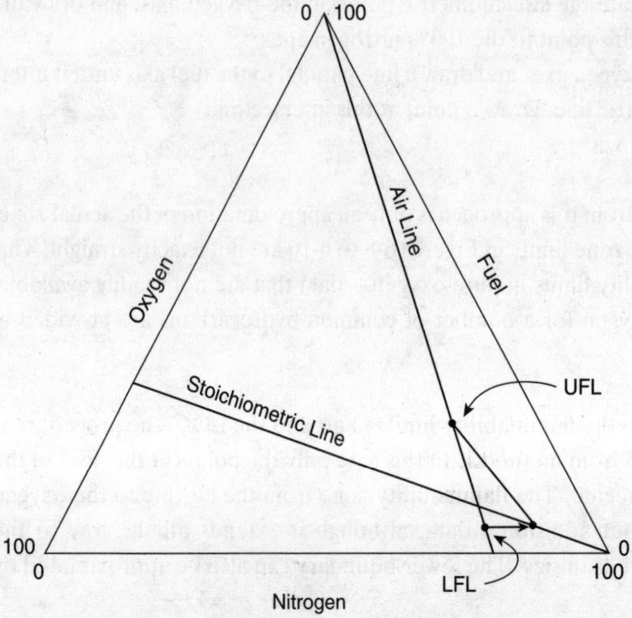

Figure 6-13 Method 3 for the approximation of the flammability zone. Only the area to the right of the air line can be determined.

6-7 Ignition Energy

The minimum ignition energy (MIE) is the minimum energy input required to initiate combustion. All flammable materials (including dusts) have MIEs. The MIE depends on the specific chemical or mixture, the concentration, pressure, and temperature. A few MIEs are given in Table 6-4.

Experimental data indicate that

- The MIE decreases with an increase in pressure
- The MIE of dusts is, in general, at energy levels somewhat higher than combustible gases
- An increase in the nitrogen concentration increases the MIE

Many hydrocarbons have MIEs of about 0.25 mJ. This is low compared with sources of ignition. For example, a static discharge of 22 mJ is initiated by walking across a rug, and an ordinary spark plug has a discharge energy of 25 mJ. Electrostatic discharges, as a result of fluid flow, also have energy levels exceeding the MIEs of flammable materials and can provide an ignition source, contributing to plant explosions (see Chapter 7).

6-8 Autoignition

The autoignition temperature (AIT) of a vapor, sometimes called the spontaneous ignition temperature (SIT), is the temperature at which the vapor ignites spontaneously from the energy of the environment. The autoignition temperature is a function of the concentration of

Table 6-4 Minimum Ignition Energy for Selected Gases[a]

Chemical	Minimum ignition energy (mJ)
Acetylene	0.020
Benzene	0.225
1,3-Butadiene	0.125
n-Butane	0.260
Cyclohexane	0.223
Cyclopropane	0.180
Ethane	0.240
Ethene	0.124
Ethylacetate	0.480
Ethylene oxide	0.062
n-Heptane	0.240
Hexane	0.248
Hydrogen	0.018
Methane	0.280
Methanol	0.140
Methyl acetylene	0.120
Methyl ethyl ketone	0.280
n-Pentane	0.220
2-Pentane	0.180
Propane	0.250

[a]Data from I. Glassman, *Combustion,* 3rd ed. (New York: Academic Press, 1996).

vapor, volume of vapor, pressure of the system, presence of catalytic material, and flow conditions. It is essential to experimentally determine AITs at conditions as close as possible to process conditions.

Composition affects the AIT; rich or lean mixtures have higher AITs. Larger system volumes decrease AITs; an increase in pressure decreases AITs; and increases in oxygen concentration decrease AITs. This strong dependence on conditions illustrates the importance of exercising caution when using AIT data.

AIT data are provided in Appendix B.

6-9 Auto-Oxidation

Auto-oxidation is the process of slow oxidation with accompanying evolution of heat, sometimes leading to autoignition if the energy is not removed from the system. Liquids with relatively low volatility are particularly susceptible to this problem. Liquids with high volatility are less susceptible to autoignition because they self-cool as a result of evaporation.

Many fires are initiated as a result of auto-oxidation, referred to as spontaneous combustion. Some examples of auto-oxidation with a potential for spontaneous combustion include oils on a rag in a warm storage area, insulation on a steam pipe saturated with certain polymers, and filter aid saturated with certain polymers (cases have been recorded where 10-year-old filter aid residues were ignited when the land-filled material was bulldozed, allowing auto-oxidation and eventual autoignition).

These examples illustrate why special precautions must be taken to prevent fires that can result from auto-oxidation and autoignition.

6-10 Adiabatic Compression

An additional means of ignition is adiabatic compression. For example, gasoline and air in an automobile cylinder will ignite if the vapors are compressed to an adiabatic temperature that exceeds the autoignition temperature. This is the cause of preignition knock in engines that are running too hot and too lean.

Several large accidents have been caused by flammable vapors being sucked into the intake of air compressors; subsequent compression resulted in autoignition. A compressor is particularly susceptible to autoignition if it has a fouled after-cooler. Safeguards must be included in the process design to prevent undesirable fires that can result from adiabatic compression.

The adiabatic temperature increase for an ideal gas is computed from the thermodynamic adiabatic compression equation:

$$T_f = T_i\left(\frac{P_f}{P_i}\right)^{(\gamma-1)/\gamma}, \tag{6-21}$$

where

T_f is the final absolute temperature,
T_i is the initial absolute temperature,
P_f is the final absolute pressure,
P_i is the initial absolute pressure, and
$\gamma = C_p/C_v$.

The potential consequences of adiabatic temperature increases within a chemical plant are illustrated in the following two examples.

Example 6-8

What is the final temperature after compressing air over liquid hexane from 14.7 psia to 500 psia if the initial temperature is 100°F? The AIT of hexane is 487°C (Appendix B), and γ for air is 1.4.

Solution

From Equation 6-21 we have

$$T_f = (37.8 + 273)\left(\frac{500}{14.7}\right)^{(0.4/1.4)}$$

$$= 851 \text{ K} = 578°\text{C}.$$

This temperature exceeds the AIT for hexane, resulting in an explosion.

Example 6-9

The lubricating oil in piston-type compressors is always found in minute amounts in the cylinder bore; compressor operations must always be maintained well below the AIT of the oil to prevent explosion.

A particular lubricating oil has an AIT of 400°C. Compute the compression ratio required to raise the temperature of air to the AIT of this oil. Assume an initial air temperature of 25°C and 1 atm.

Solution

Equation 6-21 applies. Solving for the compression ratio, we obtain

$$\left(\frac{P_f}{P_i}\right) = \left(\frac{T_f}{T_i}\right)^{\gamma/(\gamma-1)}$$

$$= \left(\frac{400 + 273}{25 + 273}\right)^{1.4/0.4}$$

$$= 17.3.$$

This ratio represents an output pressure of only (17.3)(14.7 psia) = 254 psia. The actual compression ratio or pressure should be kept well below this.

These examples illustrate the importance of careful design, careful monitoring of conditions, and the need for periodic preventive maintenance programs when working with flammable gases and compressors. This is especially important today, because high-pressure process conditions are becoming more common in modern chemical plants.

6-11 Ignition Sources[13]

As illustrated by the fire triangle, fires and explosions can be prevented by eliminating ignition sources. Various ignition sources were tabulated for over 25,000 fires by the Factory Mutual Engineering Corporation and are summarized in Table 6-5. The sources of ignition are numerous; consequently it is impossible to identify and eliminate them all. The main reason for rendering a flammable liquid inert, for example, is to prevent a fire or explosion by ignition from an unidentified source. Although all sources of ignition are not likely to be identified, engineers must still continue to identify and eliminate them.

[13]*Accident Prevention Manual for Industrial Operations* (Chicago: National Safety Council, 1974).

Table 6-5 Ignition Sources of Major Fires[a]

Electrical (wiring of motors)	23%
Smoking	18%
Friction (bearings or broken parts)	10%
Overheated materials (abnormally high temperatures)	8%
Hot surfaces (heat from boilers, lamps, etc.)	7%
Burner flames (improper use of torches, etc.)	7%
Combustion sparks (sparks and embers)	5%
Spontaneous ignition (rubbish, etc.)	4%
Cutting and welding (sparks, arcs, heat, etc.)	4%
Exposure (fires jumping into new areas)	3%
Incendiarism (fires maliciously set)	3%
Mechanical sparks (grinders, crushers, etc.)	2%
Molten substances (hot spills)	2%
Chemical action (processes not in control)	1%
Static sparks (release of accumulated energy)	1%
Lightning (where lightning rods are not used)	1%
Miscellaneous	1%

[a] *Accident Prevention Manual for Industrial Operations.*

Some special situations might occur in a process facility where it is impossible to avoid flammable mixtures. In these cases a thorough safety analysis is required to eliminate all possible ignition sources in each of the units where flammable gases are present.

The elimination of the ignition sources with the greatest probability of occurrence (see Table 6-5) should be given the greatest attention. Combinations of sources must also be investigated. The goal is to eliminate or minimize ignition sources because the probability of a fire or explosion increases rapidly as the number of ignition sources increases. The effort required increases significantly as the size of the plant increases; potential ignition sources may be in the thousands.

6-12 Sprays and Mists[14]

Static electricity is generated when mists or sprays pass through orifices. A charge may accumulate and discharge in a spark. If flammable vapors are present, a fire or explosion will occur.

Mists and sprays also affect flammability limits.[15] For suspensions with drop diameters less than 0.01 mm, the LFL is virtually the same as the substance in vapor form. This is true even at low temperatures where the liquid is nonvolatile and no vapor is present. Mists of this type are formed by condensation.

For mechanically formed mists with drop diameters between 0.01 mm and 0.2 mm the LFL decreases as the drop diameter increases. In experiments with larger drop diameters the LFL was less than one-tenth of the normal LFL. This is important when inerting in the presence of mists.

[14] Frank P. Lees, *Loss Prevention in the Process Industries,* 2nd ed. (Boston: Butterworths, 1996).
[15] J. H. Borgoyne, "The Flammability of Mists and Sprays," *Chemical Process Hazards* (1965), 2: 1.

When sprays have drop diameters between 0.6 mm and 1.5 mm, flame propagation is impossible. In this situation, however, the presence of small drops and/or disturbances that shatter the larger drops may create a hazardous condition.

6-13 Explosions

Explosion behavior depends on a large number of parameters. A summary of the more important parameters is shown in Table 6-6.

Explosion behavior is difficult to characterize. Many approaches to the problem have been undertaken, including theoretical, semiempirical, and empirical studies. Despite these efforts, explosion behavior is still not completely understood. Practicing engineers, therefore, should use extrapolated results cautiously and provide a suitable margin of safety in all designs.

An explosion results from the rapid release of energy. The energy release must be sudden enough to cause a local accumulation of energy at the site of the explosion. This energy is then dissipated by a variety of mechanisms, including formation of a pressure wave, projectiles, thermal radiation, and acoustic energy. The damage from an explosion is caused by the dissipating energy.

If the explosion occurs in a gas, the energy causes the gas to expand rapidly, forcing back the surrounding gas and initiating a pressure wave that moves rapidly outward from the blast source. The pressure wave contains energy, which results in damage to the surroundings. For chemical plants much of the damage from explosions is due to this pressure wave. Thus, in order to understand explosion impacts, we must understand the dynamics of the pressure wave.

A pressure wave propagating in air is called a *blast wave* because the pressure wave is followed by a strong wind. A *shock wave* or shock front results if the pressure front has an abrupt pressure change. A shock wave is expected from highly explosive materials, such as TNT, but it can also occur from the sudden rupture of a pressure vessel. The maximum pressure over ambient pressure is called the *peak overpressure.*

Table 6-6 Parameters Significantly Affecting the Behavior of Explosions

Ambient temperature
Ambient pressure
Composition of explosive material
Physical properties of explosive material
Nature of ignition source: type, energy, and duration
Geometry of surroundings: confined or unconfined
Amount of combustible material
Turbulence of combustible material
Time before ignition
Rate at which combustible material is released

Detonation and Deflagration

The damage effects from an explosion depend highly on whether the explosion results from a detonation or a deflagration. The difference depends on whether the reaction front propagates above or below the speed of sound in the unreacted gases. For ideal gases the speed of sound or sonic velocity is a function of temperature only and has a value of 344 m/s (1129 ft/s) at 20°C. Fundamentally, the sonic velocity is the speed at which information is transmitted through a gas.

In some combustion reactions the reaction front is propagated by a strong pressure wave, which compresses the unreacted mixture in front of the reaction front above its autoignition temperature. This compression occurs rapidly, resulting in an abrupt pressure change or shock in front of the reaction front. This is classified as a detonation, resulting in a reaction front and leading shock wave that propagates into the unreacted mixture at or above the sonic velocity.

For a deflagration the energy from the reaction is transferred to the unreacted mixture by heat conduction and molecular diffusion. These processes are relatively slow, causing the reaction front to propagate at a speed less than the sonic velocity.

Figure 6-14 shows the physical differences between a detonation and a deflagration for a combustion reaction that occurs in the gas phase in the open. For a detonation the reaction front moves at a speed greater than the speed of sound. A shock front is found a short distance in front of the reaction front. The reaction front provides the energy for the shock front and continues to drive it at sonic or greater speeds.

For a deflagration the reaction front propagates at a speed less than the speed of sound. The pressure front moves at the speed of sound in the unreacted gas and moves away from the reaction front. One way to conceptualize the resulting pressure front is to consider the reaction front as producing a series of individual pressure fronts. These pressure fronts move away from the reaction front at the speed of sound and accumulate together in a main pressure front. The main pressure front will continue to grow in size as additional energy and pressure fronts are produced by the reaction front.

The pressure fronts produced by detonations and deflagrations are markedly different. A detonation produces a shock front, with an abrupt pressure rise, a maximum pressure of greater than 10 atm, and total duration of typically less than 1 ms. The pressure front resulting from a deflagration is characteristically wide (many milliseconds in duration), flat (without an abrupt shock front), and with a maximum pressure much lower than the maximum pressure for a detonation (typically 1 or 2 atm).

The behaviors of the reaction and pressure fronts differ from those shown in Figure 6-14 depending on the local geometry constraining the fronts. Different behavior occurs if the fronts propagate in a closed vessel, a pipeline, or through a congested process unit. The gas dynamic behavior for complex geometries is beyond the scope of this text.

A deflagration can also evolve into a detonation. This is called a deflagration to detonation transition (DDT). The transition is particularly common in pipes but unlikely in vessels or open

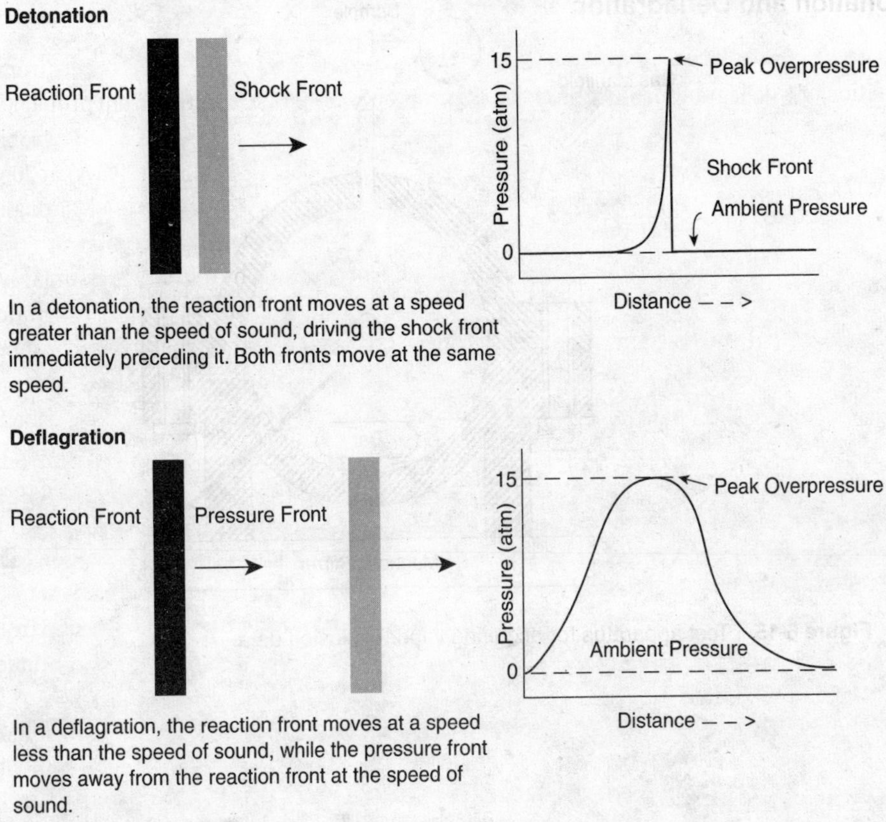
Detonation
Reaction Front
Shock Front
15
Pressure (atm)
0
Peak Overpressure
Shock Front
Ambient Pressure
Distance – – >
In a detonation, the reaction front moves at a speed greater than the speed of sound, driving the shock front immediately preceding it. Both fronts move at the same speed.
Deflagration
Reaction Front
Pressure Front
15
Pressure (atm)
0
Peak Overpressure
Ambient Pressure
Distance – – >
In a deflagration, the reaction front moves at a speed less than the speed of sound, while the pressure front moves away from the reaction front at the speed of sound.

Figure 6-14 Comparison of detonation and deflagration gas dynamics. The explosion is initiated to the far left.

spaces. In a piping system energy from a deflagration can feed forward to the pressure wave, resulting in an increase in the adiabatic pressure rise. The pressure builds and results in a full detonation.

Confined Explosions

A confined explosion occurs in a confined space, such as a vessel or a building. The two most common confined explosion scenarios involve explosive vapors and explosive dusts. Empirical studies have shown that the nature of the explosion is a function of several experimentally determined characteristics. These characteristics depend on the explosive material used and include flammability or explosive limits, the rate of pressure rise after the flammable mixture is ignited, and the maximum pressure after ignition. These characteristics are determined using two similar laboratory devices, shown in Figures 6-15 and 6-18.

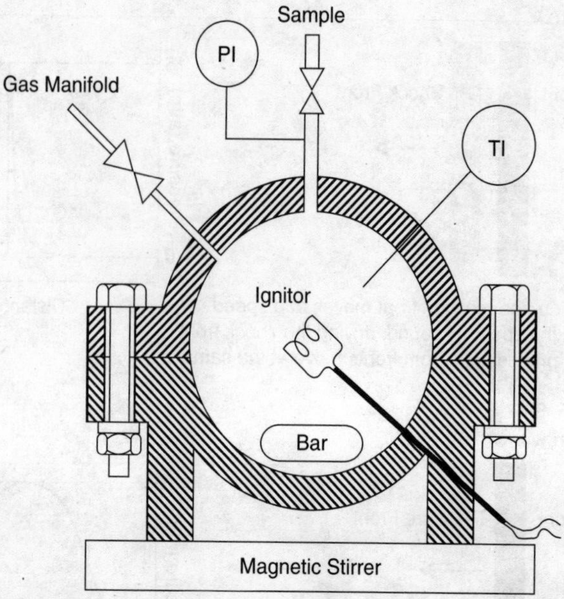

Figure 6-15 Test apparatus for acquiring vapor explosion data.

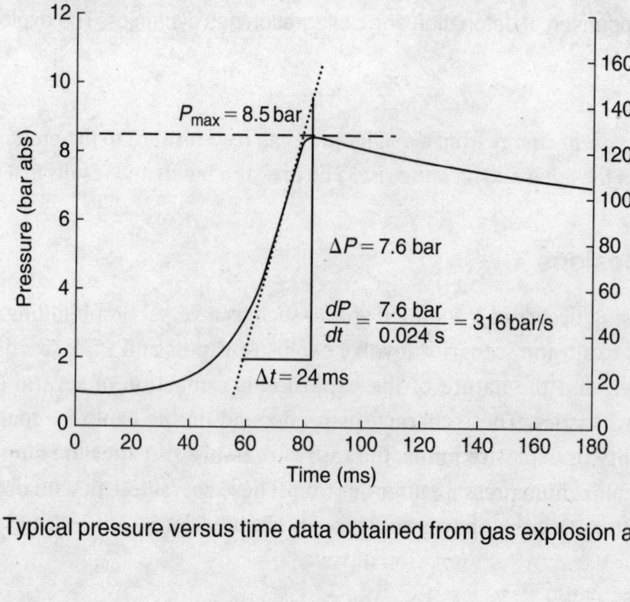

Figure 6-16 Typical pressure versus time data obtained from gas explosion apparatus shown in Figure 6-15.

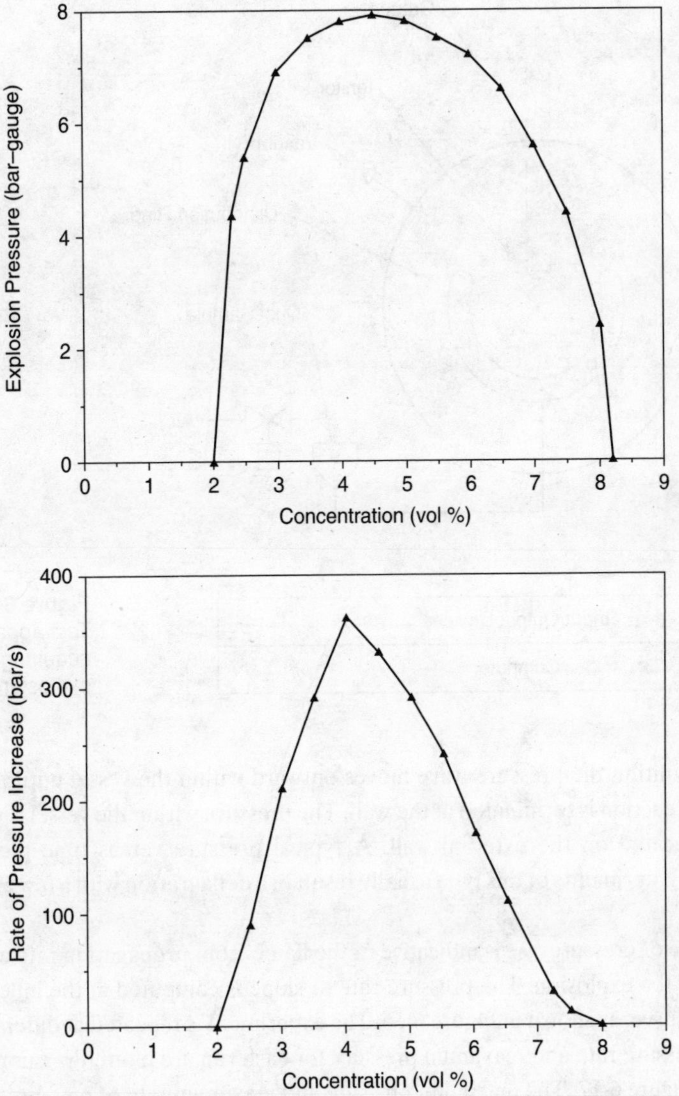

Figure 6-17 Pressure rate and maximum explosion pressure as a function of vapor concentration. The maximum pressure rate does not necessarily occur at the maximum pressure.

Explosion Apparatus for Vapors

The apparatus used to determine the explosive nature of vapors is shown in Figure 6-15. The test procedure includes (1) evacuating the vessel, (2) adjusting the temperature, (3) metering in the gases to obtain the proper mixture, (4) igniting the gas by a spark or fuse wire, and (5) measuring the pressure as a function of time.

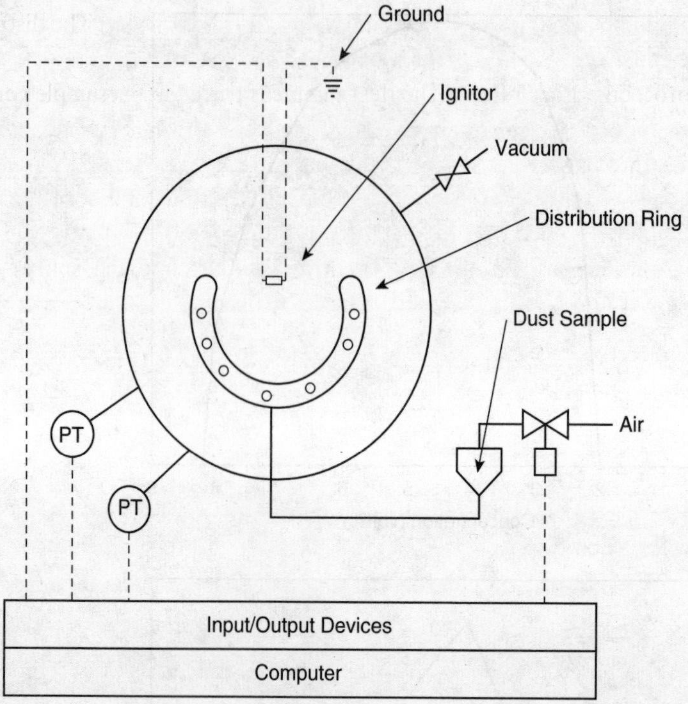

Figure 6-18
Test apparatus for acquiring dust explosion data.

After ignition the pressure wave moves outward within the vessel until it collides with the wall; the reaction is terminated at the wall. The pressure within the vessel is measured by a transducer located on the external wall. A typical pressure versus time plot is shown in Figure 6-16. Experiments of this type usually result in a deflagration with a few atmospheres of pressure rise.

The rate of pressure rise is indicative of the flame front propagation rate and thus of the magnitude of the explosion. The pressure rate or slope is computed at the inflection point of the pressure curve, as shown in Figure 6-16. The experiment is repeated at different concentrations. The pressure rate and maximum pressure for each run are plotted versus concentration, as shown in Figure 6-17. The maximum pressure and maximum rate of pressure rise are determined. Typically, the maximum pressure and pressure rates occur somewhere within the range of flammability (but not necessarily at the same concentration). By using this relatively simple set of experiments, the explosive characteristics can be completely established; in this example the flammability limits are between 2% and 8%, the maximum pressure is 7.4 bar, and the maximum rate of pressure rise is 360 bar/s.

Explosion Apparatus for Dusts

The experimental apparatus used to characterize the explosive nature of dusts is shown in Figure 6-18. The device is similar to the vapor explosion apparatus, with the exception of a larger volume and the addition of a sample container and a dust distribution ring. The distribution ring ensures proper mixing of the dust before ignition.

The experimental procedure is as follows. The dust sample is placed in the sample container. The computer system opens the solenoid valve, and the dust is driven by air pressure from the sample container through the distribution ring and into the dust sphere. After a delay of several milliseconds to ensure proper mixing and distribution of the dust, the ignitor is discharged. The computer measures the pressure as a function of time using high- and low-speed pressure transducers. The air used to drive the dust into the sphere is carefully metered to ensure a pressure of 1 atm (0.987 bar) within the sphere at ignition time. A typical pressure versus time plot from the dust explosion apparatus is shown in Figure 6-19.

The data are collected and analyzed in the same fashion as for the vapor explosion apparatus. The maximum pressure and the maximum rate of pressure increase are determined, as well as the flammability limits.

Explosion Characteristics

The explosion characteristics determined using the vapor and dust explosion apparatus are used in the following way:

1. The limits of flammability or explosivity are used to determine the safe concentrations for operation or the quantity of inert material required to control the concentration within safe regions.
2. The maximum rate of pressure increase indicates the robustness of an explosion. Thus, the explosive behavior of different materials can be compared on a relative basis. The maximum rate is also used to design a vent for relieving a vessel during an explosion before the pressure ruptures the vessel or to establish the time interval for adding an explosion suppressant (water, carbon dioxide, or other) to stop the combustion process.

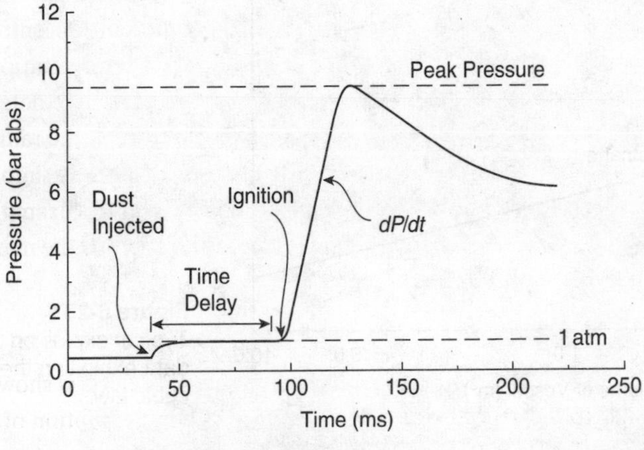

Figure 6-19 Pressure data from dust explosion device.

A plot of the logarithm of the maximum pressure slope versus the logarithm of the vessel volume frequently produces a straight line of slope −1/3, as shown in Figure 6-20. This relationship is called the cubic law:

$$(dP/dt)_{\max}V^{1/3} = \text{constant} = K_{\text{G}}, \tag{6-22}$$

$$(dP/dt)_{\max}V^{1/3} = K_{\text{St}}, \tag{6-23}$$

where K_{G} and K_{St} are the deflagration indexes for gas and dust, respectively. As the robustness of an explosion increases, the deflagration indexes K_{G} and K_{St} increase. The cubic law states that the pressure front takes longer to propagate through a larger vessel. $P_{\max}$ and K_{G} and K_{St} data for vapors and dusts are shown in Tables 6-7 and 6-8, respectively. Table 6-7 shows that good agreement is found between different investigations for the maximum pressure but that only limited agreement is found for the K_{G} values. It is postulated that the K_{G} values are sensitive to experimental configuration and conditions. Dusts are further classified into four classes, depending on the value of the deflagration index. These *St classes* are shown in Table 6-8.

Equations 6-22 and 6-23 are used to estimate the consequences of an explosion in a confined space, such as a building or a vessel, as follows:

$$\left[\left(\frac{dP}{dt}\right)_{\max} V^{1/3}\right]_{\text{in vessel}} = \left[\left(\frac{dP}{dt}\right)_{\max} V^{1/3}\right]_{\text{experimental}}. \tag{6-24}$$

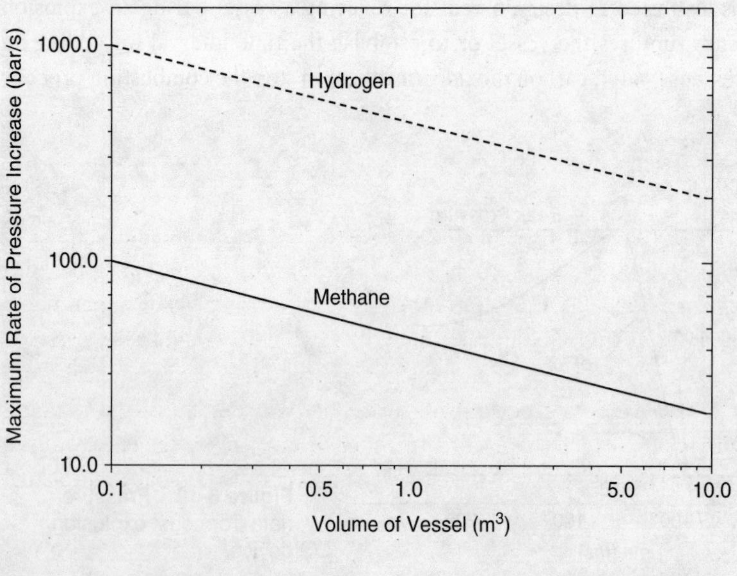

Figure 6-20 Typical explosion data exhibiting the cubic law.

Table 6-7 Maximum Pressures and Deflagration Indexes for a Number of Gases and Vapors[a]

	Maximum pressure P_{max} (bar g)			Deflagration index K_G (bar-m/s)		
Chemical	**NFPA 68 (1997)**	**Bartknecht (1993)**	**Senecal and Beaulieu (1998)**	**NFPA 68 (1997)**	**Bartknecht (1993)**	**Senecal and Beaulieu (1998)**
Acetylene	10.6	–	–	109	–	–
Ammonia	5.4	–	–	10	–	–
Butane	8.0	8.0	–	92	92	–
Carbon disulfide	6.4	–	–	105	–	–
Diethyl ether	8.1	–	–	115	–	–
Ethane	7.8	7.8	7.4	106	106	78
Ethyl alcohol	7.0	–	–	78	–	–
Ethyl benzene	6.6	7.4	–	94	96	–
Ethylene	–	–	8.0	–	–	171
Hydrogen	6.9	6.8	6.5	659	550	638
Hydrogen sulfide	7.4	–		45	–	–
Isobutane			7.4	–	–	67
Methane	7.05	7.1	6.7	64	55	46
Methyl alcohol	–	7.5	7.2	–	75	94
Methylene chloride	5.0	–	–	5	–	–
Pentane	7.65	7.8	–	104	104	–
Propane	7.9	7.9	7.2	96	100	76
Toluene	–	7.8	–	–	94	–

[a]Data selected from:

NFPA 68, *Venting of Deflagrations* (Quincy, MA: National Fire Protection Association, 1997).

W. Bartknecht, *Explosions-Schutz: Grundlagen und Anwendung* (New York: Springer-Verlag, 1993).

J. A. Senecal and P. A. Beaulieu, "K_G: Data and Analysis," in *31st Loss Prevention Symposium* (New York: American Institute of Chemical Engineers, 1997).

The subscript "in vessel" is for the reactor or building. The subscript "experimental" applies to data determined in the laboratory using either the vapor or dust explosion apparatus. Equation 6-24 allows the experimental results from the dust and vapor explosion apparatus to be applied to determining the explosive behavior of materials in buildings and process vessels. This is discussed in more detail in Chapter 10. The constants K_G and K_{St} are not physical properties of the material because they are dependent on (1) the composition of the mixture, (2) the mixing within the vessel, (3) the shape of the reaction vessel, and (4) the energy of the ignition source. It is therefore necessary to run the experiments as close as possible to the actual conditions under consideration.

Table 6-8 St Classes for Dusts and Combustion Data for Dust Clouds[a]

Deflagration index, K_{St} (bar m/s)	St class
0	St-0
1–200	St-1
200–300	St-2
>300	St-3

Dust	Median particle size (μm)	Minimum explosive dust concentration (g/m³)	P_{max} (bar g)	K_{St} (bar-m/s)	Minimum ignition energy (mJ)
Cotton, wood, peat					
Cotton	44	100	7.2	24	–
Cellulose	51	60	9.3	66	250
Wood dust	33	–	–	–	100
Wood dust	80	–	–	–	7
Paper dust	<10	–	5.7	18	–
Feed, food					
Dextrose	80	60	4.3	18	–
Fructose	200	125	6.4	27	180
Fructose	400	–	–	–	>4000
Wheat grain dust	80	60	9.3	112	–
Milk powder	165	60	8.1	90	75
Rice flour	–	60	7.4	57	>100
Wheat flour	50	–	–	–	540
Milk sugar	10	60	8.3	75	14
Coal, coal products					
Activated carbon	18	60	8.8	44	–
Bituminous coal	<10	–	9.0	55	–
Plastics, resins, rubber					
Polyacrylamide	10	250	5.9	12	–
Polyester	<10	–	10.1	194	–
Polyethylene	72	–	7.5	67	–
Polyethylene	280	–	6.2	20	–
Polypropylene	25	30	8.4	101	–
Polypropylene	162	200	7.7	38	–
Polystyrene (copolymer)	155	30	8.4	110	–
Polystyrene (hard foam)	760	–	8.4	23	–
Polyurethane	3	<30	7.8	156	–
Intermediate products, auxiliary materials					
Adipinic acid	<10	60	8.0	97	–
Naphthalene	95	15	8.5	178	<1
Salicylic acid	–	30	–	–	–

Table 6-8 *(continued)*

Dust	Median particle size (μm)	Minimum explosive dust concentration (g/m³)	P_{max} (bar g)	K_{St} (bar-m/s)	Minimum ignition energy (mJ)
Other technical, chemical products					
Organic dyestuff (blue)	<10	–	9.0	73	–
Organic dyestuff (red)	<10	50	11.2	249	–
Organic dyestuff (red)	52	60	9.8	237	–
Metals, alloys					
Aluminum powder	<10	60	11.2	515	–
Aluminum powder	22	30	11.5	110	–
Bronze powder	18	750	4.1	31	–
Iron (from dry filter)	12	500	5.2	50	–
Magnesium	28	30	17.5	508	–
Magnesium	240	500	7.0	12	–
Silicon	<10	125	10.2	126	54
Zinc (dust from collector)	<10	250	6.7	125	–
Other inorganic products					
Graphite (99.5% C)	7	<30	5.9	71	–
Sulfur	20	30	6.8	151	–
Toner	<10	60	8.9	196	4

[a]Data selected from R. K. Eckoff, *Dust Explosions in the Process Industries* (Oxford: Butterworth-Heinemann, 1997).

Experimental studies indicate that the maximum explosion pressure is usually not affected by changes in volume, and the maximum pressure and the maximum pressure rate are linearly dependent on the initial pressure. This is shown in Figure 6-21. As the initial pressure is increased, a point is reached where the deflagration turns into a detonation.

Dust explosions demonstrate unique behavior. These explosions occur if finely divided particles of solid material are dispersed in air and ignited. The dust particles can be either an unwanted by-product or the product itself.

Explosions involving dusts are most common in the flour milling, grain storage, and coal mining industries. Accidents involving dust explosions can be quite substantial; a series of grain silo explosions in Westwego near New Orleans in 1977 killed 35 people.[16]

An initial dust explosion can cause secondary explosions. The primary explosion sends a shock wave through the plant, stirring up additional dust, possibly resulting in a secondary explosion. In this fashion the explosion leapfrogs its way through a plant. Many times the secondary explosions are more damaging than the primary explosion.

[16]S. Mannan, ed., *Lees' Loss Prevention in the Process Industries*, 3rd ed. (Amsterdam: Elsevier, 2005), p. A1/48.

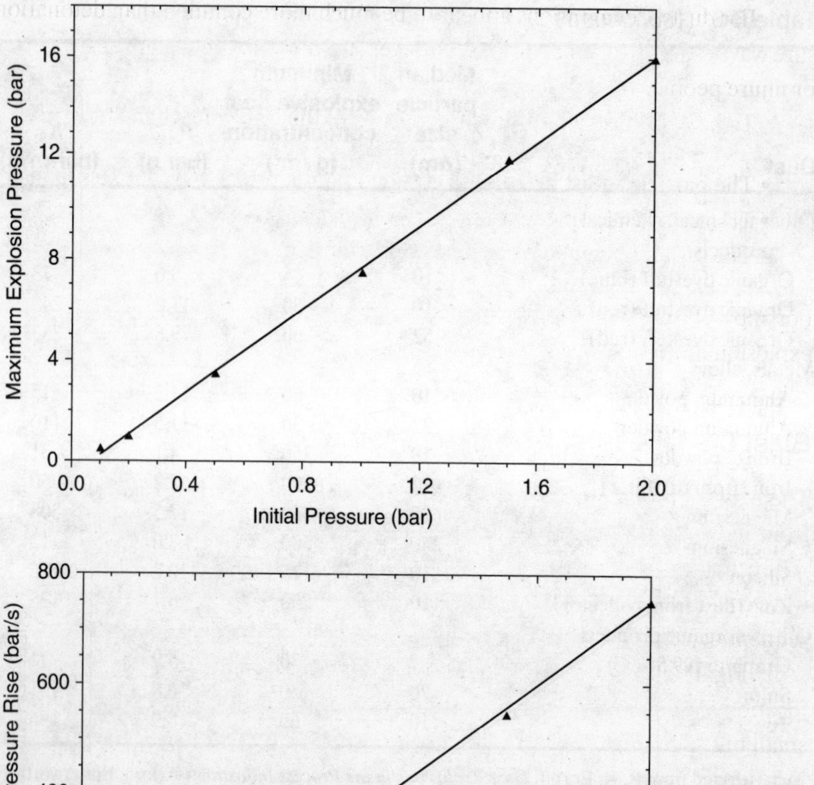

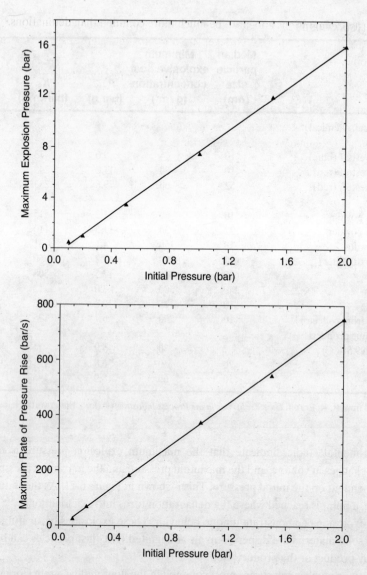

Figure 6-21 Effect of initial pressure on maximum explosion pressure and rate. Data from W. Bartknecht, *Explosions* (New York: Springer-Verlag, 1981).

Dust explosions are even more difficult to characterize than gaseous explosions. For a gas the molecules are small and of well-defined size. For dust particles the particles are of varying size and many orders of magnitude larger than molecules. Gravity also affects dust particle behavior.

For dusts, deflagrations appear to be much more common than detonations.[17] The pressure waves from dust deflagrations, however, are powerful enough to destroy structures and kill or injure people.

To be explosive, a dust mixture must have the following characteristics:

- The particles must be below a certain minimum size, typically less than 400 microns.
- The particle loading must be between certain limits.
- The dust loading must be reasonably uniform.

For most dusts[18] the lower explosion limit is between 20 g/m^3 and 60 g/m^3 and the upper explosion limit is between 2 kg/m^3 and 6 kg/m^3.

Blast Damage Resulting from Overpressure

The explosion of a dust or gas (either as a deflagration or a detonation) results in a reaction front moving outward from the ignition source preceded by a shock wave or pressure front. After the combustible material is consumed, the reaction front terminates, but the pressure wave continues its outward movement. A blast wave is composed of the pressure wave and subsequent wind. It is the blast wave that causes most of the damage.

Figure 6-22 shows the variation in pressure with time for a typical shock wave at a fixed location some distance from the explosion site. The explosion occurs at time t_0. There exists a small but finite time t_1 before the shock front travels from its explosive origin to the affected location. This time, t_1, is called the arrival time. At t_1 the shock front has arrived and a peak overpressure is observed, immediately followed by a strong transient wind. The pressure quickly decreases to ambient pressure at time t_2, but the wind continues in the same direction for a short time. The time period t_1 to t_2 is called the shock duration. The shock duration is the period of greatest destruction to free-standing structures, so its value is important for estimating damage. The decreasing pressure continues to drop below ambient pressure to a maximum underpressure at time t_3. For most of the underpressure period from t_2 to t_4 the blast wind reverses direction and flows toward the explosive origin. There is some damage associated with the underpressure period, but because the maximum underpressure is only a few psi for typical explosions, the damage is much less than that of the overpressure period. The underpressure for large explosions and nuclear explosions, however, can be quite large, resulting in considerable damage. After attaining the maximum underpressure t_3, the pressure will approach ambient pressure at t_4. At this time the blast wind and the direct destruction have terminated.

[17]Lees, *Loss Prevention in the Process Industries,* p. 17/265.
[18]Bartknecht, *Explosions*, p. 27.

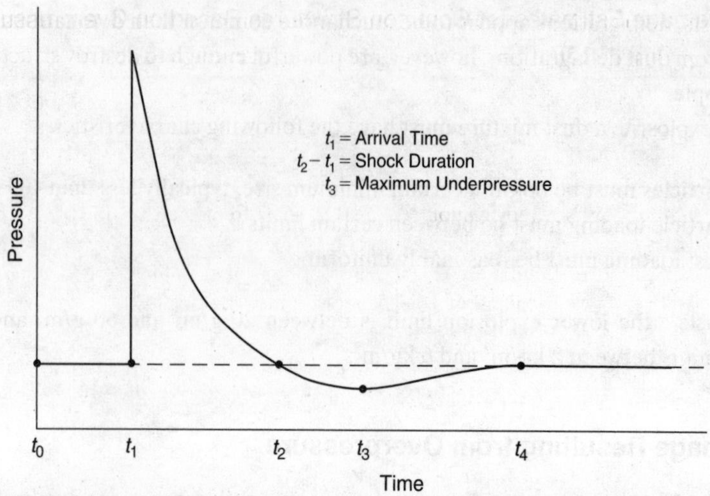

Figure 6-22 Blast wave pressure at a fixed location.

An important consideration is how the pressure is measured as the blast wave passes. If the pressure transducer is at right angles to the blast wave, the overpressure measured is called the side-on overpressure (sometimes called the free-field overpressure). At a fixed location, shown in Figure 6-22, the side-on overpressure increases abruptly to its maximum value (peak side-on overpressure) and then drops off as the blast wave passes. If the pressure transducer is placed facing toward the oncoming shock wave, then the measured pressure is the reflected overpressure. The reflected overpressure includes the side-on overpressure and the stagnation pressure. The stagnation pressure is due to deceleration of the moving gas as it impacts the pressure transducer. The reflected pressure for low side-on overpressures is about twice the side-on overpressure and can reach as high as eight or more times the side-on overpressure for strong shocks. The reflected overpressure is a maximum when the blast wave arrives normal to the wall or object of concern and decreases as the angle changes from normal. Many references report overpressure data without clearly stating how the overpressure is measured. In general, overpressure implies the side-on overpressure and frequently the peak side-on overpressure.

Blast damage is based on the determination of the peak side-on overpressure resulting from the pressure wave impacting on a structure. In general, the damage is also a function of the rate of pressure increase and the duration of the blast wave. Good estimates of blast damage, however, are obtained using just the peak side-on overpressure.

Damage estimates based on overpressures are given in Table 6-9. As illustrated, significant damage is expected for even small overpressures.

Table 6-9 Damage Estimates for Common Structures Based on Overpressure (these values are approximations)[a]

Pressure		Damage
psig	kPa	
0.02	0.14	Annoying noise (137 dB if of low frequency, 10–15 Hz)
0.03	0.21	Occasional breaking of large glass windows already under strain
0.04	0.28	Loud noise (143 dB), sonic boom, glass failure
0.1	0.69	Breakage of small windows under strain
0.15	1.03	Typical pressure for glass breakage
0.3	2.07	"Safe distance" (probability 0.95 of no serious damage below this value); projectile limit; some damage to house ceilings; 10% window glass broken
0.4	2.76	Limited minor structural damage
0.5–1.0	3.4–6.9	Large and small windows usually shatter; occasional damage to window frames
0.7	4.8	Minor damage to house structures
1.0	6.9	Partial demolition of houses, made uninhabitable
1–2	6.9–13.8	Corrugated asbestos shatters; corrugated steel or aluminum panels, fastenings fail, followed by buckling; wood panels (standard housing), fastenings fail, panels blow in
1.3	9.0	Steel frame of clad building slightly distorted
2	13.8	Partial collapse of walls and roofs of houses
2–3	13.8–20.7	Concrete or cinder block walls, not reinforced, shatter
2.3	15.8	Lower limit of serious structural damage
2.5	17.2	50% destruction of brickwork of houses
3	20.7	Heavy machines (3000 lb) in industrial buildings suffer little damage; steel frame buildings distort and pull away from foundations
3–4	20.7–27.6	Frameless, self-framing steel panel buildings demolished; rupture of oil storage tanks
4	27.6	Cladding of light industrial buildings ruptures
5	34.5	Wooden utility poles snap; tall hydraulic presses (40,000 lb) in buildings slightly damaged
5–7	34.5–48.2	Nearly complete destruction of houses
7	48.2	Loaded train wagons overturned
7–8	48.2–55.1	Brick panels, 8–12 in thick, not reinforced, fail by shearing or flexure
9	62.0	Loaded train boxcars completely demolished
10	68.9	Probable total destruction of buildings; heavy machine tools (7000 lb) moved and badly damaged, very heavy machine tools (12,000 lb) survive
300	2068	Limit of crater lip

[a] V. J. Clancey, "Diagnostic Features of Explosion Damage," paper presented at the Sixth International Meeting of Forensic Sciences (Edinburgh, 1972).

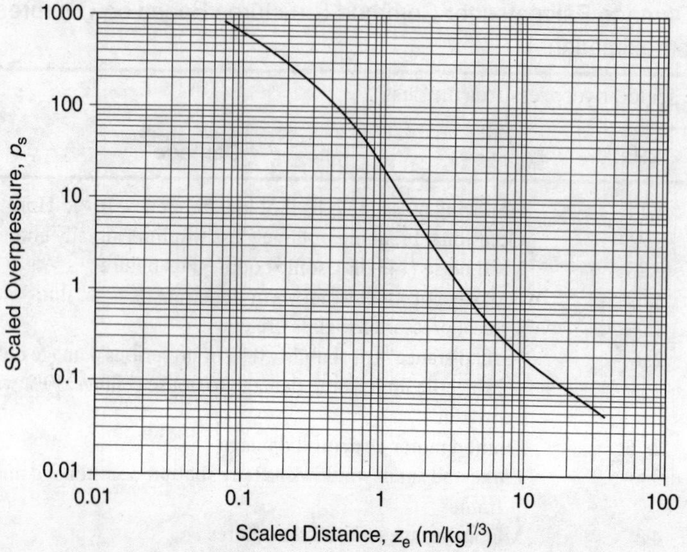

Figure 6-23 Correlation between scaled distance and explosion peak side-on overpressure for a TNT explosion occurring on a flat surface. Source: G. F. Kinney and K. J. Graham, *Explosive Shocks in Air* (Berlin: Springer-Verlag, 1985).

Experiments with explosives have demonstrated[19] that the overpressure can be estimated using an equivalent mass of TNT, denoted m_{TNT}, and the distance from the ground-zero point of the explosion, denoted r. The empirically derived scaling law is

$$\boxed{z_e = \frac{r}{m_{TNT}^{1/3}}.} \tag{6-25}$$

The equivalent energy of TNT is 1120 cal/g.

Figure 6-23 provides a correlation for the scaled overpressure p_s versus scaled distance z_e with units of m/kg$^{1/3}$. To convert ft/lb$^{1/3}$ to m/kg$^{1/3}$, multiply by 0.3967. The scaled overpressure p_s is given by

$$p_s = \frac{p_o}{p_a}, \tag{6-26}$$

[19] W. E. Baker, *Explosions in Air* (Austin: University of Texas Press, 1973); S. Glasstone, *The Effects of Nuclear Weapons* (Washington, DC: US Atomic Energy Commission, 1962).

where

p_s is the scaled overpressure (unitless),
p_o is the peak side-on overpressure, and
p_a is the ambient pressure.

The data in Figure 6-23 are valid only for TNT explosions occurring on a flat surface. For explosions occurring in the open air, well above the ground, the resulting overpressures from Figure 6-23 are multiplied by 0.5. Most explosions occurring in chemical plants are considered to originate on the ground.

The data in Figure 6-23 are also represented by the empirical equation

$$\frac{p_o}{p_a} = \frac{1616\left[1 + \left(\frac{z_e}{4.5}\right)^2\right]}{\sqrt{1 + \left(\frac{z_e}{0.048}\right)^2}\sqrt{1 + \left(\frac{z_e}{0.32}\right)^2}\sqrt{1 + \left(\frac{z_e}{1.35}\right)^2}}. \tag{6-27}$$

The procedure for estimating the overpressure at any distance r resulting from the explosion of a mass of material is as follows: (1) Compute the energy of the explosion using established thermodynamic procedures, (2) convert the energy to an equivalent amount of TNT, (3) use the scaling law and the correlations of Figure 6-23 to estimate the overpressure, and (4) use Table 6-9 to estimate the damage.

Example 6-10

One kilogram of TNT is exploded. Compute the overpressure at a distance of 30 m from the explosion.

Solution

The value of the scaling parameter is determined using Equation 6-25:

$$z_e = \frac{r}{m_{TNT}^{1/3}}$$

$$= \frac{30 \text{ m}}{(1.0 \text{ kg})^{1/3}} = 30 \text{ m kg}^{-1/3}.$$

From Figure 6-23 the scaled overpressure is 0.055. Thus, if the ambient pressure is 1 atm, then the resulting side-on overpressure is estimated at (0.055)(101.3 kPa) = 5.6 kPa (0.81 psi). From Table 6-9 this overpressure will cause minor damage to house structures.

TNT Equivalency

TNT equivalency is a simple method for equating a known energy of a combustible fuel to an equivalent mass of TNT. The approach is based on the assumption that an exploding fuel mass behaves like exploding TNT on an equivalent energy basis. The equivalent mass of TNT is estimated using the following equation:

$$m_{\text{TNT}} = \frac{\eta m \Delta H_c}{E_{\text{TNT}}}, \tag{6-28}$$

where

m_{TNT} is the equivalent mass of TNT (mass),
η is the empirical explosion efficiency (unitless),
m is the mass of hydrocarbon (mass),
ΔH_c is the energy of explosion of the flammable gas (energy/mass), and
E_{TNT} is the energy of explosion of TNT.

A typical value for the energy of explosion of TNT is 1120 cal/g = 4686 kJ/kg = 2016 Btu/lb. The heat of combustion for the flammable gas can be used in place of the energy of explosion for the combustible gas.

The explosion efficiency is one of the major problems in the equivalency method. The explosion efficiency is used to adjust the estimate for a number of factors, including incomplete mixing with air of the combustible material and incomplete conversion of the thermal energy to mechanical energy. The explosion efficiency is empirical, with most flammable cloud estimates varying between 1% and 10%, as reported by a number of sources. Explosion efficiencies can also be defined for solid materials, such as ammonium nitrate.

The TNT equivalency method also uses an overpressure curve that applies to point source detonations of TNT. Vapor cloud explosions (VCEs) are explosions that occur because of the release of flammable vapor over a large volume and are most commonly deflagrations. In addition, the method is unable to consider the effects of flame speed acceleration resulting from confinement. As a result, the overpressure curve for TNT tends to overpredict the overpressure near the VCE and to underpredict at distances away from the VCE.

The advantage to the TNT equivalency method is that it is easy to apply because the calculations are simple.

The procedure to estimate the damage associated with an explosion using the TNT equivalency method is as follows:

1. Determine the total quantity of flammable material involved in the explosion.
2. Estimate the explosion efficiency, and calculate the equivalent mass of TNT using Equation 6-28.
3. Use the scaling law given by Equation 6-25 and Figure 6-23 (or Equation 6-27) to estimate the peak side-on overpressure.
4. Use Table 6-9 to estimate the damage for common structures and process equipment.

The procedure can be applied in reverse to estimate the quantity of material involved based on damage estimates.

TNO Multi-Energy Method

The TNO method identifies the confined volumes in a process, assigns a relative degree of confinement, and then determines the contribution to the overpressure from this confined volume (TNO is the Netherlands Organization for Applied Scientific Research). Semi-empirical curves are used to determine the overpressure.

The basis for this model is that the energy of explosion depends highly on the level of congestion and depends less on the fuel in the cloud.

The procedure for using the multi-energy model for a VCE is as follows:[20]

1. Perform a dispersion model to determine the extent of the cloud. In general, this is done by assuming that equipment and buildings are not present, because of the limitations of dispersion modeling in congested areas.
2. Conduct a field inspection to identify the congested areas. Normally, heavy vapors tend to move downhill.
3. Identify potential sources of strong blast within the area covered by the flammable cloud. Potential sources of strong blast include congested areas and buildings, such as process equipment in chemical plants or refineries, stacks of crates or pallets, and pipe racks; spaces between extended parallel planes (for example, those beneath closely parked cars in parking lots; and open buildings, for instance, multistory parking garages); spaces within tubelike structures (for example, tunnels, bridges, corridors, sewage systems, culverts); and an intensely turbulent fuel-air mixture in a jet resulting from release at high pressure. The remaining fuel-air mixture in the flammable cloud is assumed to produce a blast of minor strength.
4. Estimate the energy of equivalent fuel-air charges by (a) considering each blast source separately, (b) assuming that the full quantities of fuel-air mixture present within the partially confined/obstructed areas and jets, identified as blast sources in the cloud, contribute to the blasts, (c) estimating the volumes of fuel-air mixture present in the individual areas identified as blast sources (this estimate can be based on the overall dimensions of the areas and jets; note that the flammable mixture may not fill an entire blast source volume and that the volume of equipment should be considered where it represents an appreciable proportion of the whole volume); and (d) calculating the combustion energy E (J) for each blast by multiplying the individual volumes of the mixture by 3.5×10^6 J/m^3 (this value is typical for the heat of combustion of an average stoichiometric hydrocarbon-air mixture).
5. Assign a number representative of the blast strength for each individual blast. Some companies have defined procedures for this; however, many risk analysts use their own judgment.

[20] *Guidelines for Evaluating the Characteristics of Vapor Cloud Explosions, Flash Fires, and BLEVEs* (New York: American Institute of Chemical Engineers, 1994).

A safe and most conservative estimate of the strength of the sources of a strong blast can be made if a maximum strength of 10 – representative of a detonation – is assumed. However, a source strength of 7 seems to more accurately represent actual experience. Furthermore, for side-on overpressures below about 0.5 bar, no differences appear for source strengths ranging from 7 to 10.

The blast resulting from the remaining unconfined and unobstructed parts of a cloud can be modeled by assuming a low initial strength. For extended and quiescent parts, assume a minimum strength of 1. For more nonquiescent parts, which are in low-intensity turbulent motion (for instance, because of the momentum of a fuel release), assume a strength of 3.

6. Once the energy quantities E and the initial blast strengths of the individual equivalent fuel-air charges are estimated, the Sachs-scaled blast side-on overpressure and positive-phase duration at some distance R from a blast source is read from the blast charts in Figure 6-24 after calculation of the Sachs-scaled distance:

$$\overline{R} = \frac{R}{(E/P_o)^{1/3}}, \tag{6-29}$$

where

$\overline{R}$ is the Sachs-scaled distance from the charge (dimensionless),
R is the distance from the charge (m),
E is the charge combustion energy (J), and
P_o is the ambient pressure (Pa).

The blast peak side-on overpressure and positive-phase duration are calculated from the Sachs-scaled overpressure and the Sachs-scaled positive-phase duration. The overpressure is given by

$$p_o = \Delta\overline{P}_S \cdot p_a, \tag{6-30}$$

and the positive phase duration is given by

$$t_d = \overline{t}_d \left[\frac{(E/P_o)^{1/3}}{c_o} \right], \tag{6-31}$$

where

P_S is the side-on blast overpressure (Pa),
$\Delta\overline{P}_S$ is the Sachs-scaled side-on blast overpressure (dimensionless),
p_a is the ambient pressure (Pa),

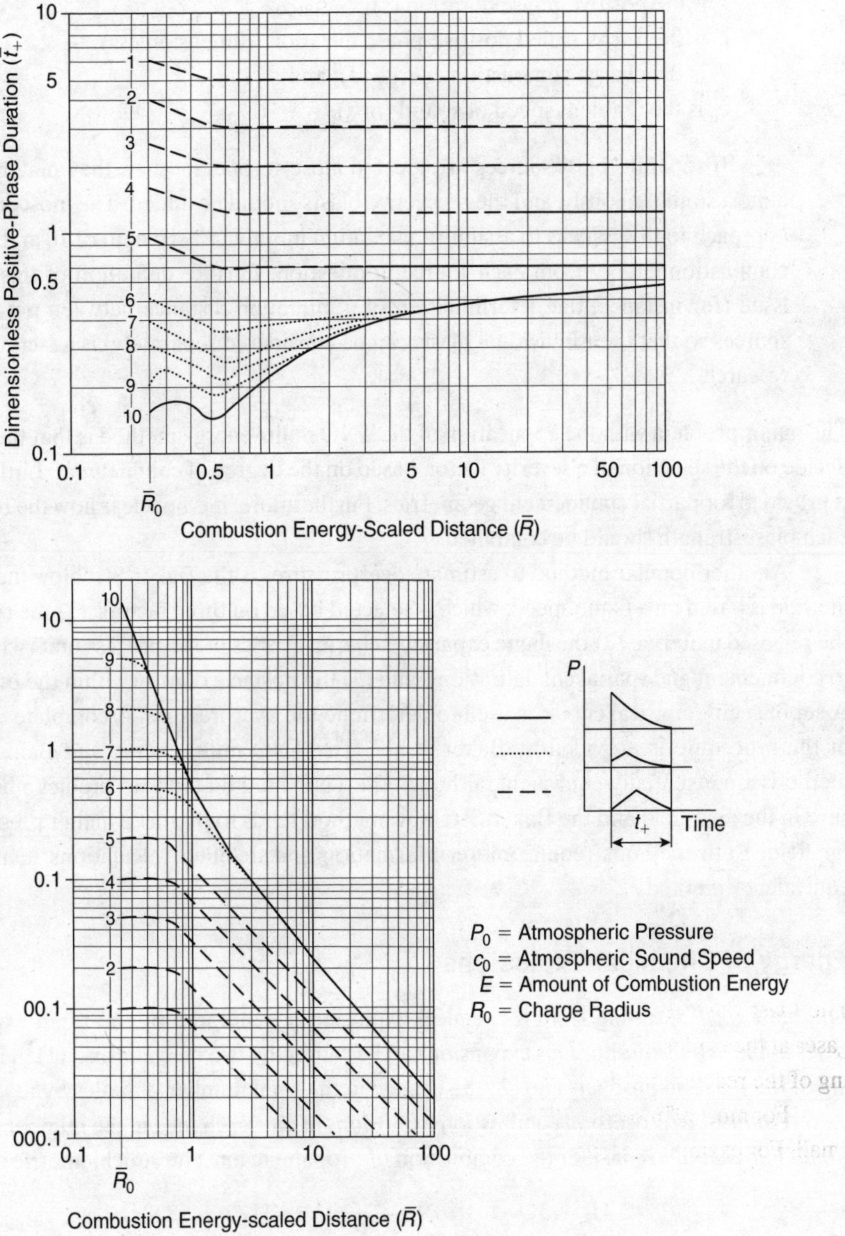

$$\Delta\bar{P}_s = \frac{\Delta P_s}{P_0};\ \bar{t}_+ = \frac{t_+ c_0}{(E/P_0)^{1/3}};\ \bar{R} = \frac{R}{(E/P_0)^{1/3}}$$

Figure 6-24 Sachs-scaled overpressure and Sachs-scaled positive-phase duration for the TNO multi-energy blast model. Source: *Guidelines for Evaluating the Characteristics of Vapor Cloud Explosions, Flash Fires, and BLEVEs* (New York: American Institute of Chemical Engineers, 1994); used with permission.

t_d is the positive-phase duration (s),
$\bar{t}_d$ is the Sachs-scaled positive-phase duration (dimensionless),
E is the charge combustion energy (J), and
c_o is the ambient speed of sound (m/s).

If separate blast sources are located close to one another, they may be initiated almost simultaneously, and the respective blasts should be added. The most conservative approach to this issue is to assume a maximum initial blast strength of 10 and to sum the combustion energy from each source in question. Further definition of this important issue (for instance, the determination of a minimum distance between potential blast sources so that their individual blasts can be considered separately) is a factor in present research.

The major problem with the application of the TNO multi-energy method is that the user must decide on the selection of a severity factor, based on the degree of confinement. Little guidance is provided for partial confinement geometries. Furthermore, it is not clear how the results from each blast strength should be combined.

Another popular method to estimate overpressures is the Baker-Strehlow method. This method is based on a flame speed, which is selected based on three factors: (1) the reactivity of the released material, (2) the flame expansion characteristics of the process unit (which relates to confinement and spatial configuration), and (3) the obstacle density within the process unit. A set of semi-empirical curves is used to determine the overpressure. A complete description of the procedure is provided by Baker et al.[21] The TNO multi-energy and Baker-Strehlow methods are essentially equivalent, although the TNO method tends to predict a higher pressure in the near field and the Baker-Strehlow method tends to predict a higher pressure in the far field. Both methods require more information and detailed calculations than the TNT equivalency method.

Energy of Chemical Explosions

The blast wave resulting from a chemical explosion is generated by the rapid expansion of gases at the explosion site. This expansion can be caused by two mechanisms: (1) thermal heating of the reaction products and (2) the change in the total number of moles by reaction.

For most hydrocarbon combustion explosions in air the change in the number of moles is small. For example, consider the combustion of propane in air. The stoichiometric equation is

$$C_3H_8 + 5O_2 + 18.8N_2 \rightarrow 3CO_2 + 4H_2O + 18.8N_2.$$

The initial number of moles on the left-hand side is 24.8, and the number of moles on the right-hand side is 25.8. In this case only a small pressure increase is expected as a result of the change in the number of moles, and almost all the blast energy must be due to thermal energy release.

[21]Q. A. Baker, C. M. Doolittle, G. A. Fitzgerald, and M. J. Tang, "Recent Developments in the Baker-Strehlow VCE Analysis Methodology," *Process Safety Progress* (1998), 17(4): 297.

The energy released during an explosion is computed using standard thermodynamics. Typically, the heat of combustion is used, but the reaction energy can be easily computed using standard heats of formation. Heat of combustion data are provided in Appendix B. Usually the lower heat of combustion is used where the water product is in the vapor phase, not liquid. Since an explosion occurs within a few milliseconds, the explosive energy is released long before the water vapor can condense into liquid.

The released explosion energy is equal to the work required to expand the gases. Crowl[22] reasoned that this expansion work is a form of mechanical energy. The thermodynamic availability is a state function used to determine the maximum mechanical energy extractable from a material as it moves into equilibrium with its surroundings. Sussman[23] showed that the thermodynamic availability for a reacting system can be computed using the standard Gibbs energy of formation. Crowl then concluded that the energy of explosion for a material exploding at room temperature and pressure is equal to the standard Gibbs energy of formation. Crowl also showed how the energy of explosion could be determined for materials exploding at different gas compositions and nonambient temperatures and pressures. However, these adjustments are normally small.

Example 6-11

One thousand kilograms of methane escapes from a storage vessel, mixes with air, and explodes. Determine (a) the equivalent amount of TNT and (b) the side-on peak overpressure at a distance of 50 m from the blast. Assume an explosion efficiency of 2%.

Solution

a. Equation 6-28 applies. The heat of combustion for methane is found in Appendix B. Substituting into Equation 6-28, we obtain

$$m_{\mathrm{TNT}} = \frac{\eta m \Delta H_{\mathrm{c}}}{E_{\mathrm{TNT}}} = \frac{(0.02)(1000\ \mathrm{kg})(1\ \mathrm{mol}/0.016\ \mathrm{kg})(802.3\ \mathrm{kJ/mol})}{4686\ \mathrm{kJ/kg}} = 214\ \mathrm{kg\ TNT}.$$

b. Equation 6-25 is used to determine the scaled distance:

$$z_{\mathrm{e}} = \frac{r}{m_{\mathrm{TNT}}^{1/3}} = \frac{50\ \mathrm{m}}{(214\ \mathrm{kg})^{1/3}} = 8.4\ \mathrm{m/kg}^{1/3}.$$

From Figure 6-23 (or Equation 6-27), the scaled overpressure is 0.25. Thus the overpressure is

$$p_{\mathrm{o}} = p_{\mathrm{s}} p_{\mathrm{a}} = (0.25)(101.3\ \mathrm{kPa}) = 25\ \mathrm{kPa}.$$

This overpressure will demolish steel panel buildings.

[22] D. A. Crowl, "Calculating the Energy of Explosion Using Thermodynamic Availability," *Journal of Loss Prevention in the Process Industries* (1992), 5(2): 109–118.

[23] M. V. Sussman, *Availability (Exergy) Analysis* (Lexington, MA: Mulliken House, 1981).

Example 6-12

Consider the explosion of a propane-air vapor cloud confined beneath a storage tank. The tank is supported 1 m off the ground by concrete piles. The concentration of vapor in the cloud is assumed to be at stoichiometric concentrations. Assume a cloud volume of 2094 m^3, confined below the tank, representing the volume underneath the tank. Determine the overpressure from this vapor cloud explosion at a distance of 100 m from the blast using the TNO multi-energy method.

Solution

The heat of combustion of a stoichiometric hydrocarbon-air mixture is approximately 3.5 MJ/m^3, and by multiplying by the confined volume, the resulting total energy is (2094 m^3)(3.5 MJ/m^3) = 7329 MJ. To apply the TNO multi-energy method, a blast strength of 7 is chosen. The Sachs-scaled energy is determined using Equation 6-25. The result is

$$\overline{R} = \frac{R}{(E/P_o)^{1/3}} = \frac{100\ \text{m}}{[(7329 \times 10^6\ \text{J})/(101{,}325\ \text{Pa})]^{1/3}} = 2.4.$$

The curve labeled 7 in Figure 6-24 is used to determine the scaled overpressure value of about 0.13. The resulting side-on overpressure is determined from Equation 6-26:

$$p_o = \Delta \overline{P}_s \cdot p_a = (0.13)(101.3\ \text{kPa}) = 13.2\ \text{kPa} = 1.9\ \text{psi}.$$

This is adequate to shatter concrete or cinder block walls.

Energy of Mechanical Explosions

For mechanical explosions a reaction does not occur and the energy is obtained from the energy content of the contained substance. If this energy is released rapidly, an explosion may result. Examples of this type of explosion are the sudden failure of a tire full of compressed air and the sudden catastrophic rupture of a compressed gas tank.

Four methods are used to estimate the energy of explosion for a pressurized gas: Brode's equation, isentropic expansion, isothermal expansion, and thermodynamic availability. Brode's method[24] is perhaps the simplest approach. It determines the energy required to raise the pressure of the gas at constant volume from atmospheric pressure to the final gas pressure in the vessel. The resulting expression is

$$E = \frac{(P_2 - P_1)V}{\gamma - 1}, \tag{6-32}$$

where

E is the energy of explosion (energy),
P_1 is the ambient pressure (force/area),

[24] H. L. Brode, "Blast Waves from a Spherical Charge," *Physics of Fluids* (1959), 2: 17.

P_2 is the burst pressure of the vessel (force/area),
V is the volume of expanding gas in the vessel (volume), and
γ is the heat capacity ratio for the gas (unitless).

Because $P_2 > P_1$, the energy calculated from Equation 6-32 is positive, indicating that the energy is released to the surroundings during the vessel rupture.

The isentropic expansion method assumes that the gas expands isentropically from its initial to final state. The following equation represents this case:

$$E = \left(\frac{P_2 V}{\gamma - 1}\right)\left[1 - \left(\frac{P_1}{P_2}\right)^{(\gamma-1)/\gamma}\right]. \tag{6-33}$$

The isothermal expansion case assumes that the gas expands isothermally. This is represented by the following equation:

$$E = R_g T_1 \ln\left(\frac{P_2}{P_1}\right) = P_2 V \ln\left(\frac{P_2}{P_1}\right), \tag{6-34}$$

where

R_g is the ideal gas constant and
T_1 is the ambient temperature (degrees).

The final method uses thermodynamic availability to estimate the energy of explosion. Thermodynamic availability represents the maximum mechanical energy extractable from a material as it comes into equilibrium with the environment. The resulting overpressure from an explosion is a form of mechanical energy. Thus thermodynamic availability predicts a maximum upper bound to the mechanical energy available to produce an overpressure.

An analysis by Crowl[25] using batch thermodynamic availability resulted in the following expression to predict the maximum explosion energy of a gas contained within a vessel:

$$E = P_2 V\left[\ln\left(\frac{P_2}{P_1}\right) - \left(1 - \frac{P_1}{P_2}\right)\right]. \tag{6-35}$$

Note that Equation 6-35 is nearly the same as Equation 6-34 for an isothermal expansion, with the addition of a correction term. This correction term accounts for the energy lost as a result of the second law of thermodynamics.

[25]D. A. Crowl, "Calculating the Energy of Explosion."

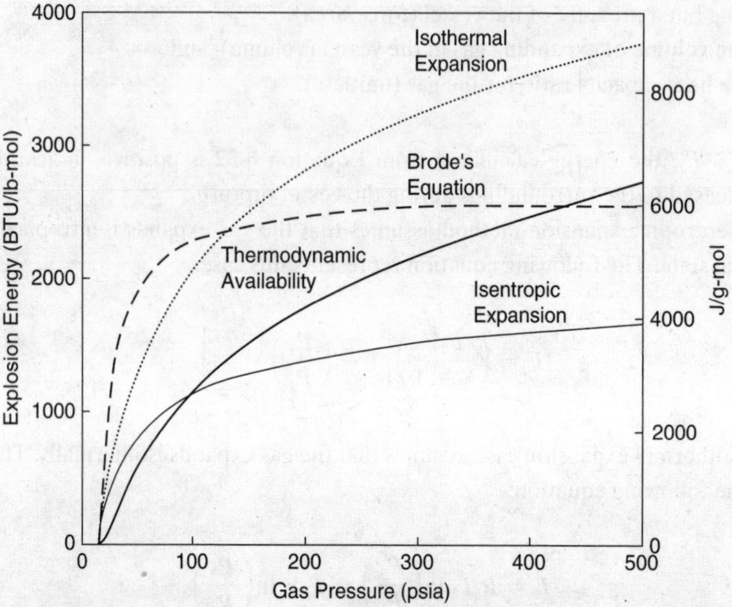

Figure 6-25 The energy of explosion for a compressed inert gas, computed using four different methods. Source: D. A. Crowl, *Understanding Explosions* (New York: American Institute of Chemical Engineers, 2003); used with permission.

The question arises as to which method to use. Figure 6-25 presents the energy of explosion using all four methods as a function of initial gas pressure in the vessel. The calculation assumes an inert gas initially at 298 K with $\gamma = 1.4$. The gas expands into ambient air at 1 atm pressure. The isentropic method produces a low value for the energy of explosion. The isentropic expansion results in a gas at a very low temperature; the expansion of an ideal gas from 200 psia to 14.7 psia results in a final temperature of 254°R, or −205°F. This is thermodynamically inconsistent because the final temperature is ambient. The isothermal expansion method predicts a large value for the energy of explosion because it assumes that all the energy of compression is available to perform work. In reality, some of the energy must be expelled as waste heat, according to the second law of thermodynamics. The thermodynamic availability method accounts for this loss through the correction term in Equation 6-35. All four methods continue to be used to estimate the energy of explosion for compressed gases.

It is thought that the Brode equation more closely predicts the potential explosion energy close to the explosion source, or near field, and that the isentropic expansion method predicts better the effects at a greater distance, or far field. However, it is unclear where this transition occurs. Also, a portion of the potential explosion energy of vessel burst is converted into kinetic energy of the vessel pieces and other inefficiencies (such as strain energy in the form of heat in the vessel fragments). For estimation purposes it is not uncommon to subtract 50% of the total potential energy to calculate the blast pressure effects from vessel burst.

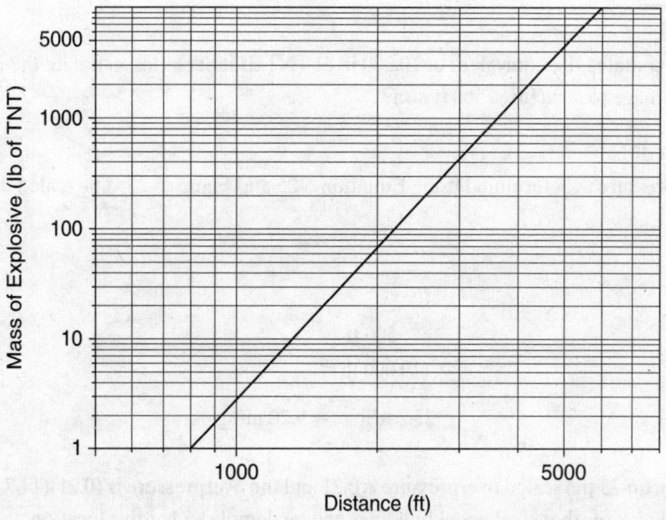

Figure 6-26 Maximum horizontal range of blast fragments. Data from Clancey, "Diagnostic Features of Explosive Damage."

Missile Damage

An explosion occurring in a confined vessel or structure can rupture the vessel or structure, resulting in the projection of debris over a wide area. This debris, or missiles, can cause appreciable injury to people and damage to structures and process equipment. Unconfined explosions also create missiles by blast wave impact and subsequent translation of structures.

Missiles are frequently a means by which an accident propagates throughout a plant facility. A localized explosion in one part of the plant projects debris throughout the plant. This debris strikes storage tanks, process equipment, and pipelines, resulting in secondary fires or explosions.

Clancey[26] developed an empirical relationship between the mass of explosive and the maximum horizontal range of the fragments, as illustrated in Figure 6-26. This relationship is useful during accident investigations for calculating the energy level required to project fragments an observed distance.

Blast Damage to People

People can be injured by explosions from direct blast effects (including overpressure and thermal radiation) or indirect blast effects (mostly missile damage).

Blast damage effects are estimated using probit analysis, discussed in Section 2-6.

[26]Clancey, "Diagnostic Features of Explosion Damage."

Example 6-13

A reactor contains the equivalent of 10,000 lb of TNT. If it explodes, estimate the injury to people and the damage to structures 500 ft away.

Solution

The overpressure is determined using Equation 6-25 and Figure 6-23. The scaled distance is

$$\begin{aligned} z_e &= \frac{r}{m_{\text{TNT}}^{1/3}} \\ &= \frac{500\text{ ft}}{(10{,}000\text{ lb})^{1/3}} \\ &= 23.2\text{ ft/lb}^{1/3} = 9.20\text{ m/kg}^{1/3}. \end{aligned}$$

From Figure 6-23 the scaled overpressure is 0.21 and the overpressure is (0.21)(14.7 psia) = 3.1 psig. Table 6-9 indicates that steel panel buildings will be demolished at this location.

Injury to personnel is determined using probit equations from Table 2-5. The probit equation for deaths resulting from lung hemorrhage is

$$Y = -77.1 + 6.91 \ln P,$$

and the probit equation for eardrum rupture is

$$Y = -15.6 + 1.93 \ln P,$$

where P is the overpressure in N/m^2. Thus

$$\begin{aligned} P &= \left(\frac{3.1\text{ psi}}{14.7\text{ psi/atm}}\right)\left(101{,}325\,\frac{\text{N/m}^2}{\text{atm}}\right) \\ &= 21{,}400\text{ N/m}^2. \end{aligned}$$

Substituting this value into the probit equations yields

$$Y_{\text{deaths}} = -77.1 + 6.91 \ln(21{,}400) = -8.20,$$

$$Y_{\text{eardrums}} = -15.6 + 1.93 \ln(21{,}400) = 3.64.$$

Table 2-4 converts the probit to percentages. The result shows that there are no deaths and that less than 10% of the exposed people suffer eardrum ruptures. This assumes complete conversion of explosion energy.

Based on Figure 6-26, this explosion could project blast fragments a maximum distance of 6000 ft, resulting in probable injuries and damage as a result of blast fragments.

Vapor Cloud Explosions

The most dangerous and destructive explosions in the chemical process industries are vapor cloud explosions (VCEs). These explosions occur in a sequence of steps:

1. Sudden release of a large quantity of flammable vapor (typically this occurs when a vessel, containing a superheated and pressurized liquid, ruptures),
2. Dispersion of the vapor throughout the plant site while mixing with air, and
3. Ignition of the resulting vapor cloud.

The accident at Flixborough, England, is a classic example of a VCE. A sudden failure of a 20-inch cyclohexane line between reactors led to vaporization of an estimated 30 tons of cyclohexane. The vapor cloud dispersed throughout the plant site and was ignited by an unknown source 45 seconds after the release. The entire plant site was leveled and 28 people were killed.

A summary of 29 VCEs[27] over the period 1974–1986 shows property losses for each event of between \$5,000,000 and \$100,000,000 and 140 fatalities (an average of almost 13 per year).

VCEs have increased in number because of an increase in inventories of flammable materials in process plants and because of operations under more severe conditions. Any process containing quantities of liquefied gases, volatile superheated liquid, or high-pressure gases is considered a good candidate for a VCE.

VCEs are difficult to characterize, primarily because of the large number of parameters needed to describe an event. Accidents occur under uncontrolled circumstances. Data collected from real events are mostly unreliable and difficult to compare.

Some of the parameters that affect VCE behavior[28] are quantity of material released, fraction of material vaporized, probability of ignition of the cloud, distance traveled by the cloud before ignition, time delay before ignition of cloud, probability of explosion rather than fire, existence of a threshold quantity of material, efficiency of explosion, and location of ignition source with respect to release.

Qualitative studies[29] have shown that (1) the ignition probability increases as the size of the vapor cloud increases, (2) vapor cloud fires are more common than explosions, (3) the explosion efficiency is usually small (approximately 2% of the combustion energy is converted into a blast wave), and (4) turbulent mixing of vapor and air and ignition of the cloud at a point remote from the release increases the impact of the explosion.[30]

From a safety standpoint the best approach is to prevent the release of material. A large cloud of combustible material is dangerous and almost impossible to control, despite any safety systems installed to prevent ignition.

[27]Richard W. Prugh, "Evaluation of Unconfined Vapor Cloud Explosion Hazards," *International Conference on Vapor Cloud Modeling* (New York: American Institute of Chemical Engineers, 1987), p. 713.

[28]Mannan, ed., *Lees' Loss Prevention in the Process Industries*, 3rd ed., p. 17/134.

[29]Mannan, ed., *Lees' Loss Prevention in the Process Industries,* 3rd ed., p. 17/140.

[30]Prugh, "Evaluation of Unconfined Vapor Cloud Explosion Hazards," p. 714.

Methods that are used to prevent VCEs include keeping low inventories of volatile, flammable materials, using process conditions that minimize flashing if a vessel or pipeline is ruptured, using analyzers to detect leaks at low concentrations, and installing automated block valves to shut systems down while the spill is in the incipient stage of development.

Boiling-Liquid Expanding-Vapor Explosions[31]

A boiling-liquid expanding-vapor explosion (BLEVE, pronounced ble′-vee) is a special type of accident that can release large quantities of materials. If the materials are flammable, a VCE might result; if they are toxic, a large area might be subjected to toxic materials. For either situation the energy released by the BLEVE process itself can result in considerable damage.

A BLEVE occurs when a tank containing a liquid held above its atmospheric pressure boiling point ruptures, resulting in the explosive vaporization of a large fraction of the tank contents.

BLEVEs are caused by the sudden failure of the container as a result of any cause. The most common type of BLEVE is caused by fire. The steps are as follows:

1. A fire develops adjacent to a tank containing a liquid.
2. The fire heats the walls of the tank.
3. The tank walls below liquid level are cooled by the liquid, increasing the liquid temperature and the pressure in the tank.
4. If the flames reach the tank walls or roof where there is only vapor and no liquid to remove the heat, the tank metal temperature rises until the tank loses it structural strength.
5. The tank ruptures, explosively vaporizing its contents.

If the liquid is flammable and a fire is the cause of the BLEVE, the liquid may ignite as the tank ruptures. Often, the boiling and burning liquid behaves as a rocket fuel, propelling vessel parts for great distances. If the BLEVE is not caused by a fire, a vapor cloud might form, resulting in a VCE. The vapors might also be hazardous to personnel by means of skin burns or toxic effects.

When a BLEVE occurs in a vessel, only a fraction of the liquid vaporizes; the amount depends on the physical and thermodynamic conditions of the vessel contents. The fraction vaporized is estimated using the methods discussed in Section 4-7.

Suggested Reading

Center for Chemical Process Safety (CCPS), *Guidelines for Evaluating Process Buildings for External Explosions and Fires* (New York: John Wiley, 1996).

Center for Chemical Process Safety (CCPS), *Guidelines for Vapor Cloud Explosion, Pressure Vessel Burst, BLEVE and Flash Fire Hazards,* 2nd ed. (New York: John Wiley, 2010).

[31] Mannan, ed., *Lees' Loss Prevention in the Process Industries,* 3rd ed., p. 17/167; Bodurtha, *Industrial Explosion Prevention and Protection* (New York: McGraw-Hill, 1980), p. 99.

D. A. Crowl, *Understanding Explosions* (New York: John Wiley, 2003).

Rolf Eckhoff, *Dust Explosions in the Process Industries,* 3rd ed. (Amsterdam: Elsevier, 2003).

Irvin Glassman and Richard A. Yetter, *Combustion,* 4th ed. (Burlington, MA: Academic Press, 2008).

Don W. Green and Robert H. Perry, *Perry's Chemical Engineers' Handbook*, 8th ed. (New York: McGraw-Hill, 2008), pp. 23–6 to 23–21.

Gilbert F. Kinney and Kenneth J. Graham, *Explosive Shocks in Air*, 2nd ed. (Berlin: Springer-Verlag, 1985).

Bernard Lewis and Guenther von Elbe, *Combustion, Flames, and Explosions of Gases*, 3rd ed. (Burlington, MA: Academic Press, 1987).

Sam Mannan, ed., *Lees' Loss Prevention in the Process Industries*, 3rd ed. (Amsterdam: Elsevier, 2005), ch. 16 and 17.

Society of Fire Protection Engineers, *SFPE Handbook of Fire Protection Engineering,* 4th ed. (Quincy, MA: National Fire Protection Association, 2008).

Daniel R. Stull, *Fundamentals of Fires and Explosion,* AICHE Monograph Series, no. 10, v. 73 (New York: American Institute of Chemical Engineers, 1977).

Problems

6-1. Estimate the flash point of a solution of 50 mol % water and 50 mol % methanol.

6-2. Estimate the LFL and the UFL of the following mixtures:

	All in volume %			
	a	**b**	**c**	**d**
Hexane	0.5	0.0	1.0	0.0
Methane	1.0	0.0	1.0	0.0
Ethylene	0.5	0.5	1.0	1.0
Acetone	0.0	1.0	0.0	1.0
Ethyl ether	0.0	0.5	0.0	1.0
Total combustibles	2.0	2.0	3.0	3.0
Air	98.0	98.0	97.0	97.0

6-3. Estimate the LFL and the UFL of Problem 6-2a at 50°C, 75°C, and 100°C.

6-4. Estimate the UFL of Problem 6-2a at 1 atm, 5 atm, 10 atm, and 20 atm of pressure.

6-5. Estimate the LFL and the UFL using the stoichiometric concentrations for methane, propylene, ethyl ether, and acetone. Compare these estimates to actual values.

6-6. Estimate the LOC of propane, hydrogen, and methane using Equations 6-15 and 6-16. Compare to the values in Table 6-3.

6-7. Determine the LOC of a mixture of 2% hexane, 3% propane, and 2% methane by volume.

6-8. Determine the minimum compression ratio required to raise the temperature of air over hexane to its AIT. Assume an initial temperature of 100°C.

6-9. A set of experiments is run on a flammable gas in a spherical vessel. The following data are obtained for two different vessel volumes. Estimate the value of K_G for this combustible gas:

$V = 1\ m^3$		$V = 20\ m^3$	
Time (s)	***P* (bar)**	**Time (s)**	***P* (bar)**
0.0	0.0	0.0	0.0
0.1	0.2	0.2	0.15
0.2	0.5	0.3	0.35
0.3	1.2	0.4	0.6
0.35	1.6	0.5	0.9
0.40	3.2	0.6	1.4
0.425	4.7	0.7	2.2
0.450	6.5	0.8	4.1
0.475	6.9	0.85	5.0
0.500	7.1	0.90	6.2
0.550	7.4	0.95	7.1
0.600	7.3	1.00	7.0
0.650	7.0	1.05	7.2
0.700	6.4	1.10	6.7
0.750	6.1	1.15	6.25
0.800	5.7	1.20	5.90
0.900	5.1	1.30	5.40
1.000	4.7	1.40	5.00
		1.50	5.60

6-10. Determine the energy of explosion for 1 lb of gaseous *n*-butane. What is the TNT equivalent?

6-11. A large cloud of propane is released and eventually ignited, producing a VCE. Estimate the quantity of propane released if the blast shatters windows 3 mi from the source of the ignition.

6-12. How many liters of gasoline are required to make a stoichiometric vapor concentration in a tank truck compartment with a volume of 11,860 liters? The stoichiometric concentration for gasoline is 1.83 vol. %. The temperature is 25°C and the pressure is 1 atm. Use the following physical properties:

Molecular weight:	106
Liquid specific gravity:	0.75

6-13. Draw a flammability diagram for *n*-butane. The experimentally reported LOC for *n*-butane is 12%. What must the oxygen concentration be reduced to before pumping in butane? What butane concentration must the vapor be reduced to before pumping air into the vessel before taking it out of service?

6-14. The following liquids are stored in a storage vessel at 1 atm and 25°C. The vessels are vented with air. Determine whether the equilibrium vapor above the liquid will be flammable. The liquids are

a. Acetone
b. Benzene
c. Cyclohexane
d. Ethyl alcohol
e. Heptane
f. Hexane
g. Pentane
h. Toluene

6-15. The table below provides the vapor pressure for liquid propane as a function of temperature:

Temperature		Vapor pressure	
(°F)	(°C)	(psig)	(bar)
−44.1	−42.2	0	0
−30	−34.4	6.8	0.5
−20	−28.9	11.5	0.8
−10	−23.3	17.5	1.2
0	−17.8	24.5	1.7
10	−12.2	34	2.3
20	−6.7	42	2.9
30	−1.1	53	3.7
40	4.4	65	4.5
50	10.0	78	5.4
60	15.6	93	6.4
70	21.1	110	7.6
80	26.7	128	8.8
90	32.2	150	10.3
100	37.8	177	12.2

A cylinder of propane contains 9 kg liquid propane at 30°C. The ambient pressure is 1 atm.

a. What is the pressure in the tank (in bar) at this temperature?

b. If the valve is equivalent to a 10-mm-diameter hole, what is the initial discharge rate of the propane (in kg/s) if the valve is opened?

c. If all of the propane leaks out and mixes with air and then ignites in the open, what is the distance (in m) to the 13.8 kPa (3 psig) peak side-on overpressure?

6-16. Many chemical operators believe that the inerted vapors above a flammable liquid are not flammable when they mix with air. This is frequently not the case: If the inerted vapors escape from the vessel and mix with air or if the vessel is purged with air after emptying, the resulting mixture might be flammable.

A storage vessel contains liquid benzene at 100°F. The vessel vapor space is inerted with pure nitrogen to a total pressure of 1/2 in of water gauge. Assume that the vapor space is saturated with benzene vapor.

a. Determine the volume percent concentration of benzene in the vapor.

b. Use a flammability diagram to show whether or not this mixture will become flammable when mixed with air.

(Hint: 1 atm = 34.4 ft of water.)

6-17. A liquid mixture containing 0.50 mole fraction benzene-toluene is contained in a storage vessel at 25°C and 1 atm. The vessel is vented to the atmosphere.

a. Is the vapor in the vessel flammable?

b. What are your resulting concerns about fire and explosion hazards with this storage vessel?

Hint: Benzene-toluene can be assumed to be an ideal liquid-vapor system.

6-18. Black powder was used as a blasting agent and a rifle propellant for hundreds, if not thousands, of years. It is a mixture of potassium nitrate, charcoal, and sulfur. The reaction that occurs during black powder combustion is

$$2KNO_3 + 3C + S ==> K_2S + 3CO_2 + N_2.$$

Estimate the TNT equivalence (in kg) of 1 kg of black powder.
The heats of formation are given below:

Species	Heat of formation (kJ/mol)
KNO_3	–494.6
CO_2	–393.6
K_2S	–380.7

6-19. Our plant site wishes to install a pressure vessel containing a total of 1000 kg of liquid propane (C_3H_8). We are concerned about the scenario of rupture of the vessel and subsequent mixing with air and explosion of the flammable mixture.

a. Our control room has a maximum side-on overpressure of 3 psi. How far (in meters) must the vessel be located from the control room? Make sure you explicitly identify and justify your explosion efficiency.

b. How far (in meters) should the vessel be located from off-site housing, in order to have no more than minor damage to the house structures?

6-20. A container in a process using a flammable vapor has dimensions of 100 m by 100 m by 10 m high. Use the TNO multi-energy model to estimate the overpressure 100 m from the process resulting from the release and ignition of the flammable vapor. Assume that 20% of the process volume is moderately congested and that the remaining 80% is lightly congested. Be sure to state any additional assumptions.

6-21. A lab worker has left an open beaker containing 1.5 liters of carbon disulfide on the desk in his lab office at the end of the workday, and he closed his office door when he left. To save energy, the company turns off the office ventilation system at the end of the workday. If the CS_2 evaporates, it might form a flammable mixture in air, and an explosion might result if the worker turns the light switch on in the morning. The temperature is 30°C and the ambient pressure is 1 atm. The floor area of the room is 3 m by 3 m, and the ceiling height is 3 m.

a. Estimate the resulting concentration of CS_2 in the room, in volume %. Compare to the flammability limit.

b. Estimate the equivalent amount of TNT from the vapor. Make sure you clearly state any assumptions.

c. If the vapor explodes, at what distance is the 3 psi overpressure found?

Physical property data for CS_2 at 30°C:

Vapor pressure:	420 mm Hg
Liquid density:	1261 kg/m^3
Molecular weight:	76.13
Normal boiling point:	46.3°C

6-22. During a particular accident, an estimated 39,000 kg of flammable material was released and ignited, resulting in an explosion and fireball and the subsequent fatalities and equipment damage. The publication *Guidelines for Evaluating the Characteristics of Vapor Cloud Explosions, Flash Fires, and BLEVES* (New York: American Institute of Chemical Engineers, 1994) provides a number of equations useful for estimating the effects of such an explosion.

The heat radiation intensity (in kW/m^2) from a ball of burning vapor is given by the empirical equation

$$I_e = 828 m_f^{0.771} / L^2.$$

The effective time duration (in seconds) of the burn is given by

$$t_e = 2.6 m_f^{1/6}.$$

The height of the center of the fireball (in meters) is assumed to be constant during the burn and is given by

$$H_{BLEVE} = 0.75 D_{max}.$$

Finally, the maximum diameter of the fireball (in meters) is given by

$$D_{max} = 5.8 m_f^{1/3}.$$

For these equations I_e is the effective radiation intensity (kW/m^2), m_f is the mass of fuel (kg), L is the distance from the center of the fireball to the receptor (m), and t_e is the effective time duration of the burn (s).

Use a spreadsheet program (such as Quattro Pro or Excel) to estimate the total number of fatalities resulting from the burning fireball. Use the probit equations provided in the text. Assume that 400 people are distributed evenly at a distance of 75 m to 1000 m from the fireball center. Divide the distance interval into a number of small increments. Use a small enough distance increment so that the results are essentially independent of the increment size.

Your spreadsheet output should have designated columns for the distance from the fireball center, radiation intensity, probit values, and percentage and number of fatalities. You should also have a single designated spreadsheet cell providing the total number of fatalities.

One way to simplify the procedure is to specify a threshold radiative flux. It is assumed that 100% fatalities will occur to anyone exposed to anything above this value. Anyone exposed to a lesser value will be unharmed. Estimate an approximate threshold radiative flux value that will result in the same number of fatalities as the detailed probit calculation.

6-23. A 60-gal hot water heater, completely filled with liquid water, catastrophically ruptures at a pressure of 290 psig. Estimate:

a. The fraction of water flashed.

b. The energy of explosion in terms of an equivalent amount of TNT, in pounds. Calculate this using the total enthalpy of the hot water in the heater when it ruptures minus the enthalpy of an equivalent amount of liquid water at the normal boiling point of 212°F.

c. What overpressure would result at a distance of 50 feet?

Use a steam table to determine the enthalpy values.

6-24. You have been assigned the task of assisting in relocating the new control room for your process. The new control room will be designed to withstand an explosive overpressure of 2 psig. Your attention is focused on a propane storage tank located 100 m from the proposed site for the new control room. What is the maximum quantity of propane (in kg) that can be stored in this tank without exceeding the overpressure rating of the control room? Make sure you state any assumptions used in your calculation.

6-25. A natural gas wellhead is located 400 m from an instrument control room. The control room is a potential ignition hazard in the event of a leak of natural gas (essentially pure methane). Studies have shown that a suitable safety margin is imposed if the downwind gas concentration is determined using one-half the LFL. For methane this represents a concentration of 2.5 vol. %.

a. What is the minimum release rate of methane (in kg/s) that will result in a concentration at the control room equal to half the LFL? Be sure to state your assumptions clearly. Assume a temperature of 298 K and an ambient pressure of 1 atm.

b. If the methane pressure in the wellhead is at 10 atm pressure, what hole size (in cm) will produce the release rate of part a?

c. If the largest pipe size in the wellhead is 4 cm (internal diameter), comment on the likelihood of an ignition hazard from the control room.

6-26. An automobile assembly line includes an operation that involves filling the gas tanks with gasoline. Estimate the ventilation rate required to reduce the vapors from this operation to below the LFL for gasoline. Assume that each tank has a volume of 14 gal and that a tank can be filled in 3 min. Assume splash filling and that only one tank is filled at a time. The molecular weight of gasoline is about 94, and its vapor pressure at 77°F is 4.6 psia. Also, calculate the ventilation air required to reduce the concentration of the gasoline vapors to below the TLV-TWA. Which problem is more difficult?

6-27. Your plant is considering installing a vessel containing 1000 kg of propane. One possible site is located 100 m from a residential area.

a. What overpressure (in kPa) can be expected in the residential area due to the sudden failure of the vessel followed by a vapor cloud explosion? What type of damage would be expected from this overpressure? Assume a 2% explosion efficiency.

b. What concentration of propane can be expected in the residential area due to the failure of the vessel? Will this be flammable? Assume urban conditions and worst-case conditions, as described in Table 4-6. The pressure is 1 atm and the temperature is 298 K.

6-28. A fair amount of variability exists in determination of the flammability limits. For example, various researchers have reported lower flammability limits for methane of 5.3%, 5.0%, and 4.85%. Rework Problem 6-2c to determine how this variability affects the mixture LFL.

6-29. The stoichiometric air/fuel mixture for gasoline is specified as a mass ratio of air to fuel of 14.7.

a. Convert this to volume percent fuel in air. Assume a molecular weight of gasoline of 106 and for air of 29.

b. An automobile has a gasoline engine with a 5-liter displacement. What is the gas consumption, in gallons per hour, if the engine is operating at 1500 rpm? Remember, the 4-cycle engine intakes air and fuel only every other stroke. Assume a specific gravity of 0.75 for gasoline. The air/fuel mixture is fed to the engine at a temperature of 1 atm and 25°C.

c. If the air/fuel vapor mixture is preheated to 150°F, what is the fuel consumption?

6-30. Benzene is stored in an inside storage area, 15 ft long and 15 ft wide with an 8-ft ceiling. This storage area has a ventilation system that changes the air in the room completely six times per hour. The storage area is also equipped with a flammable vapor detector that sounds an alarm when the flammable vapor concentration reaches 25% of the LFL for benzene. What is the minimum benzene spill rate, in lb/hr, that will set off the flammable vapor alarm in the room? Assume a pressure of 1 atm and a temperature of 80°F. Also assume average ventilation conditions.

6-31. Fires and explosions are substantial hazards in many chemical plants.

a. Describe with examples the three ingredients of any fire.

b. Create a checklist with at least six items to identify fire hazards in any workplace.

c. List six common fire prevention/protection features for chemical plants, and describe when they would be appropriate.

6-32. A butane tank is located 500 ft from a residential area. Estimate the minimum instantaneous release of butane required to produce a vapor concentration in the residential area equal to the LFL for butane. What continuous release rate is required? Assume that the release occurs at ground level. Will the minimum amount increase, decrease, or stay the same if the release occurs above ground level?

6-33. Our plant site is considering installing a propane storage tank at a location 100 m from a control room. We have been asked to evaluate the risk at this location due to flammability and explosion hazards.

a. What continuous release of propane (in kg/s) is required to result in a concentration at the control room equal to the LFL? Make sure you clearly state and validate your assumption of atmospheric stability. Assume rural conditions, a temperature of 25°C, and a pressure of 1 atm.

b. The control room is designed to withstand a side-on peak overpressure of 2 psig. How much propane (in kg) can be stored at this location? Be sure to clearly state and justify your assumption of an explosion efficiency.

6-34. The air in a 55-gal drum must be flushed and inerted with nitrogen before the drum is filled with a flammable liquid. This is accomplished by placing a nitrogen lance through the hole of the drum reaching to the bottom. A constant flow rate of nitrogen is used to achieve the inerting.

a. Show that the concentration of oxygen in the drum is represented by

$$V\frac{dC}{dt} = -kQ_vC,$$

where C is the concentration of oxygen in the drum (mass/volume), k is the nonideal mixing factor ($0.1 < k < 1$), and Q_v is the volumetric flow of nitrogen (volume/time).

b. Show that the time required to reach a target concentration C_f from an initial concentration C_o is given by

$$t = -\left(\frac{V}{kQ_v}\right)\ln\left(\frac{C_f}{C_o}\right).$$

c. Estimate the time it will take to inert a drum to 1% oxygen using 75 L/min of nitrogen. Use k as a parameter.

6-35. In the TWA Flight 800 tragedy the accident is blamed on explosion of fuel vapors in the central fuel tank. The volume of the central fuel tank is 18,000 gal.

a. If, at the time of the explosion, the fuel concentration in the tank is 1% by volume and the pressure inside the tank is 12.9 psia, determine the equivalent energy of explosion for the vapor (in pounds of TNT). Assume a temperature of 80°F. Be sure to state carefully any assumptions.

b. Estimate the overpressure at a distance of 50 ft from the fuel tank explosion from the explosion of the vapors in part a.

c. Estimate the limiting oxygen concentration (LOC) for the jet fuel, given that the LFL is 0.6% by volume and the stoichiometric coefficient for oxygen in the combustion equation is 18.9.

For jet fuel the energy of explosion is 18,590 Btu/lb and the molecular weight is 160.

6-36. A polymeric foam is expanded using gaseous propane (C_3H_8) as a blowing agent. The polymer is shipped as small pellets in shipping containers inerted with pure nitrogen to an initial shipping pressure of 1 atm abs pressure. During shipping, the propane gas comes out of the pellets and mixes with the gaseous nitrogen in the shipping container. Laboratory studies have shown that the propane out-gassing can increase the pressure in the container by 10 kPa. Will a flammable atmosphere be created when the shipping container is opened and dumped into a hopper? The ambient pressure is 1 atm.

6-37. Methyl alcohol liquid is stored in a vessel. Its vapor is inerted with nitrogen to a total pressure of 2 in of water gauge. Will the inerted vapor be flammable if it escapes the vessel? Assume a temperature of 25°C.

6-38 You have been assigned the task of assisting in relocating the new control room for your process. The new control room will be designed to withstand an explosive overpressure of 2 psig. Your attention is focused on a propane storage tank located 100 m from the proposed site for the new control room. What is the maximum quantity of propane (in kg) that can be stored in this tank without exceeding the overpressure rating of the control room? Make sure you state any assumptions used in your calculation.

6-39. For flammable gases the minimum ignition energy is typically 0.1 mJ. The mass of a penny is typically 2.6 g. How far must this penny be dropped to contain the kinetic energy equal to 0.1 mJ?

CHAPTER 7

Concepts to Prevent Fires and Explosions

A threefold strategy is used to prevent or limit the potential damage from fires and explosions: prevent flammable mixture, prevent the initiation of the fire or explosion, and minimize the damage after a fire or explosion has occurred. This strategy is presented in this chapter. The specific topics include

- Inerting
- Use of the flammability diagram introduced in Chapter 6
- Static electricity
- Controlling static electricity
- Ventilation
- Explosion-proof equipment and instruments
- Sprinkler systems
- Miscellaneous design features for preventing fires and explosions

For any fire or combustion explosion to occur, three conditions must be met (as shown in the fire triangle of Figure 6-1). First, a combustible or explosive material must be present. Second, oxygen or an oxidant must be present to support the combustion reaction. Finally, a source of ignition must be available to initiate the reaction. If any of the three conditions of the fire triangle is eliminated, the triangle is broken and it is impossible for a fire or combustion explosion to result. This is the basis for the first six design methods listed above.

Damage resulting from fires and explosions is minimized by stopping fires or explosions as quickly as possible and also by designing the process equipment (and control centers) to withstand their effects.

7-1 Inerting

Inerting is the process of adding an inert gas to a combustible mixture to reduce the concentration of oxygen below the limiting oxygen concentration (LOC). The inert gas is usually nitrogen or carbon dioxide, although steam is sometimes used. For many gases the LOC is approximately 10%, and for many dusts it is approximately 8%.

Inerting begins with an initial purge of the vessel with inert gas to bring the oxygen concentration down to safe concentrations. A commonly used control point is 4% below the LOC, that is, 6% oxygen if the LOC is 10%.

After the empty vessel has been inerted, the flammable material is charged. An inerting system is required to maintain an inert atmosphere in the vapor space above the liquid. Ideally this system should include an automatic inert gas addition feature to control the oxygen concentration below the LOC. This control system should have an analyzer to continuously monitor the oxygen concentration in relationship to the LOC and a controlled inert gas feed system to add inert gas when the oxygen concentration approaches the LOC. More frequently, however, the inerting system consists only of a regulator designed to maintain a fixed positive inert pressure in the vapor space; this ensures that inert gas is always flowing out of the vessel rather than air flowing in. The analyzer system, however, results in a significant savings in inert gas usage while improving safety.

Consider an inerting system designed to maintain the oxygen concentration below 10%. As oxygen leaks into the vessel and the concentration rises to 8%, a signal from the oxygen sensor opens the inert gas feed valve. Once again the oxygen level is adjusted to 6%. This closed-loop control system, with high (8%) and low (6%) inerting set points, maintains the oxygen concentration at safe levels with a reasonable margin of safety. NFPA recommendations are described at the end of this section.

There are several purging methods used to *initially* reduce the oxygen concentration to the low set point: vacuum purging, pressure purging, combined pressure-vacuum purging, vacuum and pressure purging with impure nitrogen, sweep-through purging, and siphon purging.

Vacuum Purging

Vacuum purging is the most common inerting procedure for vessels. This procedure is not used for large storage vessels because they are usually not designed for vacuums and usually can withstand a pressure of only a few inches of water.

Reactors, however, are often designed for full vacuum, that is −760 mm Hg gauge or 0.0 mm Hg absolute. Consequently, vacuum purging is a common procedure for reactors. The steps in a vacuum purging process include (1) drawing a vacuum on the vessel until the desired vacuum is reached, (2) relieving the vacuum with an inert gas, such as nitrogen or carbon dioxide, to atmospheric pressure, and (3) repeating steps 1 and 2 until the desired oxidant concentration is reached.

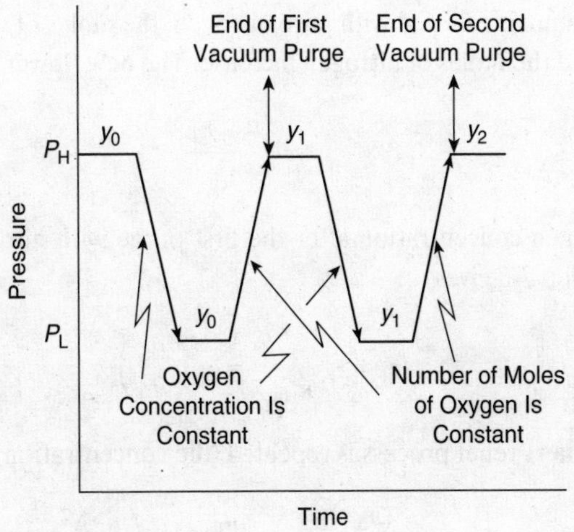

Figure 7-1 Vacuum purge cycles.

The initial oxidant concentration under vacuum (y_o) is the same as the initial concentration, and the number of moles at the initial high pressure (P_H) and initial low pressure or vacuum (P_L) are computed using an equation of state.

The process for vacuum purging is clarified using the stepwise procedure shown in Figure 7-1. A vessel of known size is vacuum-purged from an initial oxygen concentration y_o to a final target oxygen concentration y_j. The vessel is initially at pressure P_H and is vacuum-purged using a vacuum at pressure P_L. The objective of the following calculation is to determine the number of cycles required to achieve the desired oxygen concentration.

Assuming ideal gas behavior, the total moles at each pressure are

$$n_H = \frac{P_H V}{R_g T}, \tag{7-1}$$

$$n_L = \frac{P_L V}{R_g T}, \tag{7-2}$$

where n_H and n_L are the total moles in the atmospheric and vacuum states, respectively.

The number of moles of oxidant for the low pressure P_L and high pressure P_H are computed using Dalton's law:

$$(n_{oxy})_{1L} = y_o n_L, \tag{7-3}$$

$$(n_{oxy})_{1H} = y_o n_H, \tag{7-4}$$

where 1L and 1H are the first atmospheric and first vacuum states, respectively.

When the vacuum is relieved with pure nitrogen, the moles of oxidant are the same as in the vacuum state and the moles of nitrogen increase. The new (lower) oxidant concentration is

$$y_1 = \frac{(n_{\text{oxy}})_{1\text{L}}}{n_{\text{H}}}, \tag{7-5}$$

where y_1 is the oxygen concentration after the first purge with nitrogen. Substituting Equation 7-3 into Equation 7-5 gives

$$y_1 = \frac{(n_{\text{oxy}})_{1\text{L}}}{n_{\text{H}}} = y_{\text{o}}\left(\frac{n_{\text{L}}}{n_{\text{H}}}\right).$$

If the vacuum and inert relief process is repeated, the concentration after the second purge is

$$y_2 = \frac{(n_{\text{oxy}})_{2\text{L}}}{n_{\text{H}}} = y_1\frac{n_{\text{L}}}{n_{\text{H}}} = y_{\text{o}}\left(\frac{n_{\text{L}}}{n_{\text{H}}}\right)^2.$$

This process is repeated as often as required to decrease the oxidant concentration to a desired level. The concentration after j purge cycles, vacuum and relief, is given by the following general equation:

$$\boxed{y_j = y_{\text{o}}\left(\frac{n_{\text{L}}}{n_{\text{H}}}\right)^j = y_{\text{o}}\left(\frac{P_{\text{L}}}{P_{\text{H}}}\right)^j.} \tag{7-6}$$

This equation assumes that the pressure limits P_{H} and P_{L} are identical for each cycle.

The total moles of nitrogen added for each cycle is constant. For j cycles the total nitrogen is given by

$$\Delta n_{\text{N}_2} = j(P_{\text{H}} - P_{\text{L}})\frac{V}{R_g T}. \tag{7-7}$$

Example 7-1

Use a vacuum purging technique to reduce the oxygen concentration within a 1000-gal vessel to 1 ppm. Determine the number of purges required and the total nitrogen used. The temperature is 75°F, and the vessel is originally charged with air under ambient conditions. A vacuum pump is used that reaches 20 mm Hg absolute, and the vacuum is subsequently relieved with pure nitrogen until the pressure returns to 1 atm absolute.

Solution

The concentration of oxygen at the initial and final states is

$$y_{\text{o}} = 0.21 \text{ lb-mol O}_2\text{/total mol},$$

$$y_{\text{f}} = 1 \text{ ppm} = 1 \times 10^{-6} \text{ lb-mol O}_2\text{/total mol}.$$

The required number of cycles is computed using Equation 7-6:

$$y_j = y_o \left(\frac{P_L}{P_H} \right)^j,$$

$$\ln\left(\frac{y_j}{y_o} \right) = j \ln\left(\frac{P_L}{P_H} \right),$$

$$j = \frac{\ln(10^{-6}/0.21)}{\ln(20 \text{ mm Hg}/760 \text{ mm Hg})} = 3.37.$$

Number of purges $= j = 3.37$. Four purge cycles are required to reduce the oxygen concentration to 1 ppm.

The total nitrogen used is determined from Equation 7-7. The low pressure P_L is

$$P_L = \left(\frac{20 \text{ mm Hg}}{760 \text{ mm Hg}} \right)(14.7 \text{ psia}) = 0.387 \text{ psia},$$

$$\Delta n_{N_2} = j(P_H - P_L)\frac{V}{R_g T}$$

$$= 4(14.7 - 0.387) \text{ psia} \frac{(1000 \text{ gal})(1 \text{ ft}^3/7.48 \text{ gal})}{(10.73 \text{ psia ft}^3/\text{lb-mol°R})(75 + 460)\text{°R}}$$

$$= 1.33 \text{ lb-mol} = 37.2 \text{ lb of nitrogen.}$$

Pressure Purging

Vessels can be pressure-purged by adding inert gas under pressure. After this added gas is diffused throughout the vessel, it is vented to the atmosphere, usually down to atmospheric pressure. More than one pressure cycle may be necessary to reduce the oxidant content to the desired concentration.

The cycles used to reduce the oxygen concentration to a target level are shown in Figure 7-2. In this case the vessel is initially at P_L and is pressurized using a source of pure nitrogen at P_H. The objective is to determine the number of pressure purge cycles required to reach the desired concentration.

Because the vessel is pressurized with pure nitrogen, the number of moles of oxygen remains constant during pressurization, whereas the mole fraction decreases. During depressurization, the composition of the gas within the vessel remains constant, but the total number of moles is reduced. Thus the oxygen mole fraction remains unchanged.

The relationship used for this purging process is identical to Equation 7-6, where n_L is now the total moles at atmospheric pressure (low pressure) and n_H is the total moles under pressure (high pressure). In this case, however, the initial concentration of oxidant in the vessel (y_o) is computed after the vessel is pressurized (the first pressurized state). The number of moles for this pressurized state is n_H and the number of moles for the atmospheric case is n_L.

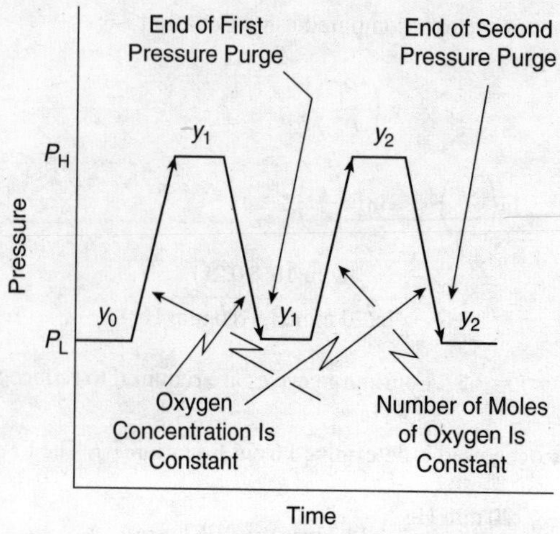

Figure 7-2 Pressure purge cycles.

One practical advantage of pressure purging versus vacuum purging is the potential for cycle time reductions. The pressurization process is much more rapid compared to the relatively slow process of developing a vacuum. Also, the capacity of vacuum systems decreases significantly as the absolute vacuum is decreased. Pressure purging, however, uses more inert gas. Therefore the best purging process is selected based on cost and performance.

Example 7-2

Use a pressure purging technique to reduce the oxygen concentration in the same vessel discussed in Example 7-1. Determine the number of purges required to reduce the oxygen concentration to 1 ppm using pure nitrogen at a pressure of 80 psig and at a temperature of 75°F. Also, determine the total nitrogen required. Compare the quantities of nitrogen required for the two purging processes.

Solution

The final oxygen concentration (y_f) is specified to be 1 ppm or 10^{-6} lb-mol oxygen/total lb-mol. The number of cycles required is computed using Equation 7-6:

$$y_j = y_o\left(\frac{P_L}{P_H}\right)^j,$$

$$j = \frac{\ln(10^{-6}/0.21)}{\ln[14.7 \text{ psia}/(80 + 14.7) \text{ psia}]} = 6.6$$

The number of purge cycles is thus 7. Thus 7 pressure purges are required, compared to 4 for the vacuum purge process. The quantity of nitrogen used for this inerting operation is determined using Equation 7-7:

$$\Delta n_{N_2} = j(P_H - P_L)\frac{V}{R_g T}$$

$$= 7(94.7 - 14.7)\text{ psia}\frac{133.7\text{ ft}^3}{(10.73\text{ psia ft}^3/\text{lb-mol}^\circ\text{R})(535^\circ\text{R})}$$

$$= 12.9\text{ lb-mol} = 363\text{ lb of nitrogen.}$$

Pressure purging requires 7 purges and 363 lb of nitrogen compared to 4 purges and 37.2 lb of nitrogen for vacuum purging. This result illustrates the need for a cost performance comparison to determine whether the time saved in pressure purging justifies the added cost for nitrogen.

Combined Pressure-Vacuum Purging

In some cases both pressure and vacuum are available and are used simultaneously to purge a vessel. The computational procedure depends on whether the vessel is first evacuated or pressurized.

The purging cycles for a pressure-first purge are shown in Figure 7-3. In this case the beginning of the cycle is defined as the end of the initial pressurization. If the initial oxygen mole fraction is 0.21, the oxygen mole fraction at the end of this initial pressurization is given by

$$y_O = 0.21\left(\frac{P_O}{P_H}\right). \tag{7-8}$$

At this point the remaining cycles are identical to pressure purging and Equation 7-6 applies. However, the number of cycles j is the number of cycles after the initial pressurization.

The purging cycles for an evacuate-first purge are shown in Figure 7-4. In this case the beginning of the cycle is defined as the end of the initial evacuation. The oxygen mole fraction at this point is the same as the initial mole fraction. Furthermore, the remaining cycles are identical to the vacuum purge operation and Equation 7-6 is directly applicable. However, the number of cycles j is the number of cycles after the initial evacuation.

Vacuum and Pressure Purging with Impure Nitrogen

The equations developed for vacuum and pressure purging apply to the case of pure nitrogen only. Many of the nitrogen separation processes available today do not provide pure nitrogen; they typically provide nitrogen in the 98%+ range with the remainder usually oxygen.

Assume that the nitrogen contains oxygen with a constant mole fraction of y_{oxy}. For a pressure purging procedure the total moles of oxygen present at the end of the first

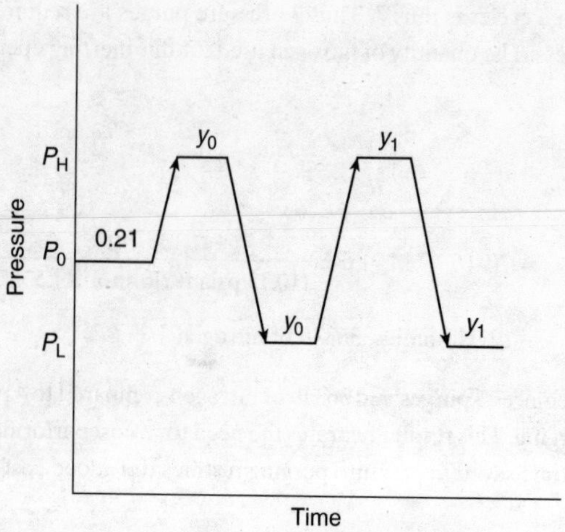

Figure 7-3 Vacuum-pressure purging with initial pressurization.

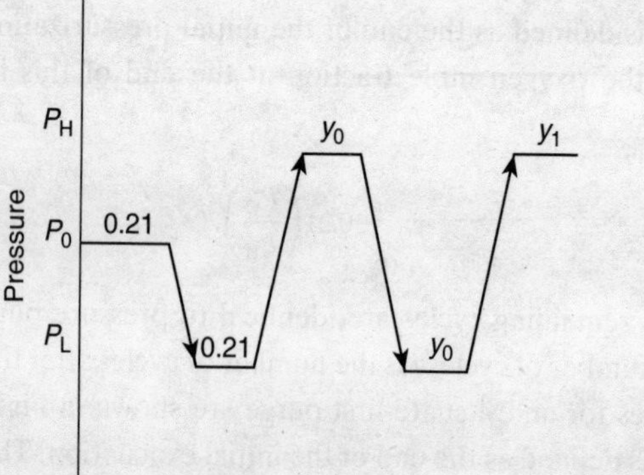

Figure 7-4 Vacuum-pressure purging with initial evacuation.

pressurization is given by the moles initially present plus the moles included with the nitrogen. This amount is

$$n_{\text{oxy}} = y_{\text{o}}\left(\frac{P_{\text{L}}V}{R_{\text{g}}T}\right) + y_{\text{oxy}}(P_{\text{H}} - P_{\text{L}})\frac{V}{R_{\text{g}}T}. \tag{7-9}$$

The total moles in the vessel at the end of the first pressurization are given in Equation 7-1. Thus the mole fraction of oxygen at the end of this cycle is

$$y_1 = \frac{n_{\text{oxy}}}{n_{\text{tot}}} = y_{\text{o}}\left(\frac{P_{\text{L}}}{P_{\text{H}}}\right) + y_{\text{oxy}}\left(1 - \frac{P_{\text{L}}}{P_{\text{H}}}\right). \tag{7-10}$$

This result is generalized into the following recursive equation (Equation 7-11) and a generalized equation (Equation 7-12) for the oxygen concentration at the end of the jth pressure cycle:

$$y_j = y_{j-1}\left(\frac{P_{\text{L}}}{P_{\text{H}}}\right) + y_{\text{oxy}}\left(1 - \frac{P_{\text{L}}}{P_{\text{H}}}\right), \tag{7-11}$$

$$(y_j - y_{\text{oxy}}) = \left(\frac{P_{\text{L}}}{P_{\text{H}}}\right)^j (y_{\text{o}} - y_{\text{oxy}}). \tag{7-12}$$

Equation 7-12 is used in place of Equation 7-6 for both pressure and vacuum purging.

Advantages and Disadvantages of the Various Pressure and Vacuum Inerting Procedures

Pressure purging is faster because the pressure differentials are greater; however, it uses more inert gas than vacuum purging. Vacuum purging uses less inert gas because the oxygen concentration is reduced primarily by vacuum. When combining vacuum and pressure purging, less nitrogen is used compared to pressure purging, especially if the initial cycle is a vacuum cycle.

Sweep-Through Purging

The sweep-through purging process adds purge gas into a vessel at one opening and withdraws the mixed gas from the vessel to the atmosphere (or scrubber) from another opening. This purging process is commonly used when the vessel or equipment is not rated for pressure or vacuum; the purge gas is added and withdrawn at atmospheric pressure.

Purging results are defined by assuming perfect mixing within the vessel, constant temperature, and constant pressure. Under these conditions the mass or volumetric flow rate for the exit stream is equal to the inlet stream. The material balance around the vessel is

$$V\frac{dC}{dt} = C_0 Q_{\text{v}} - C Q_{\text{v}}, \tag{7-13}$$

where

V is the vessel volume,
C is the concentration of oxidant within the vessel (mass or volumetric units),

C_0 is the inlet oxidant concentration (mass or volumetric units),
Q_v is the volumetric flow rate, and
t is time.

The mass or volumetric flow rate of oxidant into the vessel is C_0Q_v, and the flow rate of oxidant exiting is CQ_v. Equation 7-13 is rearranged and integrated:

$$Q_v \int_0^t dt = V \int_{C_1}^{C_2} \frac{dC}{(C_0 - C)}. \tag{7-14}$$

The volumetric quantity of inert gas required to reduce the oxidant concentration from C_1 to C_2 is Q_vt, and it is determined using Equation 7-15:

$$\boxed{Q_vt = V \ln\left(\frac{C_1 - C_0}{C_2 - C_0}\right).} \tag{7-15}$$

For many systems $C_0 = 0$.

Example 7-3

A storage vessel contains 100% air by volume and must be inerted with nitrogen until the oxygen concentration is below 1.25% by volume. The vessel volume is 1000 ft^3. How much nitrogen must be added, assuming the nitrogen contains 0.01% oxygen?

Solution

The volume of nitrogen required Q_vt is determined using Equation 7-15:

$$Q_vt = V \ln\left(\frac{C_1 - C_0}{C_2 - C_0}\right)$$

$$= (1000 \text{ ft}^3)\ln\left(\frac{21.0 - 0.01}{1.25 - 0.01}\right)$$

$$= 2830 \text{ ft}^3.$$

This is the quantity of contaminated nitrogen added (containing 0.01% oxygen). The quantity of pure nitrogen required to reduce the oxygen concentration to 1.25% is

$$Q_vt = (1000 \text{ ft}^3)\ln\left(\frac{21.0}{1.25}\right) = 2821 \text{ ft}^3.$$

Siphon Purging

As illustrated in Example 7-3, the sweep-through process requires large quantities of nitrogen. This could be expensive when purging large storage vessels. Siphon purging is used to minimize this type of purging expense.

The siphon purging process starts by filling the vessel with liquid–water or any liquid compatible with the product. The purge gas is subsequently added to the vapor space of the vessel as the liquid is drained from the vessel. The volume of purge gas is equal to the volume of the vessel, and the rate of purging is equivalent to the volumetric rate of liquid discharge.

When using the siphon purging process, it may be desirable to first fill the vessel with liquid and then use the sweep-through purge process to remove oxygen from the residual head space. By using this method, the oxygen concentration is decreased to low concentrations with only a small added expense for the additional sweep-through purging.

Using the Flammability Diagram to Avoid Flammable Atmospheres

The flammability diagram introduced in Chapter 6 is an important tool to prevent the existence of flammable mixtures. As previously stated, the elimination of ignition sources alone is not enough to prevent fires and explosions; ignition sources are too plentiful to use as the primary prevention mechanism. A more robust design is to prevent the existence of flammable mixtures as the primary control, followed by the elimination of ignition sources as a secondary control. The flammability diagram is important for determining whether a flammable mixture exists and for providing target concentrations for inerting and purging procedures.

The objective is to avoid the flammable region. The procedure for taking a vessel out of service is illustrated in Figure 7-5. The vessel is initially at point A and contains pure fuel. If air is used to purge the vessel, the composition follows line AR, which crosses the flammability zone. If nitrogen is first pumped into the vessel, the gas composition follows along line AS, as shown in Figure 7-5. One approach is to continue the nitrogen flow until the vessel contains pure nitrogen. However, this requires a large amount of nitrogen and is costly. A more efficient procedure is to inert with nitrogen until point S is reached. Then air can be introduced, and the gas composition follows along the line SR in Figure 7-5. In this case the flammability zone is avoided and a safe vessel preparation procedure is ensured.

One might suggest an even more optimized procedure. This involves first pumping air into the vessel until a point is reached on the air stoichiometric line above the UFL. This is followed by pumping nitrogen into the vessel followed by air. This approach avoids the nose of the flammability zone and minimizes the consumption of nitrogen. The problem with this approach, however, is that the air forms a flammable mixture at the entry point as the pure air mixes with the fuel-rich gas mixture in the vessel. The flammability diagram reflects only the average gas composition within the vessel. Using nitrogen first avoids this problem.

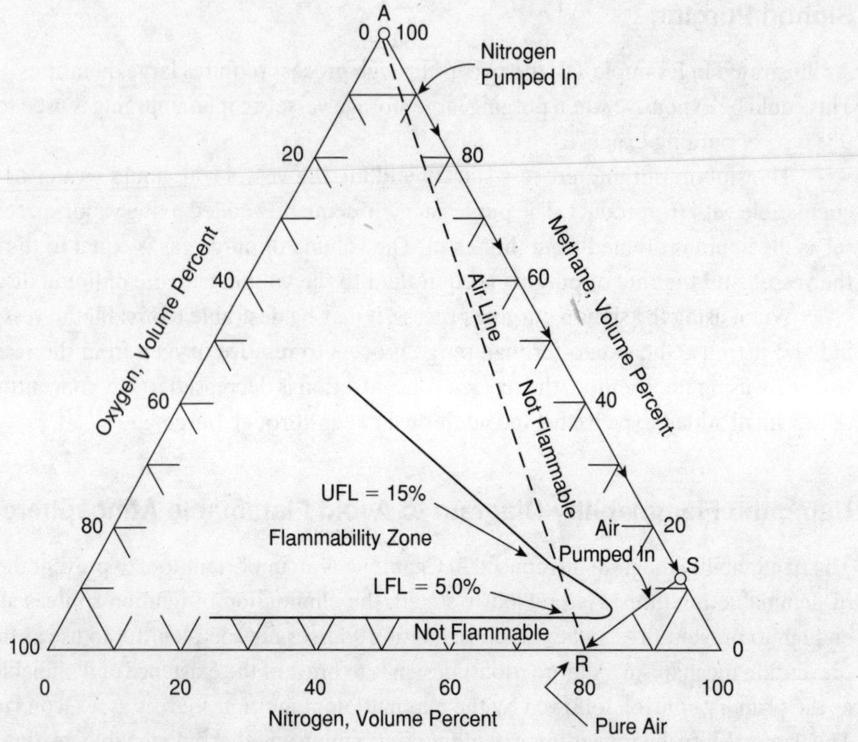

Figure 7-5 A procedure for avoiding the flammability zone for taking a vessel out of service.

When using the nitrogen purge process, one must determine the location of point S in Figure 7-5. The approach is shown in Figure 7-6. Point S is approximated by a line starting at the pure air point R and connecting through a point M at the intersection of the LFL with the stoichiometric combustion line. Because the gas compositions at points R and M are known, the composition at point S is determined graphically or with

$$\text{OSFC} = \frac{\text{LFL}}{1 - z\left(\dfrac{\text{LFL}}{21}\right)}, \tag{7-16}$$

where

OSFC is the out-of-service fuel concentration, that is, the fuel concentration at point S in Figure 7-6,

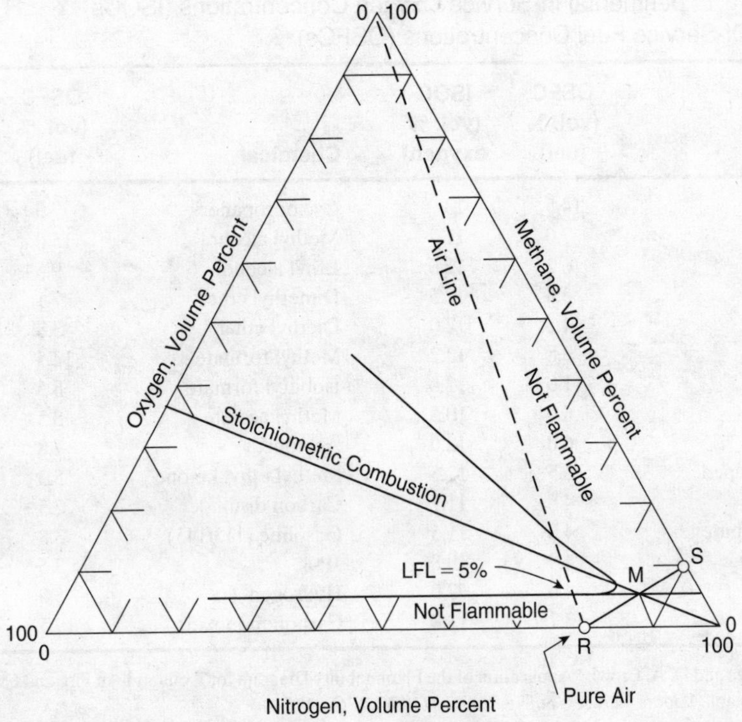

Figure 7-6 Estimating a target fuel concentration at point S for taking a vessel out of service. Point M is the intersection of the LFL line with the stoichiometric line.

LFL is the volume percent of fuel in air at the lower flammability limit, and
z is the stoichiometric oxygen coefficient from the combustion reaction given by Equation 6-9.

The derivation of Equation 7-16 is provided in Appendix C.

Another approach is to estimate the fuel concentration at point S by extending the line from point R through the intersection of the minimum oxygen concentration (M) and the stoichiometric combustion line. The analytical result is

$$\text{OSFC} = \frac{\text{LOC}}{z\left(1 - \dfrac{\text{LOC}}{21}\right)}, \tag{7-17}$$

where LOC is the limiting oxygen concentration (also called the minimum oxygen concentration) in volume percent of oxygen. Equation 7-17 is derived in Appendix C.

Table 7-1 Experimental In-Service Oxygen Concentrations (ISOCs) and Out-Of-Service Fuel Concentrations (OSFCs)[a]

Chemical	OSFC (vol. % fuel)	ISOC (vol. % oxygen)	Chemical	OSFC (vol. % fuel)	ISOC (vol. % oxygen)
Methane	14.5	13	Cyclopropane	7.0	12.0
Ethane	7.0	11.7	Methyl alcohol	15.0	10.8
Propane	6.2	12.0	Ethyl alcohol	9.5	11.0
Butane	5.8	12.5	Dimethyl ether	7.1	11.0
n-Pentane	4.2	12.0	Diethyl ether	3.8	11.0
n-Hexane	3.8	12.2	Methyl formate	12.5	11.0
Natural gas	11.0	12.8	Isobutyl formate	6.5	12.7
Ethylene	6.0	10.5	Methyl acetate	8.5	11.7
Propylene	6.0	12.0	Acetone	7.8	12.0
2-Methylpropene	5.5	12.5	Methyl ethyl ketone	5.3	11.5
1-Butene	4.8	11.7	Carbon disulfide	2.5	6.0
3-Methyl-1-butene	4.0	11.5	Gasoline (115/145)	3.8	12.0
1,3-Butadiene	4.9	10.8	JP-4	3.5	11.7
Acetylene	4.0	7.0	Hydrogen	5.0	5.7
Benzene	3.7	11.8	Carbon monoxide	19.5	7.0

[a]C. V. Mashuga and D. A. Crowl, "Application of the Flammability Diagram for Evaluation of Fire and Explosion Hazards of Flammable Vapors," *Process Safety Progress* (1998), 17(3): 176.

Equations 7-16 and 7-17 are approximations of the fuel concentration at point S. Fortunately, they are usually conservative, that is, less than the experimentally determined OSFC value. For instance, for methane the LFL is 5.3% and z is 2. Thus Equation 7-16 predicts an OSFC of 10.7% fuel. This is compared to an experimentally determined OSFC of 14.5% (Table 7-1). By using an experimental LOC of 12%, an OSFC value of 14% is determined. This is closer to the experimental value but still conservative. For ethylene, 1,3-butadiene, and hydrogen Equation 7-17 predicts a higher OSFC than the experimentally determined value. For all other species in Table 7-1, Equation 7-16 estimates an OSFC that is less than the experimental value.

Figure 7-7 shows the procedure for placing a vessel into service. The vessel begins with air, shown as point A. Nitrogen is pumped into the vessel until point S is reached. Then fuel is pumped in, following line SR until point R is reached. The problem is to determine the oxygen (or nitrogen) concentration at point S. The in-service oxygen concentration (ISOC) represents the maximum oxygen concentration at point S in Figure 7-7 that just avoids the flammability zone, with a small margin of safety.

If a detailed flammability diagram is lacking, then the ISOC is estimated. One approach is to use the intersection of the LFL with the stoichiometric combustion line. A line is drawn

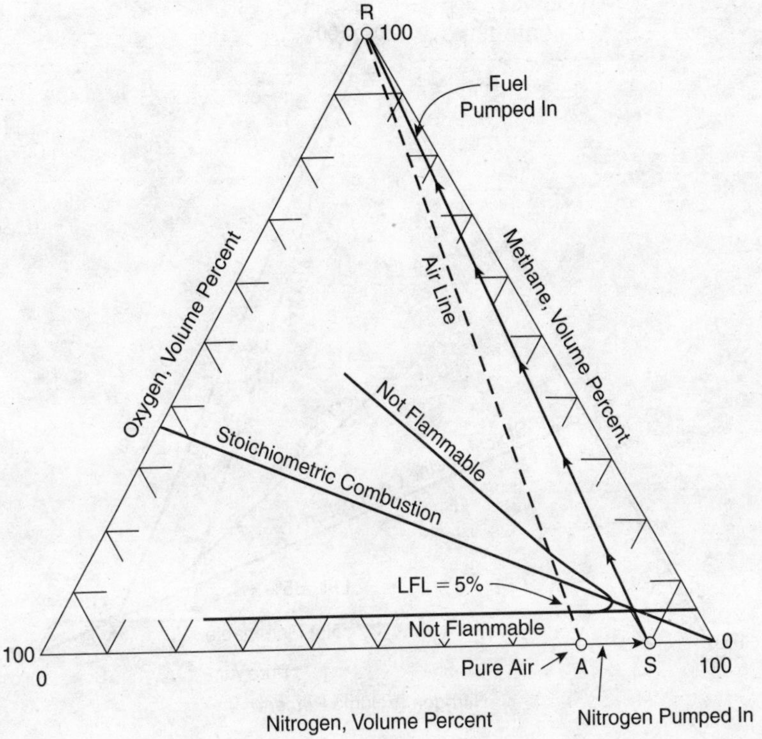

Figure 7-7 A procedure for avoiding the flammability zone for bringing a vessel into service.

from the top apex of the triangle (R) through this intersection to the nitrogen axis. This is shown in Figure 7-8. The composition at S is determined graphically or with

$$\boxed{\text{ISOC} = \frac{z\text{LFL}}{1 - \left(\dfrac{\text{LFL}}{100}\right)},} \tag{7-18}$$

where

ISOC is the in-service oxygen concentration in volume % oxygen,

z is the stoichiometric coefficient for oxygen given in Equation 6-9, and

LFL is the fuel concentration at the lower flammability limit, in volume % of fuel in air.

Equation 7-18 is derived in Appendix C.

The nitrogen concentration at point S is equal to 100 − ISOC.

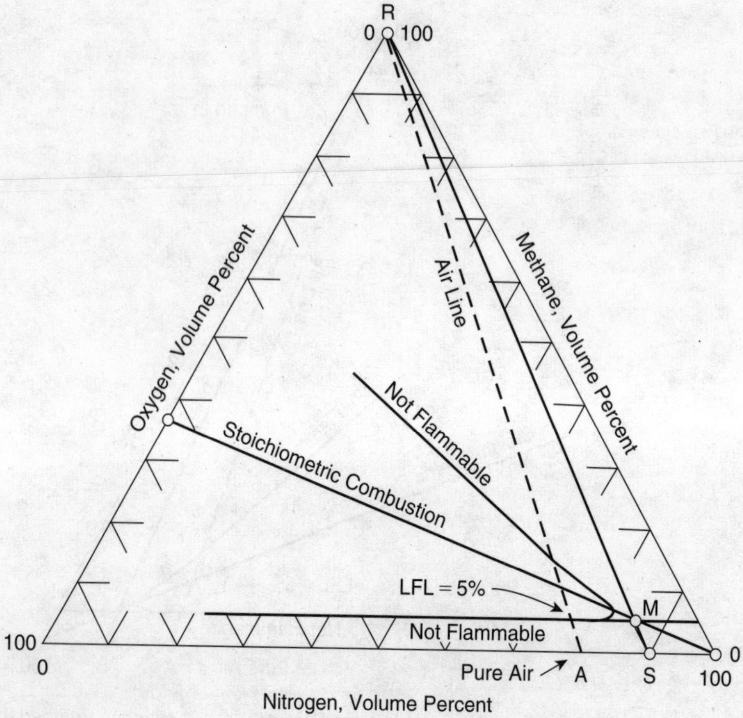

Figure 7-8 Estimating a target nitrogen concentration at point S for placing a vessel into service. Point M is the intersection of the LFL line with the stoichiometric combustion line.

An expression to estimate ISOC using the intersection of the minimum oxygen concentration and the stoichiometric line is also found using a similar procedure. The analytical result is

$$\text{ISOC} = \frac{z\text{LOC}}{z - \frac{\text{LOC}}{100}}, \tag{7-19}$$

where LOC is the minimum oxygen concentration in volume % oxygen.

A comparison of the estimates using Equations 7-18 and 7-19 with the experimental values in Table 7-1 shows that Equation 7-18 predicts a lower oxygen value than the experimental values for all species, with the exception of methyl formate. Equation 7-19 predicts a lower oxygen concentration than the experimental value for all species in Table 7-1 with the exception of butane, 3-methyl-1-butene, 1,3-butadiene, isobutyl formate, and acetone. The calculated values are deliberately not shown in Table 7-1. Direct and reliable experimental data under conditions as close as possible to process conditions are always recommended.

Other methods are available to estimate the target gas concentration for placing a vessel into or out of service. For instance, NFPA 69[1] recommends a target oxygen concentration for storage vessels of no more than 2% below the measured LOC, if the oxygen concentration is continually monitored. If the LOC is less than 5%, the target oxygen concentration is no more than 60% of the LOC. If the oxygen concentration is not continuously monitored, then the equipment must not operate at more than 60% of the LOC, or 40% of the LOC if the LOC is below 5%.

7-2 Static Electricity

A common ignition source within chemical plants is sparks resulting from static charge buildup and sudden discharge. Static electricity is perhaps the most elusive of ignition sources. Despite considerable efforts, serious explosions and fires caused by static ignition continue to plague the chemical process industry.

The best design methods for preventing this type of ignition source are developed by understanding the fundamentals relevant to static charge and by using these fundamentals to design specific features within a plant to prevent the accumulation of static charge or to recognize situations where the buildup of static electricity is inevitable and unavoidable. For unavoidable static buildup design features are added to continuously and reliably inert the atmosphere around the regions where static sparks are likely.

Fundamentals of Static Charge

Static charge buildup is a result of physically separating a poor conductor from a good conductor or another poor conductor. When different materials touch each other, the electrons move across the interface from one surface to the other. Upon separation, more of the electrons remain on one surface than on the other; one material becomes positively charged and the other negatively charged.

If both the materials are good conductors, the charge buildup as a result of separation is small because the electrons are able to scurry between the surfaces. If, however, one or both of the materials are insulators or poor conductors, electrons are not as mobile and are trapped on one of the surfaces, and the magnitude of the charge is much greater.

Household examples that result in a buildup of a static charge are walking across a rug, placing different materials in a tumble dryer, removing a sweater, and combing hair. The clinging fabrics and sometimes audible sparks are the result of the buildup of static charge.

[1]NFPA 69, *Standard on Explosion Prevention Systems,* 1997 ed. (Quincy, MA: National Fire Protection Association, 1997).

Common industrial examples are pumping a nonconductive liquid through a pipe, mixing immiscible liquids, pneumatically conveying solids, and leaking steam that contacts an ungrounded conductor. The static charges in these examples accumulate to develop large voltages. Subsequent grounding produces large and energetic sparks.

For industrial operations where flammable vapors may be present, any charge accumulation exceeding 0.1 mJ is considered dangerous. Static charges of this magnitude are easy to generate; the static buildup created by walking across a carpet averages about 20 mJ and exceeds several thousand volts.

Basic electrostatic relationships are used to understand and investigate the sample situations. These relationships may include field strengths produced by static charges, electrostatic potential, capacitance, relaxation times, currents and potentials in flow systems, and many more.

An electrostatic discharge occurs when two materials at different potentials or polarities come close enough together to generate a charge transfer. In an explosive environment this sudden transfer of charges may be energetic enough to be an ignition source. To prevent these ignitions, one must understand (1) how charges accumulate on objects, (2) how charges discharge by means of charge transfer, and (3) how to estimate the resulting energy discharged in relation to the minimum ignition energy (MIE) of the explosive environment.

Charge Accumulation

There are four charge accumulation processes[2] that are relevant to dangerous electrostatic discharges in a chemical plant:

1. Contact and frictional charging: When two materials, with one being an insulator, are brought into contact, a charge separation occurs at the interface. If the two objects are then separated, some of the charges remain separated, giving the two materials opposite but equal charges.
2. Double-layer charging: Charge separation occurs on a microscopic scale in a liquid at any interface (solid-liquid, gas-liquid, or liquid-liquid). As the liquid flows, it carries a charge and it leaves a charge of opposite sign on the other surface, for example, a pipe wall.
3. Induction charging: This phenomenon is applicable only to materials that are electrically conductive. A person with insulated shoes, for example, may approach an overhead vessel that is positively charged (previously filled with positively charged solids). Electrons in the person's body (head, shoulders, and arms) migrate toward the positive charge of the vessel, thus accumulating an equal quantity of positive charges on the opposite side of the body. This leaves the lower part of the body positively charged by induction. When a metal object is touched, there is a transfer of the electrons, creating a spark.

[2] J. A. Cross, *Electrostatics: Principles, Problems, and Applications* (Bristol: Adam Higler, 1987).

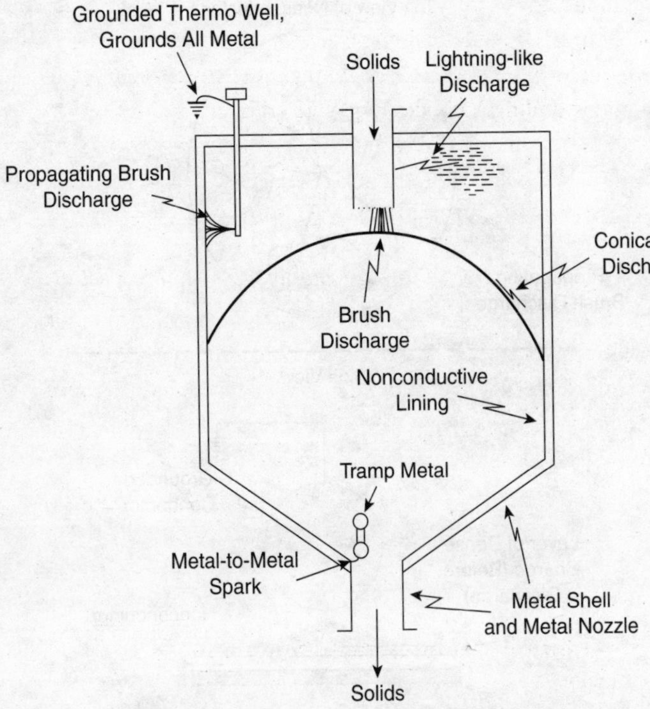

Figure 7-9 Common electrostatic discharges.

4. Charging by transport: When charged liquid droplets or solid particles settle on an isolated object, the object is charged. The transferred charge is a function of the object's capacitance and of the conductivities of the droplet, particle, and interface.

Electrostatic Discharges[3]

A charged object can be discharged to a ground or to an oppositely charged object when the field intensity exceeds 3 MV/m (breakdown voltage of air) or when the surface reaches a maximum charge density of 2.7×10^{-5} C/m^2 by six methods: (1) spark, (2) propagating brush, (3) conical pile (sometimes known as Maurer discharge), (4) brush, (5) lightning-like, and (6) corona discharges.

A *spark* discharge (Figure 7-9) is a discharge between two metallic objects. Because both objects are conductive, the electrons move to exit at a single point of the charged object, and they enter the second object at a single point. This is therefore an energetic spark that can ignite a flammable dust or gas.

A *propagating brush* discharge (Figures 7-9 and 7-10) is a discharge from a grounded conductor when it approaches a charged insulator that is backed by a conductor. These

[3]T. B. Jones and J. L. King, *Powder Handling and Electrostatics* (Chelsea, MI: Lewis Publishers, 1991).

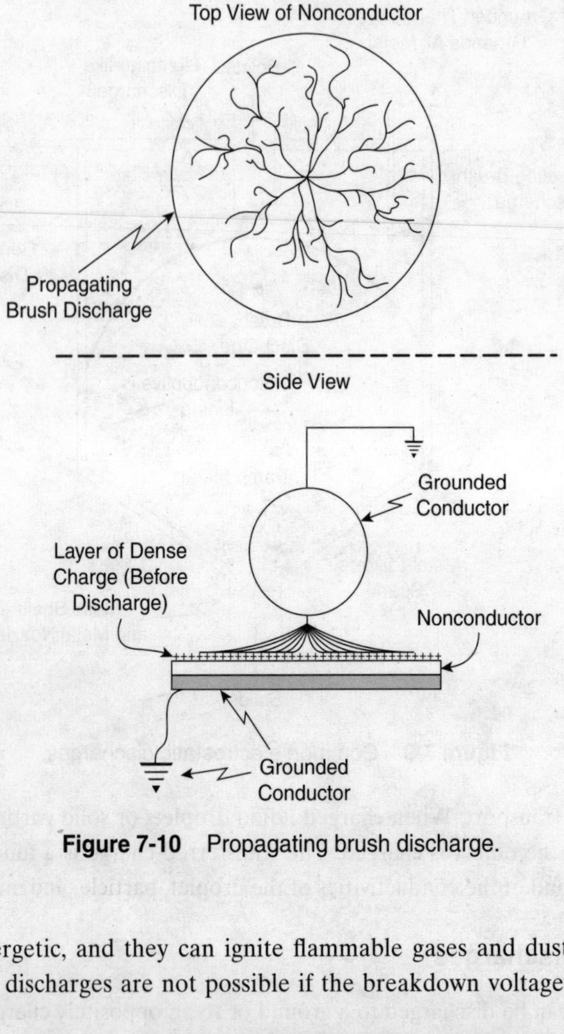

Figure 7-10 Propagating brush discharge.

discharges are energetic, and they can ignite flammable gases and dusts. Data show that propagating brush discharges are not possible if the breakdown voltage of the insulator is 4 kV or less.[4]

A *conical pile* discharge (Figure 7-9) is a form of a brush-type discharge that occurs at the conical surface of a pile of powder.[5] The necessary conditions for this discharge are (1) a powder with a high resistivity (>10^{10} ohm m), (2) a powder with coarse particles (>1 mm in diameter), (3) a powder with a high charge to mass ratio (for example, charged by

[4]B. Maurer, "Discharges due to Electrostatic Charging of Particles in Large Storage Silos," *German Chemical Engineering* (1979), 3: 189–195.

[5]M. Glor and B. Maurer, "Ignition Tests with Discharges from Bulked Polymeric Granules in Silos (Cone Discharge)," *Journal of Electrostatics* (1993), 30: 123–134.

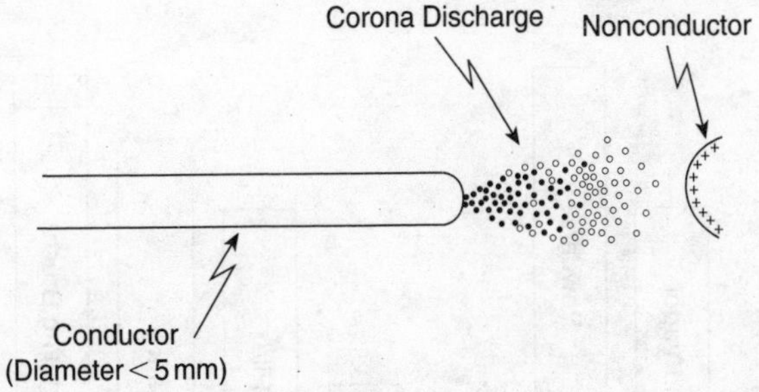

Figure 7-11 Corona discharge.

pneumatic transport), and (4) filling rates above about 0.5 kg/s. These are relatively intense discharges with energies up to several hundred millijoules; therefore they can ignite flammable gases and dusts. To ignite dusts, the coarse particles need a fraction of fines to give an explosive atmosphere.

A *brush* discharge (Figure 7-9) is a discharge between a relatively sharp-pointed conductor (radius of 0.1–100 mm) and either another conductor or a charged insulated surface. This discharge radiates from the conductor in a brush-like configuration. This discharge is less intense compared with the point-to-point spark discharge, and it is unlikely to ignite dusts. However, brush discharges can ignite flammable gases.

Lightning-like discharges (Figure 7-9) are discharges from a cloud in the air over the powder. It is known from experiments that lightning-like discharges do not occur in vessels with volumes less than 60 m^3 or in silos with diameters less than 3 m.[6] There is currently no physical evidence that lightning-like discharges have resulted in industrial deflagrations.

A *corona* discharge (Figure 7-11) is similar to a brush discharge. The electrode conductor has a sharp point. The discharge from such an electrode has sufficient energy to ignite only the most sensitive gases (for example, hydrogen).

Energy from Electrostatic Discharges

The energy generated in electrostatic discharges compared with the minimum ignition energies of gases and vapors and dusts is illustrated in Figure 7-12. In general, the results illustrate that flammable gases and vapors can be ignited by spark, brush, conical pile, and propagating brush

[6] P. Boschung, W. Hilgner, G. Luttgens, B. Maurer, and A. Wider, "An Experimental Contribution to the Question of the Existence of Lightning-like Discharges in Dust Clouds," *Journal of Electrostatics* (1977), 3: 303–310.

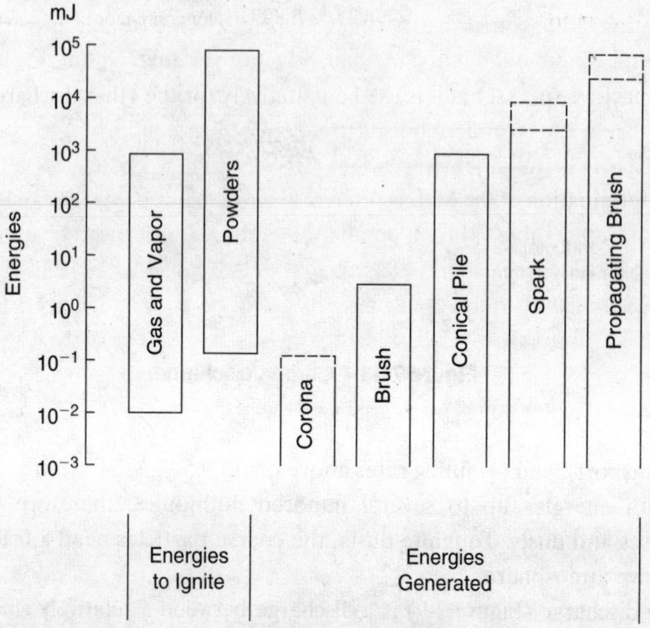

Figure 7-12 Minimum ignition energies compared to electrostatic discharge energies. Adapted from M. Glor and B. Maurer, "Ignition Tests with Discharges from Bulked Polymeric Granules in Silos (Cone Discharge)," *Journal of Electrostatics* (1993), 30: 123–134; and M. Glor, *Electrostatic Hazards in Powder Handling* (New York: Wiley, 1988).

discharges and that flammable dusts can be ignited only by sparks, propagating brush, and conical pile discharges. The regions enclosed by the dotted lines in Figure 7-12 indicate regions of uncertainty.

Energy of Electrostatic Ignition Sources

A spark is generated between two conductors when the distance between the conductors is small compared to the diameter of the conductors and when the electric field intensity between the conductors is approximately 3 MV/m. A brush discharge is generated if the distance between the conductors is large compared to the radius of curvature of the conductor.

The energy of a spark discharge is a function of the accumulated charge (Q in coulombs) on the object, the capacitance of the object (C in farads), and the potential, or voltage (V in volts), of the object. These three variables are related by the expression $C = Q/V$. The actual energy (expressed in joules) associated with the discharge process is given by

$$J = \frac{Q^2}{2C}. \tag{7-20}$$

Equation 7-20 assumes a capacitance-type discharge (that is, a spark); however, capacitance and voltage are not defined in nonconductive systems. Therefore Equation 7-20 is valid only for capacitive sparks, but it is used qualitatively for the other discharges.

A criterion that is commonly used to estimate the potential hazard of a discharge is to compare the MIE of the fuel-air mixture to the equivalent energy of the discharge. A precise experimental determination of the MIE is often required under the specific conditions of the system. MIEs are shown in Table 6-4 for a number of flammable gases and in Table 6-8 for dusts.

The static discharge energy is a function of the accumulated charge. In an industrial setting, this accumulated charge is usually the result of either contact or friction charging for flowing solids and double-layer charging for flowing liquids. In each case the charge (electrons) is transported with the material. The measure of this flow of electrons is a streaming current and is expressed in coulombs per second or amps.

Streaming Current

A streaming current I_S is the flow of electricity produced by transferring electrons from one surface to another by a flowing fluid or solid. When a liquid or solid flows through a pipe (metal or glass), an electrostatic charge develops on the streaming material. This current is analogous to a current in an electrical circuit. The relation between a liquid streaming current and the pipe diameter, pipe length, fluid velocity, and fluid properties is given by[7]

$$I_S = \left[\frac{10 \times 10^{-6}\ \text{amp}}{(\text{m/s})^2(\text{m})^2}\right](ud)^2\left[1 - \exp\left(-\frac{L}{u\tau}\right)\right], \tag{7-21}$$

where

I_S is the streaming current (amps),
u is the velocity (m/s),
d is the pipe diameter (m),
L is the pipe length (m), and
τ is the liquid relaxation time (seconds).

The relaxation time is the time required for a charge to dissipate by leakage. It is determined using

$$\tau = \frac{\varepsilon_r \varepsilon_0}{\gamma_c}, \tag{7-22}$$

[7] L. G. Britton, *Avoiding Static Ignition Hazards in Chemical Operations* (New York: American Institute of Chemical Engineers, 1999).

Table 7-2 Properties for Electrostatic Calculations[a]

Material	Specific conductivity[b] (mho/cm)	Dielectric constant
Liquids		
Benzene	7.6×10^{-8} to $<1 \times 10^{-18}$	2.3
Toluene	$<1 \times 10^{-14}$	2.4
Xylene	$<1 \times 10^{-15}$	2.4
Heptane	$<1 \times 10^{-18}$	2.0
Hexane	$<1 \times 10^{-18}$	1.9
Methanol	4.4×10^{-7}	33.7
Ethanol	1.5×10^{-7}	25.7
Isopropanol	3.5×10^{-6}	25.0
Water	5.5×10^{-6}	80.4
Other materials and air		
Air		1.0
Cellulose	1.0×10^{-9}	3.9–7.5
Pyrex	1.0×10^{-14}	4.8
Paraffin	10^{-16} to 0.2×10^{-18}	1.9–2.3
Rubber	0.33×10^{-13}	3.0
Slate	1.0×10^{-8}	6.0–7.5
Teflon	0.5×10^{-13}	2.0
Wood	10^{-10} to 10^{-13}	3.0

[a]J. H. Perry, *Chemical Engineers' Handbook*, 3rd ed. (New York: McGraw-Hill, 1950), p. 1734.
[b]Resistance = 1/conductivity = 1/(mho/cm) = ohm cm.

where

τ is the relaxation time (seconds),
ε_r is the relative dielectric constant (unitless),
ε_0 is the permittivity constant, that is,

$$8.85 \times 10^{-12} \frac{\text{coulomb}^2}{\text{N m}^2} = 8.85 \times 10^{-14} \frac{\text{s}}{\text{ohm cm}}, \text{ and}$$

γ_c is the specific conductivity (mho/cm).

Specific conductivities and relative dielectric constants are listed in Table 7-2.

Charges also accumulate when solids are transported. The buildup results from the separation of solid particle surfaces. Because solid geometries are almost always ill-defined, electrostatic calculations for solids are handled empirically.

Table 7-3 Charge Buildup for Various Operations[a]

Process	Charge (coulomb/kg)
Sieving	10^{-9} to 10^{-11}
Pouring	10^{-7} to 10^{-9}
Grinding	10^{-6} to 10^{-7}
Micronizing	10^{-4} to 10^{-7}
Sliding down an incline	10^{-5} to 10^{-7}
Pneumatic transport of solids	10^{-5} to 10^{-7}

[a] R. A. Mancini, "The Use (and Misuse) of Bonding for Control of Static Ignition Hazards," *Plant/Operations Progress* (Jan. 1988) 7(1): 24.

The streaming current that is generated while transporting solids is a function of the solids processing method (see Table 7-3) and the flow rate, as shown by

$$I_S = \left(\frac{\text{coulombs}}{\text{kg}}\right)\left(\frac{\text{kg}}{\text{s}}\right), \tag{7-23}$$

where

I_S is coulombs/second or amps,
coulombs/kg is given in Table 7-3, and
kg/s is the solids flow rate.

Some generally accepted guidelines for electrostatic calculations are shown in Table 7-4.

Table 7-4 Accepted Electrostatic Values for Calculations[a]

Voltage to produce spark between needle points 1/2 in apart	14,000 V
Voltage to produce spark between plates 0.01 mm apart	350 V
Maximum charge density before corona discharge	2.65×10^{-9} coulomb/cm^2
Minimum ignition energies (mJ)	
Vapors in air	0.1
Mists in air	1.0
Dusts in air	10.0
Approximate capacitances C (micro-microfarads)	
Humans	100 to 400
Automobiles	500
Tank truck (2000 gal)	1000
Tank (12-ft diameter with insulation)	100,000
Capacitance between two 2-in flanges (1/8-in gap)	20
Contact zeta potentials	0.01–0.1 V

[a] F. G. Eichel, "Electrostatics," *Chemical Engineering* (March 13, 1967), p. 163.

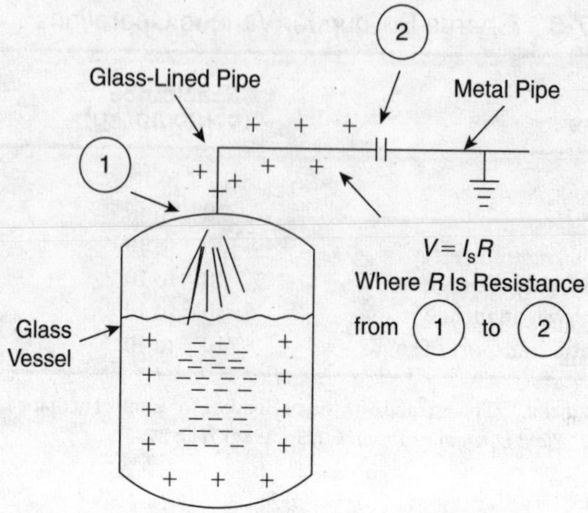

Figure 7-13 Electrical charge accumulation in a feed line resulting from fluid flow.

Electrostatic Voltage Drops

Figure 7-13 illustrates a tank with a feed line. Fluid flows through the feed line and drops into the tank. The streaming current builds up a charge and voltage in the feed line to the vessel and in the vessel itself. The voltage from the electrical ground in the metal line to the end of the glass pipe is calculated using

$$V = I_S R. \tag{7-24}$$

The resistance R (in ohms) is computed using the conductivity of the fluid γ_c (in mho/cm), the length of the conductor L (in cm), and the area A of the conductor (in cm^2):

$$R = \frac{L}{\gamma_c A}. \tag{7-25}$$

This relationship shows that as the area of the conductor increases, the resistance decreases, and if the conductor length increases, the resistance increases.

Energy of Charged Capacitors

The amount of work required to increase the charge on a capacitor from Q to $Q + dQ$ is $dJ = VdQ$, where V is the potential difference and the charge is Q. Because $V = Q/C$, the integration gives Equation 7-20, and substitutions give

Table 7-5 Capacitance of Various Objects[a]

Object	Capacitance (farad)
Small scoop, beer can, tools	5×10^{-12}
Buckets, small drums	20×10^{-12}
50–100-gal containers	100×10^{-12}
Person	200×10^{-12}
Automobile	500×10^{-12}
Tank truck	1000×10^{-12}

[a]R. A. Mancini, "The Use (and Misuse) of Bonding for Control of Static Ignition Hazards," *Plant/Operations Progress* (Jan. 1988), 7(1): 24.

$$J = \frac{CV^2}{2}, \tag{7-26}$$

$$J = \frac{QV}{2}. \tag{7-27}$$

The units used in Equations 7-26 and 7-27 are usually C in farads, V in volts, Q in coulombs, and J in joules.

Capacitances of various materials used in the chemical industry are given in Table 7-5.

Charges can accumulate as a result of a streaming current $dQ/dt = I_S$. Assuming a constant streaming current,

$$Q = I_S t, \tag{7-28}$$

where I_S is in amps and t is in seconds. Equation 7-28 assumes that the system starts with no accumulation of charge, only one constant source of charge I_S, and no current or charge loss terms (see the section "Balance of Charges" on page 350 for a more complex system).

Example 7-4

Determine the voltage developed between a charging nozzle and a grounded tank, as shown in Figure 7-14. Also, compute the energy stored in the nozzle and the energy accumulated in the liquid. Explain the potential hazards in this process for a flow rate of

a. 1 gpm
b. 150 gpm

The data are

Hose length:	20 ft
Hose diameter:	2 in

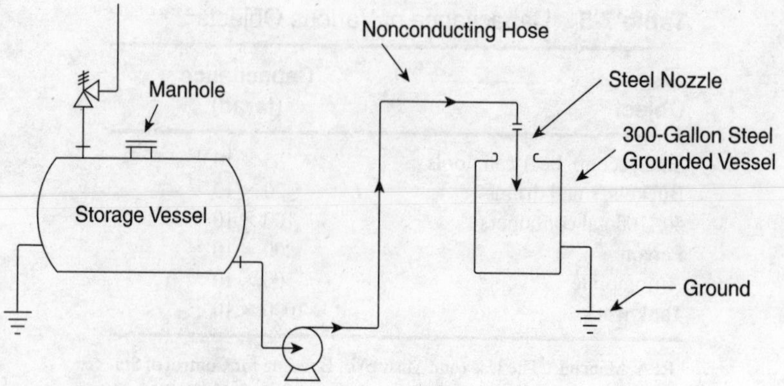

Figure 7-14 System for Example 7-4.

Liquid conductivity:	10^{-8} mho/cm
Dielectric constant ε_r:	25.7
Density:	0.88 g/cm^3

Solution

a. Because the hose and nozzle are not grounded, the voltage generated at the nozzle tip is $V = IR$. The resistance is computed using Equation 7-25 for the conducting fluid with a resistance length equivalent to the hose length (from the ground near the pump to the nozzle) and a resistance area equivalent to the cross-sectional area of the conducting fluid:

$$L = (20\text{ ft})(12\text{ in/ft})(2.54\text{ cm/in}) = 610\text{ cm},$$

$$A = \pi r^2 = (3.14)(1\text{ in})^2(2.54\text{ cm/in})^2 = 20.3\text{ cm}^2.$$

Using Equation 7-25, we obtain

$$R = \left(\frac{1}{\gamma_c}\right)\left(\frac{L}{A}\right)$$

$$= (10^8\text{ ohm cm})\left(\frac{610\text{ cm}}{20.3\text{ cm}^2}\right)$$

$$= 3.00 \times 10^9\text{ ohm}.$$

The streaming current is a function of the velocity and the pipe diameter. The average velocity in the pipe is

$$u = \left(\frac{1\text{ gal/min}}{3.14\text{ in}^2}\right)\left(\frac{\text{ft}^3}{7.48\text{ gal}}\right)\left(\frac{144\text{ in}^2}{\text{ft}^2}\right)\left(\frac{1\text{ min}}{60\text{ s}}\right)$$

$$= 0.102\text{ ft/s} = 3.1 \times 10^{-2}\text{ m/s}.$$

The relaxation time is estimated using Equation 7-22:

$$\tau = \frac{\varepsilon_r \varepsilon_0}{\gamma_c} = \frac{(25.7)\left(8.85 \times 10^{-14} \dfrac{\text{mho} \times \text{s}}{\text{cm}}\right)}{10^{-8}\ \text{mho/cm}}$$

$$= 22.7 \times 10^{-5}\ \text{s}.$$

The streaming current is now determined using Equation 7-21:

$$I_S = \left[\frac{10 \times 10^{-6}\ \text{amp}}{(\text{m/s})^2(\text{m})^2}\right](ud)^2\left[1 - \exp\left(-\frac{L}{u\tau}\right)\right]$$

$$= \left[\frac{10 \times 10^{-6}\ \text{amp}}{(\text{m/s})^2(\text{m})^2}\right]\left[(3.1 \times 10^{-2})\left(\frac{2}{12 \times 3.28}\right)\right]^2\left[1 - \exp\left(-\frac{20}{0.102 \times 2.27 \times 10^{-4}}\right)\right]$$

$$= (9.6 \times 10^{-9})(2.58 \times 10^{-3})(1 - 0) = 2.48 \times 10^{-11}\ \text{amp}.$$

Method 1: Compute the energy accumulated in the capacitor formed between the flanges at the nozzle. A spark between the flanges may be an ignition source. The voltage drop down the 20-ft line is the same as the voltage drop from the hose flange to the nozzle flange, assuming that the nozzle is grounded. The voltage is therefore

$$V = IR = (2.48 \times 10^{-11}\ \text{amp})(3.0 \times 10^9\ \text{ohm})$$

$$= 0.074\ \text{volt}.$$

The capacitance between the two 1-in flanges is given in Table 7-4, that is,

$$C = 20 \times 10^{-12}\ \text{farads} = 20 \times 10^{-12}\ \text{coulomb/volt}.$$

The energy is determined using Equation 7-26:

$$J = \frac{CV^2}{2} = \left[\frac{20 \times 10^{-12}(0.074)^2}{2}\right] = 5.49 \times 10^{-14}\ \text{Joules}.$$

This is significantly lower than the energy required to ignite a flammable gas (0.1 mJ); therefore there is no hazard at the nozzle.

Method 2: Compute the energy accumulated in the capacitor formed by the tank of liquid. A brush discharge can jump from this liquid to a metal component, such as a grounded thermocouple. The accumulated charge is computed using Equation 7-28:

$$Q = I_S t,$$

with the time equal to the filling time of the vessel:

$$t = (300\ \text{gal}/1\ \text{gpm})(60\ \text{s/min}) = 18{,}000\ \text{s}.$$

Substitution into Equation 7-28 gives

$$Q = I_S t = (2.48 \times 10^{-11}\ \text{amp})(18{,}000\ \text{s})$$
$$= 4.46 \times 10^{-7}\ \text{coulomb}.$$

The capacitance of the liquid is estimated to be one-tenth of the capacitance of a 2000-gal vessel, shown in Table 7-4; therefore

$$C = 100 \times 10^{-12}\ \text{farads} = 100 \times 10^{-12}\ \text{coulomb/volt},$$

and the accumulated energy is determined using Equation 7-20:

$$J = \frac{Q^2}{2C} = \frac{(4.46 \times 10^{-7}\ \text{coulomb})^2}{2(100 \times 10^{-12}\ \text{farads})} = 9.9 \times 10^{-4}\ \text{Joule} = 0.99\ \text{mJ}.$$

This exceeds the energy required to ignite a flammable gas (0.1 mJ). In this situation the vessel should be purged with nitrogen to keep the concentration of the flammable vapor below the LFL.

b. This case is identical to case a except that the flow rate is higher, 150 gpm versus 1 gpm for case a:

$$u = \left(0.102\,\frac{\text{ft}}{\text{s}}\right)\left(\frac{150\ \text{gpm}}{1\ \text{gpm}}\right) = 4.66\,\frac{\text{m}}{\text{s}}.$$

The resistance is the same as for case a, that is, 3.0×10^9 ohm:

$$\tau = 22.7 \times 10^{-5}\ \text{s}.$$

The streaming current is, from Equation 7-21,

$$I_S = \left[\frac{10 \times 10^{-6}\ \text{amp}}{(\text{m/s})^2(\text{m})^2}\right][(4.66\ \text{m/s})(0.051\ \text{m})]^2\left[1 - \exp\left(-\frac{20\ \text{ft}}{15.3\ \text{ft/s} \times 2.27 \times 10^{-4}\ \text{s}}\right)\right]$$
$$= 5.65 \times 10^{-7}(1 - 0) = 5.65 \times 10^{-7}\ \text{amp}.$$

Method 1: Compute the energy accumulated in the capacitor formed between the flanges at the nozzle:

$$V = IR = (5.65 \times 10^{-7}\ \text{amp})(3 \times 10^9\ \text{ohm}) = 1695\ \text{volts}.$$

The accumulated energy is again computed using Equation 7-26:

$$J = \frac{CV^2}{2} = \frac{(20 \times 10^{-12})(1695)^2}{2} = 0.000029\ \text{J} = 0.029\ \text{mJ}.$$

This is less than the energy required to ignite a flammable gas (0.1 mJ).

Method 2: Compute the energy accumulated in the capacitor formed by the tank of fluid:

$$t = \frac{300 \text{ gal}}{150 \text{ gpm}}\left(\frac{60 \text{ s}}{\text{min}}\right) = 160 \text{ s},$$

$$Q = I_S t = (5.65 \times 10^{-7})(160) = 9 \times 10^{-5} \text{ coulombs},$$

$$J = \frac{Q^2}{2C} = \frac{(9 \times 10^{-5})^2}{2(100 \times 10^{-12})} = 40 \text{ Joules} \gg 0.1 \text{ mJ}.$$

This energy exceeds 0.1 mJ. This problem illustrates the importance of inerting. It is relatively easy to build up energies that exceed 0.1 mJ.

Capacitance of a Body

The buildup of a charge on one surface relative to another surface produces a capacitor. In the chemical industry the properties of the developed capacitor are estimated by assuming parallel flat plate or spherical geometries. For example, the capacitance of a tank or a person is estimated by assuming spherical geometries, and the capacitance of a person's shoe sole or of a noncorrosive tank lining is estimated assuming parallel flat plates. Several examples are shown in Figure 7-15.

The capacitance C of a body is Q/V. For a sphere with radius r the voltage developed when a charge Q is accumulated is derived with elementary physics:

$$V = \frac{1}{4\pi\varepsilon_0}\frac{Q}{\varepsilon_r r}. \tag{7-29}$$

Therefore, because $C = Q/V$, the capacitance for a spherical body is

$$\boxed{C = 4\pi\varepsilon_r \varepsilon_0 r,} \tag{7-30}$$

where

ε_r is the relative dielectric constant (unitless),
ε_0 is the permittivity (8.85×10^{-12} coulomb^2/N m^2 = 2.7×10^{-12} coulomb/volt ft),
r is the sphere radius, and
C is the capacitance.

For two parallel plates

$$V = \frac{QL}{\varepsilon_r \varepsilon_0 A}. \tag{7-31}$$

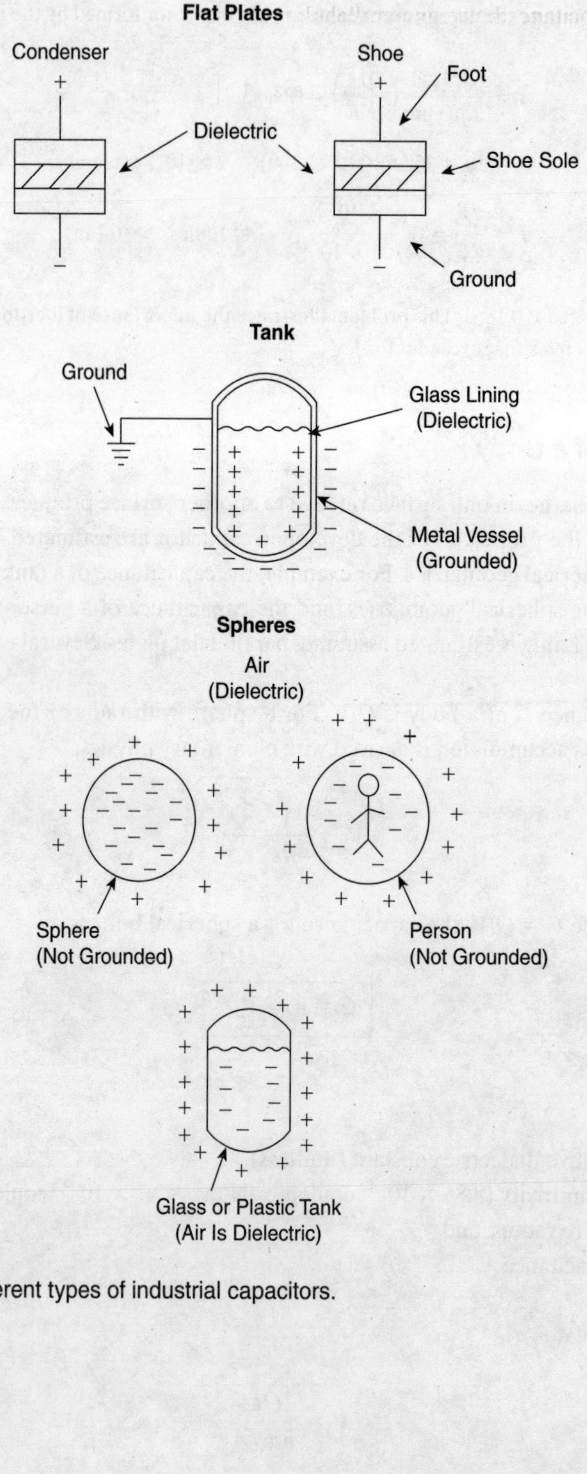

Figure 7-15 Different types of industrial capacitors.

Therefore the capacitance between parallel plates is

$$\boxed{C = \frac{\varepsilon_r \varepsilon_0 A}{L},} \qquad (7\text{-}32)$$

where

A is the area of the surface and
L is the thickness of the dielectric.

Example 7-5

Estimate the capacitance of a person (6 ft, 2 in tall) standing on a dry wooden floor.

Solution

This person's capacitance is estimated assuming that the person's shape is spherical and that the "sphere" is surrounded by air (ε_r is 1.0 for air). Using Equation 7-30 for a sphere, we have

$$C = 4\pi\varepsilon_r\varepsilon_0 r$$

$$= 4(3.14)(1.0)\left(2.7 \times 10^{-12}\,\frac{\text{coulomb}}{\text{volt ft}}\right)\left(\frac{6.17\text{ ft}}{2}\right)$$

$$= 1.05 \times 10^{-10}\,\frac{\text{coulomb}}{\text{volt}}.$$

The calculated capacitance is close to the value listed for a person in Table 7-5.

Example 7-6

Estimate the capacitance of a person standing on a conductive floor. Assume that the person's shoe soles separate the person from the floor; that is, the shoe sole is the dielectric of the capacitor. Given

Shoe sole area (ft^2) = 2 shoes (0.4 ft^2 each)
Shoe sole thickness = 0.2 in
Dielectric constant of shoe soles = 3.5

Solution

Use Equation 7-32, which for flat parallel plates is

$$C = \frac{\varepsilon_r \varepsilon_0 A}{L}$$

$$= \frac{(3.5)\left(2.7 \times 10^{-12}\,\frac{\text{coulomb}}{\text{volt ft}}\right)(0.8\text{ ft}^2)}{\left(\frac{0.2\text{ in}}{12\text{ in/ft}}\right)}$$

$$= 4.54 \times 10^{-10}\text{ farads.}$$

Example 7-7

Estimate the charge buildup, and accumulated energy, as a result of a person (insulated from the floor) charging 30 lb of a dry powder, using a scoop, into a 20-gal insulated drum. Assume that the person's capacitance is 300×10^{-12} farad.

Solution

This operation is a sliding-contact type operation. From Table 7-3 this operation gives a charge of 10^{-5} coulomb/kg. Therefore the charge buildup is

$$Q = \left(10^{-5}\,\frac{\text{coulombs}}{\text{kg}}\right)(30\ \text{lb})\left(0.454\,\frac{\text{kg}}{\text{lb}}\right) = 1.36 \times 10^{-4}\ \text{coulombs}.$$

The accumulated energy, using Equation 7-20, is

$$J = \frac{Q^2}{2C} = \frac{(1.36 \times 10^{-4}\ \text{coulombs})^2}{2(300 \times 10^{-12}\ \text{farad})} = 30.8\ \text{Joules}.$$

These results illustrate that the energy exceeds the requirement for generating a spark capable of igniting a flammable gas. This spark would be discharged if the person approached a ground with a hand or with the scoop.

An equal and opposite charge is also accumulated in the powder in the insulated drum. Therefore the charged powder is another ignition source. For example, if a grounded object of any kind is placed close to the solids, an energetic spark could be generated.

Balance of Charges

Some systems are more complex than those previously discussed; for example, a vessel may have several inlet lines and several outlet lines. An example is illustrated in Figure 7-16.

For this type of system a charge balance is required to establish the charge and accumulated energy as a function of time. The charge balance is developed by considering the currents streaming in, the charge carried away by flows going out, and charge loss resulting from relaxation. The result is

$$\boxed{\frac{dQ}{dt} = \sum^{n}(I_S)_{i,\text{in}} - \sum^{m}(I_S)_{j,\text{out}} - \frac{Q}{\tau},} \qquad (7\text{-}33)$$

where

$(I_S)_{i,\text{in}}$ is the streaming current entering the tank through a specific inlet line i from a set of n lines,

$(I_S)_{j,\text{out}}$ is the current leaving through one specific outlet line j from a set of m lines,

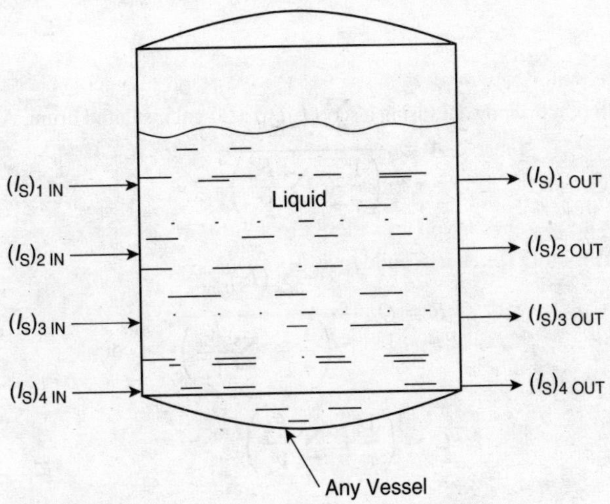

Figure 7-16 Vessel with multiple inlets and outlets.

Q/τ is the charge loss resulting from relaxation, and
τ is the relaxation time.

$(I_S)_{j,\text{out}}$ is a function of the charge accumulated in the tank and the rate of discharge F from the specific outlet nozzle j:

$$(I_S)_{j,\text{out}} = \frac{F_j}{V_c} Q, \tag{7-34}$$

where

V_c is the container or tank volume and
Q is the total charge in the tank.

Substituting Equation 7-34 into Equation 7-33 gives

$$\frac{dQ}{dt} = \sum (I_S)_{i,\text{in}} - \sum \frac{F_j}{V_c} Q - \frac{Q}{\tau}. \tag{7-35}$$

If the flows, streaming currents, and relaxation times are constant, Equation 7-35 is a linear differential equation that can be solved using standard techniques. The result is

$$Q = A + Be^{-C}t, \tag{7-36}$$

where

$$A = \frac{\sum (I_S)_{i,\,\text{in}}}{\left(\dfrac{1}{\tau} + \sum \dfrac{F_n}{V_c}\right)},$$

$$B = Q_0 - \frac{\sum (I_S)_{i,\,\text{in}}}{\left(\dfrac{1}{\tau} + \sum \dfrac{F_n}{V_c}\right)},$$

$$C = \left(\frac{1}{\tau} + \sum \frac{F_n}{V_c}\right).$$

Q_0 is the initial charge in the tank at $t = 0$. These equations plus the equations described previously (equations for I_S and J) are used to compute Q and J as a function of time. Therefore the hazards of relatively complex systems can be evaluated.

Equation 7-36 is also used when the filling and discharge rates are sequential. In this case Q is computed for each step with the specified $\Sigma\ (I_S)_{i,\,\text{in}}$ and $\Sigma\ (F_n/V_c)$ for that particular step, and the initial Q_0 is the result from the previous step.

An example of a sequential operation is (1) charging benzene to a vessel at a specific rate through a specific line of known size, (2) charging methanol and toluene through two different lines at different rates, (3) holding the batch for a specified time, and (4) discharging the batch through a different line at a specified rate. If the line sizes, rates, and materials of construction are known, the potential hazard of each step of the operation can be estimated.

Example 7-8

A large vessel (50,000 gal) is being filled with toluene. Compute Q and J during the filling operation when the vessel is half full (25,000 gal) and where

$F = 100$ gpm,
$I_S = 1.5 \times 10^{-7}$ amp,
Liquid conductivity $= 10^{-14}$ mho cm^{-1}, and
Dielectric constant $= 2.4$.

Solution

Because there is only one inlet line and no outlet lines, Equation 7-33 reduces to

$$\frac{dQ}{dt} = I_S - \frac{Q}{\tau}.$$

Therefore

$$Q = I_S\tau + (Q_0 - I_S\tau)e^{-t/\tau}.$$

Because the vessel is initially empty, $Q_0 = 0$. The relaxation time is computed using Equation 7-22:

$$\tau = \frac{\varepsilon_r \varepsilon_0}{\gamma_c} = \frac{(2.4)\left(8.85 \times 10^{-14} \dfrac{\text{s}}{\text{ohm cm}}\right)}{(10^{-14}\ \text{mho cm}^{-1})} = 21.2\ \text{s}.$$

The charge buildup as a function of time is

$$Q(t) = I_S\tau(1 - e^{-t/\tau}) = \left(1.5 \times 10^{-7} \frac{\text{coulomb}}{\text{s}}\right)(21.2\ \text{s})(1 - e^{-t/21.2}).$$

When the vessel contains 25,000 gal, the elapsed time is 15,000 s. Therefore

$$Q(15{,}000\ \text{s}) = 3.19 \times 10^{-6}\ \text{coulombs}.$$

The capacitance of this vessel is estimated by assuming a spherical geometry surrounded by air:

$$V_t = \frac{4}{3}\pi r^3,$$

$$r = \left(\frac{3V_t}{4\pi}\right)^{1/3}$$

$$= \left(\frac{3}{4\pi}\frac{25{,}000\ \text{gal}}{7.48\ \text{gal ft}^{-3}}\right)^{1/3} = 9.27\ \text{ft}.$$

Using Equation 7-30 and assuming a dielectric of 1 for air, we obtain

$$C = 4\pi\varepsilon_r\varepsilon_0 r = 4(3.14)(1.0)\left(2.7 \times 10^{-12}\frac{\text{coulomb}}{\text{volt ft}}\right)(9.27\ \text{ft})$$

$$= 3.14 \times 10^{-10}\ \text{farads}.$$

The energy stored in this vessel (25,000 gal of toluene) is computed using Equation 7-20:

$$J = \frac{Q^2}{2C} = \frac{(3.19 \times 10^{-6}\ \text{coulomb})^2}{2(3.14 \times 10^{-10}\ \text{farad})} = 16.2\ \text{mJ}.$$

The minimum condition for an ignition is 0.10 mJ; therefore the operating conditions for this vessel are extremely hazardous.

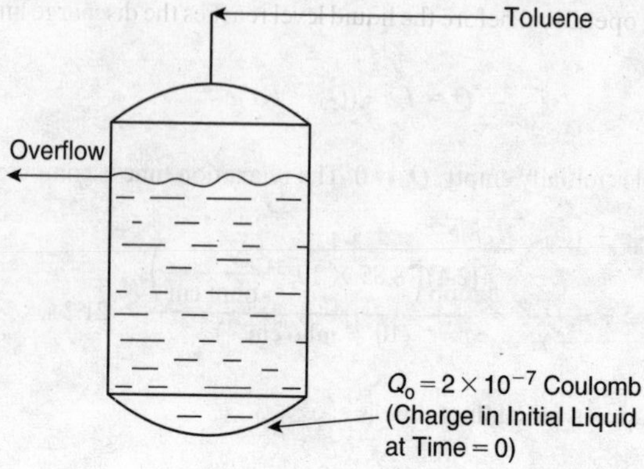

Figure 7-17 Charge buildup with complex vessel system.

Example 7-9

Figure 7-17 shows an in-line trap for removing water from a process stream. Compute:

a. Q and J when the vessel fluid just reaches the overflow line (start with an empty vessel).
b. Q and J under equilibrium conditions ($t = \infty$).
c. The time required to reduce the accumulated charge to half the equilibrium charge if the flows are stopped after equilibrium conditions are reached.
d. The charge removed with the discharge under equilibrium conditions.

Given:

Volume of vessel = 5 gal
Flow rate = 100 gpm toluene
Streaming current $I_S = 1.5 \times 10^{-7}$ amp (high value due to filter in line)
Liquid conductivity = 10^{-14} mho/cm
Dielectric constant = 2.4
Initial vessel charge = 2×10^{-7} coulomb

Solution

a. The residence time of this vessel is

$$\text{Residence time} = \left(\frac{5\text{ gal}}{100\text{ gpm}}\right)\left(\frac{60\text{ s}}{\text{min}}\right) = 3.00\text{ s}.$$

The relaxation time is determined using Equation 7-22:

$$\tau = \frac{\varepsilon_r \varepsilon_0}{\gamma_c} = \frac{(2.4)\left(8.85 \times 10^{-14} \dfrac{\text{s}}{\text{ohm cm}}\right)}{10^{-14} \dfrac{\text{mho}}{\text{cm}}} = 21.2\text{ s}.$$

During the filling operation, before the liquid level reaches the discharge line, Equations 7-35 and 7-36 reduce to

$$\frac{dQ}{dt} = I_S - \frac{Q}{\tau},$$

$$Q(t) = I_S\tau + (Q_0 - I_S\tau)e^{-t/\tau}$$

$$= 1.5 \times 10^{-7} \frac{\text{coulomb}}{\text{s}}(21.2\ \text{s})$$

$$+ [2 \times 10^{-7}\ \text{coulomb} - 1.5 \times 10^{-7}\ \text{amp}(21.24\ \text{s})]e^{-t/21.2}$$

$$= 3.18 \times 10^{-6} - 2.98 \times 10^{-6} e^{-t/21.2},$$

with $Q(t)$ in coulombs and t in seconds. At 3 seconds

$$Q(t = 3\ \text{s}) = 5.93 \times 10^{-7}\ \text{coulombs}.$$

This is the charge buildup just before reaching the overflow line.

The vessel capacitance is calculated by assuming a spherical geometry with the surrounding air serving as the dielectric. Because 5 gal = 0.668 ft^3, the radius of this sphere is

$$r = \left[\frac{3(0.668\ \text{ft}^3)}{4\pi}\right]^{1/3} = 0.542\ \text{ft}.$$

The capacitance is estimated using Equation 7-30:

$$C = 4\pi\varepsilon_r\varepsilon_0 r = 4\pi(1.0)\left(2.7 \times 10^{-12}\ \frac{\text{coulomb}}{\text{volt ft}}\right)(0.542\ \text{ft})$$

$$= 1.84 \times 10^{-11}\ \text{farads}.$$

The energy accumulated in this vessel is estimated using Equation 7-20:

$$J = \frac{Q^2}{2C} = \frac{(5.93 \times 10^{-7}\ \text{coulomb})^2}{2(1.84 \times 10^{-11}\ \text{farads})} = 9.55\ \text{mJ}.$$

The accumulated energy (9.55 mJ) greatly exceeds the quantity required for ignition of flammable materials. This system is operating under hazardous conditions.

b. This vessel will gradually level off to steady-state equilibrium conditions when the operating time significantly exceeds the relaxation time; therefore the exponential term of Equation 7-36 is 0. Equation 7-36 for this case reduces to

$$Q(t = \infty) = \frac{I_S}{\left(\frac{1}{\tau} + \frac{F}{V_c}\right)} = \frac{(1.5 \times 10^{-7}\ \text{amps})}{\left(\frac{1}{21.2} + \frac{1}{3}\right)\text{s}^{-1}} = 3.94 \times 10^{-7}\ \text{coulomb}.$$

From part a the capacitance is $C = 1.84 \times 10^{-11}$ farads. The energy is determined by using Equation 7-20:

$$J = \frac{Q^2}{2C} = \frac{(3.94 \times 10^{-7}\ \text{coulombs})^2}{2(1.84 \times 10^{-11}\ \text{farads})} = 4.22\ \text{mJ}.$$

Although there is an additional loss of charge with the overflowing liquid, the system is still operating under hazardous conditions.

c. After the inlet flow is stopped, $(I_S)_{in}$ and $(I_S)_{out}$ are zero, and Equation 7-36 reduces to

$$Q = Q_0 e^{-t/\tau}.$$

For $Q/Q_0 = 0.5$, from the problem definition,

$$0.5 = e^{-t/\tau}$$

$$t = (21.2\ \text{s})\ln 2 = 14.7\ \text{s}.$$

Therefore it only takes about 15 s to reduce the accumulated charge to one-half its original charge.

d. Under equilibrium conditions Equation 7-35 is set to zero:

$$\frac{dQ}{dt} = I_S - \left(\frac{1}{\tau} + \frac{F}{V_c}\right)Q = 0,$$

and from part b, $Q(t = \infty) = 3.94 \times 10^{-7}$ coulomb, and

$$\text{Charge loss via relaxation} = \frac{Q}{\tau} = 1.86 \times 10^{-8}\ \frac{\text{coulomb}}{\text{s}},$$

$$\text{Charge loss via the overflow} = \frac{F}{V_c}Q = 1.31 \times 10^{-7}\ \frac{\text{coulomb}}{\text{s}}.$$

For this example the charge loss resulting from flow out of a system is greater than the loss resulting from relaxation.

Sparks resulting from static charge and discharge continue to cause major fires and explosions within the chemical industry. The examples and fundamentals developed in these sections were designed to emphasize the importance of this subject. Hopefully this emphasis on the fundamentals will make the subject less elusive and destructive.

7-3 Controlling Static Electricity

Charge buildup, resulting sparks, and the ignition of flammable materials are inevitable events if control methods are not appropriately used. In practice, however, design engineers recognize this problem and install special features to prevent (1) sparks by eliminating the buildup and accumulation of static charge and (2) ignition by inerting the surroundings.

Inerting (section 7-1) is the most effective and reliable method for preventing ignition. It is always used when working with flammable liquids that are 5°C (or less) below the flash point (closed cup). Methods for preventing charge buildup are described in the following paragraphs.

General Design Methods to Prevent Electrostatic Ignitions

The design objective is to prevent the buildup of charges on a product (liquid or powder) as well as on surrounding objects (equipment or personnel). For every charged object there exists its oppositely charged counterpart. Three methods are used to achieve this objective:

1. Prevent charges from accumulating to dangerous levels by reducing the rate of charge generation and increasing the rate of charge relaxation. This method is generally used when handling liquids.
2. Prevent charges from accumulating to dangerous levels by designing the system to include charge reduction by means of low-energy discharges. This method is generally used when handling powders.
3. When dangerous discharges cannot be eliminated, then prevent the possibility of an ignition by maintaining oxidant levels below the combustible levels (inerting) or by maintaining fuel levels below the LFL or above the UFL. Measures to mitigate the consequences of an explosion are also options for consideration (for example, deflagration venting and explosion suppression).

The special design features for preventing electrostatic ignitions are described in the following paragraphs.

Sparks are prevented by grounding and bonding. This procedure prevents two metallic objects (close to each other) from having different potentials. Grounding and bonding are used especially to prevent the existence of isolated metal parts or objects. Isolated objects are notorious for building up large potentials and energetic sparks when they are approached by another conductor at a lower potential.

Propagating brush discharges are prevented by keeping the nonconductive surfaces or coatings thin enough or conductive enough to have a breakdown voltage below 4 kV. These discharges are also prevented by keeping the metallic backings grounded, to eliminate the accumulation of a high-density charge on the metallic interface and a countercharge on the nonconductor surface.

Conical pile discharges are prevented by increasing the conductivity (additives), by decreasing the charge rate below 0.5 kg/s, or by using containers with a volume less than 1 m^3. The most effective way of preventing ignitions from conical pile discharges is inerting.

Brush discharges are prevented by keeping the nonconductive surfaces thin enough or conductive enough to have a breakdown voltage (U_d) of 4 kV. Nonconductive coatings with a thickness greater than 2 mm, however, are capable of brush discharges even with a U_d less than 4 kV. To prevent brush discharges, a thickness of less than 2 mm is necessary. This fixes the charges accumulated on the nonconductor, and fixed charges cannot be transferred in a brush discharge. Brush discharges from nonconductive liquids are prevented by increasing the conductivity using conductive additives. The most effective way of preventing ignitions from brush discharges is inerting.

Lightning-like discharges are prevented by keeping the vessel volume to less than 60 m^3 or the vessel diameter to less than 3 m. If this condition is not met, then the system needs to be inerted.

Relaxation

When pumping fluids into a vessel through a pipe on top of the vessel, the separation process produces a streaming current I_S, which is the basis for charge buildup. It is possible to substantially reduce this electrostatic hazard by adding an enlarged section of pipe just before entering the tank. This hold provides time for charge reduction by relaxation. The residence time in this relaxation section of pipe should be about twice the relaxation time determined from Equation 7-22.

In actual practice,[8] it was found that a hold time equal to or greater than one-half the calculated relaxation time is sufficient to eliminate charge buildup. The "twice the relaxation time" rule, therefore, provides a safety factor of 4. The American Petroleum Institute[9] recommends a *ud*, from Equation 7-21, of less than 0.5 m^2/s for road tanker filling and 0.8 m^2/s for railcar filling.

Bonding and Grounding

The voltage difference between two conductive materials is reduced to zero by bonding the two materials, that is, by bonding one end of a conducting wire to one of the materials and bonding the other end to the second material.

When comparing sets of bonded materials, the sets may have different voltages. The voltage difference between sets is reduced to zero by bonding each set to ground, that is, by *grounding.*

Bonding and grounding reduces the voltage of an entire system to ground level or zero voltage. This also eliminates the charge buildup between various parts of a system, eliminating the potential for static sparks. Examples of grounding and bonding are illustrated in Figures 7-18 and 7-19.

[8] F. G. Eichel, "Electrostatics," *Chemical Engineering* (Mar. 13, 1967), p. 153.

[9] API RP 2003, *Protection Against Ignitions Arising Out of Static, Lightning, and Stray Currents* (Washington, DC: American Petroleum Institute, 1991).

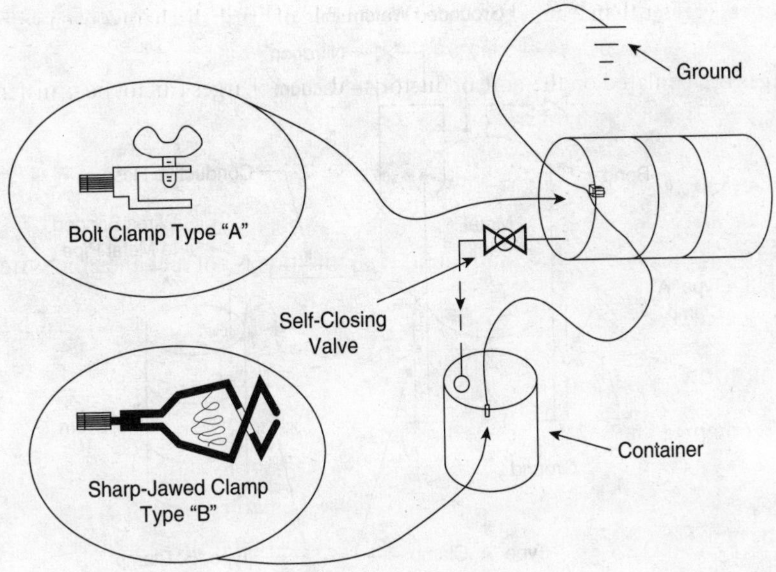

Figure 7-18 Bonding and grounding procedures for tanks and vessels. Adapted from Eichel, "Electrostatics," p. 153. (*continues*)

Glass- and plastic-lined vessels are grounded using tantalum inserts or metal probes, as illustrated in Figure 7-20. This technique, however, is not effective when handling liquids with low conductivity. In this case the fill line should extend to the bottom of the vessel (see Figure 7-21), to help eliminate the charge generation (and accumulation) resulting from separation during the filling operation. Also, the inlet velocities should be low enough to minimize the charge generated by streaming current I_S.

Dip Pipes

An extended line, sometimes called a dip leg or dip pipe, reduces the electrical charge that accumulates when liquid is allowed to free fall. When using dip pipes, however, care must be taken to prevent siphoning back when the inlet flow is stopped. A commonly used method is to place a hole in the dip pipe near the top of the vessel. Another technique is to use an angle iron instead of a pipe and to let the liquid flow down the angle iron (see Figure 7-21). These methods are also used when filling drums.

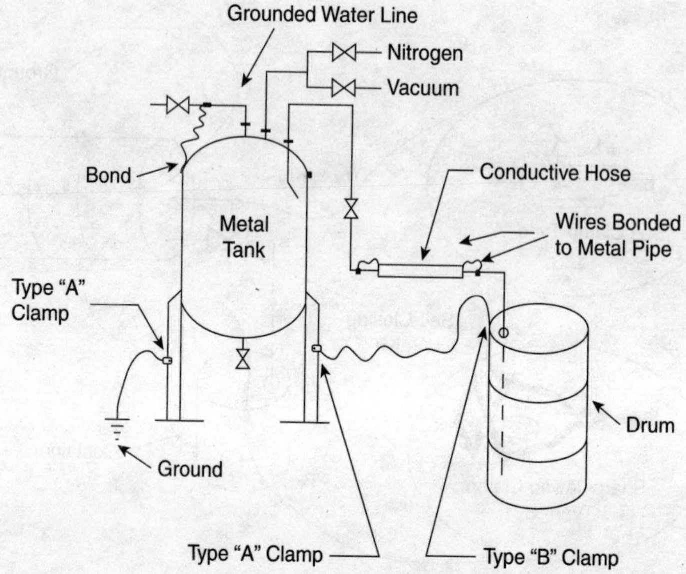

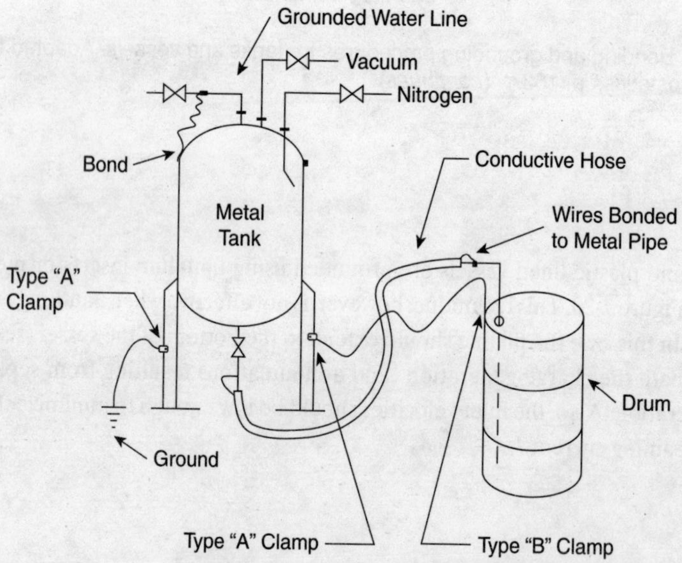

Figure 7-18 (*continues*)

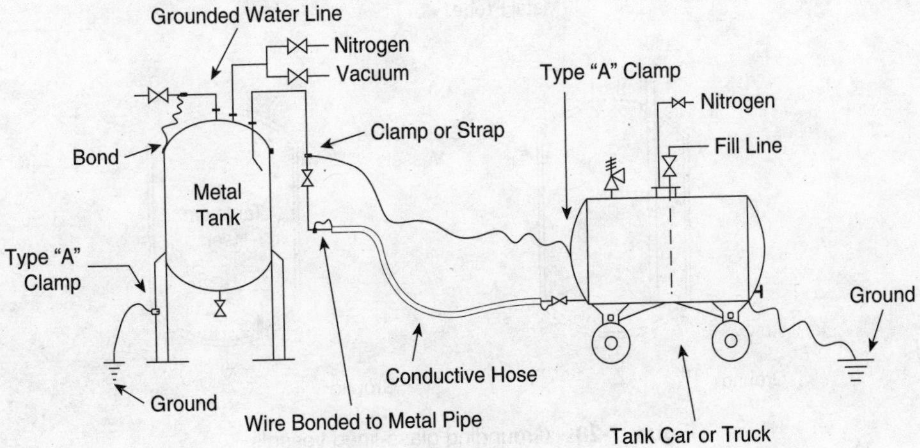

Unloading Tank Trucks or Cars

Figure 7-18 *(continued)*

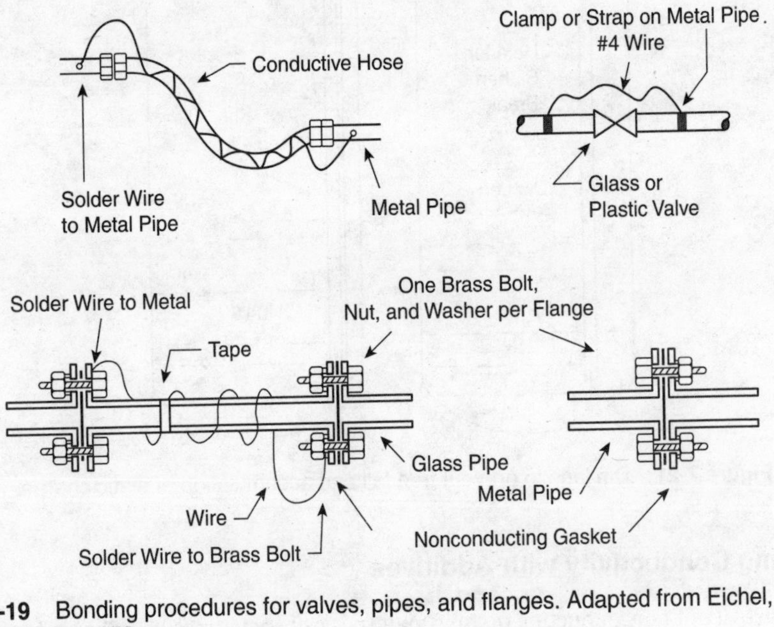

Figure 7-19 Bonding procedures for valves, pipes, and flanges. Adapted from Eichel, "Electrostatics," p. 153.

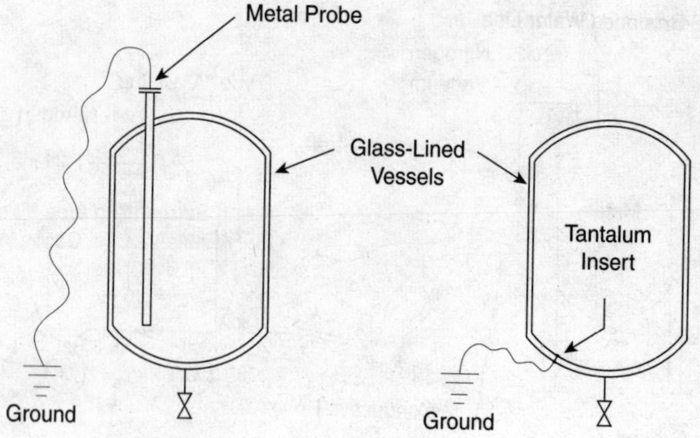

Figure 7-20 Grounding glass-lined vessels.

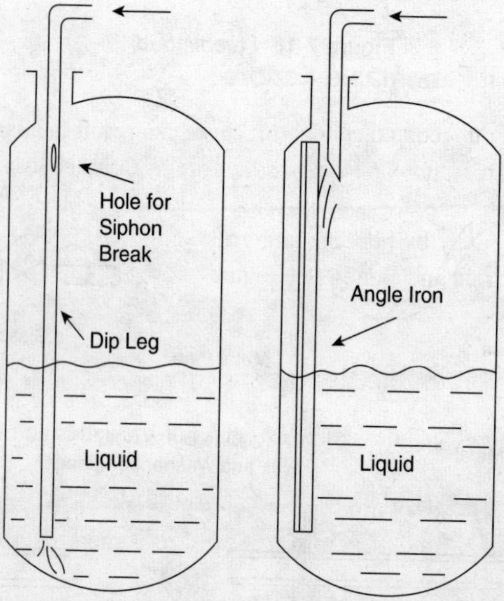

Figure 7-21 Dip legs to prevent free fall and accumulation of static charge.

Increasing Conductivity with Additives

The conductivity of nonconducting organic materials can sometimes be increased using additives called antistatic additives. Examples of antistatic additives include water and polar solvents, such as alcohols. Water is effective only when it is soluble in the offending liquid, because an insoluble phase gives an additional source of separation and charge buildup.

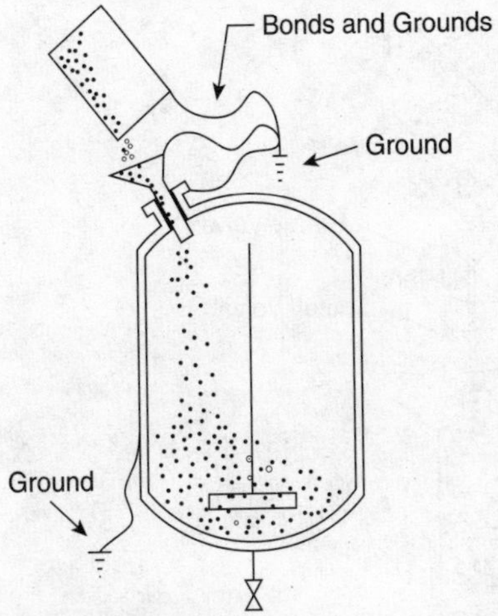

Permissible: Vessel and Surrounding Area Must Be Free from Flammable Vapors, Gases, and Liquids

Figure 7-22 Handling solids with no flammable vapors present. Adapted from Expert Commission for Safety in the Swiss Chemical Industry, "Static Electricity: Rules for Plant Safety," *Plant/Operations Progress* (Jan. 1988), 7(1): 19.

Handling Solids without Flammable Vapors

Charging solids with a nongrounded and conductive chute can result in a buildup of a charge on the chute. This charge can accumulate and finally produce a spark that may ignite a dispersed and flammable dust.

Solids are transferred safely by bonding and grounding all conductive parts and/or by using nonconductive parts (drum and chute). See Figure 7-22.

Handling Solids with Flammable Vapors

A safe design for this operation includes closed handling of the solids and liquids in an inert atmosphere (see Figure 7-23).

For solvent-free solids the use of nonconductive containers is permitted. For solids containing flammable solvents, only conductive and grounded containers are recommended.[10]

7-4 Explosion-Proof Equipment and Instruments

All electrical devices are inherent ignition sources. Special design features are required to prevent the ignition of flammable vapors and dusts. The fire and explosion hazard is directly proportional to the number and type of electrically powered devices in a process area.

[10]Expert Commission for Safety in the Swiss Chemical Industry, "Static Electricity: Rules for Plant Safety," p. 1.

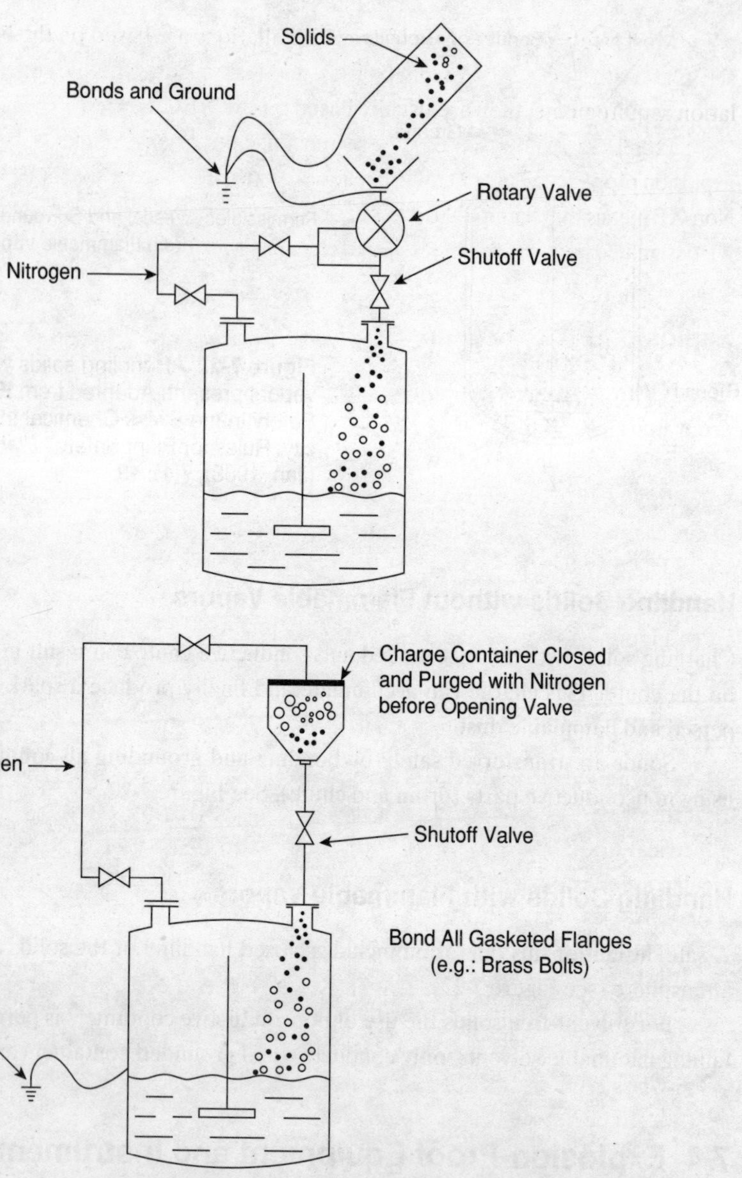

Figure 7-23 Handling solids with flammable vapors present. Source: Expert Commission for Safety in the Swiss Chemical Industry, "Static Electricity: Rules for Plant Safety," p. 19.

Most safety practices for electrical installations are based on the National Electric Code (NEC).[11] Although states, municipalities, and insurance companies may have their own installation requirements, they are usually based on the NEC.

Process areas are divided into two major types of environments: XP and non-XP. XP, for explosion proof, means flammable materials (particularly vapors) might be present at certain times. Non-XP means that flammable materials are not present, even under abnormal conditions. For non-XP designated areas open flames, heated elements, and other sources of ignition may be present.

Explosion-Proof Housings

In an XP area the electrical equipment and some instrumentation must have special explosion-proof housings. The housings are not designed to prevent flammable vapors and gases from entering but are designed to withstand an internal explosion and prevent the combustion from spreading beyond the inside of the enclosure. A motor starter, for example, is enclosed in a heavy cast walled box with the strength needed to withstand explosive pressures.

The explosion-proof design includes the use of conduit with special sealed connections around all junction boxes.

Figure 7-24 shows features of electrical equipment rated for an XP area.

Area and Material Classification

The design of electrical equipment and instrumentation is based on the nature of the process hazards or specific process classifications. The classification method is defined in the National Electrical Code; it is a function of the nature and degree of the process hazards within a particular area. The rating method includes Classes I, II, and III, Groups A-G, and Divisions 1 or 2.

The classes are related to the nature of the flammable material:

Class I: Locations where flammable gases or vapors are present.
Class II: Same for combustible dusts.
Class III: Hazard locations where combustible fibers or dusts are present but not likely to be in suspension.

The groups designate the presence of specific chemical types. Chemicals that are grouped have equivalent hazards:

Group A: acetylene
Group B: hydrogen, ethylene
Group C: carbon monoxide, hydrogen sulfide

[11] NFPA 70, *The National Electrical Code* (Quincy, MA: National Fire Protection Association, 2008).

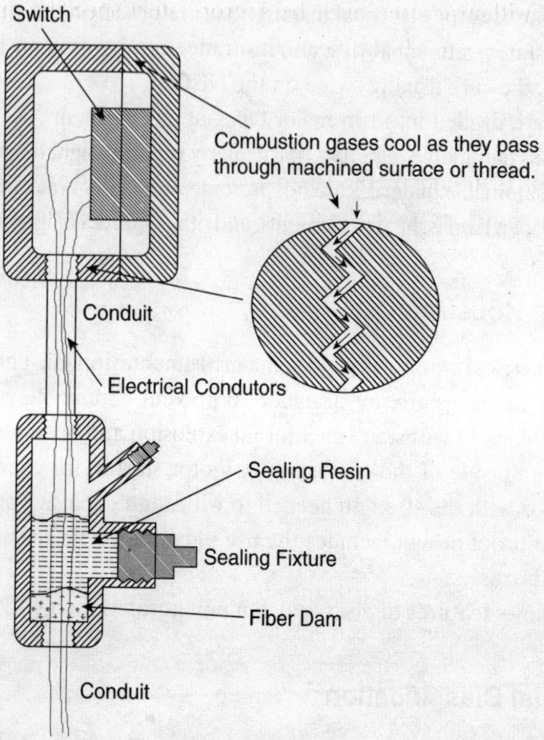

Figure 7-24 Design features of electrical fixtures rated for an XP area. Source: D. A. Crowl, *Understanding Explosions* (New York: American Institute of Chemical Engineers, 2003). Used by permission.

Group D: butane, ethane, ethyl alcohol
Group E: aluminum dust
Group F: carbon black
Group G: flour

Division designations are categorized in relationship to the probability of the material being within the flammable or explosive regions:

Division 1: Probability of ignition is high; that is, flammable concentrations are normally present.

Division 2: Hazardous only under abnormal conditions. Flammable materials are normally contained in closed containers or systems.

Design of an XP Area

When designing an XP area, all pieces of electrical equipment and instrumentation are specified for the class, group, and division, as discussed previously. All pieces of equipment and instrumentation within an area must be appropriately specified and installed. The overall classification is only as good as the piece of equipment in an area with the lowest classification.

7-5 Ventilation

Proper ventilation is another method used to prevent fires and explosions. The purpose of ventilation is to dilute the explosive vapors with air to prevent explosion and to confine the hazardous flammable mixtures.

Open-Air Plants

Open-air plants are recommended because the average wind velocities are high enough to safely dilute volatile chemical leaks that may exist within a plant. Although safety precautions are always practiced to minimize leaks, accidental releases from pump seals and other potential release points may occur.

Example 7-10

A plant handling substantial quantities of flammable toluene is located 1000 ft from a residential area. There is some concern that a sizable leak of flammable vapors will form a flammable cloud with subsequent ignition in the residential area. Determine the minimum mass flow rate of toluene leakage required to produce a vapor cloud in the residential area with a concentration equal to the LFL. Assume a 5 mph wind and D atmospheric stability.

Solution

Assume a continuous leak at ground level. The plume concentration directly downwind along the cloud centerline is given by Equation 5-48:

$$\langle C \rangle = \frac{Q_{\mathrm{m}}}{\pi \sigma_y \sigma_z u}.$$

Solving for Q_{m}, the mass flow rate from the leak, we obtain

$$Q_{\mathrm{m}} = \langle C \rangle \pi \sigma_y \sigma_z u.$$

The LFL for toluene is 1.2% in air (from Appendix B). Converting the units, we obtain

$$\left(0.012 \frac{\text{m}^3 \text{ toluene}}{\text{m}^3 \text{ air}}\right)\left(\frac{1 \text{ g-mol toluene}}{22.4 \times 10^{-3} \text{ m}^3 \text{ toluene}}\right)\left(\frac{92 \text{ g toluene}}{1 \text{ g-mol toluene}}\right) = 49.3 \text{ g/m}^3.$$

The wind speed is 5 mph = 2.23 m/s. The distance downwind is 1000 ft = 304 m. From Figure 5-10, $\sigma_y = 22$ m and $\sigma_z = 12$ m. Substituting, we obtain

$$\begin{aligned} Q_{\mathrm{m}} &= (49.3 \text{ g/m}^3)(3.14)(22 \text{ m})(12 \text{ m})(2.23 \text{ m/s}) \\ &= 9.11 \times 10^4 \text{ g/s} \\ &= 201 \text{ lb/s}. \end{aligned}$$

Any leak with a flow rate greater than 201 lb/s is capable of producing a flammable cloud in the residential area. Of course, the toxic effects of this cloud must also be considered. The LFL of 1.2% = 12,000 ppm is much above the toluene TLV of 20 ppm.

Plants Inside Buildings

Frequently, processes cannot be constructed outside. In this case local and dilution ventilation systems are required. These ventilation systems were discussed in detail in Chapter 3, section 3-4.

Local ventilation is the most effective method for controlling flammable gas releases. Dilution ventilation, however, is also used because the potential points of release are usually numerous and it may be mechanically or economically impossible to cover every potential release point with only local ventilation.

There are empirically determined design criteria for designing ventilation systems for flammable materials inside storage and process areas. These design criteria are given in Table 7-6.

The effectiveness of a ventilation system is determined using material balance equations, described in Chapter 3 in the section "Estimating Worker Exposures to Toxic Vapors," and as illustrated in the following example.

Table 7-6 Ventilation Data for Handling Flammable Materials[a]

Type of area	Rate	Conditions
Ventilation for inside storage areas	1 $ft^3/min/ft^2$ of floor area	(a) System interlocked to sound an alarm when ventilation fails (b) Locate inlet and exhausts to provide air movement across entire area (c) Recirculation is permitted but stopped when air concentrations exceed 25% of LFL
Ventilation for inside process areas	1 $ft^3/min/ft^2$ of floor area or more; see (d)	(a) to (c) as for inside storage areas (d) Design ventilation system to keep concentrations at a 5-ft radius from all sources to below 25% of LFL

Class I: Flash point (closed cup) below 37.8°C (100°F)
Class II: Flash point from 37.8°C to 60°C (100°F to 140°F)
Class III: Flash point above 60°C (140°F)
[a]Data taken from NFPA 30, *Flammables and Combustible Liquids Code* (Quincy, MA: National Fire Protection Association, 2008).

Example 7-11

Determine the concentration of toluene over a diked area (100 ft^2) that contains toluene as a result of a spill. Assume that the process area (2500 ft^2) is designed to handle Class I flammable materials and that the liquid and air temperature is 65°F. The vapor pressure of toluene at 65°F is 20 mm Hg. The LEL is 1.2% by volume.

Solution

The source models for spills are described in Chapter 3, Equations 3-14 and 3-18. The concentration of volatiles in a ventilated area resulting from the evaporation from a pool is given by Equation 3-14:

$$C_{\text{ppm}} = \frac{KAP^{\text{sat}}}{kQ_{\text{v}}P} \times 10^6,$$

where

K is the mass transfer coefficient, determined using Equation 3-18,
A is the area of the pool,
P^{sat} is the saturation vapor pressure of the liquid,
k is the nonideal mixing factor,
Q_{v} is the volumetric ventilation rate, and
P is the pressure.

The ventilation capacity for this process area is based on the design criterion of 1 ft^3/min/ft^2 (Table 7-6); therefore

$$Q_{\text{v}} = \left(\frac{1\ \text{ft}^3}{\text{min ft}^2}\right)(2500\ \text{ft}^2) = 2500\,\frac{\text{ft}^3}{\text{min}}.$$

Also,

$$M = 92,$$
$$P^{\text{sat}} = 20\ \text{mm Hg},$$
$$A = 100\ \text{ft}^2.$$

The mass transfer coefficient is computed using Equation 3-18 with M_0, and K_0 for water, that is, 18 and 0.83 cm/s, respectively:

$$K = K_0\left(\frac{M_0}{M}\right)^{1/3} = 0.83\left(\frac{18}{92}\right)^{1/3} = 0.482\ \text{cm/s} = 0.948\ \text{ft/min}.$$

The nonideal mixing factor k ranges between 0.1 and 0.5. Because no information is given about the ventilation, k is used as a parameter. Substituting into Equation 3-14, we obtain

$$kC_{\text{ppm}} = \frac{KAP^{\text{sat}} \times 10^6}{Q_{\text{v}}P}$$

$$= \frac{(0.948\ \text{ft/min})(100\ \text{ft}^2)(20/760)\ \text{atm} \times 10^6}{(2500\ \text{ft}^3/\text{min})(1\ \text{atm})} = 998\ \text{ppm}.$$

The concentration range is estimated to be

$$C_{ppm} = 1996 \text{ ppm} = 0.1996\% \text{ by volume}, \qquad \text{for } k = 0.5,$$

$$C_{ppm} = 9980 \text{ ppm} = 0.998\% \text{ by volume}, \qquad \text{for } k = 0.1.$$

These concentrations are considerably below the LFL of 1.2% by volume, which illustrates that the specified ventilation rate for Class I liquids is satisfactory for handling relatively large spills of flammable materials. The concentrations do, however, exceed the TLV for this substance.

7-6 Sprinkler Systems

Sprinkler systems are an effective way to contain fires. The system consists of an array of sprinkler heads connected to a water supply. The heads are mounted in a high location (usually near ceilings) and disperse a fine spray of water over an area when activated. The heads are activated by a variety of methods. A common approach activates the heads individually by the melting of a fusible link holding a plug in the head assembly. Once activated, the sprinklers cannot be turned off unless the main water supply is stopped. This approach is called a wet pipe system. These systems are used for storage areas, laboratories, control rooms, and small pilot areas. Another approach activates the entire sprinkler array from a common control point. The control point is connected to an array of heat and/or smoke detectors that start the sprinklers when an abnormal condition is detected. If a fire is detected, the entire sprinkler array within an area is activated, possibly in areas not even affected by the fire. This approach is called a deluge system. This system is used for plant process areas and larger pilot plants.

Sprinkler systems can cause considerable water damage when activated, depending on the contents of the building or process structure. Statistically, the amount of water damage is never as great as the damage from fires in areas that should have had sprinklers.

Sprinkler systems require maintenance to ensure that they remain in service and have an adequate and uninterrupted water supply.

There are various fire classes that require different sprinkler designs. The detailed descriptions of these classes and sprinkler specifications are given in NFPA 13.[12] An average chemical plant is classified as an ordinary hazard (Group 3) area. Various sprinkler specifications for this type of area are given in Table 7-7.

Sometimes vessels need special water protection to keep the vessel walls cool during fires. High surface temperatures can result in metal failure at pressures far below the vessel's maximum allowable working pressure (MAWP) with potentially disastrous consequences. In hydrocarbon spill fires unprotected vessels (no insulation or water spray) can fail within minutes.

A water spray protection system around vessels is recommended to prevent this type of failure. These water spray protection systems, commonly called deluge systems, are designed to

[12]NFPA 13, *Installation of Sprinkler Systems* (Quincy, MA: National Fire Protection Association, 2010).

Table 7-7 Fire Protection for Chemical Plants[a]

Sprinkler system types

Antifreeze sprinkler system: a wet pipe system that contains an antifreeze solution and that is connected to a water supply.

Deluge sprinkler system: open sprinklers and an empty line that is connected to a water supply line through a valve that is opened upon detection of heat or a flammable material.

Dry pipe sprinkler system: a system filled with nitrogen or air under pressure. When the sprinkler is opened by heat, the system is depressurized, allowing water to flow into the system and out the open sprinklers.

Wet pipe sprinkler system: a system containing water that discharges through the opened sprinklers via heat.

Design densities (see NFPA documents for details)

Source of fire: not less than 0.50 gpm/ft^2 of floor area.

Pumps and related equipment: 0.50 gpm/ft^2 of projected area.

Vessels: 0.25 gpm/ft^2 of exposed surface, including top and bottom. Vertical distance of nozzle should not exceed 12 ft.

Horizontal structural steel: 0.10 gpm/ft^2 of surface area. This may not be necessary if the steel is insulated or designed to withstand the worst-case scenario.

Vertical structural steel: 0.25 gpm/ft^2 of surface area. This may not be necessary if the steel is insulated or designed to withstand the worst-case scenario.

Metal pipe, tubing, and conduit: not less than 0.15 gpm/ft^2 of surface area and directed toward the undersides.

Cable trays: not less than 0.3 gpm/ft^2 of projected plane area (horizontal or vertical).

Combined systems: The NFPA standards specify acceptable methods for combining the above requirements.

Nominal discharge rates for 0.5-in orifice spray nozzles are

gpm:	18	25	34	50	58
psi:	10	20	35	75	100

[a]Data taken from NFPA 13, *Standard for the Installation of Sprinkler Systems* (Quincy, MA: National Fire Protection Associates, 2010); and NFPA 15, *Standards for Water Spray Fixed Systems for Fire Protection* (Quincy, MA: National Fire Protection Association, 2007).

keep the vessel cool, flush away potentially hazardous spills, and help to knock down gas clouds.[13] Deluge systems can also provide enough time to transfer material out of a storage tank into another (safe) area.

Vessel deluge systems are usually designed as open-head systems, which are activated when a fire is detected and/or a flammable gas mixture is detected. The deluge system is usually opened when the flammable gas concentration is a fraction of the LFL (approximately 25%) or when a fire is detected through heat. Table 7-7 provides descriptions and design specifications for these systems.

[13]D. C. Kirby and J. L. De Roo, "Water Spray Protection for a Chemical Processing Unit: One Company's View," *Plant/Operations Progress* (Oct. 1984), 13(4).

Monitors are fixed water hydrants with an attached discharge gun. They are also installed in process areas and storage tank areas. Fire hydrants and monitors are spaced 150–250 ft apart around process units, located so that all areas of the plant can be covered by 2 streams. The monitor is usually located 50 ft from the equipment being protected.[14] Fire monitors discharge water at a rate of 500–2000 gpm.

Example 7-12

Determine the sprinkler requirements for a chemical process area within a building with an area of 100 ft by 30 ft that handles reactive solvents. Determine the number of sprinkler spray nozzles and pump specifications. Assume 0.5-in orifice sprinklers with 35 psig at each nozzle, giving 34 gpm each, a 10-psig frictional loss within the system, and a 15-ft elevation of the sprinkler system above the pump.

Solution

Data for designing this system are found in Table 7-7.

$$\text{Total water requirement} = (0.50 \text{ gpm/ft}^2)(100 \text{ ft})(30 \text{ ft})$$

$$= 1500 \text{ gpm},$$

$$\text{Number of sprinkler nozzles} = \frac{(1500 \text{ gpm})}{(34 \text{ gpm/nozzle})} = 44.1,$$

which is rounded to the next even number for layout convenience, or 44.

The pressure required at the pump is the sum of the minimum pressure at the nozzle (specified as 35 psi), the pressure loss resulting from friction (10 psi), and the pressure resulting from the pipe elevation over the pump (15 ft water or 6.5 psi). Therefore the total pressure is 51.5 psi, which is rounded up to 52 psi. The pump power is now determined:

$$\frac{\text{ft-lb}_f}{\text{s}} = \left(\frac{52 \text{ lb}_f}{\text{in}^2}\right)\left(\frac{144 \text{ in}^2}{\text{ft}^2}\right)\left(\frac{1500 \text{ gal}}{\text{min}}\right)\left(\frac{\text{min}}{60 \text{ s}}\right)\left(\frac{\text{ft}^3}{7.48 \text{ gal}}\right) = 25{,}029,$$

$$\text{Horsepower} = (25{,}029 \text{ ft-lb}_f/\text{s})\left(\frac{\text{HP}}{550 \dfrac{\text{ft-lb}_f}{\text{s}}}\right) = 45.5 \text{ HP}.$$

Therefore this sprinkler requires a pump with a capacity of 1500 gpm and a 45.5-HP motor, assuming an efficiency of 100%.

Actually, fire pumps are usually designed with discharge pressures of 100–125 psig so that the hose and monitor nozzle streams will have an effective reach. In addition, the size of the monitor is governed by requirements in the fire codes.[15]

[14] Orville M. Slye, "Loss Prevention Fundamentals for the Process Industry," paper presented at AIChE Symposium, New Orleans, LA, March 6–10, 1988.

[15] NFPA 1, *Fire Code* (Quincy, MA: National Fire Protection Association, 2009).

Table 7-8 Miscellaneous Concepts for Preventing Fires and Explosions[a]

Feature	Explanation
Maintenance programs	The best way to prevent fires and explosions is to stop the release of flammable materials. Preventive maintenance programs are designed to upgrade system before failures occur.
Fireproofing	Insulate vessels, pipes, and structures to minimize damage resulting from fires. Add deluge systems and design to withstand some damage from fires and explosions; e.g., use multiple deluge systems with separate shutoffs.
Control rooms	Design control rooms to withstand explosions.
Water supplies	Provide supply for maximum demand. Consider many deluge systems running simultaneously. Diesel-engine pumps are recommended.
Control valves for deluge	Place shutoffs well away from process areas.
Manual fire protection	Install hydrants, monitors, and deluge systems. Add good drainage.
Separate units	Separate (space) plants on a site, and separate units within plants. Provide access from two sides.
Utilities	Design steam, water, electricity, and air supplies to be available during emergencies. Place substations away from process areas.
Personnel areas	Locate personnel areas away from hazardous process and storage areas.
Group units	Group units in rows. Design for safe operation and maintenance. Create islands of risk by concentrating hazardous process units in one area. Space units so hot work can be performed on one group while another is operating.
Isolation valves	Install isolation valves for safe shutdowns. Install in safe and accessible locations at edge of unit or group.
Railroads and flares	Process equipment should be separated from flares and railroads.
Compressors	Place gas compressors downwind and separated from fired heaters.
Dikes	Locate flammable storage vessels at periphery of unit. Dike vessels to contain and carry away spills.
Block valves	Automated block valves should be placed to stop and/or control flows during emergencies. Ability to transfer hazardous materials from one area to another should be considered.
On-line analyzers	Add appropriate on-line analyzers to (1) monitor the status of the process, (2) detect problems at the incipient stage, and (3) take appropriate action to minimize effects of problems while still in initial phase of development.
Fail-safe designs	All controls need to be designed to fail safely. Add safeguards for automated and safe shutdowns during emergencies.

[a]John A. Davenport, "Prevent Vapor Cloud Explosions," *Hydrocarbon Processing* (March 1977), pp. 205–214; and Orville M. Slye, "Loss Prevention Fundamentals for the Process Industry," paper presented at AIChE Loss Prevention Symposium, New Orleans, LA, March 6–10, 1988.

7-7 Miscellaneous Concepts for Preventing Fires and Explosions

The successful prevention of fires and explosions in chemical plants requires a combination of many design techniques, including those mentioned previously and many more. A complete description of these techniques is far beyond the scope of this text. A partial list, shown in Table 7-8, is given to illustrate that safety technology is relatively complex (the appropriate application requires significant knowledge and experience) and to serve as a checklist for engineers to help them include the critical features for preventing fires and explosions.

Suggested Reading

R. Beach, "Preventing Static Electricity Fires," *Chemical Engineering* (Dec. 21, 1964), pp. 73–78; (Jan. 4, 1965), pp. 63–73; and (Feb. 2, 1965), pp. 85–88.

John Bond, *Sources of Ignition, Flammability Characteristics of Chemicals and Products* (Oxford: Butterworth-Heinemann, 1991).

L. G. Britton, *Avoiding Static Ignition Hazards in Chemical Operations* (New York: American Institute of Chemical Engineers, 1999).

D. A. Crowl, *Understanding Explosions* (New York: American Institute of Chemical Engineers, 2003).

H. Deichelmann, *The Electrostatic Charge of Glass-Lined Vessels and Piping,* Pfaudler PWAG Report 326e.

J. S. Dorsey, "Static Sparks: How to Exorcise the 'Go Devils,'" *Chemical Engineering* (Sept. 13, 1976), pp. 203–205.

Fire Protection Handbook, 14th ed. (Boston: National Fire Protection Association, 1976), ch. 5.

S. K. Gallym, "Elements of Static Electricity," *Gas* (March 1949), pp. 12–46.

M. Glor, *Electrostatic Hazards in Powder Handling* (New York: Wiley, 1988).

H. Haase, *Electrostatic Hazards* (New York: Verlag Chemie-Weinheim, 1977).

Thomas B. Jones and Jack L. King, *Powder Handling and Electrostatics* (Chelsea, MI: Lewis Publishers, 1991).

T. M. Kirby, "Overcoming Static Electricity Problems in Lined Vessels," *Chemical Engineering* (Dec. 27, 1971), p. 90.

T. A. Kletz, *What Went Wrong?* 5th ed. (London: Butterworth Heinemann, 2009).

A. Klinkenberg and J. L. Van der Mine, *Electrostatics in the Petroleum Industry* (New York: Elsevier, 1958).

L. B. Loeb, "The Basic Mechanisms of Static Electrification," *Science* (Dec. 7, 1945), pp. 573–576.

"Loss Prevention," *Chemical Engineering Progress* (1977), v. 11.

J. F. Louvar, B. Maurer, and G. W. Boicourt, "Tame Static Electricity," *Chemical Engineering Progress* (Nov. 1994), pp. 75–81.

G. Luttgens and M. Glor, *Understanding and Controlling Static Electricity* (Goethestrasse, Germany: Expert Veriag, 1989).

S. S. MacKeown and V. Wouk, "Electrical Charges Produced by Flowing Gasoline," *Industrial Engineering Chemistry* (June 1942), pp. 659–664.

NFPA 77, *Recommended Practice on Static Electricity* (Boston: National Fire Protection Association, 2007).

T. H. Pratt, *Electrostatic Ignitions of Fires and Explosions* (Marietta, GA: Burgoyne, 1997).

D. I. Saletan, “Static Electricity Hazards,” *Chemical Engineering* (June 1, 1959), pp. 99–102; and (June 29, 1959), pp. 101–106.

F. B. Silsbee, *Static Electricity,* Circular C-438 (Washington, DC: National Bureau of Standards, 1942).

Static Electricity, Bulletin 256 (Washington, DC: US Department of Labor, 1963).

Problems

7-1. What bonding and grounding procedures must be followed to transfer a drum of flammable solvent into a storage tank?

7-2. Ethylene oxide is a flammable liquid having a normal boiling temperature below room temperature. Describe a system and a procedure for transferring ethylene oxide from a tank car through a pumping system to a storage tank. Include both inerting and purging as well as bonding and grounding procedures.

7-3. Using the sweep-through purging method, inert a 100-gal vessel containing 100% air until the oxygen concentration is 1%. What volume of nitrogen is required? Assume nitrogen with no oxygen and a temperature of 77°F.

7-4. A 150-ft^3 tank containing air is to be inerted to 1% oxygen concentration. Pure nitrogen is available for the job. Because the tank's maximum allowable working pressure is 150 psia, it is possible to use either the sweep-through or a pressurization technique. For the pressurization technique, multiple pressurization cycles might be necessary, with the tank being returned to atmospheric pressure at the end of each cycle. The temperature is 80°F.

a. Determine the volume of nitrogen required for each technique.

b. For the pressurization technique, determine the number of cycles required if the pressure purge includes increasing the pressure to 140 psia with nitrogen and then venting to 0 psig.

7-5. Use a vacuum purging technique to purge oxygen from a 150-ft^3 tank containing air. Reduce the oxygen concentration to 1% using pure nitrogen as the inert gas. The temperature is 80°F. Assume that the vacuum purge goes from atmospheric pressure to 20 mm Hg absolute. Determine the number of purge cycles required and the total moles of nitrogen used.

7-6. Repeat Problem 7-5 using a combined vacuum and pressure purge. Use a vacuum of 20 mm Hg absolute and a pressure of 200 psig.

7-7. Design a generalized pressure vessel storage tank for a flammable material. Include the following design features:

a. Vacuum and pressure purging.

b. Vacuum charging of material from a 55-gal drum.

c. Draining the tank contents.

Provide precise details on the location of valves, regulators, and process lines.

7-8. Use the system described in Figure 7-14 to determine the voltage developed between the charging nozzle and the grounded tank, and the energy stored in the nozzle. Explain the potential hazard for cases a and b from the following table:

	Case a	Case b
Hose length (ft)	20	20
Hose diameter (in)	02	2
Flow rate (gpm)	25	25
Liquid conductivity (mho/cm)	10^{-8}	10^{-18}
Dielectric constant	02.4	19
Density (g/cm^3)	00.8	0.8

7-9. Use the system described in Problem 7-8, part b, to determine the hose diameter required to eliminate the potential hazard resulting from static buildup.

7-10. Repeat Example 7-2 with a 40,000-gal storage vessel. Assume that the vessel height is equal to the diameter.

7-11. Review Problem 7-8, part b. What is the most effective way to reduce the hazard of this situation?

7-12. Estimate the charge buildup and accumulated energy as a result of pneumatically conveying a dry powder through a Teflon duct. The powder is collected in an insulated vessel. Repeat the calculation for a transport rate of 50 lb/min and 100 lb/min for transport times of 1 hr and 5 hr. Discuss ways to improve the safety of this situation.

7-13. Compute the accumulated charge and energy for a 100,000-gal vessel being filled with a fluid at a rate of 200 gpm and having a streaming current of 2×10^{-6} amp. Make the calculation for a fluid having a conductivity of 10^{-18} mho/cm and a dielectric constant of 2.0. Repeat the calculation for (a) a half full vessel, (b) a full vessel, and (c) a full vessel with an overflow line.

7-14. What electrical classification would be specified for an area that has Classes I and II, Groups A and E, and Divisions 1 and 2 motors?

7-15. Determine the recommended ventilation rate for an inside process area (30,000 ft^3) that will handle Class I liquids and gases.

7-16. For the process area described in Problem 7-15, determine the concentration of propane in the area as a function of time if at $t = 0$ a 3/4-in propane line breaks (the propane main header is at 100 psig). The temperature is 80°F. See Chapter 4 for the appropriate source model and Chapter 3 for material balance models.

7-17. Using the results of Problem 7-16, describe what safety features should be added to this process area.

7-18. Determine the fire water requirements (gpm, number of sprinkler heads, and pump horsepower) to protect an inside process area of 2000 ft^2. Assume that the sprinkler nozzles have a 0.5-in orifice and that the nozzle pressure is 75 psig.

7-19. Repeat Problem 7-18 assuming that the nozzle pressure is 100 psig and that the rate is 58 gpm.

7-20. Your plant is considering installing a 5000 m^3 low-pressure cone-roof storage tank. The tank will store toluene (C_7H_8). The plant is considering several options:

a. A single tank within 10 m of the process.

b. Multiple, smaller tanks within 10 m of the process. This option requires 200 m of additional piping plus additional valves.

c. A single tank 100 m from the process. This requires 150 m of additional piping.

d. Multiple, smaller tanks 100 m from the process. This requires 1000 m of additional piping plus additional valves.

Consider each option and list the inherently safer features associated with each. Select the single option that represents the most inherently safe design. Please make sure to provide support for your selection.

What additional questions should you ask to improve the inherent safety of this installation?

7-21. The plant has asked you to consider the consequences of a tank explosion with resulting overpressure for options a and c in Problem 7-20. For both cases assume that the storage tank is drained of all liquid and contains only the saturation vapor pressure for liquid toluene at 25°C and 1 atm total pressure with air.

a. What is the volume percent concentration of toluene in the vapor of each tank?

b. If the tank contains air, is this concentration flammable?

c. What is the stoichiometric concentration for toluene in air? Is the vapor in the tank fuel rich or fuel lean?

d. If an ignition and explosion occur within the storage tank, estimate the overpressure at the process boundary for each case.

e. Which case is acceptable? Discuss.

f. What additional design features will you recommend to reduce the probability of an explosion?

7-22. Determine the water requirement (gpm) and number of nozzles for a deluge system required to protect a 10,000-gal storage tank that has a diameter of 15 ft. Use 0.5-in nozzles with a nozzle pressure of 35 psig, and assume that the vessel contains a reactive solvent.

7-23. A propane storage tank with a volume of 10,000 liters is being taken out of service for maintenance. The tank must be drained of its liquid propane, depressurized to atmospheric pressure, and then inerted with nitrogen prior to opening the tank to air.

The temperature is 25°C and the ambient pressure is 1 atm.

a. Determine the required target fuel concentration in the tank prior to opening the tank.

b. A sweep purge will be used for the inerting procedure. If pure nitrogen is available at a delivery rate of 0.5 kg/min, what is the minimum time (in min) required to reduce the fuel concentration to the target value?

c. What is the total amount (in kg) of nitrogen required to do the job?

7-24. Determine the sprinkler requirements for a chemical process area 150 ft by 150 ft. Determine the number of sprinkler heads and the pump specifications for this system (HP and gpm). Assume that the friction loss from the last sprinkler head to the pump is 50 psi and that the nozzles (0.5-in orifice) are at 75 psig.

7-25. A 1000 m^3 storage vessel contains liquid methyl alcohol (CH_4O). The vessel is padded with a gas mix obtained from a membrane separation unit. The gas from the membrane unit contains 98% nitrogen (plus 2% oxygen). The vessel is padded to a total pressure of 10 mm Hg gauge.

We must prepare the vessel for entry for the annual inspection of the inside of the vessel. The liquid is first drained from the tank prior to this operation, and then the empty tank must be inerted using a sweep purging method prior to opening the vessel and allowing air to enter.

Assume an ambient temperature of 25°C and 1 atm.

a. What is the concentration of gas (in vol. %) within the tank after draining the liquid and prior to inerting?

b. Use a triangle diagram to estimate the target fuel concentration (in vol. %) for the inerting operation.

c. If we use a sweep purging inerting procedure, using the 98% nitrogen sweep gas from the membrane unit, how much total sweep gas (in m^3 at 25°C and 1 atm) is required to achieve the desired target concentration?

d. If the gas from the membrane unit is supplied at the rate of 5 kg/min, how long (in min) will it take to achieve the desired target concentration?

7-26. We are considering the installation of a storage vessel to hold 5000 kg of liquid hydrogen. The hydrogen will be stored in an insulated vessel at 1 atm absolute pressure at its normal boiling point of 20 K.

Physical properties for liquid hydrogen at 20 K:

Density:	70.8 kg/m^3
Heat capacity:	9.668 kJ/kg °C
Heat of vaporization:	446.0 kJ/kg
Molecular weight:	2.02

a. We wish to store the liquid hydrogen in a vertical cylindrical storage tank with an inside diameter of 3 m. A vapor volume equal to 10% of the liquid volume must also be included. What is the volume of the liquid and the tank (in m^3)? What height tank (in m) is required?

b. A 25-mm schedule 40 pipe (ID: 26.64 mm; OD: 30.02 mm) is connected to the bottom of the tank to drain the liquid hydrogen. If the pipe breaks off, producing a hole with a diameter equal to the OD of the pipe, what is the initial discharge rate of the liquid hydrogen from the hole? Assume the liquid height is at the full 5000 kg level.

c. What distance (in m) from the storage will the 3 psi side-on overpressure occur in the event of an unconfined vapor cloud explosion involving the entire 5000 kg contents of the vessel?

d. We need to develop a procedure to inert the vessel prior to charging it with hydrogen. To what target nitrogen concentration do we need to inert the vessel in order to prevent the formation of a flammable gas mixture during the filling process?

7-27. A storage vessel must be prepared for filling with carbon monoxide. The vessel currently contains fresh air.

a. What is the target oxygen concentration for this operation in order to prevent the existence of a flammable vapor when the carbon monoxide is added?

b. If nitrogen containing 2% by volume oxygen is available at 2 barg, how many pressure cycles are required to inert the vessel properly?

7-28. Acetone (C_3H_6O) is to be stored in a cylindrical process vessel with a diameter of 5 ft and a height of 8 ft. The vessel must be inerted with pure nitrogen before storage of the acetone. A limited supply of pure nitrogen is available at 80 psig and 80°F. A vacuum is available at 30 mm Hg absolute pressure.

a. Determine the target oxygen concentration for the inerting procedure.

b. Decide whether a pressure or vacuum purge, or a combination of both, is the best procedure.

c. Determine the number of cycles required for your selected procedure.

d. Determine the total amount of nitrogen used. The final pressure in the tank after the inerting procedure is atmospheric. The ambient temperature is 80°F.

CHAPTER 8

Chemical Reactivity

Reactive chemical hazards have resulted in many accidents in industrial operations and laboratories. Preventing reactive chemical accidents requires the following steps, which are discussed in this chapter:

1. Background understanding. This includes case histories and important definitions. Case histories provide an understanding of the consequences, frequency, and breadth of reactive chemical accidents. Definitions provide a common fundamental basis for understanding. This is presented in Section 8-1 and supplemented with Chapter 14, "Case Histories."
2. Commitment, awareness, and identification of reactive chemical hazards. This is achieved through proper management and the application of several methods to identify reactive chemical hazards. This is discussed in Section 8-2.
3. Characterization of reactive chemical hazards. A calorimeter is typically used to acquire reaction data, and a fundamental model is used to estimate important parameters to characterize the reaction. This is described in Section 8-3.
4. Control of reactive chemical hazards. This includes application of inherent, passive, active, and procedural design principles. This is discussed in Section 8-4 and supplemented by additional material in Chapters 9, "Introduction to Reliefs"; 10, "Relief Sizing"; and 13, "Safety Procedures and Designs."

8-1 Background Understanding

In October 2002, the U.S. Chemical Safety and Hazard Investigation Board (CSB) issued a report on reactive chemical hazards.[1] They analyzed 167 serious accidents in the U.S. involving reactive chemicals from January 1980 through June 2001. Forty-eight of these accidents resulted in a total of 108 fatalities. These accidents resulted in an average of five fatalities per year. They concluded that reactive chemical incidents are a significant safety problem. They recommended that awareness of chemical reactive hazards be improved for both chemical companies and other companies that use chemicals. They also suggested that additional resources be provided so that that these hazards can be identified and controlled.

On December 19, 2007, an explosion occurred at T2 Laboratories in Jacksonville, Florida. Four people were killed and 32 injured due to the explosion. The facility was producing a chemical product to be used as a gasoline octane additive. The explosion was caused by the bursting of a large reactor vessel due to a runaway reaction. A **runaway reaction** occurs when the process is unable to remove adequate heat from the reactor to control the temperature. The reactor temperature subsequently increases, resulting in a higher reaction rate and an even faster rate of heat generation. Large commercial reactors can achieve heating rates of several hundred degrees Celsius per minute during a runaway.

The CSB investigated the T2 Laboratories accident and found that the company engineers did not recognize the runaway hazards associated with this chemistry and process and were unable to provide adequate controls and safeguards to prevent the accident. They found that, even though the engineers were degreed chemical engineers, they did not have any instruction on reactive hazards. The CSB recommended adding reactive hazard awareness to chemical engineering curriculum requirements.

A **chemical reactivity hazard** is "a situation with the *potential* for an *uncontrolled chemical reaction* that can result directly or indirectly in serious harm to people, property or the environment."[2] The resulting reaction may be very violent, releasing large quantities of heat and possibly large quantities of toxic, corrosive, or flammable gases or solids. If this reaction is confined in a container, the pressure within the container may increase very quickly, eventually exceeding the pressure capability of the container, resulting in an explosion. The reaction may occur with a single chemical, called a **self-reacting chemical** (e.g., monomer), or with another chemical, called either a chemical **interaction** or **incompatibility**.

Note that the hazard is due to the potential for a chemical reaction. Something else must occur for this hazard to result in an accident. However, as long as reactive chemicals are stored and used in a facility, the reactive chemical hazard is always present.

One of the difficulties with reactive chemicals hazards is that they are difficult to predict and identify. Common materials that we use routinely by themselves with negligible hazard

[1]*Improving Reactive Hazard Management* (Washington, DC: US Chemical Safety and Hazard Investigation Board, October 2002).

[2]R. W. Johnson, S. W. Rudy, and S. D. Unwin, *Essential Practices for Managing Chemical Reactivity Hazards* (New York: AIChE Center for Chemical Process Safety, 2003).

may react violently when mixed with other common materials, or react violently when the temperature or pressure is changed.

Chemical reactivity occurs in chemical plants due to the following scenarios:

1. Chemicals reacting by design, for example, in your process reactor, to produce a desired product.
2. Chemicals reacting by accident, for example, due to an upset in the process, loss of containment, etc.

Human factors are also important in reactive chemical incidents. Suppose an operator is given the task to "Charge 10 kg of catalyst to reactor B at 3:00 PM" Table 8-1 lists some of the ways in which this operator may fail to perform this task properly. As can be seen, many failure modes are possible, and this is only one instruction in a sequence of possibly hundreds of steps.

Table 8-1 Possible Failure Modes for the Single Instruction "Charge 10 kg of Catalyst to Reactor B at 3:00 PM"

1. Charge more catalyst.
2. Charge less catalyst.
3. Fail to charge catalyst.
4. Charge catalyst too early.
5. Charge catalyst too late.
6. Charge wrong catalyst.
7. Charge catalyst to wrong reactor.
8. Charge catalyst that is contaminated.
9. Charge something else besides catalyst.
10. Operator goes to wrong catalyst storage container and charges wrong catalyst.
11. Operator spills catalyst while charging.
12. Operator uses wrong scoop and catalyst is contaminated with other material during measuring process.
13. Catalyst in storage is contaminated with other material.
14. Catalyst is contaminated with an incompatible chemical and a vigorous reaction ensues.
15. Catalyst storage is contaminated with an incompatible chemical and a vigorous reaction ensues in the storage container.
16. Operator is exposed to catalyst during charging operation, either via skin, eyes, ingestion, or inhalation.
17. Other workers are exposed to catalyst.
18. Catalyst becomes airborne and is distributed throughout work site.
19. Catalyst catches on fire.
20. Catalyst is spilled and washed into waste drain.
21. Catalyst in storage is not catalyst or wrong catalyst—wrong material charged.
22. Catalyst storage container is empty—catalyst not charged.
23. Catalyst scoop cannot be found—catalyst not charged at correct time.
24. Catalyst scale used to weigh catalyst is not available—catalyst not charged at correct time.
25. Catalyst scale is not working properly or improperly calibrated—wrong amount of catalyst charged.
26. Clock stops working or displays incorrect time—catalyst not charged at correct time.
27. Operator distracted by upset in adjacent unit—catalyst not charged at correct time.

8-2 Commitment, Awareness, and Identification of Reactive Chemical Hazards

The first step in this process is to commit to manage reactive chemical hazards properly. This requires commitment from all employees, especially management, to properly identify and manage these hazards throughout the entire life cycle of a process. This includes laboratory research and development; pilot plant studies; and plant design, construction, operation, maintenance, expansion, and decommissioning.

Figure 8-1 is a flowchart useful for preliminary screening for reactive chemicals hazards. Figure 8-1 contains seven questions to help identify reactive chemical hazards.

1. *Is intentional chemistry performed at your facility?* In most cases this is easy to determine. The bottom line is: Are the products that come out of your facility in a different molecular configuration from the raw materials? A precise answer to this question is required prior to moving forward in the flowchart.

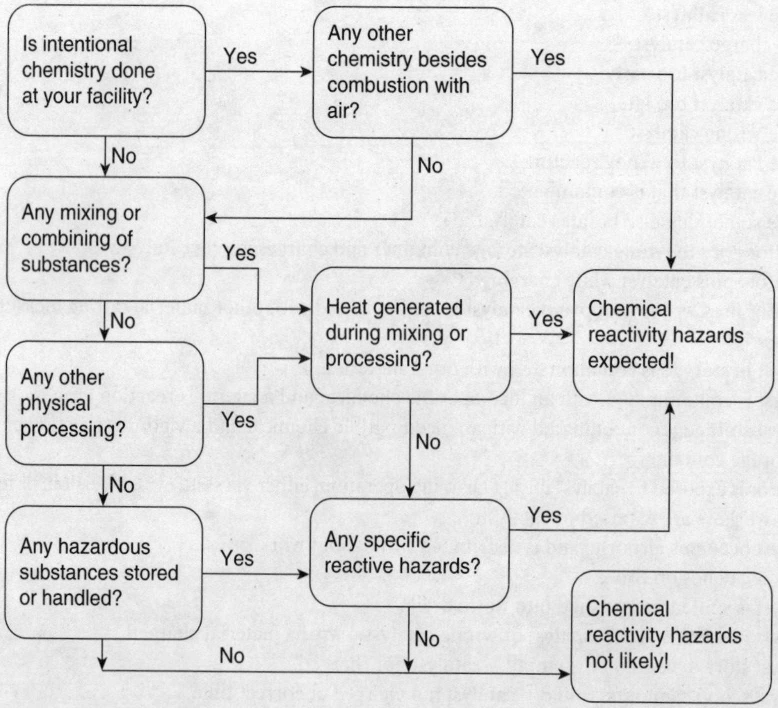

Figure 8-1 Screening flowchart for reactive chemical hazards. An answer of "yes" at any decision point moves more toward reactive chemisty. See Section 8.2 for more details. Source: R. W. Johnson, S. W. Rudy, and S. D. Unwin, *Essential Practices for Managing Chemical Reactivity Hazards* (New York: AIChE Center for Chemical Process Safety, 2003.)

2. *Is there any mixing or combining of different substances?* If substances are mixed or combined, or even dissolved in a liquid or water, then it is possible that a reaction, either intended or unintended, may occur.
3. *Does any other physical processing of substances occur in your facility?* This could include size reduction, heating/drying, absorption, distillation, screening, storage, warehousing, repackaging, and shipping and receiving.
4. *Are there any hazardous substances stored or handled at your facility?* The Materials Safety Data Sheet (MSDS) is a good source of information here.
5. *Is combustion with air the only chemistry intended at your facility?* This includes combustion of common fuels such as natural gas, propane, fuel oil, etc. Combustion is a special reactive hazard that is handled by separate codes and standards and is not addressed here.
6. *Is any heat generated during the mixing, phase separation, or physical processing of substances?* Heat generation when chemicals are mixed is a prime indication that a reaction is taking place. Note that many chemicals do not release much heat during the reaction, so even if limited heat is released, a chemical reaction may still be occurring. There are also some physical heat effects, such as absorption or mechanical mixing, that can cause heat generation. This heat release, even though not caused by chemical reaction, may increase the temperature and cause a chemical reaction to occur.
7. *Are there any specific reaction hazards that occur?* Specific reaction hazards are shown in Table 8-2 with detailed lists of chemical categories and chemicals provided in Appendix F. Functional groups that are typically associated with reactive chemistry are shown in Table 8-3.

One of the most difficult reactive chemical hazards to characterize is incompatible chemicals, shown at the bottom of Table 8-2. Common materials that we use routinely and safely by themselves may become highly reactive when mixed. These materials may react very quickly, possibly producing large amounts of heat and gas. The gas may be toxic or flammable.

The easiest way to show graphically the various interactions between chemicals is a chemical compatibility matrix, as shown in Table 8-4. The chemicals are listed on the left-hand side of the table. The chemicals selected may be all of the chemicals in a facility, or the chemicals that may come in contact with each other during routine or emergency situations. Clearly, listing all the chemicals provides a conservative result, but may result in a large and unwieldy matrix.

Each table entry in the chemical compatibility matrix shows the interaction between two chemicals in the table. Thus, the table entry just to the right of acetic anhydride represents the binary interaction between acetic anhydride and hydrochloric acid solution.

Table 8-2 Specific Reactive Chemical Hazards[a]

Pyrophoric and spontaneously combustible: Substances that will readily react with the oxygen in the atmosphere, igniting and burning even without an ignition source. Ignition may be immediate or delayed.

Identification: MSDS or labeling identifies this as "spontaneously combustible."

NFPA Flammability rating of 4.

DOT/UN Hazard Class 4.2 (spontaneously combustible solids).

Examples: Aluminum alkyl, Grignard reagent, finely divided metals, iron sulfide, triethyl aluminum.

See Table F-1 in Appendix F.

Peroxide-forming: Reacts with oxygen in the atmosphere to form unstable peroxides.

Identification: Not easily identified as a peroxide former from MSDS or other resources.

Examples: 1,3-butadiene, 1,1-dichloro-ethylene, isopropyl and other ethers, alkali metals.

See Table F-2.

Water-reactive chemicals: Chemically reacts with water, particularly at normal ambient conditions.

Identification: Usually identified as water-reactive on MSDS.

May be identified as DOT/UN Hazard Class 4.3 (dangerous when wet).

May be labeled as "dangerous when wet."

NFPA Special Rating with symbol.

Examples: Sodium, titanium tetrachloride, boron trifluoride, acetic anhydride.

See Tables F-3 and F-4.

Oxidizers: Readily yields oxygen or other oxidizing gas, or readily reacts to promote or initiate combustion of combustible materials.

Identification: Identified as an oxidizer on MSDS.

DOT/UN Hazard Class 5.1 (oxidizing agent) or other rating groups.

NFPA Special Rating with symbol OX.

Examples: Chlorine, hydrogen peroxide, nitric acid, ammonium nitrate, ozone, hypochlorites, benzyl peroxide.

See Table F-5.

Self-Reactive: Substances that self-react, often with accelerating or explosive rapidity.

Identification: Generally identified on MSDS or labeling as "polymerizing," "decomposing," or "unstable."

NFPA reactivity/stability rating of 1 or higher.

Polymerizing: monomers combining together to form very large, chain-like or cross-linked polymer molecules.

Examples: acrolein, ethylene and propylene oxide, styrene, vinyl acetate.

See Table F-6.

Shock-sensitive: react on impact.

Example: picric acid.

Thermally decomposing: large molecules breaking into smaller, more stable molecules.

Rearranging: atoms in the molecule rearranging into a different molecular structure, such as a different isomer.

Incompatible materials: Incompatible materials contacting each other.

Examples: Ammonia + methacrylic acid; caustic soda + epichlorohydrin; acids + bases.

[a]See Johnson et al., *Essential Practices for Managing Chemical Reactivity Hazards*, for additional detail on these classifications, as well as Appendix F for more detailed lists of these materials.

Table 8-3 Reactive Functional Groups[a]

Azide	N_3
Diazo	$-N{=}N-$
Diazonium	$-N_2^+ X^-$
Nitro	$-NO_2$
Nitroso	$-NO$
Nitrite	$-ONO$
Nitrate	$-ONO_2$
Fulminate	$-ONC$
Peroxide	$-O-O-$
Peracid	$-CO_3H$
Hydroperoxide	$-O-O-H$
Ozonide	O_3
N-haloamine	$-N(X)-Cl$
Amine oxide	$\equiv NO$
Hypohalites	$-OX$
Chlorates	ClO_3
Acetylides of heavy metals	$-C{\equiv}CM$

[a]Conrad Schuerch, "Safe Practice in the Chemistry Laboratory: A Safety Manual," in *Safety in the Chemical Laboratory,* v. 3, Norman V. Steere, ed. (Easton, PA: Division of Chemical Education, American Chemical Society, 1974), pp. 22–25.

The chemical compatibility matrix only considers binary interactions between two chemicals. Binary interactions would be expected during routine operations, while combinations of several chemicals may occur during emergency situations. However, once the hazards are identified using the binary interactions of all chemicals, additional hazards due to combinations of more than two chemicals are unlikely.

Once the chemicals are identified, the binary interactions are filled in. Information for these interactions can be obtained from a variety of sources, as shown in Table 8-5. Perhaps the easiest source to use is the Chemical Reactivity Worksheet (CRW).[3] This worksheet is provided free of charge by the Office of Emergency Management of the U.S. Environmental Protection Agency, the Emergency Response Division of the National Oceanic and Atmospheric Administration (NOAA), and the AIChE Center for Chemical Process Safety. The software contains a library of 5000 common chemicals and mixtures and considers 43 different organic

[3]Lewis E. Johnson and James K. Farr, "CRW 2.0: A Represetative-Compound Approach to Functionality-Based Prediction of Chemical Hazards," *Process Safety Progress* (Sept. 2008), 27(3): 212–218.

Table 8-4 Chemical Compatibility Matrix and Hazards for Example 8-1, as Predicted by CRW 2.02

No.	Chemical name	1	2	3
1	Hydrochloric acid solution			
2	Acetic anhydride	C, D7, E, G		
3	Methanol	C	B5, C	
4	Caustic soda, beads	B4, C, D3, D5, D6, D7, G	A6, C, D4	B1, B5, C

Key:

A6	Reaction proceeds with explosive violence and/or forms explosive products.
B1	May become highly flammable or may initiate a fire, especially if other combustible materials are present.
B4	Spontaneous ignition of reactants or products due to reaction heat.
B5	Combination liberates gaseous products, at least one of which is flammable. May cause pressurization.
C	Exothermic reaction. May generate heat and/or cause pressurization.
D3	Combination liberates gaseous products, at least one of which is toxic. May cause pressurization.
D4	Combination liberates nonflammable, nontoxic gas. May cause pressurization.
D5	Combination liberates combustion-enhancing gas (e.g., oxygen). May cause pressurization.
D6	Exothermic generation of toxic and corrosive fumes.
D7	Generation of corrosive liquid.
E	Generates water-soluble toxic products.
G	Reaction may be intense or violent.

Individual Chemical Hazards and Functional Groups

Chemical	Reactive hazard	Functional group
Acetic anhydride	Water-reactive	Anhydride
Caustic soda, beads	Water-reactive	Base
Hydrochloric acid solution	Mildly air-reactive	Acid, inorganic, non-oxidizing
Methanol	Highly flammable	Alcohol

and inorganic reactive groups. CRW also provides information on the hazards associated with specific chemicals and also the reactive group(s) associated with those chemicals, as shown at the bottom of Table 8-4. CRW tends to be conservative on its predictions of binary interactions so the results must be carefully interpreted.

Another source of information on reactive chemicals is a program called CHETAH. CHETAH stands for Chemical Thermodynamics and Energy Release Evaluation. This program is able to predict the reactive chemical hazards using functional groups. CHETAH was originally developed by Dow Chemical and is very useful as an initial screening tool for reactive chemical hazards.

Table 8-5 Sources of Information on Chemical Reactivity Hazards

Source	Location
Material Safety Data Sheet (MSDS)	Provided by chemical manufacturer or on web
Chemical Reactivity Worksheet	National Oceanic and Atmospheric Administration (NOAA) *http://response.restoration.noaa.gov/*
Brethericks Handbook of Reactive Chemical Hazards, P. Urben, ed. (2006)	Elsevier Publishers *www.elsevier.com*
Sax's Dangerous Properties of Industrial Materials, R. J. Lewis, ed. (2007)	John Wiley and Sons, Inc. *www.wiley.com*
Sigma Aldrich Library of Chemical Safety Data, R. E. Lenga, ed. (1988)	Sigma-Aldrich *www.sigmaaldrich.com*
Fire Protection Guide to Hazardous Materials (2010)	National Fire Protection Association (NFPA) *www.nfpa.org*
CHETAH: Computer Program for Chemical Thermodynamics and Energy Release Evaluation	American Society for Testing and Materials (ASTM) *www.astm.org*

Example 8-1

A laboratory contains the following chemicals: hydrochloric acid solution, acetic anhydride, methanol, and caustic soda (NaOH) beads. Draw a chemical compatibility matrix for these chemicals. What are the major hazards associated with these chemicals?

Solution

The chemicals are entered into the Chemical Reactivity Worksheet (CRW) software and the chemical compatibility matrix is shown in Table 8-4. Table 8-4 also lists the major hazard and reactive group associated with each chemical.

From Table 8-4 it is clear that the mixing of any of these chemicals will result in a hazardous situation! All of these chemicals must be stored separately, and management systems must be enforced to ensure that accidental mixing does not occur.

Since each combination in the matrix contains the letter C, it is clear that an exothermic reaction is expected with the mixing of any pair of chemicals. Three combinations (hydrochloric acid + caustic soda; acetic anhydride + methanol; methanol + caustic soda) liberate a gaseous product, at least one of which is flammable. Two combinations (hydrochloric acid + acetic anhydride; hydrochloric acid + caustic soda) result in an intense or violent reaction. One combination (acetic anhydride + caustic soda) results in a reaction with explosive violence and/or forms explosive products. Other hazards are listed in Table 8-4.

From the individual hazards table at the bottom of Table 8-4, two of the chemicals (acetic anhydride and caustic soda) are water-reactive, one chemical (hydrochloric acid solution) is mildly air-reactive, and methanol is flammable. The prediction of air reactivity with the hydrochloric acid solution is probably a bit conservative.

All personnel using these chemicals in the laboratory must be aware of both the individual chemical hazards and the reactive hazards that result when these chemicals are mixed.

8-3 Characterization of Reactive Chemical Hazards Using Calorimeters

Chemical plants produce products using a variety of complex reactive chemistries. It is essential that the behavior of these reactions be well characterized prior to using these chemicals in large commercial reactors. Calorimeter analysis is important to understand both the desired reactions and also undesired reactions.

Some of the important questions that must be asked in order to characterize reactive chemicals are shown in Table 8-6. The answers to these questions are necessary to design control systems to remove heat from the reaction to prevent a runaway; to design safety systems, such as a reactor relief, to protect the reactor from the effects of high pressure (see Chapters 9 and 10); and to understand the rate at which these processes occur. The answers must be provided at conditions as close as possible to actual process conditions.

For exothermic reactions, heat is lost through the walls of the reactor vessel to the surroundings. The higher these heat losses, the lower the temperature inside the reactor. Conversely, the lower the heat losses, the higher the temperature within the reactor. We can thus conclude that we will reach the highest reaction temperatures and highest self-heating rates when the reactor has no heat losses, that is, adiabatic.

The heat losses through the walls of the reactor are proportional to the surface area of the reactor vessel. As the vessel becomes larger, the surface-to-volume ratio becomes smaller and the heat losses through the walls have a smaller effect. Thus, as the vessel becomes larger, the behavior of the vessel approaches adiabatic behavior.

Many chemical plant personnel believe that a large reactor will self-heat at a rate that is a lot slower than a much smaller vessel. In reality the reverse is true: A larger reactor vessel will approach adiabatic conditions and the self-heat rates will be a lot faster.

Table 8-6 Important Questions for the Characterization of Reactive Chemicals

1. At what temperature does the reaction rate become large enough for adequate energy to be produced for heating of the reaction mixture to be detected?
2. What is the maximum temperature increase due to adiabatic self-heating of the reactants?
3. What is the maximum self-heat rate? At what time and temperature does this occur?
4. What is the maximum pressure during the reaction? Is this pressure due to the vapor pressure of the liquid, or due to the generation of gaseous reaction products?
5. What is the maximum pressure rate? At what time and temperature does this occur?
6. Are there any other side reactions that occur, particularly at temperatures higher than the normal reaction temperature? If so, can questions 1 through 5 be answered for this reaction?
7. Can the heat generation from the desired chemistry heat the reaction mass under adiabatic conditions to a temperature at which another reaction occurs?
8. Can the heat generated by chemical reaction (desired or undesired) exceed the capability of the vessel/process to remove heat? At what temperature does this occur?

As discussed above, heat removal rates do not scale linearly with increased reactor volume. This scaling problem has been the cause of many incidents. Reactions tested in the laboratory or pilot plant frequently showed slow self-heat rates that were controlled easily using ice baths or small cooling coils. However, when these reactions were scaled up to large commercial reactors, sometimes having volumes of 20,000 gallons or more, the self-heat rates were sometimes orders of magnitude higher, resulting in an uncontrollable temperature increase and explosion of the reaction vessel. Large commercial reactors with energetic chemicals such as acrylic acid, ethylene or propylene oxide, and many others can achieve self-heat rates as high as hundreds of degrees Celsius per minute!

Introduction to Reactive Hazards Calorimetry

The idea behind the calorimeter is to safely use small quantities of material in the laboratory to answer the questions shown in Table 8-6. Most of the calorimeters discussed in this chapter have test volumes from a few ml to as high as 150 ml. Larger test volumes more closely match industrial reactors but also increase the hazards associated with the laboratory test.

The calorimeter technology presented here was developed mostly in the 1970s. Much of the early development was done by Dow Chemical[4,5,6] although numerous researchers have made significant contributions since then.

Table 8-7 summarizes the commonly used calorimeters that are available for reactive chemicals testing. All of the calorimeters hold the sample in a small sample cell. All of the calorimeters have a means to heat the test sample and measure the temperature of the sample as a function of time. Most also have the capability to measure the pressure inside the closed sample cell.

It is important that the calorimeter be as close as experimentally possible to adiabatic behavior in order to ensure that the results are representative of a large reactor. The adiabatic conditions will also ensure the "worst-case" results, i.e.: highest temperature and pressure and highest self-heat rates and pressure rates.

All of the calorimeters have two modes of operation. The most common mode, called the thermal scan mode, is to heat the sample at a constant temperature rate (for example, 2°C per minute) until the reaction rate becomes large enough for adequate energy to be produced for the calorimeter to detect the reaction heating. This is called the thermal scan mode. Two of the calorimeters in Table 8-7—DSC and Advanced Reactive System Screening Tool (ARSST)—continue to heat beyond this temperature. All of the other calorimeters stop the heating once

[4]D. L. Townsend and J. C. Tou, "Thermal Hazard Evaluation by an Accelerating Rate Calorimeter," *Thermochimica Acta* (1980), 37: 1–30.

[5]US Patent 4,208,907, June 24, 1980.

[6]US Patent 4,439,048, March 27, 1984.

Table 8-7 Types of Calorimeters Most Commonly Used to Study Reactive Chemicals

Calorimeter	Supplier	Type	Typical test vessel volume ml	Nominal phi-factor ϕ	Adiabatic reaction tracking limits K/min	Operation time	Comments
DSC Differential Scanning Calorimeter	Various	Open	<1	Not applicable	Not applicable	1 hour	Used mostly for initial screening. Closed sample cells can be used.
ARRST Advanced Reactive System Screening Tool	Fauske and Associates *www.fauske.com*	Open	10	1.05	0.1–200	Hours	Used mostly for initial screening due to short operation time.
ARC Accelerating Rate Calorimeter	Various	Closed	10	1.5	0.04–20	1+ day	Most effective for reactions with low self-heat rates. Need to adjust temperatures for Φ factor.
VSP2 Vent Sizing Package 2	Fauske and Associates *www.fauske.com*	Closed	100	1.05	0.05–600	1+ day	Useful for reactions with very high self-heat rates. Can also be used to identify if two-phase flow occurs during relief discharge.
APTAC Automatic Pressure Tracking Adiabatic Calorimeter	NETZSCH *www.netzsch.com*	Closed	130	1.10	0.04–400	1+ day	Useful for reactions with high self-heat rates. Also has capability to automatically inject reactants and collect products.

the reaction heating is detected and then switched to an adiabatic state by matching the outside temperature to the sample temperature.

The other mode of heating is to heat the sample up to a fixed temperature and then wait for a specified time to see if any reaction self-heating is detected. If self-heating is detected, the calorimeter is placed immediately in adiabatic mode. If no self-heating is detected after a specific time, the temperature is again incremented and the process is repeated. This is called the heat-wait-search mode.

Several calorimeters – the Accelerating Rate Calorimeter (ARC), Vent Sizing Package (VSP2), and Automatic Pressure Tracking Adiabatic Calorimeter (APTAC) – have the capability to do both heating modes during the same run.

The thermal scan mode is most often used for reactive chemicals studies. The heat-wait-search mode is used for chemicals that have a long induction time, meaning they take a long time to react.

In adiabatic mode, the calorimeter attempts to adjust the heaters outside the sample cell to match the temperature inside the sample cell. This ensures that there is no heat flow from the sample cell to the surroundings, resulting in adiabatic behavior.

The calorimeters are classified as either open or closed. An open calorimeter is one in which the sample cell is either open to the atmosphere or open to a large containment vessel. Two calorimeters in Table 8-7 – the DSC and ARSST – are classified as open. For the traditional DSC, the sample cell is completely open to the atmosphere, and no pressure data are collected. Some DSCs have been modified to use sealed capillary tubes or sealed high-pressure metal holders. For the ARSST, the small sample cell (10 ml) is open to a much larger (350 ml) containment vessel. A pressure gauge is attached to the containment vessel, but only qualitative pressure data are collected from this gauge. The ARSST containment vessel is also pressurized with nitrogen during most runs to prevent the liquid sample from boiling so that higher reaction temperatures can be reached.

Since the ARC is a closed system, this calorimeter can also be used to determine the vapor pressure of the liquid mixture. This is done by first evacuating the ARC and then adding the test sample. The pressure measured by the ARC is then the vapor pressure; this can be measured as a function of temperature.

It is fairly easy to insulate a small sample cell to approach near adiabatic conditions. However, the sample cell must be capable of withstanding reaction pressures that may be as high as hundreds of atmospheres. The easiest approach to achieve high-pressure capability is to use a thick-walled vessel capable of withstanding the pressure. The problem with this is that the thick walls of the sample cell will absorb heat from the test sample, resulting in less than adiabatic conditions. The presence of a vessel that absorbs heat increases the thermal inertia of the test device and reduces both the maximum temperature and also the maximum temperature rate.

The thermal inertia of the apparatus is represented by a phi-factor, defined by

$$\phi = \frac{\text{Combined heat capacity of sample and container}}{\text{Heat capacity of sample}} \tag{8-1}$$

$$= 1 + \frac{\text{Heat capacity of container}}{\text{Heat capacity of sample}}.$$

Clearly, a phi-factor as close as possible to 1 represents less thermal inertia. Most large commercial reactors have a phi-factor of about 1.1.

Table 8-7 lists the phi-factors for the most common calorimeters. The ARC uses a thick-walled vessel to contain the reaction pressure; it has a high phi-factor as a result. The ARSST uses a thin-walled glass sample cell that is open to the containment vessel. Since this glass vessel contains only the test sample and does not need to withstand the pressure developed by the reaction, it has a low phi-factor.

The VSP2 and the APTAC use a unique control method to reduce the phi-factor. Both of these calorimeters use thin-walled containers to reduce the heat capacity of the sample cell. Figure 8-2 shows a schematic of the VSP2 calorimeter. The sample is contained in a closed, thin-walled test cell, which is held in a containment vessel. The control system measures the pressure inside the test cell and also the pressure inside the containment vessel. The control system is able to rapidly adjust the pressure inside the containment vessel to match the pressure inside the test cell. The pressure difference between the inside of the test cell and the

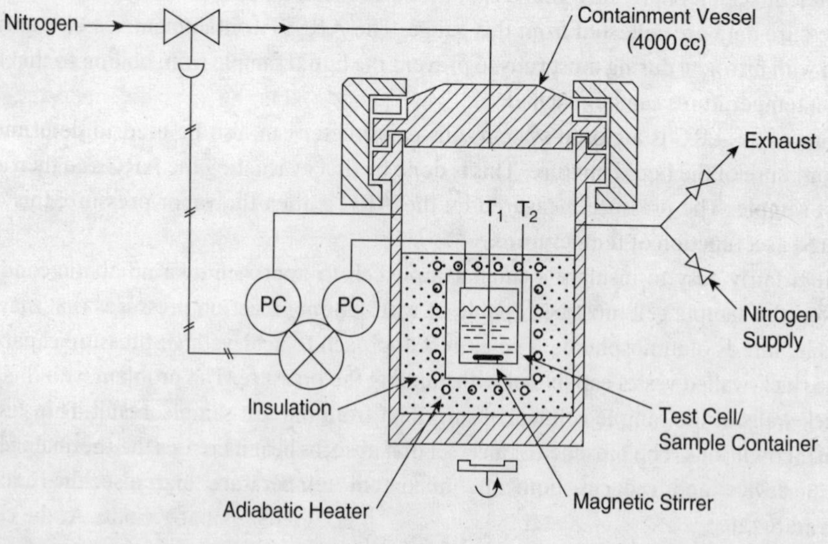

Figure 8-2 Vent Sizing Package (VSP2) showing the control system to equalize the pressure between the sample cell and the containment vessel.

containment device is kept as low as possible, usually less than 20 psi. As a result, the thin-walled sample cell does not rupture.

The adiabatic reaction tracking limits shown in Table 8-7 relate to the lower rate at which the self-heating is detected and the upper reaction rate that the calorimeter can follow.

The operation time in Table 8-7 is an approximate idea of how long it takes to do a single, standard run on the apparatus. Some of the calorimeters (DSC and ARSST) have short run times; these calorimeters are useful for doing numerous screening studies to get an initial idea of the reactive nature of the material before moving to a more capable, but longer operation time, calorimeter.

The Differential Scanning Calorimeter (DSC) consists of two small sample cells, one containing the unknown sample and the other containing a reference material. The two samples are heated and the DSC measures the difference in heat required to maintain the two samples at the same temperature during this heating. This apparatus can be used to determine the heat capacity of the unknown sample, the temperature at which a phase change occurs, the heat required for the phase change, and also the heat changes due to a reaction. For a traditional DSC the trays are open to the atmosphere, so this type of calorimeter is classified as an open type, as shown in Table 8-7. The DSC can also be modified to use sealed glass capillary tubes or small metal containers. The DSC is mostly used for quick screening studies to identify if a reactive hazard is present and to get an initial idea of the temperatures at which the reaction occurs. The traditional DSC does not provide any pressure information since the pans are open. If sealed glass capillary tubes are used, limited pressure information can be obtained from the pressure at which the tube ruptures.

Figures 8-3 and 8-4 show typical temperature and pressure scans for an APTAC device. In Figure 8-3 the sample is heated at a constant temperature rate until an exotherm is detected as shown. The calorimeter then switches to adiabatic mode. In adiabatic mode, the calorimeter measures the temperature of the sample and attempts to match the external temperature to the sample temperature. This ensures near-adiabatic behavior. During adiabatic mode, the sample self-heats by the energy released by the reaction. Eventually, the reactants are all consumed and the reaction terminates. Self-heating stops at this point and the temperature remains constant. At the end of the run, the calorimeter heating is turned off and the sample cools.

The plot at the bottom of Figure 8-3 shows the pressure scan for this APTAC run. The pressure increase is due to the vapor pressure of the liquid sample. This pressure increases exponentially with temperature. The decrease and then increase in pressure after the reaction is finished would merit additional study – it might be due to the decomposition of one of the reaction products.

Figure 8-4 shows a calorimeter run using the heat-wait-search mode. The sample is incrementally heated using a user-defined temperature step, and then the calorimeter waits for a specified time, looking for any reaction heating. Several heat-wait-search cycles are required before an exotherm is detected and the calorimeter goes into adiabatic mode. At the completion of the reaction, the calorimeter goes back into the heat-wait-search mode, looking for additional reactions at higher temperatures.

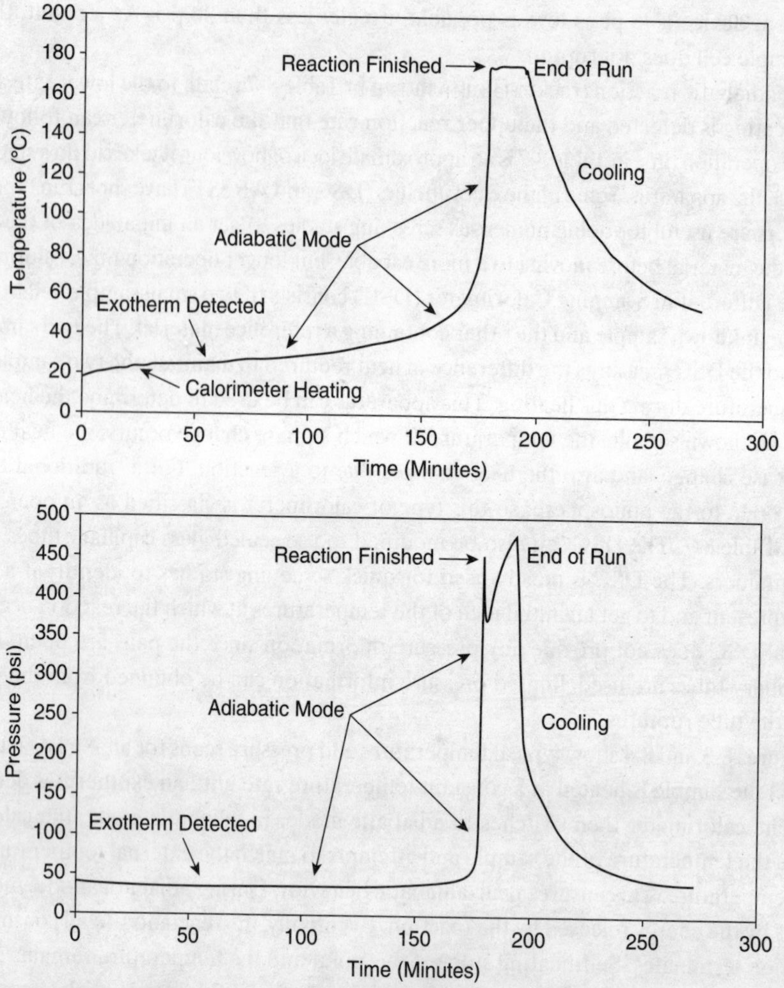

Figure 8-3 APTAC data for the reaction of methanol and acetic anhydride.

Another mode of calorimeter operation is to inject a chemical at a specified temperature. It is also possible to heat the calorimeter with chemical A in the sample container, and then inject chemical B at a specified temperature. Both of these methods will result in an injection endotherm as the cold liquid is injected, but the calorimeter will quickly recover.

The calorimeter selected for a particular study depends on the nature of the reactive material. Many companies do screening studies using the DSC or ARSST and then, depending on the screening results, move to a more capable calorimeter. If a very slow reaction is expected,

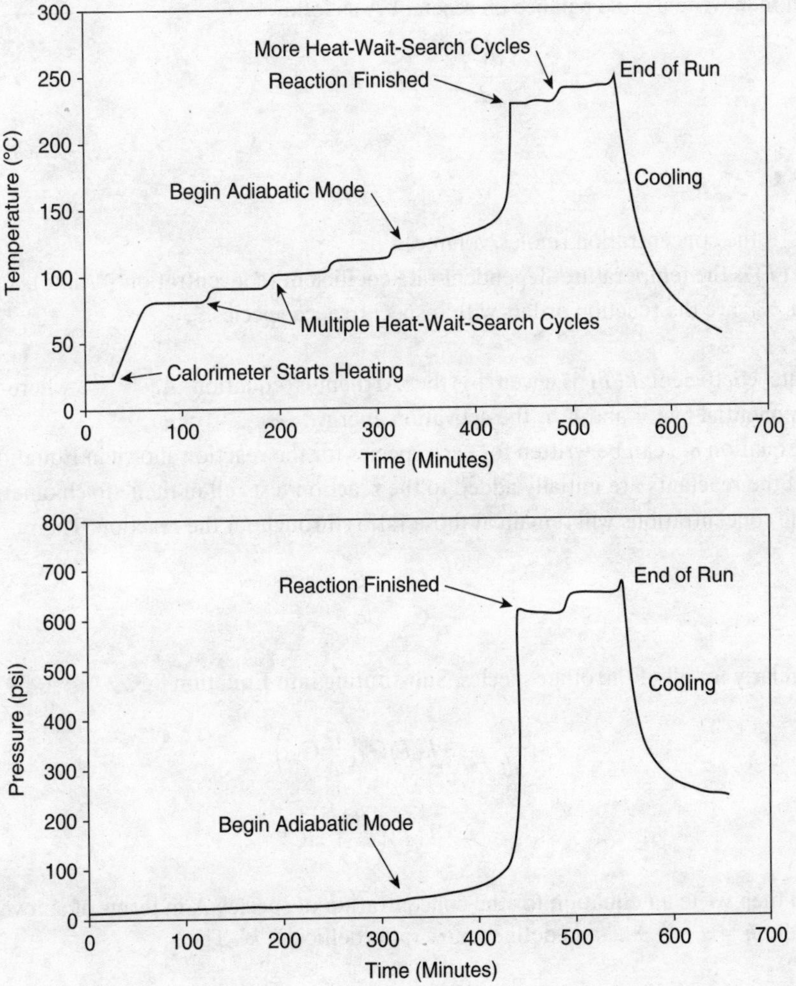

Figure 8-4 APTAC data for the thermal decomposition of di-tert-butyl peroxide.

then the ARC has the best ability to detect very low heating rates. If the reaction has a very high self-heat rate, then the VSP2 or APTAC is the calorimeter of choice.

Theoretical Analysis of Calorimeter Data

Assume that we have a reaction occurring in a closed, well-stirred reaction test cell. Assume a general reaction of the form

$$\alpha A + \beta B + ... = \text{Products}. \tag{8-2}$$

We can then write a mole balance on reactant A as follows:

$$\frac{dC_A}{dt} = -k(T)C_A^a C_B^b....., \tag{8-3}$$

where

C is the concentration (moles/volume),
$k(T)$ is the temperature-dependent rate coefficient (concentration^{1-n}/time), and
a, b ... are the reaction orders with respect to each species.

The rate coefficient $k(T)$ is given by the Arrhenius equation Ae^{-E_a/R_gT}, where A is the pre-exponential factor and E_a is the activation energy.

Equation 8-3 can be written for each species for the reaction shown in Equation 8-2.

If the reactants are initially added to the reaction test cell in their stoichiometric ratios, then the concentrations will remain at those ratios throughout the reaction. Then

$$\frac{C_B}{C_A} = \frac{\beta}{\alpha}, \tag{8-4}$$

and similarly for all of the other species. Substituting into Equation 8-3,

$$\begin{aligned} \frac{dC_A}{dt} &= -k(T)C_A^a\left(\frac{\beta}{\alpha}C_A\right)^b.... \\ &= -k(T)\left(\frac{\beta}{\alpha}\right)^b ...C_A^{a+b+}.... \end{aligned} \tag{8-5}$$

We can then write an equation for the concentration of species A in terms of an overall reaction order $n = a + b +$ ... and define a new rate coefficient k'. Then

$$\frac{dC_A}{dt} = -k'(T)C_A^n. \tag{8-6}$$

This approach only works if all of the species are stoichiometric.

Another approach is to have all the reactants, except one, be in excess. In this case the excess reactant concentrations can be assumed to be approximately constant during the reaction. Suppose that all the reactants, except species A, are in excess. Then

$$\begin{aligned} \frac{dC_A}{dt} &= -k(T)C_A^a C_{Bo}^b C_{Co}^c... \\ &= -k(T)(C_{Bo}^b C_{Co}^c...)C_A^a \\ &= -k'(T)C_A^a, \end{aligned} \tag{8-7}$$

where C_{Bo} is the initial concentration of species B. This approach is useful for determining the reaction order with respect to an individual species.

Consider now a situation where the reaction order is not known. Assume that the reaction can be represented by an overall nth-order reaction of the following form:

$$\frac{dC}{dt} = -k(T)C^n. \tag{8-8}$$

We can define a reaction conversion x in terms of the initial concentration C_o:

$$x = \frac{C_o - C}{C_o}. \tag{8-9}$$

Note that when $C = C_o, x = 0$ and when $C = 0, x = 1$.

Substituting Equation 8-9 into Equation 8-8,

$$\frac{dx}{dt} = k(T)C_o^{n-1}(1 - x)^n: \tag{8-10}$$

Dividing both sides of Equation 8-10 by $k(T_o)C_o^{n-1}$,

$$\frac{1}{k(T_o)C_o^{n-1}}\frac{dx}{dt} = \frac{k(T)}{k(T_o)}(1 - x)^n. \tag{8-11}$$

Now define a dimensionless time τ as

$$\begin{aligned} \tau &= k(T_o)C_o^{n-1}t \\ d\tau &= k(T_o)C_o^{n-1}dt, \end{aligned} \tag{8-12}$$

and Equation 8-11 simplifies to

$$\frac{dx}{d\tau} = \frac{k(T)}{k(T_o)}(1 - x)^n \tag{8-13}$$

Up to this point all our equations are cast with respect to the concentration within our reaction vessel. Unfortunately, the concentration is very difficult to measure, particularly when the reaction is very fast and the concentrations are changing very rapidly. On-line instruments to measure the concentration directly are still very limited. A more direct approach would be to withdraw a very small sample from the reactor and cool and quench the reaction instantaneously to get a representative result. Withdrawing the sample would also have an impact on the test sample since we are removing mass and energy from the vessel. Thus, measuring the concentration in real time is very difficult to do.

The easiest system parameter to measure is the temperature. This can be done easily with a thermocouple and can be done very rapidly in real time. We can relate the temperature to the conversion by assuming that the conversion is proportional to the entire temperature change during the reaction. This gives us the following equation:

$$x = \frac{T - T_o}{\Delta T_{ad}} = \frac{T - T_o}{T_F - T_o}, \tag{8-14}$$

where

T_o is the initial reaction temperature, also called the reaction onset temperature,
T_F is the final reaction temperature when the reaction is completed, and
ΔT_{ad} is the adiabatic temperature change during the reaction.

Equation 8-14 contains two important assumptions. These are

1. The reaction is characterized by an initial and final temperature, and these temperatures can be determined experimentally with a fair amount of precision.
2. The heat capacity of the test sample is constant during the reaction.

Assumption 1 is perhaps the more important. The initial or onset temperature must be the temperature at which the reaction rate becomes large enough for adequate energy to be produced for heating of the reaction mixture to be detected by a thermocouple. This temperature has been misinterpreted by many investigators in the past. Some investigators have incorrectly concluded that if a reactive material is stored below the initial or onset temperature, then that reactive mixture will not react. This is totally incorrect, since the reaction proceeds at a finite, albeit often undetectable rate, even below the onset temperature. Different calorimeters will also give different initial or onset temperatures since this is a function of the temperature measurement sensitivity of the calorimeter. The initial or onset temperature is used only to relate the concentration of the reactant to the temperature of the reactor, and nothing more.

Assumption 2 will fail if the heat capacity of the products is significantly different from the heat capacity of the reactants. Fortunately, the heat capacities for most liquid materials are about the same. If the reactants are mostly liquids and a significant fraction of the products are gases, then this assumption may fail. This assumption is approximately true if one or more of the reactants are in excess or the system contains a solvent in high concentration, resulting in a nearly constant liquid heat capacity.

The kinetic term in Equation 8-13 can be expanded as follows:

$$\frac{k(T)}{k(T_o)} = \frac{Ae^{-E_a/R_gT}}{Ae^{-E_a/R_gT_o}} = \exp\left[\frac{E_a}{R_g}\left(\frac{1}{T_o} - \frac{1}{T}\right)\right] \tag{8-15}$$

$$= \exp\left[\frac{E_a}{R_gT_o}\left(1 - \frac{T_o}{T}\right)\right]$$

$$= \exp\left[\frac{E_a}{R_gT_o}\left(1 - \frac{T_o}{T_o + \Delta T_{ad}x}\right)\right]$$

$$= \exp\left[\frac{\dfrac{E_a}{R_g T_o}\dfrac{\Delta T_{ad}}{T_o}x}{1 + \dfrac{\Delta T_{ad}}{T_o}x}\right]. \tag{8-16}$$

Now define B as the dimensionless adiabatic temperature rise and Γ as the dimensionless activation energy, given by the following equations:

$$B = \frac{\Delta T_{ad}}{T_o} = \frac{T_F - T_o}{T_o} \tag{8-17}$$

$$\Gamma = \frac{E_a}{R_g T_o}. \tag{8-18}$$

Then Equation 8-13 reduces to the following dimensionless equation:

$$\boxed{\frac{dx}{d\tau} = (1 - x)^n \exp\left(\frac{\Gamma B x}{1 + Bx}\right).} \tag{8-19}$$

If the dimensionless adiabatic temperature rise B is small, that is, less than about 0.4, then Equation 8-19 simplifies to

$$\boxed{\frac{dx}{d\tau} \cong (1 - x)^n \exp(\Gamma B x).} \tag{8-20}$$

Equations 8-19 and 8-20 contain the following very important assumptions:

1. The reaction vessel is well mixed. This means that the temperature and concentration gradients in the liquid sample are small.
2. The physical properties — heat capacity and heat of reaction — of the sample are constant.
3. The heat released by the reaction is proportional to the conversion.
4. The reaction conversion x is directly proportional to the temperature increase during the reaction.

By converting our dimensional equations into dimensionless form we reduce the equations to their simplest form, thus allowing easy algebraic manipulation of the equations. We also identify the least number of dimensionless parameters required to describe our system. In this case there are three parameters: reaction order n, dimensionless adiabatic temperature rise B, and dimensionless activation energy Γ. Finally, the equations are easier to solve numerically since all variables are scaled, typically between 0 and 1.

The problem with using a dimensionless approach is that the dimensionless parameters and variables are difficult to interpret physically. Also, some effort might be required to convert from dimensional variables to dimensionless variables.

The reaction order, n, has typical values between 0 and 2. The reaction order is almost always greater than 1 and fractional orders are likely. The dimensionless adiabatic temperature rise, B, has typical values from 0 to about 2. The dimensionless activation energy, Γ, can have values ranging from about 5 to 50 or higher depending on the activation energy.

Our dimensionless Equations 8-19 and 8-20 depend on a number of dimensional parameters. These includes onset temperature T_o, final temperature T_F, activation energy E_a, and the value of the Arrhenius equation at the onset temperature $k(T_o)$. Note that the onset and final temperatures are implicitly related to the Arrhenius reaction rate equation and cannot be specified independently.

Equations 8-19 and 8-20 can be easily integrated. This can be done using a spreadsheet and the trapezoid rule, or a mathematical package. A spreadsheet using the trapezoid rule might require a small step size; this should be checked to ensure that the results are converged.

Figures 8-5 and 8-6 show the results for the integration of Equation 8-19. The conversion is plotted versus the dimensionless time. The time scale is logarithmic to show a much larger range. Figure 8-5 shows how increasing the dimensionless adiabatic temperature rise B results in a reaction that occurs over a shorter time period with a steeper slope. Figure 8-6 shows how increasing the dimensionless activation energy Γ also results in a reaction that occurs over a shorter time period and a steeper slope. For the case with $\Gamma = 20$, the conversion responds very quickly.

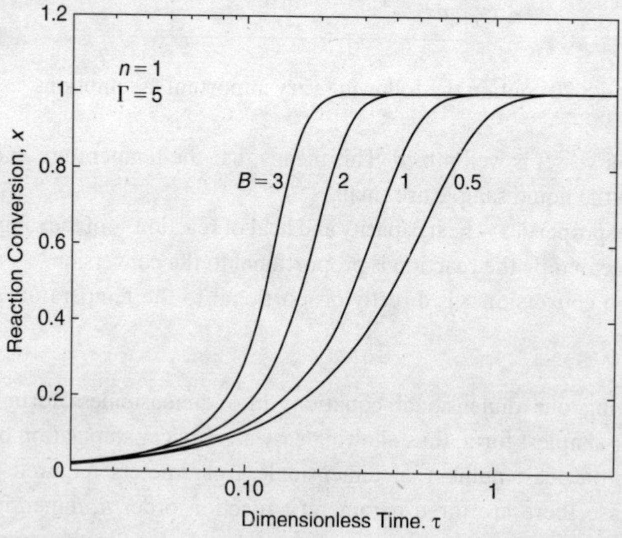

Figure 8-5 Equation 8-20 solved for increasing dimensionless adiabatic temperature rise B.

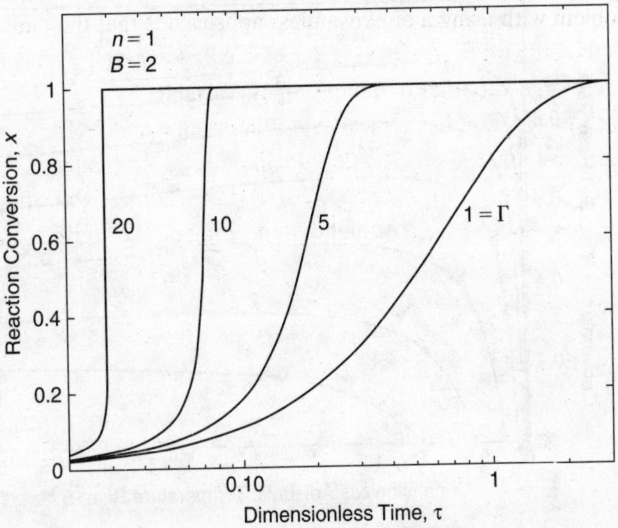

Figure 8-6 Equation 8-20 solved for increasing dimensionless activation energy Γ.

One of the important questions in Table 8-6 is the maximum self-heat rate and the time at which this occurs. The maximum self-heat rate is important for designing heat transfer equipment to remove the heat of reaction – larger self-heat rates require larger heat transfer equipment. Some chemicals, such as ethylene oxide and acrylic acid, will self-heat at rates of several hundred degrees Celsius per minute. The time at which the maximum self-heat rate occurs is also important for designing heat transfer equipment as well as for emergency response procedures.

The maximum self-heat rate can be found by differentiating Equation 8-19 with respect to the dimensionless time τ and then setting the result to zero to find the maximum. This equation can be solved for the conversion x_m at which the maximum self-heat rate occurs. After a lot of algebra, the following equation is obtained:

$$x_m = \frac{1}{2nB}\left[-(\Gamma + 2n) + \sqrt{\Gamma[\Gamma + 4n(1 + B)]}\right], \tag{8-21}$$

where x_m is the conversion at the maximum rate. The maximum rate is then found by substituting x_m into Equation 8-19.

Figure 8-7 is a plot of Equation 8-21 for a first-order reaction. As Γ increases, an asymptotic function is approached. This function is close to the $\Gamma = 64$ curve shown. Also, there is a maximum x_m for each curve. The maximum x_m increases as Γ increases and also occurs at lower B values. Each curve intersects the x axis.

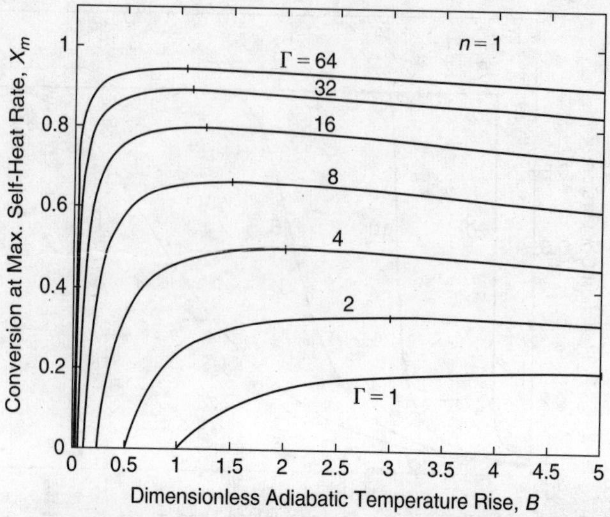

Figure 8-7 Conversion at maximum self-heat rate for a first-order reaction. The vertical line on each curve represents the maximum value.

Equation 8-21 can be differentiated one more time with respect to B to find the maximum value of x_m. After a fair amount of algebra, the maximum value is found to occur at

$$B = \frac{4n}{\Gamma} + 1, \qquad x_m = \frac{\Gamma}{4n + \Gamma}. \tag{8-22}$$

The intersection of the curves on Figure 8-7 with the x axis means that the self-heat rate occurs at the onset temperature, that is, when $\tau = 0$. The value of B at this intersection can be found from Equation 8-21 by setting $x_m = 0$ and solving for B. The result is

$$B = \frac{n}{\Gamma}. \tag{8-23}$$

The time to the maximum self-heat rate is found by separating variables in Equation 8-19 and integrating. The result is

$$\int_0^{x_m} \frac{dx}{(1-x)^n \exp\left(\dfrac{\Gamma B x}{1 + Bx}\right)} = \int_0^{\tau_m} d\tau = \tau_m, \tag{8-24}$$

where τ_m is the dimensionless time at which the maximum rate occurs. Note that this time is relative to the onset temperature.

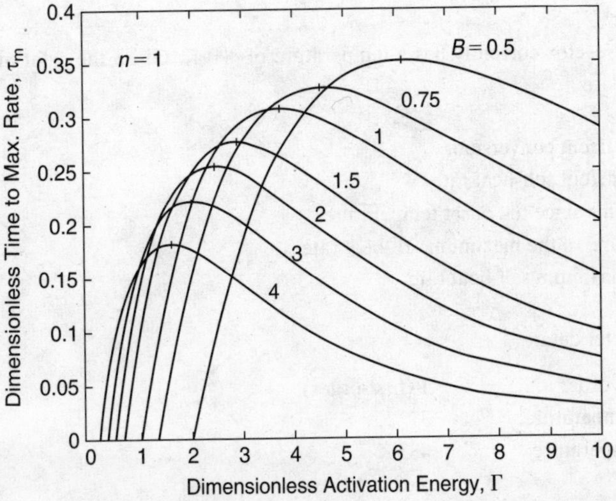

Figure 8-8 Time to maximum self-heat rate for a first-order reaction—low Γ range. The vertical lines on each curve represent the maximum value.

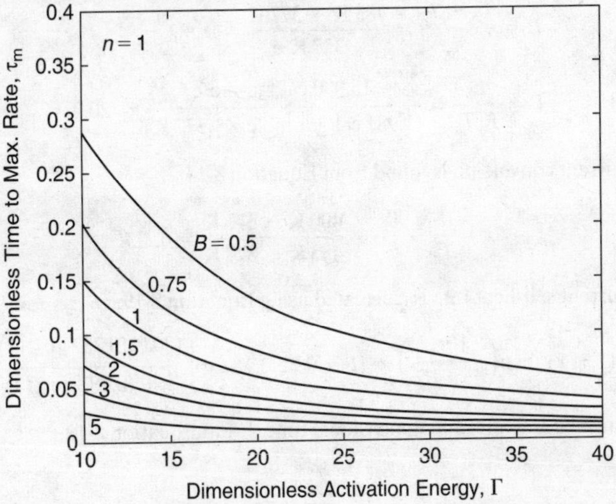

Figure 8-9 Time to maximum self-heat rate for a first-order reaction—high Γ range.

Equation 8-24 can be solved numerically for τ_m. The results are shown in Figures 8-8 and 8-9 for two different ranges of Γ. Each curve has a maximum, shown by the vertical tick mark. This maximum occurs at lower Γ values as the dimensionless adiabatic temperature rise B increases. This maximum must be solved for numerically – an algebraic solution is not possible.

Example 8-2

A chemical reactor currently has a temperature of 400 K. Given the calorimetry data provided below, calculate:

a. The current conversion.
b. The current self-heat rate.
c. The time since the onset temperature.
d. The time to the maximum self-heat rate.
e. The maximum self-heat rate.

Calorimeter data:

Reaction order n:	1 (first-order)
Onset temperature:	377 K
Final temperature:	483 K
$k(T_o)$:	$5.62 \times 10^{-5}\ \text{sec}^{-1}$
Activation energy E_a:	15,000 cal/gm-mole K

Solution

From the calorimetry data provided:

$$B = \frac{T_F - T_o}{T_o} = \frac{483\ \text{K} - 377\ \text{K}}{377\ \text{K}} = 0.282,$$

$$\Gamma = \frac{E_a}{R_g T_o} = \frac{15{,}000\ \text{cal/gm-mole}}{(1.987\ \text{cal/gm-mole K})(377\ \text{K})} = 20.0.$$

a. The current conversion is found from Equation 8-14:

$$x = \frac{T - T_o}{T_F - T_o} = \frac{400\ \text{K} - 377\ \text{K}}{483\ \text{K} - 377\ \text{K}} = 0.217.$$

b. The current self-heat rate is calculated using Equation 8-19:

$$\frac{dx}{d\tau} = (1 - x)^n \exp\left(\frac{\Gamma B x}{1 + Bx}\right) = (1 - 0.217) \times \exp\left[\frac{(20.0)(0.282)(0.217)}{1 + (0.282)(0.217)}\right] = 2.48.$$

This must be converted to dimensional time. From Equation 8-12,

$$t = \frac{\tau}{k(T_o) C_o^{n-1}}. \tag{8-25}$$

and using the definition of the conversion given by Equation 8-14:

$$\frac{dT}{dt} = (T_F - T_o) k(T_o) C_0^{n-1} \left(\frac{dx}{d\tau}\right). \tag{8-26}$$

And it follows for $n = 1$,

$$\frac{dT}{dt} = (T_F - T_o) k(T_o) \frac{dx}{d\tau} = (483\ \text{K} - 377\ \text{K})(5.62 \times 10^{-5}\ \text{sec}^{-1})(2.48)$$
$$= 0.0148\ \text{K/s} = 0.886\ \text{K/min}.$$

The dimensionless time since the onset temperature is found by integrating Equation 8-19. This can be done easily using either a spreadsheet or a numerical package. The results are shown in Figure 8-10. From Figure 8-10, at a conversion of 0.217 the dimensionless time is 0.141. The dimensionless time can be converted to actual time using Equation 8-25. For a first-order reaction, $n = 1$ and

$$t = \frac{\tau}{k(T_o)} = \frac{0.141}{5.62 \times 10^{-5}\ \text{sec}^{-1}} = 2{,}510\ \text{sec} = 41.8\ \text{min}.$$

This is the time since the onset temperature.

c. The conversion at the maximum rate is given by Equation 8-21. Substituting the known values:

$$x_m = \frac{1}{2nB}\left[-(\Gamma + 2n) + \sqrt{\Gamma[\Gamma + 4n(1 + B)]}\right]$$

$$x_m = \frac{1}{(2)(1)(0.282)}\left[-(20 + 2) + \sqrt{(20)[20 + (4)(1 + 0.282)]}\right]$$

$$x_m = 0.741.$$

From the numerical solution, Figure 8-10, the dimensionless time at this conversion is 0.249. The actual time is

$$t = \frac{\tau}{k(T_o)} = \frac{0.249}{5.62 \times 10^{-5}\ \text{sec}^{-1}} = 4{,}432\ \text{sec} = 73.9\ \text{min}.$$

This is with respect to the time the onset temperature is reached. The time from the current reaction state ($x = 0.217$) to the time at the maximum rate is

$$73.9\ \text{min} - 41.8\ \text{min} = 32.1\ \text{min}.$$

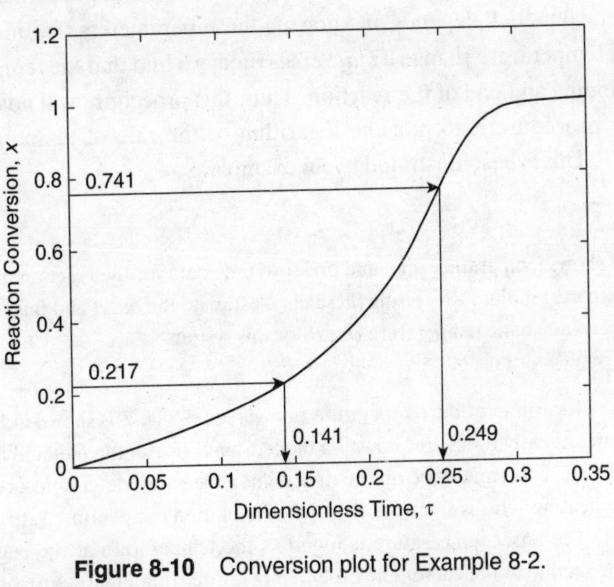

Figure 8-10 Conversion plot for Example 8-2.

Thus, the reaction will reach the maximum rate in 32.1 min.

Figure 8-8 or 8-9 could be used to solve this problem directly. However, it is not as precise.

d. The maximum self-heat rate is found using Equation 8-19:

$$\frac{dx}{d\tau} = (1 - x)^n \exp\left(\frac{\Gamma Bx}{1 + Bx}\right) = (1 - 0.741) \times \exp\left[\frac{(20.0)(0.282)(0.741)}{1 + (0.282)(0.741)}\right] = 8.21.$$

It follows that

$$\frac{dT}{dt} = (T_F - T_o)k(T_o)\frac{dx}{d\tau} = (483\text{ K} - 377\text{ K})(5.62 \times 10^{-5}\text{ sec}^{-1})(8.21)$$
$$= 0.0489\text{ K/s} = 2.93\text{ K/min}.$$

The maximum self-heat rate, along with the heat capacity of the reacting liquid, could be used to estimate the minimum cooling requirements for this reactor. Also, the time to maximum rate could be used to estimate the residence time, operating temperature, and conversion for the reactor.

Estimation of Parameters from Calorimeter Data

Prior to using the theoretical model, we need to estimate from calorimeter data the parameters required for the model. These include onset temperature T_o, final temperature T_F, reaction order n, activation energy E_a, and the value of the Arrhenius equation at the onset temperature $k(T_o)$. The calorimeter typically provides temperature versus time data so a procedure is required to estimate these parameters from these data.

The onset and final temperatures are perhaps the most important since the conversion, and the theoretical model, depends on knowing these parameters reasonably precisely. If we plot the rate of temperature change dT/dt versus time, we find that the temperature rate is very low at the beginning and end of the reaction. Thus, this procedure will not work.

A better procedure is to plot the logarithm of the rate of temperature change dT/dt versus $-1000/T$. This is best illustrated by an example.

Example 8-3

Figure 8-3 shows temperature time and pressure time data for the reaction of methanol and acetic anhydride in a 2:1 molar ratio. Using these data, estimate the onset and final temperatures and the dimensionless adiabatic temperature rise B for this system.

Solution

A plot of the logarithm of the temperature rate versus $-1000/T$ is shown in Figure 8-11. The temperature rates at early times are shown on the left-hand side of the plot and the temperature rates at the end of the experiment are on the right. When the calorimeter detects exothermic behavior, it stops the heating. This is shown as a drop in the plotted temperature rate on the far left side of Figure 8-11. The onset temperature is found as the temperature at the beginning of the nearly straight-line section of the curve. The onset temperature from Figure 8-10 is found to be 298 K.

The final temperature is found from the right-hand side of the plot where the temperature rate drops off suddenly and returns to almost the same temperature rate as the onset temperature. The final temperature identified from Figure 8-11 is 447 K.

Figure 8-11 can also be used to identify the maximum temperature rate as well as the temperature at which this occurs. This is found from the peak value in Figure 8-11. From the data, the maximum temperature rate is 104 K/min (1.73 K/sec), and this occurs at a temperature of 429 K.

The dimensionless adiabatic temperature rise is given by Equation 8-17. Thus,

$$B = \frac{T_F - T_o}{T_o} = \frac{447\text{ K} - 298\text{ K}}{298\text{ K}} = 0.500.$$

At this point in the procedure we have the onset and final temperatures and the dimensionless adiabatic temperature rise B.

The next parameter to estimate is the reaction order. The reaction order can be estimated by rearranging Equation 8-19 as follows:

$$\frac{1}{(1-x)^n}\frac{dx}{d\tau} = \exp\left(\frac{\Gamma B x}{1 + Bx}\right). \tag{8-27}$$

From Equation 8-12, $d\tau = k(T_o)C_o^{n-1}\,dt$, and it follows that

$$\frac{1}{(1-x)^n}\frac{dx}{d\tau} = \frac{1}{(1-x)^n\,k(T_o)C_o^{n-1}}\frac{dx}{dt} = \exp\left(\frac{\Gamma B x}{1 + Bx}\right)$$

$$\frac{(dx/dt)}{(1-x)^n\,C_o^{n-1}} = k(T_o)\exp\left(\frac{\Gamma B x}{1 + Bx}\right)$$

$$\ln\left[\frac{(dx/dt)}{(1-x)^n\,C_o^{n-1}}\right] = \ln[k(T_o)] + \Gamma\left(\frac{Bx}{1 + Bx}\right). \tag{8-28}$$

Equation 8-28 can be modified in terms of the actual temperature. Since $dx = dT/(T_F - T_o)$,

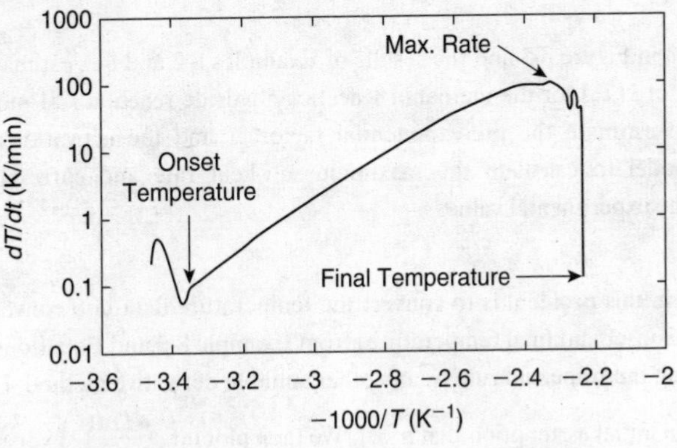

Figure 8-11 Graphical procedure to estimate the onset and final temperatures.

errors!

$$\ln\left[\frac{(dT/dt)}{(T_F - T_o)(1-x)^n C_o^{n-1}}\right] = \ln[k(T_o)] + \Gamma\left(\frac{Bx}{1+Bx}\right). \tag{8-29}$$

For a first-order reaction, $n = 1$, and $(1 - x) = (T_F - T)/(T_F - T_o)$ and Equation 8-29 can be simplified even further:

$$\ln\left[\frac{(dT/dt)}{T_F - T}\right] = \ln[k(T_o)] + \Gamma\left(\frac{Bx}{1+Bx}\right) \tag{8-30}$$

The procedure for determining the overall reaction order n, using either Equation 8-28, 8-29, or 8-30, is as follows. The onset and final temperatures, and the dimensionless adiabatic temperature rise B, are already known from Example 8-3. First, the overall reaction order is guessed. First-order ($n = 1$) is a good place to start. The conversion x can be calculated from the temperature data using Equation 8-14. Then the left-hand side of either Equation 8-28, 8-29, or 8-30 is plotted versus $Bx/(1 + Bx)$. If the reaction order is correct, a straight line is obtained. It is possible to have fractional overall reaction orders, so some effort might be required to estimate the reaction order that produces the best fit to the data. For any reaction order not equal to unity, the initial concentration of reactant must be known. Finally, as a bonus, once the reaction order is identified, the intercept of the straight line with the y axis provides an estimate of $k(T_o)$.

If we assume a first-order reaction ($n = 1$) and substitute to convert Equation 8-30 into dimensional form, the following equation is obtained:

$$\ln\left[\frac{dT/dt}{T_F - T}\right] = \ln A - \frac{E_a}{R_g T}. \tag{8-31}$$

Equation 8-31 states that if a system is first-order, then a plot of the left-hand side versus $-1/R_g T$ should produce a straight line with slope of E_a and intercept $-\ln A$. Equation 8-31 is commonly seen in the literature as a means to determine the kinetic parameters. It is not as general as Equation 8-28.

Example 8-4

Using the data in Figure 8-3 and the results of Examples 8-2 and 8-3, estimate the reaction order and the value of $k(T_o)$ for the methanol + acetic anhydride reaction (2:1 molar ratio). Use these parameters to estimate the pre-exponential factor A and the activation energy E_a. Use the theoretical model to calculate the maximum self-heat rate and corresponding temperature. Compare to the experimental values.

Solution

The first step in this problem is to convert the temperature data into conversion data, x. This is done using the onset and final temperatures from Example 8-3 and Equation 8-14. Then (dx/dt) is calculated using the trapezoid rule or any other suitable derivative method. Equation 8-29 is then applied with an initial assumption that $n = 1$. We then plot $\ln\left(\frac{dT/dt}{T_F - T}\right)$ versus $\left(\frac{Bx}{1+Bx}\right)$. These

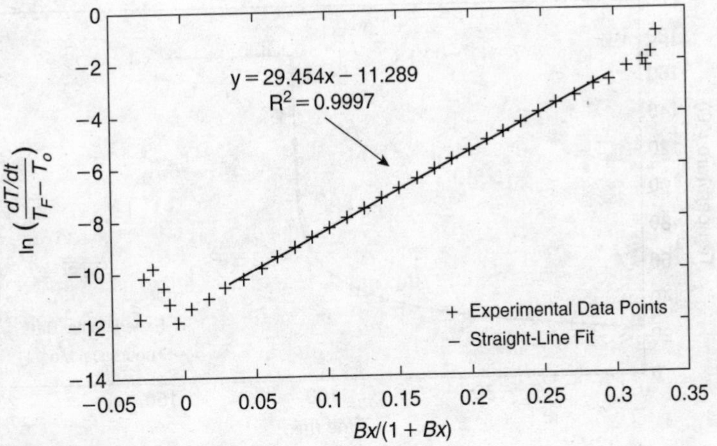

Figure 8-12 Determination of the kinetic parameters n, Γ, and $k(T_o)$.

results are shown in Figure 8-12. If we eliminate some of the early and later points in the data that diverge from the straight line—these points have less precision—and fit a straight line to the remaining data, we get a very straight line with an R^2 value of 0.9997. This confirms that the reaction is first-order.

From the straight-line fit, the slope is equal to our dimensionless parameter Γ and the intercept is equal to ln $k(T_o)$. Thus, $\Gamma = 29.4$ and $\ln k(T_o) = -11.3$. It follows that $k(T_o) = 1.24 \times 10^{-5}\ \text{sec}^{-1}$.

From the definition for Γ given by Equation 8-18, the activation energy E_a is computed as 72.8 kJ/mol, and since $k(T_o) = A \exp(-E_a / R_g T_o)$, we can calculate the pre-exponential factor as $A = 7.27 \times 10^7\ \text{sec}^{-1}$.

The conversion at the maximum self-heat rate is given by Equation 8-21:

$$x_m = \frac{1}{2nB}\left[-(\Gamma + 2n) + \sqrt{\Gamma[\Gamma + 4n(1 + B)]}\right].$$

Substituting the known values,

$$x_m = \frac{1}{(2)(0.5)}\left[-(29.4 + 2) + \sqrt{29.4[29.4 + 4(1 + 0.5)]}\right] = 0.861.$$

The temperature at this conversion is

$$\frac{T - T_o}{T_F - T_o} = x_m = 0.861$$

$$T = 426\ \text{K}.$$

This compares very well to the experimental maximum rate temperature of 429 K.

The maximum self-heat rate is estimated from Equation 8-19, with $n = 1$:

$$\frac{dx}{d\tau} = (1 - x)\exp\left(\frac{\Gamma Bx}{1 + Bx}\right) = (1 - 0.861)\exp\left[\frac{(29.4)(0.500)(0.861)}{1 + (0.5)(0.861)}\right] = 967.$$

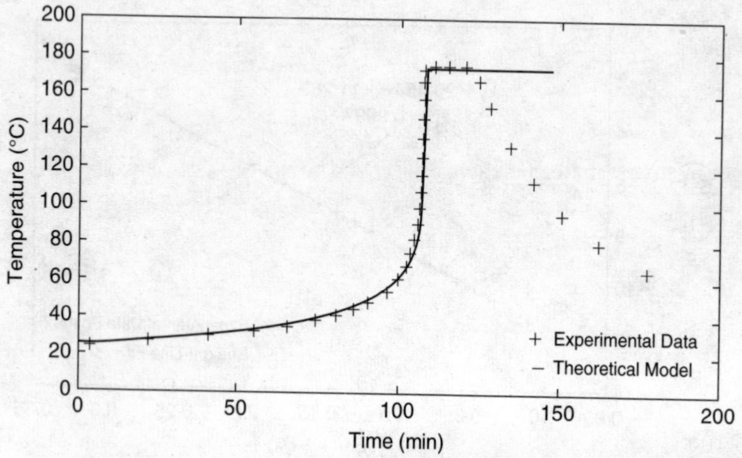

Figure 8-13 Comparison of experimental data with theoretical model prediction.

The maximum self-heat rate in dimensional units is calculated from Equation 8-26:

$$\frac{dT}{dt} = (T_F - T_o)k(T_o)\frac{dx}{d\tau} = (447\text{ K} - 298\text{ K})(1.24 \times 10^{-5}\text{ sec}^{-1})(967) = 1.78\text{ K/sec} = 107\text{ K/min.}$$

This compares to the experimental value of 1.73 K/sec (104 K/min). The experimental maximum self-heat rate is usually lower than the theoretical value due to the dampening effect of the sample container heat capacity. Figure 8-13 is a plot of the experimental and theoretical temperature-time plots. The agreement is very good.

Summary of Calorimeter Analysis: Ethanol + Acetic Anhydride

Reaction order n:	1
Onset temperature T_o:	298 K
Final temperature T_F:	447 K
Dimensionless adiabatic temperature rise B:	0.500
Dimensionless activation energy Γ:	29.4
Activation energy E_a:	72.8 kJ/mol
Pre-exponential factor A:	7.27×10^7 sec^{-1}
Maximum self-heat rate, experimental:	104 K/min
Maximum self-heat rate, theoretical:	107 K/min
Temp. at max. self-heat rate, experimental:	429 K
Temp. at max. self-heat rate, theoretical:	426 K

Adjusting the Data for the Heat Capacity of the Sample Vessel

Up to now, the calorimeter data analysis has assumed that the sample vessel container has a negligible heat capacity. This situation is not realistic — the sample vessel always has a heat capacity that absorbs heat during the chemical reaction.

The sample container absorbs heat during the reaction and reduces the total temperature change during the reaction. Thus, without the container, the final reaction temperature would be higher.

The effect of the sample container on the temperature can be estimated from a heat balance. The goal is to estimate the change in temperature of the isolated sample, without the container. The heat generated by the isolated reacting sample is distributed between the sample and the sample container. In equation form,

$$[mC_P\Delta T_{ad}]_{\text{Isolated Sample}} = [mC_P\Delta T_{ad}]_{\text{Sample + Container}}$$

$$[m_S C_P^S \Delta T_{ad}^S]_{\text{Isolated Sample}} = \left[(m_S C_P^S + m_C C_P^C)\Delta T_{ad}^{S+C}\right]_{\text{Sample + Container}}$$

$$\Delta T_{ad}^S = \left[\frac{m_S C_P^S + m_C C_P^C}{m_S C_P^S}\right]\Delta T_{ad}^{S+C}$$

$$\Delta T_{ad}^S = \Phi \Delta T_{ad}^{S+C}, \tag{8-32}$$

where Φ is the phi-factor presented earlier in Equation 8-1.

Equation 8-32 shows that, for example, if the reaction occurs in a reaction container with a phi-factor of 2, then the container absorbs half of the heat generated by the reaction and the measured adiabatic temperature increase is half of the temperature increase that would be measured by an isolated sample.

The theoretical model can be adjusted by replacing the dimensionless adiabatic temperature rise B by ΦB to account for the heat capacity of the container.

The initial reaction temperature is not affected much by the container presence. However, the final reaction temperature is estimated from the following equation:

$$T_F = T_o + \Phi \Delta T_{ad}^{S+C}. \tag{8-33}$$

Heat of Reaction Data from Calorimeter Data

Calorimeter analysis can provide additional information beyond the kinetic model analysis discussed so far.

Calorimeter data can be used to estimate the heat of reaction of the reacting sample. This is done using the following equation:

$$\Delta H_{rx} = \frac{\Phi C_V \Delta T_{ad}}{m_{LR}/m_T}, \tag{8-34}$$

where

ΔH_{rx} is the heat of reaction, energy/mass, based on the limiting reactant;

Φ is the phi-factor for the vessel container, given by Equations 8-1 and 8-33, unitless;

C_V is the heat capacity at constant volume for the reacting liquid, energy/mass-deg;

ΔT_{ad} is the adiabatic temperature rise during the reaction, deg;

m_{LR} is the initial mass of limiting reactant, mass; and

m_T is the total mass of reacting mixture, mass.

Using Pressure Data from the Calorimeter

The pressure information provided by the calorimeter is very important, especially for relief system and pressure vessel design. If the calorimeter is the closed vessel type, the vessel can be evacuated prior to addition of the sample. The pressure data are then representative of the vapor pressure of the reacting liquid – important data required for relief sizing.

The pressure data are used to classify reaction systems into four different types.[7] These classifications are important for relief system design, discussed in Chapter 10. The classifications are based on the dominant energy term in the liquid reaction mass as material is discharged through the relief system.

1. Volatile/tempered reaction: This is also called a vapor system. In this case the heat of vaporization of the liquid cools, or tempers, the reaction mass during the relief discharge. Tempered reactions are inherently safer since the cooling mechanism is part of the reaction mass.
2. Hybrid/tempered reaction: Non-condensable gases are produced as a result of the reaction. However, the heat of vaporization of the liquid dominates to cool the reaction mass during the entire relief discharge.
3. Hybrid/non-tempered reaction: Non-condensable gases are produced but the heat of vaporization of the liquid does not always dominate during the entire relief discharge.
4. Gassy/non-tempered reaction: The reaction produces non-condensable gases and the liquid is not volatile enough for the heat of vaporization of the liquid to have much effect during the entire relief discharge.

The pressure data from the calorimeter are used for classifying the type of system.

1. The initial and final pressure in the closed vessel calorimeter can be used to determine if the system produces a gaseous product. In this case the calorimeter must be operated

[7]H. G. Fisher et al., *Emergency Relief System Design Using DIERS Technology* (New York: AIChE Design Institute for Emergency Relief Systems, 1992).

so that the starting and ending temperatures are the same. If the initial pressure is equal to the final pressure, then no gaseous products are produced and the pressure is due to the constant vapor pressure of the liquid – this is a volatile/tempered reaction system. If the final pressure is higher than the starting pressure, then vapor products are produced and the reaction system is either hybrid or gassy.

2. If the system is classified as hybrid or gassy from part 1, then the time and temperature at which the peak in the temperature rate and pressure rate occurs is used. If the peaks occur at the same time and temperature, then the system is hybrid. If the peaks do not occur at the same temperature, then the system is gassy.

Application of Calorimeter Data

The calorimeter data are used to design and operate processes so that reactive chemical incidents do not occur. This is, perhaps, the most difficult part of this procedure since each process has its unique problems and challenges. Experience is essential in this procedure. Expert advice is recommended for interpreting calorimetry data and for designing controls and emergency systems.

The calorimeter data are most useful for designing relief systems to prevent high pressures due to runaway reactors. This is done using the procedures discussed in Chapter 10.

Calorimeter data are also useful for estimating or developing:

1. Heat exchanger duty to achieve required reactor cooling.
2. Cooling water requirements and cooling water pump size.
3. Condenser size in a reactor reflux system.
4. Maximum concentrations of reactants to prevent overpressure in the reactor.
5. Reactor vessel size.
6. Reactor vessel pressure rating.
7. Type of reactor: batch, semi-batch or tubular.
8. Reactor temperature control and sequencing.
9. Semi-batch reactor reactant feed rates.
10. Catalyst concentrations.
11. Alarm/shutdown setpoints.
12. Maximum fill factor for batch and semi-batch reactors.
13. Solvent concentrations required to control reactor temperature.
14. Operating procedures.
15. Emergency procedures.
16. Reactant storage vessel design and storage temperature.
17. Relief effluent treatment systems.

8-4 Controlling Reactive Hazards

If the flowchart shown in Figure 8-1 and discussed in section 8-1 shows that reactive hazards are present in your plant or operation, then the methods shown in Table 8-8 are useful to control these hazards and prevent reactive chemicals incidents. Table 8-8 is only a partial list of methods – many more methods are available. The methods are classified as inherent, passive, active or procedural. The methods at the top of the list are preferred since inherent and passive methods are always preferred over active and procedural methods.

The procedural methods in Table 8-8, even though they are low on the hierarchy, are essential for any effective reactive chemicals management system. These are discussed in detail in Johnson, et al.[8]

A chemical reactive hazards program requires a considerable amount of technology, experience, and management to prevent incidents in any facility handling reactive chemicals. This requires awareness and commitment from all employees, from upper management on down, and the resources necessary to make it all work.

Table 8-8 Hierarchy of methods to improve reactive chemicals safety. This is only a partial list of possibilities.

Inherent

- Use a reaction pathway that uses less hazardous chemicals.
- Use a reaction pathway that is less energetic, slower, or easier to control.
- Use smaller inventories of reactive chemicals both in the process and in storage. Reduce pipe length and size to reduce inventory.
- Eliminate or reduce inventories of reactive intermediates.
- Use reactive chemicals at lower concentrations or temper reactions with a solvent.
- Control reactor stoichiometry and charge mass so that in the event of a runaway reaction the pressure rating of the vessel will not be exceeded and the relief devices will not open.
- Reduce shipping of reactive chemicals — produce on site by demand if possible.
- Design equipment and/or procedures to prevent an incident in the event of a human error.
- Reduce pipe sizes to reduce leak rate. Provide orifice plates or flow restrictors.
- Apply principles of human error to the design and operation of the process. Simplify both the process design and operation. Use simpler processes and chemistry.

Passive

- Ensure that incompatible chemicals are always separated.
- Provide adequate separation distances between storage vessels, reactors and other process equipment using reactive chemicals.
- Provide passive engineering controls, such as dikes and containment, to control reactive chemical spills.

[8] Johnson, et al., *Essential Practices for Managing Reactivity Hazards.*

Table 8-8 Hierarchy of methods to improve reactive chemicals safety. This is only a partial list of possibilities. *(continued)*

Passive
• Provide passive fire protection for chemical reactors, storage vessels, and process equipment. This includes insulation of reactors and storage vessels, and thermal coating of all mechanical supports. • Ensure adequate separation of the plant from local communities.
Active
• Screen all chemicals for reactive chemical hazards. • Provide or have access to experimental calorimeter characterization of reactive chemicals. • Provide properly designed control systems to control reactive chemicals in the process. • Provide properly designed heat transfer equipment to remove energy released by reactive chemistry. • Identify and characterize all possible reactions, including reactions or decompositions at higher temperatures, reactions induced by fire exposure, and reactions due to contamination. • Use quench, stop, or dump systems to quickly stop out-of-control reactive chemistry. • Provide active fire protection and emergency response to reduce the size of reactive chemical incidents. • Provide reliable mixing systems on all chemical reactors and sensors capable of identifying mixing failures. • Provide double block and bleed systems and other systems to prevent backflow of reactor contents to storage vessels. • Provide properly designed relief systems to prevent high pressures in the process due to reactive chemistry. • Ensure that all reactive chemicals requiring inhibitors in storage, particularly monomers, are tested regularly to ensure that inhibitor concentrations are adequate. • Provide reliable cooling water systems to exothermic reactors. • Provide an explicit measure of cooling water flow to a reactor, with proper alarms and control system interlocks to provide safe control in the event of cooling water failure. • Use semi-batch reactors rather than batch – the flow rate of reactant to the semi-batch reactor provides a means to control the heat release rate from the exothermic reaction. • Prevent a "sleeping reactor" in a semi-batch reactor by properly measuring and controlling temperatures and reactant concentrations.
Procedural
• Provide reactive chemical reviews of existing processes and new processes. • Document chemical reactivity risks and management decisions. • Communicate and train on chemical reactivity hazards. • Manage process changes that may involve reactive chemicals. • Review and audit your reactive chemicals program to ensure that it is operating properly. • Investigate chemical reactivity incidents. • Provide proper resource allocation for reactive chemicals programs. • Ensure management line responsibility for reactive chemicals. • Provide quality control procedures to ensure that all reactive chemicals received are the correct chemicals at the correct concentrations, without hazardous impurities.

Suggested Reading

Center for Chemical Process Safety (CCPS), *Guidelines for Safe Storage and Handling of Reactive Chemicals* (New York: American Institute of Chemical Engineers, 1995).

H. G. Fisher, H. S. Forrest, S. S. Grossel, J. E. Huff, A. R. Muller, J. A. Noronha, D. A. Shaw, and B. J. Tilley, *Emergency Relief System Design Using DIERS Technology* (New York: AIChE Design Institute for Emergency Relief Systems, 1992).

R. W. Johnson, "Chemical Reactivity," pp. 23–24 to 23–30, *Perry's Chemical Engineers' Handbook*, 8th ed., D. W. Green, ed. (New York: McGraw-Hill, 2008).

D. C. Hendershot, "A Checklist for Inherently Safer Chemical Reaction Process Design and Operation," *International Symposium on Risk, Reliability and Security* (New York: American Institute of Chemical Engineers Center for Chemical Process Safety, 2002).

Improving Reactive Hazard Management (Washington, DC: US Chemical Safety and Hazard Investigation Board, October 2002).

L. E. Johnson and J. K. Farr, "CRW 2.0: A Representative-Compound Approach to Functionality-Based Prediction of Reactive Chemical Hazards," *Process Safety Progress* (2008), 27(3): 212–218.

R. W. Johnson, S. W. Rudy, and S. D. Unwin, *Essential Practices for Managing Chemical Reactivity Hazards* (New York: AIChE Center for Chemical Process Safety, 2003).

A. Kossoy and Y. Akhmetshin, "Identification of Kinetic Models for the Assessment of Reeaction Hazards," *Process Safety Progress* (2007), 26(3): 209.

D. L. Townsend and J. C. Tou, "Thermal Hazard Evaluation by an Accelerating Rate Calorimeter," *Thermochimica Acta* (1980), 37: 1–30.

Problems

8-1. Professor Crowl's laboratory contains the following inventory of chemicals: methanol, sodium hydroxide in solid beads, acetic anhydride, methane, hydrogen, nitrogen, and oxygen. The methane, nitrogen, and oxygen are contained in K-cylinders, which hold about 200 SCF of gas. Please help Professor Crowl by preparing a chemical compatibility matrix for these chemicals. Provide recommendations on what represents the greatest hazard.

8-2. A contract manufacturer is contracted to prepare one 8100 lb batch of a gold precipitating agent. Ingredients are mixed in a 125 ft^3 (6 m^3) cone blender which is insulated and has a steel jacket to allow cooling and heating with a water/glycol mixture. The precipitating agent consists of approximately 66% sodium hydrosulfite, 22% aluminum powder, and 11% potassium carbonate by weight. After blending these dry ingredients, a small amount of liquid benzaldehyde is added for odor control. The product blend is packaged into eighteen 55 gal drums for shipment.[9]

[9]Problem statement from Johnson et al., *Essential Practices for Managing Chemical Reactivity Hazards.*

This operation is entirely a blending procedure. This same blender is also used for other formulations and has cooling capability that uses a water/ethylene glycol mixture as the cooling medium. Apply the screening method of Figure 8-1 to determine if any chemical reactivity hazards are expected.

8-3. Redo Figures 8-5 and 8-6 for a second-order reaction using the same parameters. How does the reaction order affect the behavior?

8-4. Redo Figure 8-7 for second-order reaction. How does the reaction order affect the behavior?

8-5. Derive Equation 8-21 by differentiating Equation 8-19 with respect to , solving for the maximum by setting the result to zero, and then solving for x_m.

8-6. Derive Equation 8-23.

8-7. Derive Equation 8-22. Note: This is a lot of tedious algebra!

8-8. Starting from Equation 8-20, show that the maximum self-heat rate for small values of B is given by

$$x_m = 1 - \frac{n}{\Gamma B}.$$

What happens for large Γ? At $x_m = 0$? At $\Gamma B = n$?

8-9. A commonly used equation in calorimetry analysis to determine the temperature at the maximum rate is given by

$$T_{\max} = \frac{E_a}{2nR_g}\left[\sqrt{1 + \frac{4nR_g T_F}{E_a}} - 1\right]. \tag{8-35}$$

Derive this equation from Equation 8-21. Use this equation to calculate $T_{\max}$ for the ethanol acetic anhydride system of Examples 8-3 and 8-4. Compare to the experimental value.

8-10. 3.60 gm of vacuum-distilled acrylic acid is placed in a titanium test vessel in an ARC. Estimate the phi-factor for this experiment.

Heat capacity of liquid acrylic acid:	2.27 J/gm-K
Heat capacity of titanium:	0.502 J/gm-K
Mass of titanium test vessel:	8.773 gm

8-11. Using the data and information from Examples 8-3 and 8-4, estimate the heat of reaction for the methanol + acetic anhydride system. Assume a constant heat capacity for the liquid of 2.3 J/gm K and a phi-factor of 1.04. This experiment was done in the APTAC, with 37.8 gm of methanol combined with 61.42 gm of acetic anhydride, and injected into a titanium bomb of 135 ml.

8-12. Shown below are calorimetry data from an ARC for the reaction of 50 wt. % epichlorohydrin in water. In this case there are two exotherms, one following the other. The second exotherm is most likely the decomposition of one of the products of the first reaction. Determine the following parameters for both exotherms: T_o, T_F, B, Γ, $\ln k(T_o)$, A, and E_a.

For the first exotherm, determine the reaction order. For the second exotherm, the initial concentration of reactant is not known; assume a first-order reaction and check if this fits the data.

Use the model to predict the maximum self-heat rate for both exotherms; compare to experimental results.

Calculate the phi-factor and adjust your final results.

Experimental conditions:

	Sample	Bomb
Mass (gm)	4.000	18.480
Heat capacity (J/gm-K)	3.490	0.385
Density (gm/mL)	1.07428	
Volume (mL)	3.72	9.1

Initial concentration of limiting reactant (epichlorohydrin): 0.537 gm/mL

Status	Time (min)	Temperature (°C)	Temp. rate (°C/min)	Pressure (psia)	Pressure rate (psi/min)
Exotherm 1 begin:	320.84	71.2	0.029	22.4	0.01
	382.13	73.2	0.033	22.9	0.01
	435.7	75.2	0.038	23.2	0
	481.78	77.2	0.045	23.7	0.01
	523.25	79.21	0.049	24.1	0.01
	559.84	81.21	0.057	24.7	0.01
	592.91	83.22	0.062	25.4	0.02
	621.43	85.22	0.072	26.2	0.03
	646.07	87.22	0.083	26.8	0.03
	668.31	89.24	0.091	27.6	0.03
	687.61	91.26	0.107	28.3	0.03
	704.06	93.26	0.124	29.1	0.05
	718.63	95.26	0.141	29.8	0.06
	731.88	97.27	0.155	30.6	0.08
	743.94	99.31	0.173	31.3	0.05
	754.69	101.32	0.191	32.2	0.08
	764.28	103.34	0.215	33.1	0.08
	773.03	105.34	0.233	34	0.09
	781.05	107.38	0.262	35	0.16
	787.6	109.2	0.286	35.8	0.14
	794.25	111.22	0.307	36.9	0.15
	800.36	113.24	0.34	37.9	0.17
	805.96	115.26	0.368	39	0.22
	811.01	117.31	0.412	40.2	0.24
	815.61	119.34	0.451	41.4	0.27
	819.79	121.36	0.492	42.6	0.29

(*continues*)

Status	Time (min)	Temperature (°C)	Temp. rate (°C/min)	Pressure (psia)	Pressure rate (psi/min)
	823.57	123.38	0.546	43.9	0.33
	826.68	125.21	0.609	45	0.38
	829.99	127.31	0.656	46.4	0.37
	832.94	129.34	0.701	47.9	0.56
	835.67	131.38	0.755	49.3	0.52
	838.11	133.25	0.76	50.8	0.58
	840.68	135.26	0.781	52.5	0.7
	843.36	137.31	0.75	54.4	0.74
	846.15	139.35	0.715	56.4	0.76
	849.34	141.4	0.608	58.4	0.6
	853.13	143.23	0.443	60	0.3
	866.88	145.24	0.094	60.8	0.06
Exotherm 1 end:	898.12	147.25	0.063	66	0.23
Exotherm 2 start:	926.14	149.26	0.075	76.8	0.42
	948.94	151.27	0.091	90.5	0.65
	966.87	153.27	0.119	103.5	0.74
	981.41	155.29	0.146	116.6	0.97
	993.06	157.3	0.184	128.8	1.08
	1002.74	159.31	0.216	140.3	1.24
	1010.8	161.33	0.259	151.3	1.41
	1017.58	163.34	0.306	161.8	1.56
	1023.39	165.34	0.357	171.7	1.71
	1028.41	167.37	0.412	181.3	1.94
	1032.32	169.21	0.478	189.7	2.18
	1036.12	171.23	0.564	198.8	2.46
	1039.46	173.27	0.639	207.8	2.8
	1042.3	175.28	0.731	216.4	3.19
	1044.91	177.37	0.841	225.6	3.65
	1046.92	179.21	0.964	233.7	4.24
	1048.95	181.3	1.084	242.8	4.63
	1050.65	183.33	1.228	251.8	5.54
	1052.18	185.37	1.342	260.7	5.92
	1053.39	187.22	1.627	268.9	7.06
	1054.58	189.28	1.821	277.9	7.68
	1055.65	191.4	2	287.5	8.87
	1056.51	193.25	2.17	296.6	10.85
	1057.4	195.37	2.523	307	12.38
	1058.09	197.28	2.944	316.2	13.33
	1058.68	199.21	3.222	325.7	15.93
	1059.29	201.3	3.551	337.6	22.76
	1059.86	203.4	3.655	350.1	22.41
	1060.29	205.34	4.652	361.1	25.65
	1060.69	207.35	5.142	374.4	33.81
	1061.04	209.43	5.85	387.1	35.5
	1061.34	211.4	6.75	400.6	66.25

(*continues*)

Status	Time (min)	Temperature (°C)	Temp. rate (°C/min)	Pressure (psia)	Pressure rate (psi/min)
	1061.59	213.25	7.75	412.4	49.17
	1061.83	215.29	8.833	425.2	55
	1062.06	217.4	9	439.1	60
	1062.26	219.33	9.909	453.4	73.64
	1062.46	221.35	10.3	468.3	77
	1062.64	223.39	11.5	483.6	89
	1062.8	225.33	12.625	498.6	97.5
	1062.96	227.4	13	504.9	25
	1063.1	229.2	13	532.6	135
	1063.26	231.39	14.125	553.5	135
	1063.38	233.25	15.833	561.3	20
	1063.52	235.44	16	592.6	166.67
	1063.64	237.39	15.5	606.7	58.33
	1063.76	239.4	16.833	632.2	398.33
	1063.88	241.34	16	638.8	6.67
	1064	243.4	17.833	640.4	15
	1064.12	245.44	16.666	711.9	801.67
	1064.24	247.3	15.666	746.9	225
	1064.38	249.51	16.833	750.7	46.67
	1064.5	251.52	17	768.4	11.67
	1064.62	253.39	15.333	796.2	426.67
	1064.74	255.23	15	882.5	1423.33
	1064.92	257.44	12.4	936.2	270
	1065.08	259.43	12.375	975.5	243.75
	1065.24	261.29	11.5	1012.1	230
	1065.42	263.28	10.8	1051.4	215
	1065.61	265.26	10.111	1089.1	195.56
	1065.82	267.34	9.909	1127.9	179.09
	1066.05	269.46	9.083	1166.3	161.67
	1066.25	271.22	8.777	1196	146.67
	1066.5	273.27	8	1228.1	125.83
	1066.77	275.28	7.2	1264.7	135.33
	1067.12	277.39	5.85	1311.5	131
	1067.48	279.4	5.35	1356.4	120.5
	1067.82	281.2	4.842	1399.1	125.79
	1068.26	283.22	4.888	1451.5	112.78
	1068.69	285.23	4.5	1506.6	129
	1069.19	287.37	4.076	1570.3	128.08
	1069.73	289.37	3.793	1626	93.45
	1070.31	291.25	2.971	1670.4	70.86
	1071.26	293.29	1.905	1709.7	32.45
	1072.95	295.34	0.98	1728.5	9.12
	1078.36	297.34	0.292	1778.8	8.65
Exotherm 2 end:	1090.55	299.35	0.141	1839.7	3.84

8-13. Your company is designing a reactor to run the methanol + acetic anhydride reaction. You have been assigned the task of designing the cooling coil system within the reactor. The reactor is designed to handle 10,000 kg of reacting mass. Assume a heat capacity for the liquid of 2.3 J/kg-K.

a. Using the results of Examples 8-3 and 8-4, estimate the heat load, in J/s, on the cooling coils at the maximum reaction rate. What additional capacity and other considerations are important to ensure that the cooling coils are sized properly to prevent a runaway reaction?

b. Using the results of part a, estimate the cooling water flow required, in kg/s. The cooling water is available at 30 °C with a maximum temperature limit of 50 °C.

8-14. Your company proposes to use a 10 m^3 batch reactor to react methanol + acetic anhydride in a 2:1 molar ratio. The reactor has cooling coils with a maximum cooling rate of 30 MJ/min. Since the cooling is limiting, the decision was made to operate the reactor in semi-batch mode. In this mode, the methanol is first added to the reactor, then heated to the desired temperature, and the limiting reactant, acetic anhydride, is added at a constant rate to control the heat release.

The following data are available:

Reaction: $CH_3OH + (CH_3CO)_2O \rightarrow CH_3COOCH_3 + CH_3COOH$

Methanol + acetic anhydride methyl acetate + acetic acid

Specific gravity of final liquid mixture: 0.97

Heat of reaction: 67.8 kJ/mol

Additional data are also available in Examples 8-3 and 8-4.

a. The company wants to produce this product as quickly as possible. To achieve this, at what temperature should it operate the reactor?

b. Assuming a maximum reactor fill factor of 80%, calculate the total amount of methanol, in kg, initially charged to the reactor. How much acetic anhydride, in kg, will be added?

c. What is the maximum addition rate of acetic anhydride, in kg/min, to result in a reaction heat release rate equal to the cooling capacity of the cooling coils?

d. How long, in hours, will it take to do the addition?

8-15. The data below are raw data from the ARSST. Assume a first-order reaction for this system. The heating rate for the calorimeter is 0.3 °C/min.

a. Plot the temperature rate versus −1000/T to estimate the onset and final temperatures.

b. Use Equation 8-32 to determine the kinetic parameters A and E_a for the original raw data.

Time (min)	Temperature (ºC)
0	12.0
5.1	15.0
10.1	17.1
15.2	19.3
20.2	21.4
25.3	23.4
30.3	25.3
35.4	25.7
40.4	26.6
45.5	27.6
50.6	28.9
55.6	30.4
60.7	32.4
65.7	34.8
70.7	37.6
75.8	41.0
80.8	45.0
85.9	50.0
90.9	57.1
95.1	67.1
96.16	71.1
97.25	77.1
98.25	85.6
99.2	100.7
99.53	110.3
99.63	114.5
99.75	120.2
99.87	127.0
99.93	131.2
100.01	138.4
100.06	142.5
100.13	149.3
100.21	158.0
100.3	165.5
100.39	170.1
100.48	172.6
101.2	171.9

8-16. The ARSST continues to heat the test sample during the entire exotherm. Thus, the data must be adjusted for this continuous heating. This adjustment is done by realizing that the temperature rise measured by the calorimeter, $\Delta T^{\text{Measured}}$, is composed of both the adiabatic temperature increase due to the reaction, $\Delta T_{ad}^{\text{Reac}}$, and the temperature increase due to the calorimeter heating, $\Delta T_{\text{External}}$:

$$\Delta T^{\text{Measured}} = \Delta T_{\text{ad}}^{\text{Reac}} + \Delta T_{\text{External}} \tag{8-36}$$

The temperature increase due to the calorimeter heating is given by

$$\Delta T_{\text{External}} = \left(\frac{dT}{dt}\right)_{\text{Applied}} (t_F - t_o), \tag{8-37}$$

where

$(dT/dt)_{\text{Applied}}$ is the applied heating rate, deg/time;
t_F is the time at the final temperature; and
t_o is the time at the onset temperature.

Use Equations 8-36 and 8-37 to adjust the temperatures of the raw data from Problem 8-15 for the imposed heating rate from the calorimeter. Repeat Problem 8-15 to determine the kinetic parameters with the adjusted data.

8-17. The phi-factor for the ARSST is about 1.05 (Table 8-7). Adjust the data from Problem 8-15 for the phi-factor and estimate the kinetic parameters.

8-18. Using the raw data from Problem 8-15, calculate A and E_a for each case shown below. How does each case affect the quantities calculated?

a. Reduce the time period over which the reaction occurs by one-half.
b. Keep the same times, but double the adiabatic temperature rise.
c. Comment on how these changes affect the results.

9.16 The Pyrex thermometer [illegible] the [illegible] used for [illegible] the [illegible] [illegible] [illegible]

[illegible]

[illegible] is the applied heating [illegible] [illegible] [illegible]

[illegible]

9.17 The [illegible]

[illegible]

CHAPTER 9

Introduction to Reliefs

Despite many safety precautions within chemical plants, equipment failures or operator errors can cause increases in process pressures beyond safe levels. If pressures rise too high, they may exceed the maximum strength of pipelines and vessels. This can result in rupturing of process equipment, causing major releases of toxic or flammable chemicals.

The defense against this type of accident is to prevent the accident in the first place. Inherent safety, described in Chapter 1, is the first line of defense. The second line of defense is better process control. A major effort is always directed toward controlling the process within safe operating regions. Dangerous high-pressure excursions must be prevented or minimized.

The third line of defense against excessive pressures is to install relief systems to relieve liquids or gases before excessive pressures are developed. The relief system is composed of the relief device and the associated downstream process equipment to safely handle the material ejected.

The method used for the safe installation of pressure relief devices is illustrated in Figure 9-1. The first step in the procedure is to specify where relief devices must be installed. Definitive guidelines are available. Second, the appropriate relief device type must be selected. The type depends mostly on the nature of the material relieved and the relief characteristics required. Third, scenarios are developed that describe the various ways in which a relief can occur. The motivation is to determine the material mass flow rate through the relief and the physical state of the material (liquid, vapor, or two phases). Next, data are collected on the relief process, including physical properties of the ejected material, and the relief is sized. Finally, the worst-case scenario is selected and the final relief design is achieved.

Every step in this method is critical to the development of a safe design; an error in any step of this procedure can result in catastrophic failures.

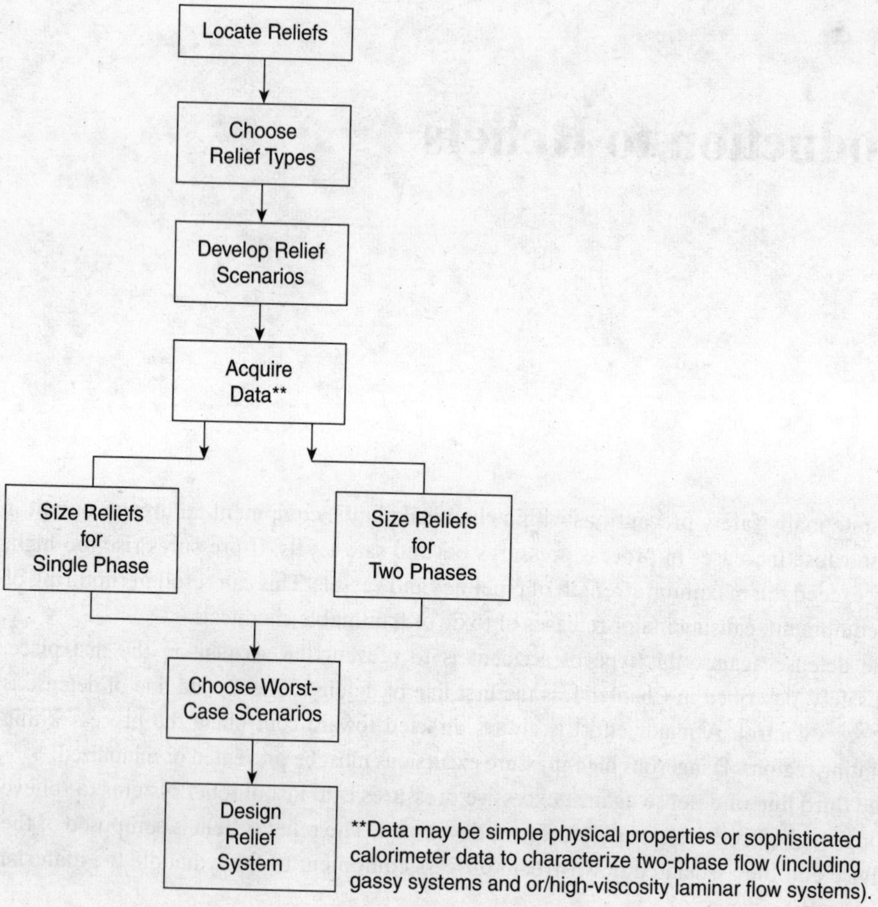

Figure 9-1 Relief method.

In this chapter we introduce relief fundamentals and the steps in the relief design procedure. Relief sizing methods are covered in Chapter 10.

9-1 Relief Concepts

Pressure relief systems are required for the following reasons:[1]

- To protect personnel from the dangers of overpressurizing equipment
- To minimize chemical losses during pressure upsets
- To prevent damage to equipment

[1] Marx Isaacs, "Pressure Relief Systems," *Chemical Engineering* (Feb. 22, 1971), pp. 113–124.

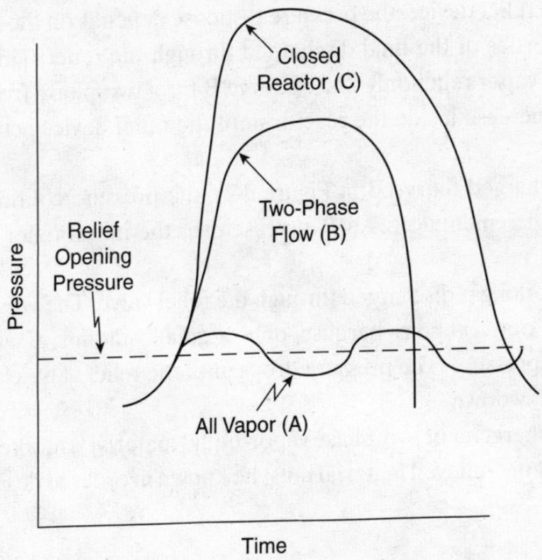

Figure 9-2 Pressure versus time for runaway reactions: (A) relieving vapor, (B) relieving froth (two-phase flow), and (C) closed reaction vessel.

- To prevent damage to adjoining property
- To reduce insurance premiums
- To comply with governmental regulations

Typical pressure versus time curves for runaway reactions are illustrated in Figure 9-2. Assume that an exothermic reaction is occurring within a reactor. If cooling is lost because of a loss of cooling water supply, failure of a valve, or other scenario, then the reactor temperature will rise. As the temperature rises, the reaction rate increases, leading to an increase in heat production. This self-accelerating mechanism results in a runaway reaction.

The pressure within the reactor increases because of increased vapor pressure of the liquid components and/or gaseous decomposition products resulting from the high temperature.

Reaction runaways for large commercial reactors can occur in minutes, with temperature and pressure increases of several hundred degrees per minute and several hundred psi per minute, respectively. For the curves in Figure 9-2 the cooling is lost at $t = 0$.

If the reactor has no relief system, the pressure and temperature continue to rise until the reactants are completely consumed, as shown by curve C (Figure 9-2). After the reactants are consumed, the heat generation stops and the reactor cools; the pressure subsequently drops. Curve C assumes that the reactor is capable of withstanding the full pressure of the runaway reaction.

If the reactor has a relief device, the pressure response depends on the relief device characteristics and the properties of the fluid discharged through the relief. This is illustrated by curve A (Figure 9-2) for vapor relief only and by curve B for a two-phase froth (vapor and liquid). The pressure will increase inside the reactor until the relief device activates at the pressure indicated.

When froth is discharged (curve B in Figure 9-2), the pressure continues to rise as the relief valve opens. The incremental pressure increase over the initial relief pressure is called overpressure.

Curve A is for vapor or gas discharged through the relief valve. The pressure drops immediately when the relief device opens because only a small amount of vapor discharge is required to decrease the pressure. The pressure drops until the relief valve closes; this pressure difference is called the blowdown.

Because the relief character of two-phase vapor-liquid material is markedly different from vapor relief, the nature of the relieved material must be known in order to design a proper relief.

9-2 Definitions[2]

Definitions that are commonly used within the chemical industry to describe reliefs are given in the following paragraphs.

Set pressure: The pressure at which the relief device begins to activate.

Maximum allowable working pressure (MAWP): The maximum gauge pressure permissible at the top of a vessel for a designated temperature. This is sometimes called the design pressure. As the operating temperature increases, the MAWP decreases because the vessel metal loses its strength at higher temperatures. Likewise, as the operating temperature decreases, the MAWP decreases because of metal embrittlement at lower temperatures. Vessel failure typically occurs at 4 or 5 times the MAWP, although vessel deformation may occur at as low as twice the MAWP.

Operating pressure: The gauge pressure during normal service, usually 10% below the MAWP.

Accumulation: The pressure increase over the MAWP of a vessel during the relief process. It is expressed as a percentage of the MAWP.

Overpressure: The pressure increase in the vessel over the set pressure during the relieving process. Overpressure is equivalent to the accumulation when the set pressure is at the MAWP. It is expressed as a percentage of the set pressure.

[2]API RP 521, *Guide for Pressure-Relieving and Depressuring Systems,* 4th ed. (Washington, DC: American Petroleum Institute, 1997), pp. 1–3.

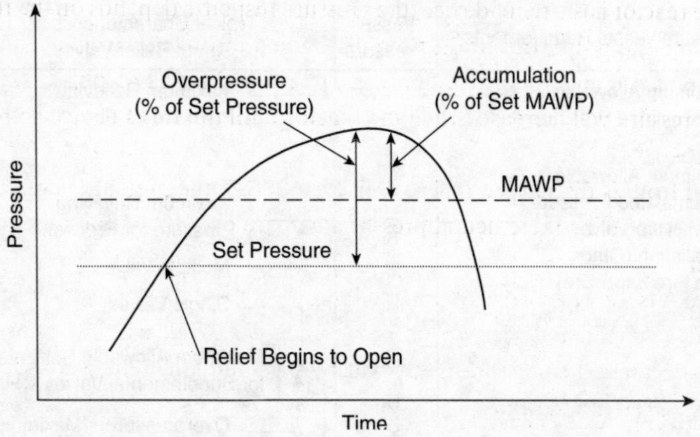

Figure 9-3 Description of overpressure and accumulation.

Backpressure: The pressure at the outlet of the relief device during the relief process resulting from pressure in the discharge system.

Blowdown: The pressure difference between the relief set pressure and the relief reseating pressure. It is expressed as a percentage of the set pressure.

Maximum allowable accumulated pressure: The sum of the MAWP and the allowable accumulation.

Relief system: The network of components around a relief device, including the pipe to the relief, the relief device, discharge pipelines, knockout drum, scrubber, flare, or other types of equipment that assist in the safe relief process.

The relationship between these terms is illustrated in Figures 9-3 and 9-4.

9-3 Location of Reliefs[3]

The procedure for specifying the location of reliefs requires the review of every unit operation in the process and of every process operating step. The engineer must anticipate the potential problems that may result in increased pressures. Pressure relief devices are installed at every point identified as potentially hazardous, that is, at points where upset conditions create pressures that may exceed the MAWP.

[3]Robert Kern, "Pressure-Relief Valves for Process Plants," *Chemical Engineering* (Feb. 28, 1977), pp. 187–194.

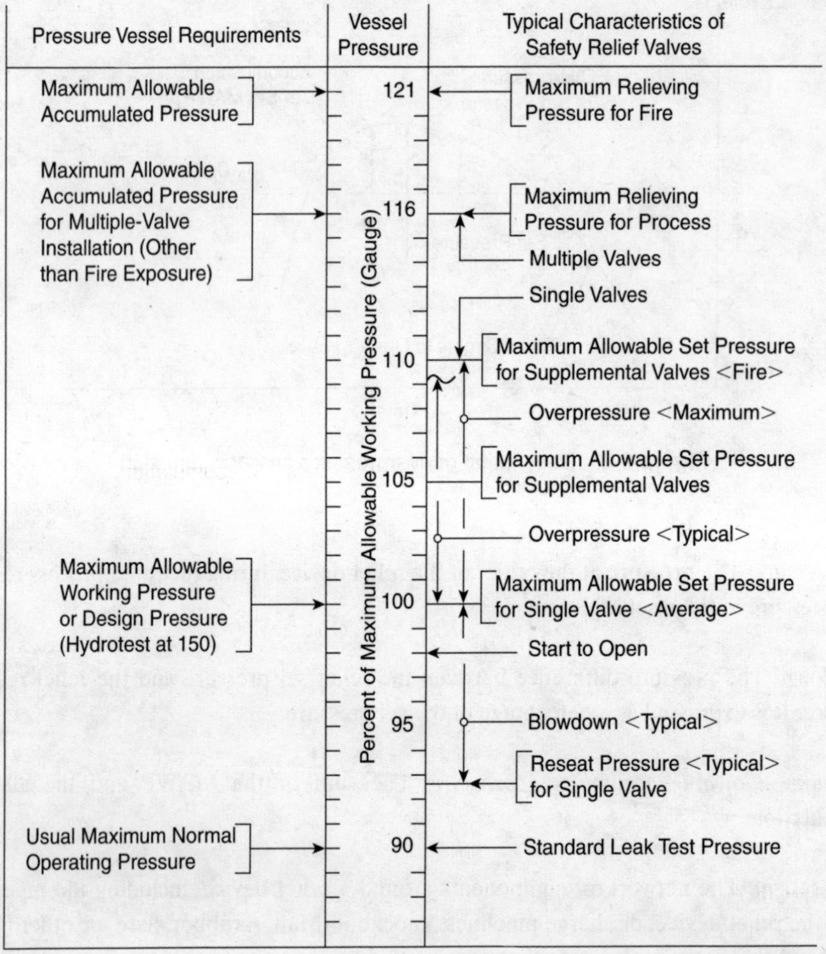

Figure 9-4 Guidelines for relief pressures. Adapted from API RP 521, *Guide for Pressure-Relieving and Depressuring Systems,* 4th ed. (Washington, DC: American Petroleum Institute, 1997), p. 30.

The types of questions asked in this review process are

- What happens with loss of cooling, heating, or agitation?
- What happens if the process is contaminated or has a mischarge of a catalyst or monomer?
- What happens if the operator makes an error?
- What is the consequence of closing valves (block valves) on vessels or in lines that are filled with liquids and exposed to heat or refrigeration?
- What happens if a line fails, for example, a failure of a high-pressure gas line into a low-pressure vessel?

Table 9-1 Guidelines for Specifying Relief Positions[a]

All vessels need reliefs, including reactors, storage tanks, towers, and drums.
Blocked-in sections of cool liquid-filled lines that are exposed to heat (such as the sun) or refrigeration need reliefs.
Positive displacement pumps, compressors, and turbines need reliefs on the discharge side.
Storage vessels need pressure and vacuum reliefs to protect against pumping in or out of a blocked-in vessel or against the generation of a vacuum by condensation.
Vessel steam jackets are often rated for low-pressure steam. Reliefs are installed in jackets to prevent excessive steam pressures due to operator error or regulator failure.

[a]Marx Isaacs, "Pressure-Relief Systems," *Chemical Engineering* (Feb. 22, 1971), pp. 113–124.

- What happens if the unit operation is engulfed in a fire?
- What conditions cause runaway reactions, and how are relief systems designed to handle the discharge as a result of runaway reactions?

Some guidelines for locating reliefs are summarized in Table 9-1.

Example 9-1

Specify the location of reliefs in the simple polymerization reactor system illustrated in Figure 9-5. The major steps in this polymerization process include (1) pumping 100 lb of initiator into reactor R-1, (2) heating to the reaction temperature of 240°F, (3) adding monomer for a period of 3 hr, and (4) stripping the residual monomer by means of a vacuum using valve V-15. Because the reaction is exothermic, cooling during monomer addition with cooling water is necessary.

Solution

The review method for specifying the location of reliefs follows. Refer to Figures 9-5 and 9-6 and Table 9-1 for relief locations.

a. Reactor (R-1): A relief is installed on this reactor because, in general, every process vessel needs a relief. This relief is labeled PSV-1 for pressure safety valve 1.

b. Positive displacement pump (P-1): Positive displacement pumps are overloaded, overheated, and damaged if they are dead-headed without a pressure-relieving device (PSV-2). This type of relief discharge is usually recycled back to the feed vessel.

c. Heat exchanger (E-1): Heat exchanger tubes can rupture from excessive pressures when water is blocked in (V-10 and V-11 are closed) and the exchanger is heated (by steam, for example). This hazard is eliminated by adding PSV-3.

d. Drum (D-1): Again, all process vessels need relief valves, PSV-4.

e. Reactor coil: This reactor coil can be pressure-ruptured when water is blocked in (V-4, V-5, V-6, and V-7 are closed) and the coil is heated with steam or even the sun. Add PSV-5 to this coil.

This completes the specification of the relief locations for this relatively simple process. The reason for the two relief devices PSV-1A and PSV-1B is described in the next section.

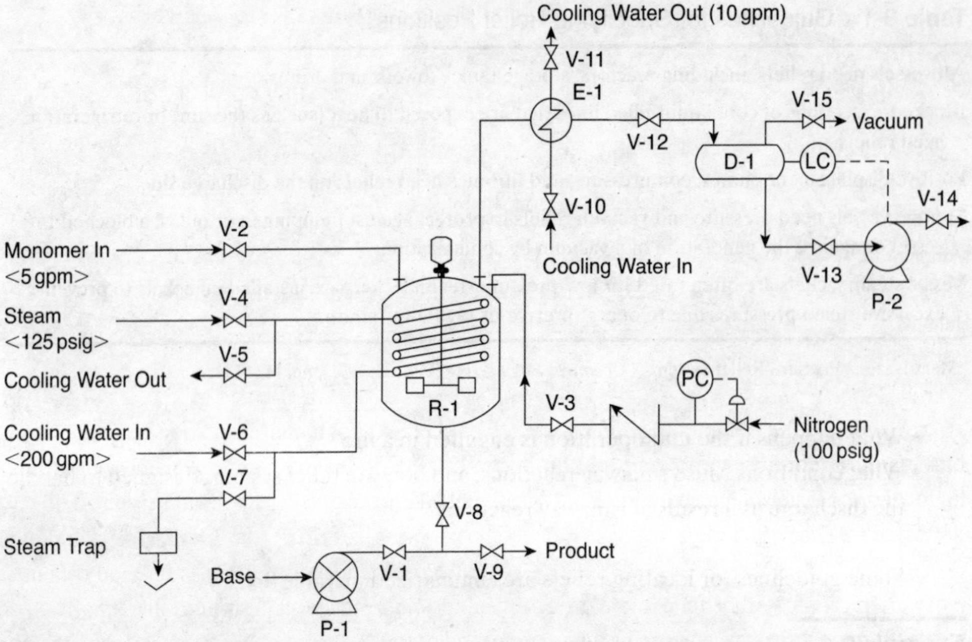

Specifications

Name	Description	Max. psig	Gpm at 50 psig
D-1	100 Gal Drum	50	—
R-1	1000 Gal Reactor	50	—
P-1	Gear Pump	100	100
P-2	Centrifugal Pump	50	20

Piping	Size
Steam and Water Lines	2 inch
Nitrogen	1 inch
Vapor Lines	0.5 inch

Figure 9-5 Polymerization reactor without safety reliefs.

Example 9-1 illustrates the engineering rationale for installing relief valves at various locations within a chemical plant. After the relief locations are specified, the type of relief is chosen, depending on the specific application.

9-4 Relief Types and Characteristics

Spring-Operated and Rupture Discs

Specific types of relief devices are chosen for specific applications, such as for liquids, gases, liquids and gases, solids, and corrosive materials; they may be vented to the atmosphere or vented

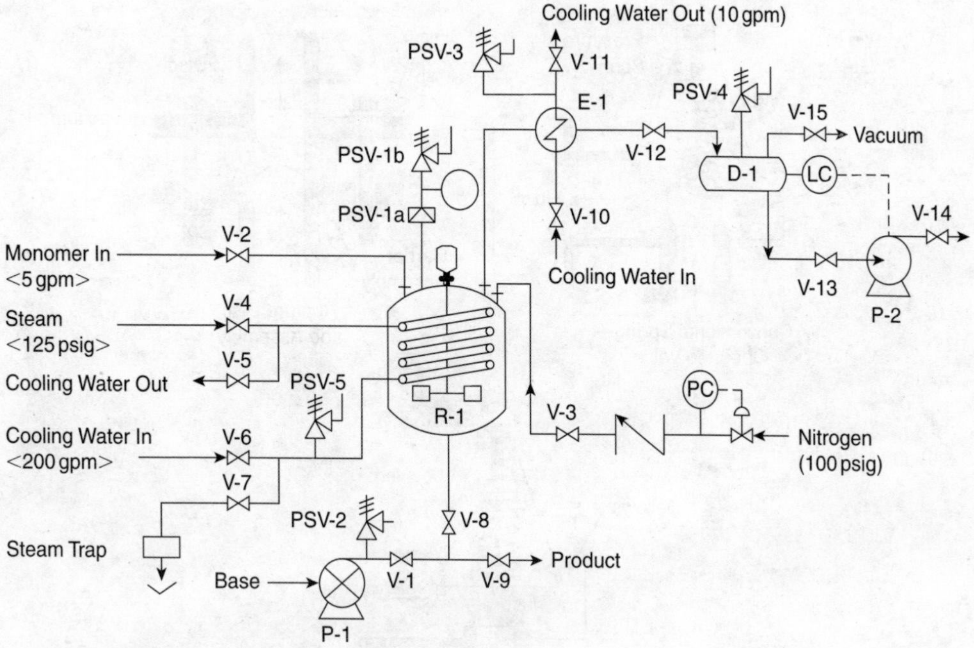

Figure 9-6 Polymerization reactor with safety reliefs.

to containment systems (scrubber, flare, condenser, incinerator, and the like). In engineering terms the type of relief device is specified on the basis of the details of the relief system, process conditions, and physical properties of the relieved fluid.

There are two general categories of relief devices (spring-operated and rupture discs) and two major types of spring-operated valves (conventional and balanced-bellows), as illustrated in Figure 9-7.

On spring-operated valves the adjustable spring tension offsets the inlet pressure. The relief set pressure is usually specified at 10% above the normal operating pressure. To avoid the possibility of an unauthorized person changing this setting, the adjustable screw is covered with a threaded cap.

For a conventional spring-operated relief, the valve opens based on the pressure drop across the valve seat; that is, the set pressure is proportional to the pressure drop across the seat. Thus, if the backpressure downstream of the valve increases, the set pressure will increase and the valve may not open at the correct pressure. In addition, the flow through the conventional relief is proportional to the difference in pressure across the seat. The flow through the relief, therefore, is reduced as the backpressure increases.

For the balanced-bellows design the bellows on the backside of the valve seat ensures that the pressure on that side of the seat is always atmospheric. Thus the balanced-bellows valve will always open at the desired set pressure. However, the flow through the balanced-bellows relief is proportional to the difference in pressure between the inlet and the outlet of the valve. Therefore the flow is reduced as the backpressure increases.

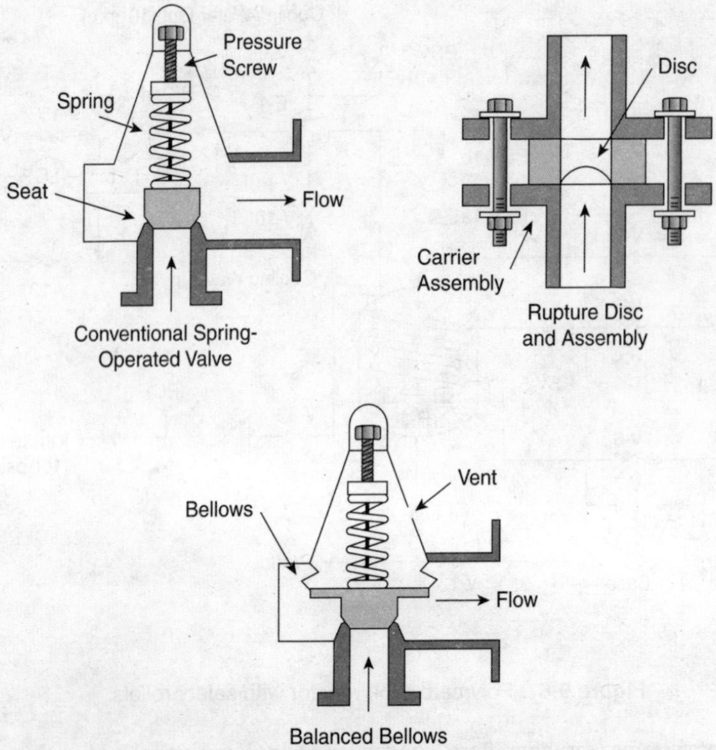

Figure 9-7 Major types of relief devices.

Rupture discs are specially designed to rupture at a specified relief set pressure. They usually consist of a calibrated sheet of metal designed to rupture at a well-specified pressure. They are used alone, in series, or in parallel to spring-loaded relief devices. They can be made from a variety of materials, including exotic corrosion-resistant materials.

An important problem with rupture discs is the flexing of the metal as process pressures change. Flexing could lead to premature failure at pressures below the set pressure. For this reason some rupture disc systems are designed to operate at pressures well below the set pressure. In addition, vacuum service may cause rupture disc failure if the relief system is not specifically designed for this service.

Another problem with rupture disc systems is that once they open, they remain open. This may lead to the complete discharge of process material. It may also allow air to enter the process, leading to a possible fire and/or explosion. In some accidents discs were ruptured without the process operator being aware of the situation. To prevent this problem, rupture discs are available with embedded wires that are cut when the disc ruptures; this can activate an alarm in the control room to alert the operator. Also, when rupture discs rupture, pieces of the disc may become dislodged, creating potential downstream plugging problems. Recent advances in rupture disc design have minimized this problem.

In all these examples the problems are eliminated if the rupture disc and system are specified and designed appropriately for the specific operating conditions of the process.

Rupture discs are available in much larger sizes than spring-operated relief valves, with commercial sizes available up to several feet in diameter. Rupture discs typically cost less than equivalently sized spring-operated relief valves.

Rupture discs are frequently installed in series to a spring-loaded relief (1) to protect an expensive spring-loaded device from a corrosive environment, (2) to give absolute isolation when handling extremely toxic chemicals (spring-loaded reliefs may weep), (3) to give absolute isolation when handling flammable gases, (4) to protect the relatively complex parts of a spring-loaded device from reactive monomers that could cause plugging, and (5) to relieve slurries that may plug spring-loaded devices.

When rupture discs are used before a spring-loaded relief, a pressure gauge is installed between the two devices. This telltale gauge is an indicator that shows when the disc ruptures. The failure can be the result of a pressure excursion or of a pinhole caused by corrosion. In either case the telltale gauge indicates that the disc needs to be replaced.

There are three subcategory types of spring-loaded pressure reliefs:

1. The *relief valve* is primarily for liquid service. The relief valve (liquid only) begins to open at the set pressure. This valve reaches full capacity when the pressure reaches 25% overpressure. The valve closes as the pressure returns to the set pressure.
2. The *safety valve* is for gas service. Safety valves pop open when the pressure exceeds the set pressure. This is accomplished by using a discharge nozzle that directs high-velocity material toward the valve seat. After blowdown of the excess pressure, the valve reseats at approximately 4% below the set pressure; the valve has a 4% blowdown.
3. The *safety relief valve* is used for liquid and gas service. Safety relief valves function as relief valves for liquids and as safety valves for gases.

Example 9-2

Specify the types of relief devices needed for the polymerization reactor in Example 9-1 (see Figure 9-6).

Solution

Each relief is reviewed in relation to the relief system and the properties of the relieved fluids:

a. PSV-1a is a rupture disc to protect PSV-1b from the reactive monomers (plugging from polymerization).

b. PSV-1b is a safety relief valve because a runaway reaction will give two-phase flow, both liquid and vapor.

c. PSV-2 is a relief valve because this relief is in a liquid service line. A conventional valve is satisfactory.

d. PSV-3 is a relief valve because it is for liquid only. A conventional relief device is satisfactory in this service.

e. PSV-4 is a safety relief valve because liquid or vapor service is possible. Because this vent will go to a scrubber with possibly large backpressures, a balanced bellows is specified.

f. PSV-5 is a relief valve for liquid service only. This relief provides protection for the following scenario: The liquid is blocked in by closing all valves; the heat of reaction increases the temperature of the surrounding reactor fluid; and pressures are increased inside the coil because of thermal expansion.

After specifying the location and type of all relief devices, the relief scenarios are developed.

Buckling-Pin Reliefs

A buckling-pin relief is similar to a rupture disc; that is, when the pressure buckles the pin, the valve opens fully. As shown in Figure 9-8, this is a relatively simple device. The major advantage of a buckling-pin relief is that the pin buckles at a precise pressure, and the major disadvantage of this device is that when the pin buckles, the valve opens and stays open.

Pilot-Operated Reliefs

The main valve of a pilot-operated relief valve is controlled by a smaller pilot valve that is a spring-operated relief valve as shown in Figure 9-9. When the pilot valve reaches the set pressure, it opens

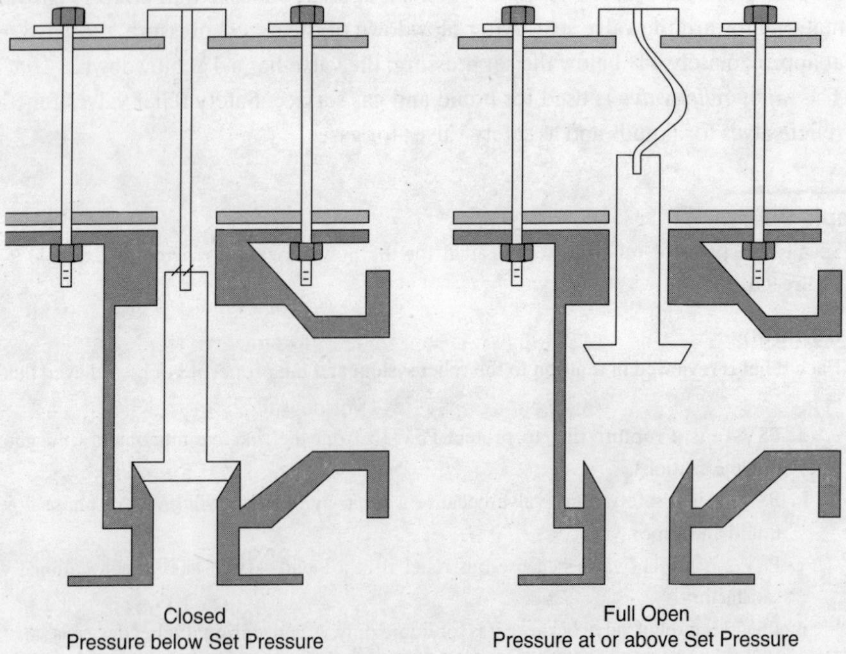

Figure 9-8 Buckling-pin relief valve.

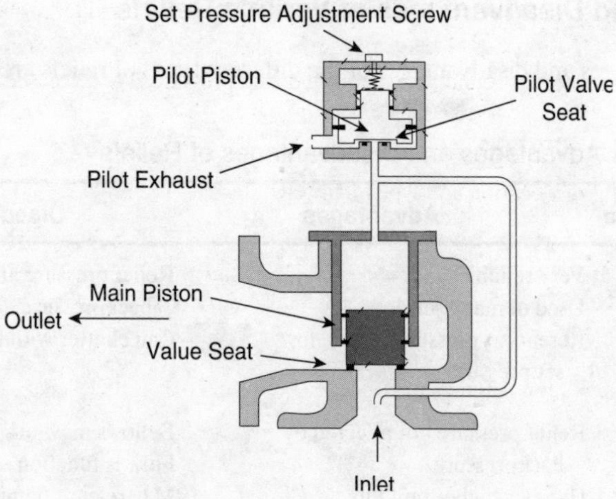

Figure 9-9 Pilot-operated relief valve.

and releases the pressure above the main valve. The large valve piston then opens and exhausts the system fluid. The pilot and main valves reseat when the inlet pressure drops below the set pressure.

Pilot-operated relief valves are commonly used when a large relieving area at high set pressures is required. The set pressure of this type of valve can be very close to the operating pressure. Pilot-operated valves are frequently chosen when operating pressures are within 5% of set pressures. The pilot valve exhausts either to the outlet of the main valve or to the atmosphere. Pilot-operated relief valves are commonly used in clean services.

Chatter

In general, relief systems must be designed appropriately to prevent unwanted and dangerous problems. Included in this design are the sizing of the relief and also the mechanical piping details. For example, if a system is not designed correctly, the valve may chatter violently. Chattering is the rapid opening and closing of a relief valve that can cause valve seat damage or the mechanical failure of the internals.

The major cause of valve chatter is an oversized relief valve. In this case the valve opens a short time to reduce the pressure and the pressure then rises rapidly to open the valve again. This pulsating action can be very destructive. The major causes of chatter are excessive inlet pressure drop, high backpressures, and oversized valves.

These problems have design solutions; for example, (1) excessive inlet pressure drops can be prevented with larger inlet pipe sizes and fewer elbows and constrictions; (2) high backpressures can be prevented by increasing the size of the exit lines and eliminating elbows and constrictions; and (3) oversized valves can be prevented by adding different-size valves to cover the range of release scenarios.

Advantages and Disadvantages of Various Reliefs

The major advantages and disadvantages of the different types of reliefs are shown in Table 9-2.

Table 9-2 Major Advantages and Disadvantages of Reliefs

Type of relief valve	Advantages	Disadvantages
Spring-operated (conventional)	Very reliable Used in many services Reseats at pressures 4% below set pressure	Relief pressure affected by backpressure Can chatter with high backpressures
Spring-operated (balanced bellows)	Relief pressure not affected by backpressure Handles higher buildup backpressures Protects spring from corrosion	Bellows may fatigue/rupture Flow is function of backpressure May release flammables/toxics to atmosphere
Rupture discs	No fugitive emissions; i.e., no seal leakage Low cost and easy to replace Good for high-volume releases Less fouling or plugging Good for second relief requiring large relief area	Stay open after relief Burst pressure can't be tested Require periodic replacement Sensitive to mechanical damage Greater problems with high temperatures Fatigue problems with pressure cycling
Buckling-pin	No fatigue problems Relief pressures are more accurate than conventional devices Set pressure is not sensitive to operating temperature Replacing pins is very easy and not expensive	Elastomer seals limit temperature to about 450°F Initial cost is greater than for rupture discs
Pilot-operated	Relief pressure is not affected by backpressure Can operate at pressures up to 98% of set pressure Seals tightly even at pressures approaching set pressure Main valve snaps fully open at low overpressures Less susceptible to chatter Chattering due to backpressure is not possible	Pilot is susceptible to plugging Limited to the chemical and temperature constraints of the seals Condensation and liquid accumulated above the main piston may cause problems Potential for backflow

9-5 Relief Scenarios

A relief scenario is a description of one specific relief event. Usually each relief has more than one relief event, and the worst-case scenario is the scenario or event that requires the largest relief vent area. Examples of relief events are

1. A pump is dead-headed; the pump relief is sized to handle the full pump capacity at its rated pressure.
2. The same pump relief is in a line with a nitrogen regulator; the relief is sized to handle the nitrogen if the regulator fails.
3. The same pump is connected to a heat exchanger with live steam; the relief is sized to handle steam injected into the exchanger under uncontrolled conditions, for example, a steam regulator failure.

This is a list of scenarios for one specific relief. The relief vent area is subsequently computed for each event (scenario) and the worst-case scenario is the event requiring the largest relief vent area. The worst cases are a subset of the overall developed scenarios for each relief.

For each specific relief all possible scenarios are identified and cataloged. This step of the relief method is extremely important: The identification of the actual worst-case scenario frequently has a more significant effect on the relief size than the accuracy of relief sizing calculations.

The scenarios developed for the reactor system described in Figure 9-6 are summarized in Table 9-3. The worst-case scenarios are identified later by means of the computed maximum relief area for each scenario and relief (see Chapter 10). In Table 9-3 only three reliefs have multiple scenarios that require the comparative calculations to establish the worst cases. The other three reliefs have only single scenarios; therefore they are the worst-case scenarios.

Table 9-3 Relief Scenarios for Example 9-2 (see Figure 9-6)

Relief identifications	Scenarios
PSV-1a and PSV-1b	(a) Vessel full of liquid and pump P-1 is accidentally actuated. (b) Cooling coil is broken and water enters at 200 gpm and 50 psig. (c) Nitrogen regulator fails, giving critical flow through 1-in line. (d) Loss of cooling during reaction (runaway).
PSV-2	V-1 is accidentally closed; system needs relief for 100 gpm at 50 psig.
PSV-3	Confined water line is heated with 125-psig steam.
PSV-4	(a) Nitrogen regulator fails, giving critical flow through 0.5-in line. (b) Note: The other R-1 scenarios will be relieved via PSV-1.
PSV-5	Water blocked inside coil, and heat of reaction causes thermal expansion.

9-6 Data for Sizing Reliefs

Physical property data and sometimes reaction rate characteristics are required for making relief sizing calculations. Data estimated using engineering assumptions are almost always acceptable when designing unit operations because the only result is poorer yields or poorer quality. In the relief design, however, these types of assumptions are not acceptable because an error may result in catastrophic and hazardous failures.

When designing reliefs for gas or dust explosions, special deflagration data for the scenario conditions are required. These data are acquired with the apparatus already described in Section 6-13.

A runaway reaction is another scenario that requires special data.

It is known that runaway reactions nearly always result in two-phase flow reliefs.[4] The two phases discharge through the relief system similar to a champagne and carbon dioxide mixture exiting a freshly opened bottle. If the champagne is heated before opening, the entire contents of the bottle may be "relieved." This result has also been verified for runaway reactions in the chemical industry.

Two-phase flow calculations are relatively complex, especially when conditions change rapidly, as in a runaway reaction scenario. As a result of this complexity, special methods have been developed for acquiring relevant data and for making the relief vent sizing calculations. See Chapter 8 for a detailed discussion of these experimental methods and Chapter 10 for the sizing calculations.

9-7 Relief Systems

After the relief type has been chosen and the relief size computed, the engineer takes the responsibility for completing the design of the relief system, including deciding how to install the relief in the system and how to dispose of the exiting liquids and vapors.

Pressure-relieving systems are unique compared with other systems within a chemical plant; ideally they will never need to operate, but when they do, they must do so flawlessly. Other systems, such as extraction and distillation systems, usually evolve to their optimum performance and reliability. This evolution requires creativity, practical knowledge, hard work, time, and the cooperative efforts of the plant, design, and process engineers. This same effort and creativity are essential when developing relief systems; however, in this case the relief system development must be optimally designed and demonstrated within a research environment before the plant startup.

To develop the necessary optimum and reliable relief systems, it is essential to understand this technology. The objective of this section is to give students and design engineers the details necessary for understanding relief systems.

[4]Harold G. Fisher, "DIERS Research Program on Emergency Relief Systems," *Chemical Engineering Progress* (Aug. 1985), pp. 33–36.

Relief Installation Practices

Regardless of how carefully the relief is sized, specified, and tested, a poor installation can result in completely unsatisfactory relief performance. Some installation guidelines are illustrated in Figure 9-10. During field construction, sometimes expediency or construction convenience leads to modifications and deviations from acceptable practice. The engineer must take the responsibility for adhering to standard practices, especially when installing relief systems.

System	Recommendations
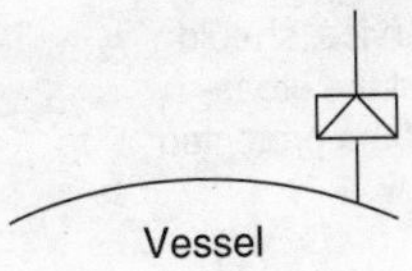	• Rupture disc in corrosive service. • Or for highly toxic materials where spring-loaded valve may weep.
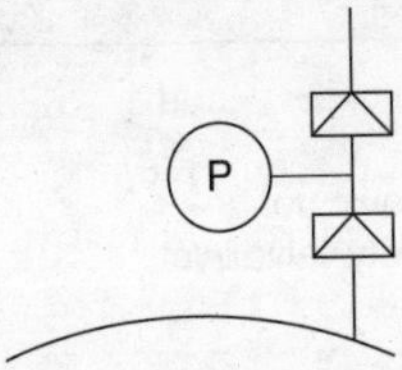	• Two rupture discs in extremely corrosive service. The 1st may periodically need to be replaced.
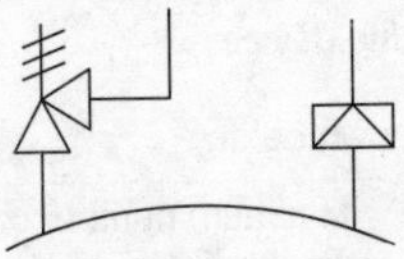	• Rupture disc and spring-loaded relief. Normal relief may go through spring-loaded device, and rupture disc is backup for larger reliefs.
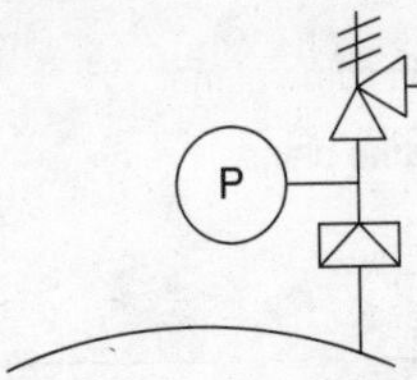	• Two reliefs in series. The rupture disc protects against toxicity and corrosion. The spring-loaded relief closes and minimizes losses.
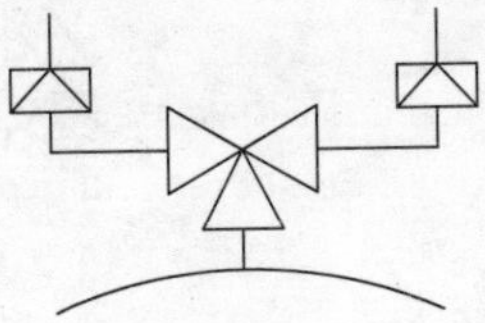	• Two rupture discs with special valve which keeps one valve always directly connected to vessel. This type of design is good for polymerization reactors where periodic cleaning is necessary.

Figure 9-10 Relief installation practices. Adapted from Eric Jennett, "Components of Pressure-Relieving Systems," *Chemical Engineering* (Aug. 19, 1963), pp. 151–158. (*continues*)

<table>
<tr><th>System</th><th>Recommendations</th></tr>
<tr><td>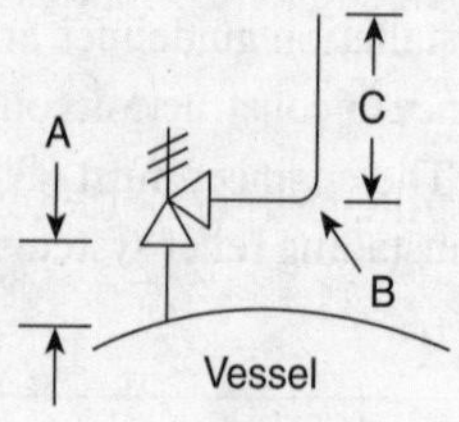</td><td>A. Pressure drop not more than 3% of set pressure

B. Long radius elbow

C. If distance is greater than 10 feet, weight and reaction forces should be supported below the long radius elbow.</td></tr>
<tr><td>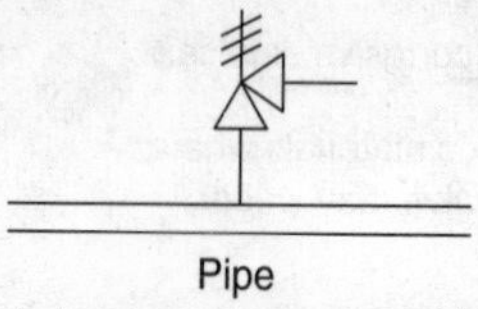</td><td>• Orifice area of a single safety relief in vapor service, should not exceed 2% of the cross-sectional area of the protected line.

• Multiple values with staggered settings may be required.</td></tr>
<tr><td>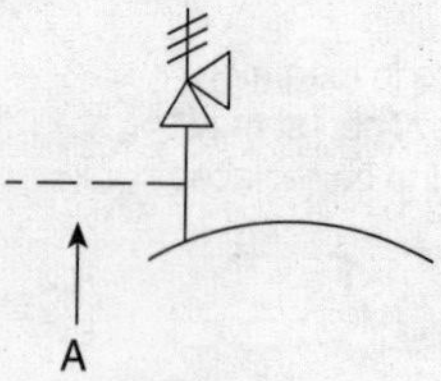</td><td>A. Process lines should not be connected to safety valve inlet piping.</td></tr>
<tr><td>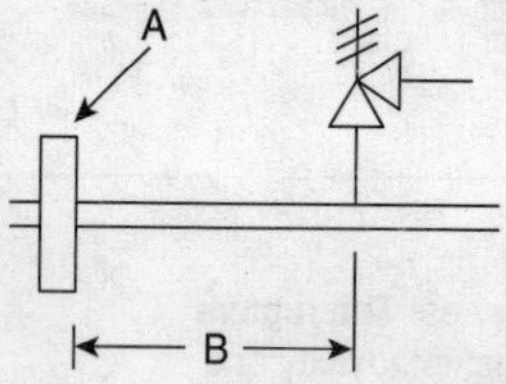</td><td>A. Turbulence-causing device

B. Dimension (B) shown below:<table>
<tr><th>Device causing turbulence</th><th>Minimum number of straight pipe diameters</th></tr>
<tr><td>Regulator or valve:</td><td>25</td></tr>
<tr><td>2 ells or bends not in same plane:</td><td>20</td></tr>
<tr><td>2 ells or bends in same plane:</td><td>15</td></tr>
<tr><td>1 ell or bend:</td><td>10</td></tr>
<tr><td>Pulsation damper:</td><td>10</td></tr>
</table></td></tr>
</table>

Figure 9-10 (*continued*)

Relief Design Considerations

A designer of relief systems must be familiar with governmental codes, industrial standards, and insurance requirements. This is particularly important because local government standards may vary. Codes of particular interest are published by the American Society of Mechanical Engineers, the American Petroleum Institute, and the National Board of Fire Underwriters. Specific references have already been cited. It is recommended that relief designers carefully consider all codes and, where feasible, select the one that is most suited to the particular installation.

Another important consideration is the reaction forces generated when the relieved materials flow through the relief system at high speed. The API RP 520[7] has some guidelines; however, normal stress analysis is the recommended method.

It is also important to recognize that company philosophy and the regulatory authorities have a significant influence on the design of the final disposal system, primarily from the standpoint of pollution. For this reason reliefs are now rarely vented to the atmosphere. In most cases a relief is first discharged to a knockout system to separate the liquid from the vapor; here the liquid is collected and the vapor is discharged to another treatment unit. This subsequent vapor treatment unit depends on the hazards of the vapor; it may include a condenser, scrubber, incinerator, flare, or a combination of them. This type of system is called a total containment system; one is illustrated in Figure 9-11. Total containment systems are commonly used, and they are becoming an industrial standard.

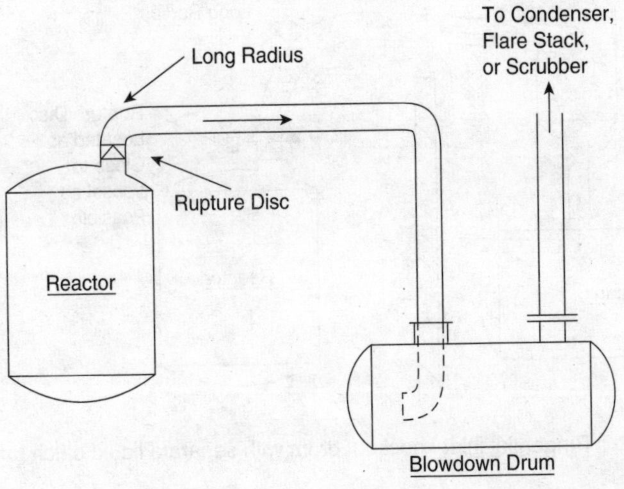

Figure 9-11 Relief containment system with blowdown drum. The blowdown drum separates the vapor from the liquid.

[7] API 520, *Sizing, Selection, and Installation of Pressure-Relieving Devices in Refineries, pt. 2, Installation*, 4th ed. (Washington, DC: American Petroleum Institute, 1994).

Horizontal Knockout Drum

Knockout drums are sometimes called catch tanks or blowdown drums. As illustrated in Figure 9-11, this horizontal knockout drum system serves as a vapor-liquid separator as well as a hold-up vessel for the disengaged liquid. The two-phase mixture usually enters at one end, and the vapor leaves at the opposite end. Inlets may be provided at each end, with a vapor exit in the center to minimize vapor velocities. When space within a plant is limited, a tangential knockout drum is used, as shown in Figure 9-12.

The design method for sizing this type of system was published by Grossel[8] and in API 521.[9] The method is based on the maximum allowable velocity for minimizing liquid entrainment. The dropout velocity of a particle in a stream is

$$u_d = 1.15\sqrt{\frac{g d_p(\rho_L - \rho_V)}{\rho_V C}}, \tag{9-1}$$

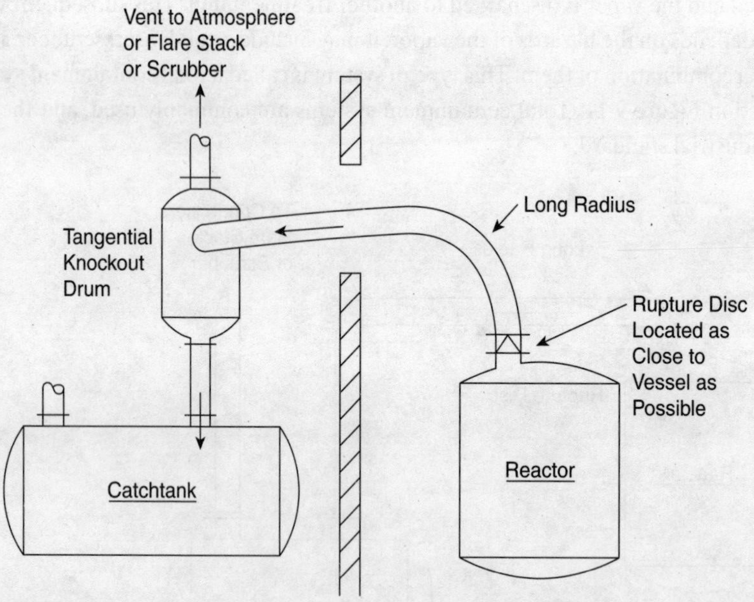

Figure 9-12 Tangential inlet knockout drum with separate liquid catch tank.

[8]S. S. Grossel, "Design and Sizing of Knockout Drums/Catchtanks for Reactor Emergency Relief Systems," *Plant/Operations Progress* (July 1986).

[9]API RP 521, *Guide for Pressure-Relieving and Depressurizing Systems,* 4th ed. (Washington, DC: American Petroleum Institute, 1997), pp. 63–67.

where

u_d is the dropout velocity,
g is the acceleration due to gravity,
d_p is the particle diameter,
ρ_L is the liquid density,
ρ_V is the vapor density, and
C is the drag coefficient given by Figure 9-13.

The abscissa of Figure 9-13 is

$$C(Re)^2 = \left[0.95 \times 10^8 \frac{\text{centipoise}^2}{\left(\frac{\text{lb}}{\text{ft}^3}\right)^2 \text{ft}^3} \right] \frac{\rho_V d_p^3(\rho_L - \rho_V)}{\mu_V^2}, \tag{9-2}$$

where

μ_V is the vapor viscosity in centipoise and
$C(Re)^2$ is unitless.

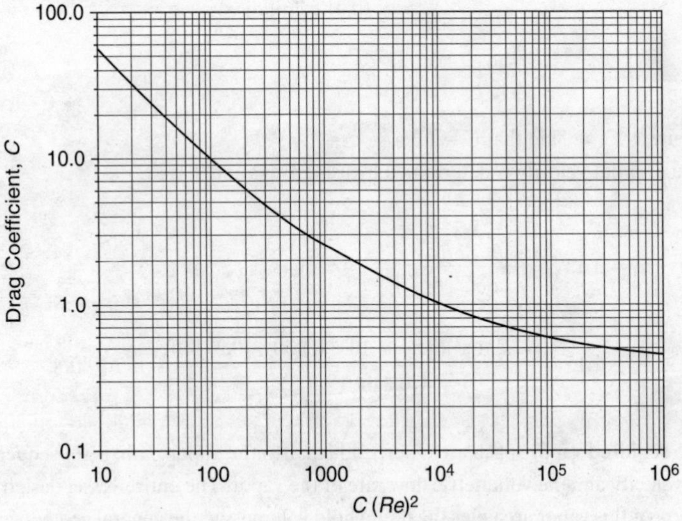

Figure 9-13 Drag coefficient correlation. Data from API RP 521, *Guide for Pressure-Relieving and Depressurizing Systems*, 2nd ed. (Washington, DC: American Petroleum Institute, 1982).

Example 9-3

Determine the maximum vapor velocity in a horizontal knockout drum to dropout liquid particles with particle diameters of 300 μm, where

Vapor rate = 170 lb/hr,
$\rho_V = 0.20\ \text{lb/ft}^3$,
$\rho_L = 30\ \text{lb/ft}^3$,
$\mu_V = 0.01$ centipoise, and
$d_p = 300\ \mu\text{m} = 9.84 \times 10^{-4}$ ft.

Solution

To determine the dropout velocity, the drag coefficient is first determined, using Figure 9-13. The graph abscissa is computed using Equation 9-2:

$$C(Re)^2 = \left[0.95 \times 10^8 \frac{\text{centipoise}^2}{\left(\frac{\text{lb}}{\text{ft}^3}\right)^2 \text{ft}^3} \right] \frac{\rho_V d_p^3 (\rho_L - \rho_V)}{\mu_V^2}$$

$$= \left[0.95 \times 10^8 \frac{\text{centipoise}^2}{\left(\frac{\text{lb}_m}{\text{ft}^3}\right)^2 \text{ft}^3} \right]$$

$$\times \frac{(0.2\ \text{lb}_m/\text{ft}^3)(9.84 \times 10^{-4}\ \text{ft})^3 (30 - 0.2)\ \text{lb}_m/\text{ft}^3}{(0.01\ \text{centipoise})^2}$$

$$= 5394.$$

Using Figure 9-13, we find that $C = 1.3$.

The dropout velocity is determined by using Equation 9-1:

$$u_d = 1.15 \sqrt{\frac{g d_p (\rho_L - \rho_V)}{\rho_V C}}$$

$$= 1.15 \sqrt{\frac{(32.2\ \text{ft/s}^2)(9.84 \times 10^{-4}\ \text{ft})(30 - 0.2)\ \text{lb/ft}^3}{(0.2\ \text{lb/ft}^3)(1.3)}} = 2.19\ \text{ft/s}.$$

The required vapor space area, perpendicular to the vapor path, is subsequently computed using the velocity and the volumetric flow rate of the vapor. The entire vessel design is determined as a function of this vapor area plus the liquid hold volume and the general geometric configuration of the vessel.

Flares[10]

Flares are sometimes used after knockout drums. The objective of a flare is to burn the combustible or toxic gas to produce combustion products that are neither toxic nor combustible. The diameter of the flare must be suitable to maintain a stable flame and to prevent a blowout (when vapor velocities are greater than 20% of the sonic velocity).

The height of a flare is fixed on the basis of the heat generated and the resulting potential damage to equipment and humans. The usual design criterion is that the heat intensity at the base of the stack is not to exceed 1500 Btu/hr/ft^2. The effects of thermal radiation are shown in the following table:

Heat intensity (Btu/hr/ft^2)	Effect
2000	Blisters in 20 s
5300	Blisters in 5 s
3000–4000	Vegetation and wood are ignited
350	Solar radiation

Using the fundamentals of radiation, we know that the heat intensity q at a specific point is a function of the heat generated by the flame Q_f, the emissivity ε, and the distance R from the flame:

$$q = \frac{\varepsilon Q_f}{4\pi R^2}. \tag{9-3}$$

Assuming a flame height of $120d_f$, an emissivity $\varepsilon = 0.048\sqrt{M}$, and a heating value of 20,000 Btu/lb, Equation 9-3 can be algebraically modified to give the flare height H_f (in ft) as a function of the flare stack diameter d_f (in ft) and the desired heat intensity q_f (in Btu/hr/ft^2) at a distance X_f from the base of the flare (in ft) for a burning fuel with a molecular weight M and a vapor rate Q_m (in lb/hr):

$$H_f = -60d_f + 0.5\sqrt{(120d_f)^2 - \left(\frac{4\pi q_f X_f^2 - 960Q_m\sqrt{M}}{\pi q_f}\right)}. \tag{9-4}$$

Example 9-4

Determine the stack height required to give a heat intensity of 1500 Btu/hr/ft^2 at a distance of 410 ft from the base of the flare. The flare diameter is 4 ft, the flare load is 970,000 lb/hr, and the molecular weight of the vapor is 44.

[10]Soen H. Tan, "Flare System Design Simplified," *Hydrocarbon Processing* (Jan. 1967).

Solution

The flare height is computed using Equation 9-4. The units are consistent with those required:

$$H_f = -60d_f + 0.5\sqrt{(120d_f)^2 - \left(\frac{4\pi q_f X_f^2 - 960Q_m\sqrt{M}}{\pi q_f}\right)}$$

$$= -(60)(4) + 0.5\sqrt{[(120)(4)]^2 - \left[\frac{(4)(3.14)(1500)(410)^2 - (960)(970{,}000)\sqrt{44}}{(3.14)(1{,}500)}\right]}$$

$$= 226 \text{ ft.}$$

Scrubbers

The fluid from reliefs, sometimes two-phase flow, must first go to a knockout system, where the liquids and vapors are separated. Liquids are subsequently collected and the vapors may or may not be vented. If the vapors are nontoxic and nonflammable, they may be vented unless some regulation prohibits this type of discharge.

If the vapors are toxic, a flare (described previously) or a scrubber system may be required. Scrubber systems can be packed columns, plate columns, or venturi-type systems. Details of scrubber designs are covered by Treybal.[11]

Condensers

A simple condenser is another possible alternative for treating exiting vapors. This alternative is particularly attractive if the vapors have a relatively high boiling point and if the recovered condensate is valuable. This alternative should always be evaluated because it is simple and usually less expensive and because it minimizes the volume of material that may need additional post-treatment. The design of condenser systems is covered by Kern.[12]

Suggested Reading

General Articles on Relief Valves and Systems

Floyd E. Anderson, "Pressure Relieving Devices," in *Safe and Efficient Plant Operations and Maintenance,* Richard Greene, ed. (New York: McGraw-Hill, 1980), p. 207.

G. W. Boicourt, "Emergency Relief System (ERS) Design: An Integrated Approach Using DIERS Methodology," *Process Safety Progress* (Apr. 1995), pp. 93–106.

R. Darby, *Emergency Relief System Design* (New York: American Institute of Chemical Engineers, 1997).

[11] R. E. Treybal, *Mass Transfer Operations,* 3rd ed. (New York: McGraw-Hill, 1958).

[12] D. Q. Kern, *Process Heat Transfer* (New York: McGraw-Hill, 1950).

Ron Darby, "Relief Vent Sizing for Deflagrations," *Process Safety Progress* (June 2006), 25(2): 130–134.

S. S. Grossel and J. F. Louvar, *Design for Overpressure and Underpressure Protection* (New York: American Institute of Chemical Engineers, 2000).

Marx Isaacs, "Pressure-Relief Systems," *Chemical Engineering* (Feb. 22, 1971), p. 113.

Robert Kern, "Pressure-Relief Valves for Process Plants," *Chemical Engineering* (Feb. 28, 1977), p. 187.

J. C. Leung, "Simplified Vent Sizing Equations for Emergency Relief Requirements in Reactors and Storage Vessels," *AICHE Journal* (Oct. 1986), pp. 1622–1634.

J. C. Leung, H. K. Fauske, and H. G. Fisher, "Thermal Runaway Reactions in a Low Thermal Inertia Apparatus," *Thermochimica Acta* (1986), 104: 13–29.

G. A. Melhem, "Relief System's Last Line of Defense, Only Line of Defense?" *Process Safety Progress* (Dec. 2006), 25(4): 290–297.

Stanley A. Urbanik, "Evaluating Relief Valve Reliability When Extending the Test and Maintenance Interval," *Process Safety Progress* (Sept. 2004), 23(3): 191–196.

Problems

9-1. Can gate valves be placed between a vessel relief and its vessel?

9-2. Describe the process of creating a vacuum in a storage vessel as a result of condensation. Develop an example to illustrate the potential magnitude of the vacuum.

9-3. Give four examples of situations requiring a combination of spring-operated reliefs in series with rupture discs.

9-4. PSV-2 of Figure 9-6 is a relief to protect the positive displacement pump P-1. If the fluid being handled is extremely volatile and flammable, what design modifications would you make to this relief system?

9-5. One defense against runaway reactions is better process control. Using the system illustrated in Figure 9-6, what control features (safeguards) would you add to this reactor system?

9-6. If a scrubber is installed after PSV-1b and it has a pressure drop of 30 psig, how would this affect the size (qualitatively) of this relief system?

9-7. Referring to Problem 9-6, qualitatively describe the algorithm you would use to compute the relief size for this system.

9-8. Review Figure 9-14, and determine the locations for relief devices.

9-9. Review Figure 9-14 and Problem 9-8 to determine what types of relief devices should be used at each location.

9-10. Review Figure 9-14 and Problems 9-8 and 9-9, and make recommendations for total containment systems.

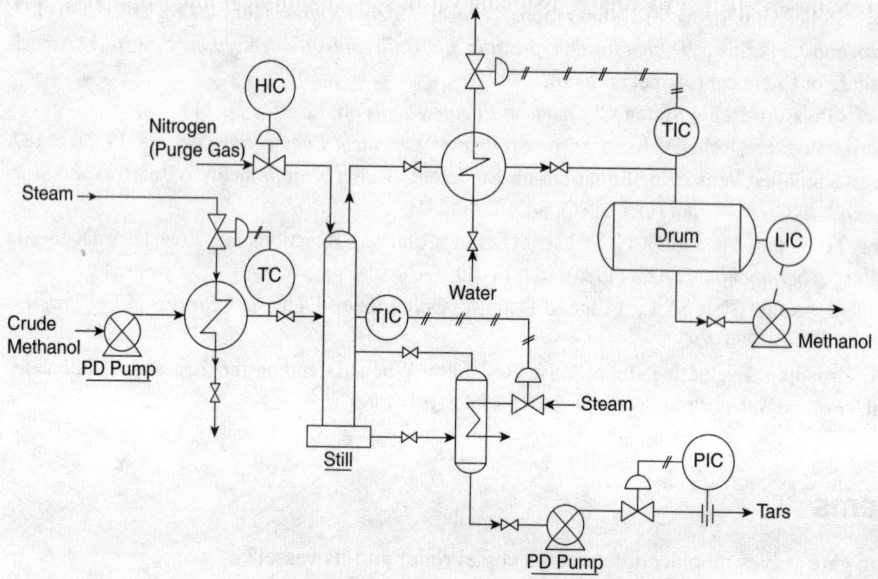

Figure 9-14 Distillation system.

9-11. Develop sketches of reactor vent systems for the following four cases:

	Case a	Case b	Case c	Case d
Reactor relief is vapor only	x			x
Reactor relief is two-phase flow		x	x	
Reactor contents are corrosive		x		x
Reactor contents are plugging type		x		
Relieved vapors are toxic	x			x
Relieved vapors are high boilers	x	x		
Vapors are low boilers			x	x

9-12. Determine the vapor velocity inside a horizontal knockout drum for the following three systems:

	System a	System b	System c
ρ_V (lb/ft^3)	0.03	0.04	0.05
ρ_L (lb/ft^3)	64.0	64.5	50.0
Vapor viscosity (centipoise)	0.01	0.02	0.01
Particle diameter (μm)	300	400	350

9-13. Determine the height of a flare, assuming various maximum heat intensities at ground level at the specified distances from the flare, for the following three cases:

	Case a	Case b	Case c
Vapor flow (lb/hr)	60,000	70,000	80,000
Molecular weight	30	60	80
Heat intensity (Btu/hr/ft^2)	2,000	3,000	4,000
Distance from base (ft)	5	10	50
Stack diameter (ft)	2	3	5

9-14. Describe a runaway that is a "hybrid." See Grossel and Louvar (2000).

9-15. When using a rupture disc followed by a spring-operated relief, it is important to periodically check the pressure gauge to be sure that there is no pinhole leak in the rupture disc. Describe several methods to satisfy this requirement.

9-16. Identify the problems with the relief valve configurations shown in Figure 9-16.

9-17. When designing the inlet piping to a relief valve, what pressure losses are recommended? See API 520, *Sizing, Selection, and Installation* (1994).

9-18. Describe a runaway that is "gassy." See Grossel and Louvar (2000).

9-19. The outlet piping of a relief system is normally supported to resist two mechanical stresses. What are these two stresses? See API 520, *Sizing, Selection, and Installation* (1994).

9-20. Describe a runaway reaction scenario that is the result of a sleeper reaction. See Grossel and Louvar (2000).

9-21. Describe a tempered runaway reaction. See Grossel and Louvar (2000).

9-22. Sometimes isolation valves are needed between the vessel and the relief. What management system is recommended for isolation valves? See API 520, *Sizing, Selection, and Installation* (1994).

CHAPTER 10

Relief Sizing

Relief sizing calculations are performed to determine the vent area of the relief device. The relief sizing calculation procedure involves, first, using an appropriate source model to determine the rate of material release through the relief device (see Chapter 4) and, second, using an appropriate equation based on fundamental hydrodynamic principles to determine the relief device vent area.

The relief vent area calculation depends on the type of flow (liquid, vapor, or two-phase) and the type of relief device (spring or rupture disc).

In Chapter 9 we showed that for liquids and two-phase relief, the relieving process begins at the relief set pressure with the pressure normally continuing to rise past the set pressure (see curve B in Figure 9-2). These overpressures frequently exceed the set pressure by 25% or more. A relief device designed to maintain the pressure at the set pressure could require an excessively large vent area. As shown in Figure 10-1, the relief vent area is reduced substantially as the overpressure increases. This is one example that illustrates this typical result. The optimal vent area for a particular relief depends on the specific application. The overpressure specification is part of the relief design. Normally, relief devices are specified for overpressures from 10% to 25%, depending on the requirements of the equipment protected and the type of material relieved.

Spring relief devices require 25–30% of maximum flow capacity to maintain the valve seat in the open position. Lower flows result in "chattering," caused by rapid opening and closing of the valve disc. This can lead to destruction of the relief device and a dangerous situation. A relief device with an area that is too large for the required flow may chatter. For this reason reliefs must be designed with the proper vent area, neither too small nor too large.

Experimental data at the actual relief conditions are recommended for sizing relief vents for runaway reaction scenarios. See Chapter 8 for details. As always, manufacturers' technical specifications are used for selection, purchase, and installation.

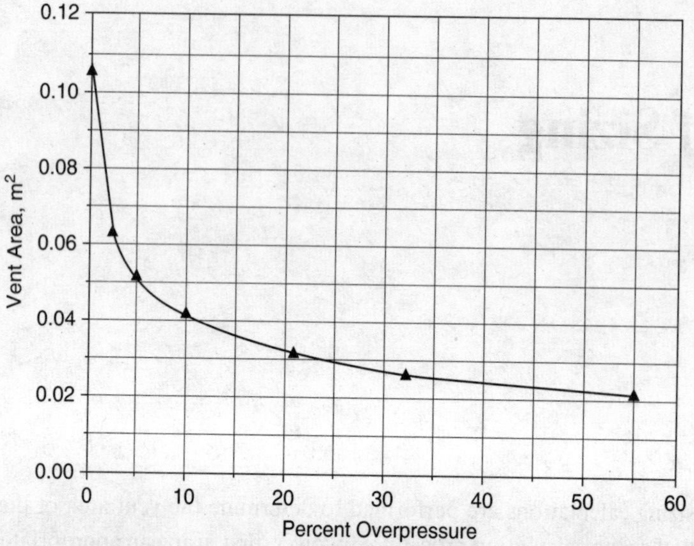

Figure 10-1 Required vent area as a function of overpressure for two-phase flow. The vent area is decreased appreciably as the overpressure increases. Data from J. C. Leung, "Simplified Vent Sizing Equations for Emergency Relief Requirements in Reactors and Storage Vessels," *AIChE Journal* (1986), 32(10).

In this chapter we present methods for calculating the relief device vent areas for the following configurations:

- Conventional spring-operated reliefs in liquid or vapor-gas service
- Rupture discs in liquid or vapor-gas service
- Two-phase flow during runaway reactor relief
- Reliefs for dust and vapor explosions
- Reliefs for fires external to process vessels
- Reliefs for thermal expansion of process fluids

10-1 Conventional Spring-Operated Reliefs in Liquid Service

Flow through spring-type reliefs is approximated as flow through an orifice. An equation representing this flow is derived from the mechanical energy balance (Equation 4-1). The result is similiar to Equation 4-6, except that the pressure is represented by a pressure difference across the spring relief:

$$\overline{u} = C_o \sqrt{\frac{2g_c \Delta P}{\rho}}, \tag{10-1}$$

where

$\bar{u}$ is the liquid velocity through the spring relief,
C_o is the discharge coefficient,
ΔP is the pressure drop across the relief, and
ρ is the liquid density.

The volumetric flow Q_v of liquid is the product of the velocity times the area, or $\bar{u}A$. Substituting Equation 10-1 and solving for the vent area A of the relief, we obtain

$$A = \frac{Q_v}{C_o\sqrt{2g_c}}\sqrt{\frac{\rho}{\Delta P}}. \tag{10-2}$$

A working equation with fixed units is derived from Equation 10-2 by (1) replacing the density ρ with the specific gravity (ρ/ρ_{ref}) and (2) making the appropriate substitutions for the unit conversions. The result is

$$\boxed{A = \left[\frac{\text{in}^2(\text{psi})^{1/2}}{38.0\text{ gpm}}\right]\frac{Q_v}{C_o}\sqrt{\frac{(\rho/\rho_{ref})}{\Delta P}},} \tag{10-3}$$

where

A is the computed relief area (in^2),
Q_v is the volumetric flow through the relief (gpm),
C_o is the discharge coefficient (unitless),
(ρ/ρ_{ref}) is the specific gravity of the liquid (unitless), and
ΔP is the pressure drop across the spring relief (lb$_f$/in^2).

In reality, flow through a spring-type relief is different from flow through an orifice. As the pressure increases, the relief spring is compressed, increasing the discharge area and increasing the flow. A true orifice has a fixed area. Also, Equation 10-3 does not consider the viscosity of the fluid. Many process fluids have high viscosities. The relief vent area must increase as the fluid viscosity increases. Finally, Equation 10-3 does not consider the special case of a balanced-bellows-type relief.

Equation 10-3 has been modified by the American Petroleum Institute to include corrections for the above situations. The result[1] is

$$\boxed{A = \left[\frac{\text{in}^2(\text{psi})^{1/2}}{38.0\text{ gpm}}\right]\frac{Q_v}{C_oK_vK_pK_b}\sqrt{\frac{(\rho/\rho_{ref})}{1.25P_s - P_b}},} \tag{10-4}$$

[1] API RP 520, *Recommended Practice for the Sizing, Selection, and Installation of Pressure-Relieving Systems in Refineries,* 6th ed. (Washington, DC: American Petroleum Institute, 1993).

where

A is the computed relief area (in^2),
Q_v is the volumetric flow through the relief (gpm),
C_o is the discharge coefficient (unitless),
K_v is the viscosity correction (unitless),
K_p is the overpressure correction (unitless),
K_b is the backpressure correction (unitless),
(ρ/ρ_{ref}) is the specific gravity of the liquid (unitless),
P_s is the gauge set pressure (lb_f/in^2), and
P_b is the gauge backpressure (lb_f/in^2).

Note that the ΔP term in Equation 10-3 has been replaced by a term involving the difference between the set pressure and the backpressure. Equation 10-3 appears to assume a maximum pressure equal to 1.25 times the set pressure. Discharge at other maximum pressures is accounted for in the overpressure correction term K_b.

C_o is the discharge coefficient. Specific guidelines for the selection of an appropriate value are given in Chapter 4, Section 4-2. If this value is uncertain, a conservative value of 0.61 is used to maximize the relief vent area.

The viscosity correction K_v corrects for the additional frictional losses resulting from flow of high-viscosity material through the valve. This correction is given in Figure 10-2. The required relief vent area becomes larger as the viscosity of the liquid increases (lower Reynolds numbers). Because the Reynolds number is required to determine the viscosity correction and because the vent area is required to calculate the Reynolds number, the procedure is iterative. For most reliefs the Reynolds number is greater than 5000 and the correction is near 1. This assumption is frequently used as an initial estimate to begin the calculations.

Darby and Molavi[2] developed an equation to represent the viscosity correction factor shown in Figure 10-2. This equation applies only to Reynolds numbers greater than 100:

$$K_v = 0.975\sqrt{\frac{1}{\dfrac{170}{Re} + 0.98}}, \qquad (10\text{-}5)$$

where

K_v is the viscosity correction factor (unitless) and
Re is the Reynolds number (unitless).

The overpressure correction K_p includes the effect of discharge pressures greater than the set pressure. This correction is given in Figure 10-3. The overpressure correction K_p is a

[2] R. Darby and K. Molavi, "Viscosity Correction Factor for Safety Relief Valves," *Process Safety Progress* (1997), 16(2).

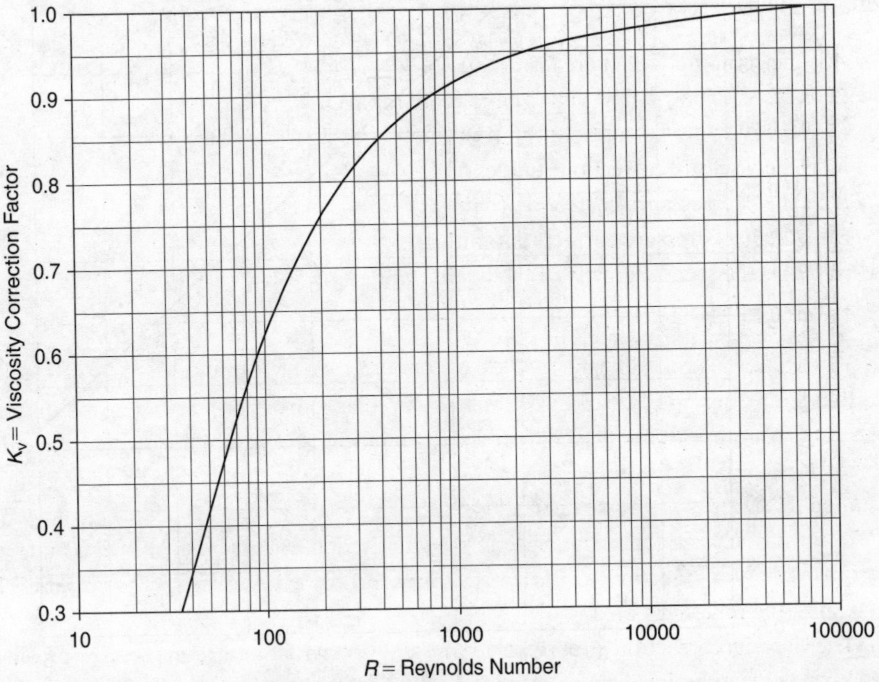

Figure 10-2 Viscosity correction factor K_v for **conventional and balanced bellows reliefs** in liquid service. This is drawn using equation $\ln K_v = 0.08547 - 0.9541/\ln R - 35.571/R$ using data from API RP 520, *Recommended Practice for the Sizing, Selection, and Installation of Pressure-Relieving Systems in Refineries*, 7th ed. (2000), p. 54.

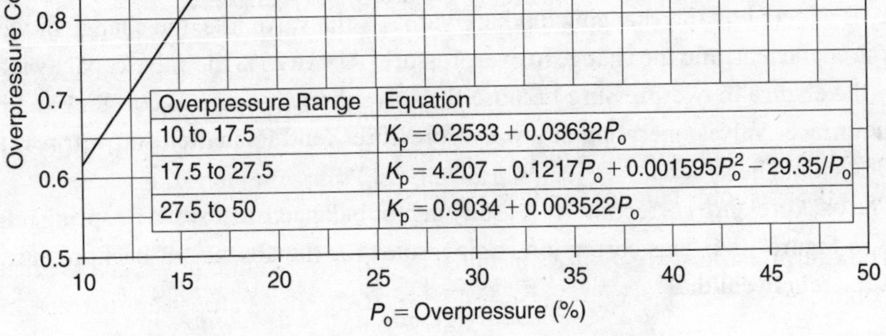

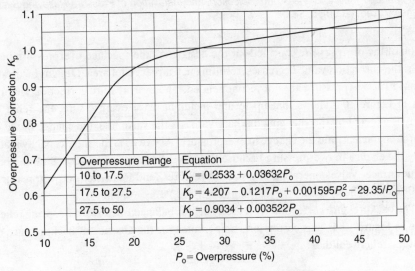

Figure 10-3 Overpressure correction K_p for spring operated reliefs **(conventional and balanced bellows)** in liquid service. Figure drawn using the equations shown, derived from data from API RP 520, *Recommended Practice for the Sizing, Selection, and Installation of Pressure-Relieving Systems in Refineries*, 7th ed. (2000), p. 55.

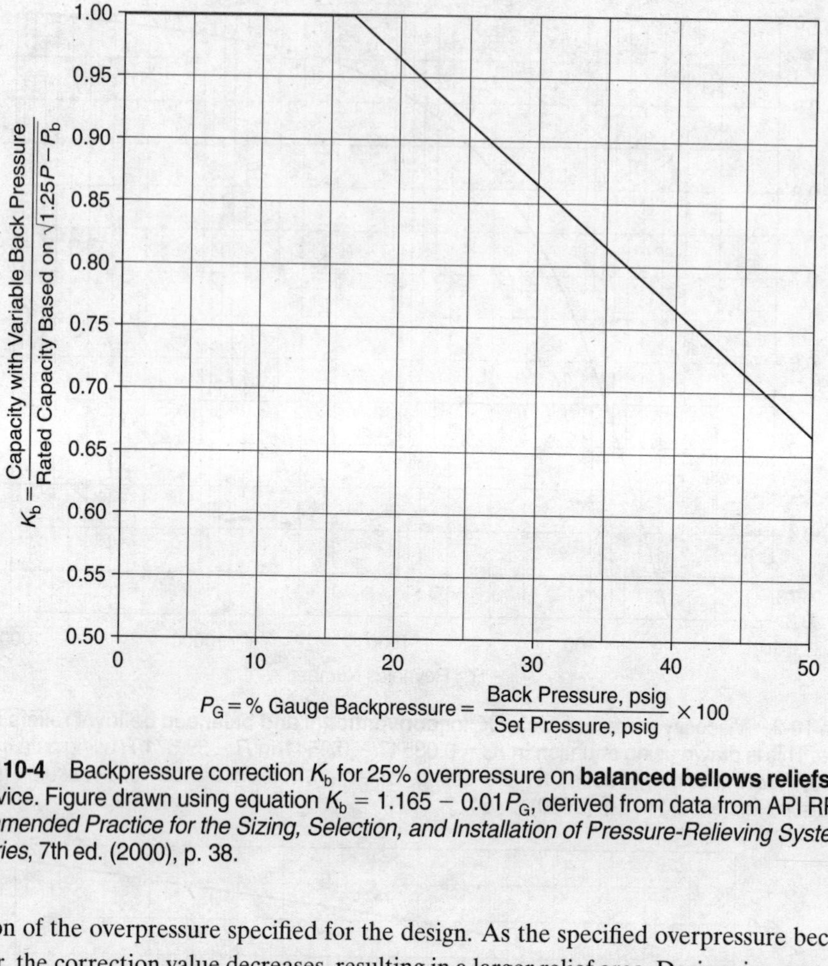

Figure 10-4 Backpressure correction K_b for 25% overpressure on **balanced bellows reliefs** in liquid service. Figure drawn using equation $K_b = 1.165 - 0.01P_G$, derived from data from API RP 520, *Recommended Practice for the Sizing, Selection, and Installation of Pressure-Relieving Systems in Refineries*, 7th ed. (2000), p. 38.

function of the overpressure specified for the design. As the specified overpressure becomes smaller, the correction value decreases, resulting in a larger relief area. Designs incorporating less than 10% overpressure are not recommended. The overpressure correction factor curve shown in Figure 10-3 shows that up to and including 25% overpressure, the relief device capacity is affected by the changing discharge area as the valve lifts, the change in the orifice discharge coefficient, and the change in overpressure. Above 25% the valve capacity is affected only by the change in overpressure because the valve discharge area is constant and behaves as a true orifice. Valves operating at low overpressures tend to chatter, so overpressures less than 10% should be avoided.

The backpressure correction K_b is used only for balanced-bellows-type spring reliefs and is given in Figure 10-4. This correction compensates for the absence of backpressure on the back of the relief vent disc.

Example 10-1

A positive displacement pump pumps water at 200 gpm at a pressure of 200 psig. Because a dead-headed pump can be easily damaged, compute the area required to relieve the pump, assuming a backpressure of 20 psig and (a) a 10% overpressure and (b) a 25% overpressure.

Solution

a. The set pressure is 200 psig. The backpressure is specified as 20 psig and the overpressure is 10% of the set pressure, or 20 psig.

The discharge coefficient C_o is not specified. However, for a conservative estimate a value of 0.61 is used.

The quantity of material relieved is the total flow of water; so $Q_v = 200$ gpm.

The Reynolds number through the relief device is not known. However, at 200 gpm the Reynolds number is assumed to be greater than 5000. Thus the viscosity correction is, from Figure 10-2, $K_v = 1.0$.

The overpressure correction K_p is given in Figure 10-3. Because the percentage of overpressure is 10%, from Figure 10-3, $K_p = 0.6$.

The backpressure correction is not required because this is not a balanced-bellows spring relief. Thus $K_b = 1.0$.

These numbers are substituted directly into Equation 10-4:

$$A = \left[\frac{\text{in}^2(\text{psi})^{1/2}}{38.0\ \text{gpm}}\right]\frac{Q_v}{C_o K_v K_p K_b}\sqrt{\frac{(\rho/\rho_{\text{ref}})}{1.25P_s - P_b}}$$

$$= \left[\frac{\text{in}^2(\text{psi})^{1/2}}{38.0\ \text{gpm}}\right]\frac{200\ \text{gpm}}{(0.61)(1.0)(0.6)(1.0)}\sqrt{\frac{1.0}{(1.25)(200\ \text{psig}) - 20\ \text{psig}}}$$

$$= 0.948\ \text{in}^2,$$

$$d = \sqrt{\frac{4A}{\pi}} = \sqrt{\frac{(4)(0.948\ \text{in}^2)}{(3.14)}} = 1.10\ \text{in.}$$

b. For an overpressure of 25%, $K_p = 1.0$ (Figure 10-3), and

$$A = (0.948\ \text{in}^2)\left(\frac{0.6}{1.0}\right) = 0.569\ \text{in}^2,$$

$$d = \sqrt{\frac{(4)(0.569\ \text{in}^2)}{(3.14)}} = 0.851\ \text{in.}$$

As expected, the relief vent area decreases as the overpressure increases.

Manufacturers do not provide relief devices to the nearest 0.01 in. Thus a selection must be made depending on relief device sizes available commercially. The next largest available size is normally selected. For all relief devices the manufacturers' technical specifications must be checked before selection and installation.

10-2 Conventional Spring-Operated Reliefs in Vapor or Gas Service

For most vapor discharges through spring reliefs the flow is critical. However, the downstream pressure must be checked to ensure that it is less than the choked pressure computed using Equation 4-49. Thus for an ideal gas Equation 4-50 is valid:

$$(Q_m)_{\text{choked}} = C_o AP \sqrt{\frac{\gamma g_c M}{R_g T}\left(\frac{2}{\gamma+1}\right)^{(\gamma+1)/(\gamma-1)}}, \tag{4-50}$$

where

$(Q_m)_{\text{choked}}$ is the discharge mass flow,
C_o is the discharge coefficient,
A is the area of the discharge,
P is the absolute upstream pressure,
γ is the heat capacity ratio for the gas,
g_c is the gravitational constant,
M is the molecular weight of the gas,
R_g is the ideal gas constant, and
T is the absolute temperature of the discharge.

Equation 4-50 is solved for the area of the relief vent given a specified mass flow rate Q_m:

$$A = \frac{Q_m}{C_o P}\sqrt{\frac{T/M}{\frac{\gamma g_c}{R_g}\left(\frac{2}{\gamma+1}\right)^{(\gamma+1)/(\gamma-1)}}}. \tag{10-6}$$

Equation 10-6 is simplified by defining a function χ:

$$\chi = \sqrt{\frac{\gamma g_c}{R_g}\left(\frac{2}{\gamma+1}\right)^{(\gamma+1)/(\gamma-1)}}. \tag{10-7}$$

Then the required relief vent area for an ideal gas is computed using a simplified form of Equation 10-6:

$$\boxed{A = \frac{Q_m}{C_o \chi P}\sqrt{\frac{T}{M}}}. \tag{10-8}$$

For nonideal gases and real vents Equation 10-8 is modified by (1) including the compressibility factor z to represent a nonideal gas and (2) including a backpressure correction K_b. The result is

$$\boxed{A = \frac{Q_m}{C_o \chi K_b P}\sqrt{\frac{Tz}{M}}}, \tag{10-9}$$

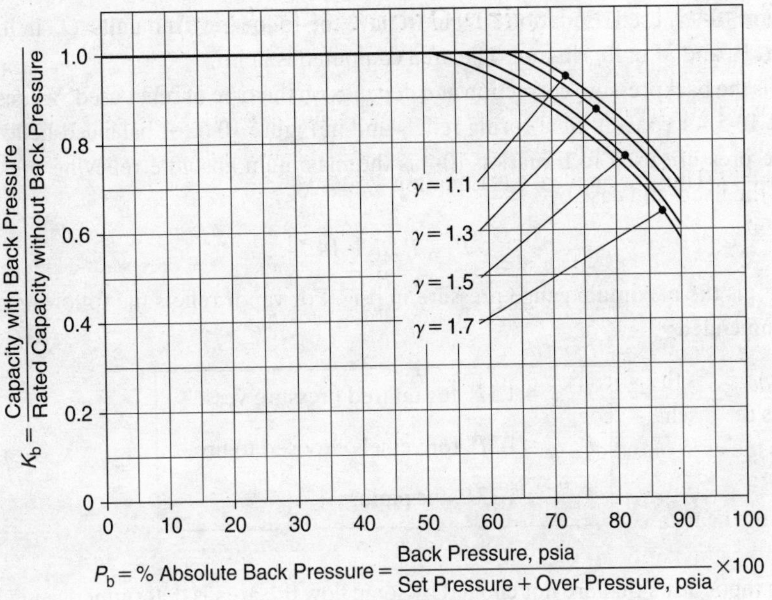

$K_b = a + bP_b^3$

γ	Range	a	b
1.1	66–90	1.3026	-1.137×10^{-6}
1.3	63–90	1.294	-1.1703×10^{-6}
1.5	56–90	1.203	-1.143×10^{-6}
1.7	51–90	1.148	-1.109×10^{-6}

Figure 10-5 Backpressure correction K_b for **conventional spring-type reliefs** in vapor or gas service. Equations shown derived from data in API RP 520 *Recommended Practice for the Sizing, Selection, and Installation of Pressure-Relieving Systems in Refineries*, 7th ed. (2000), p. 49.

where

A is the area of the relief vent,
Q_m is the discharge flow,
C_o is the effective discharge coefficient, usually 0.975 (unitless),
K_b is the backpressure correction (unitless),
P is the maximum absolute discharge pressure,
T is the absolute temperature,
z is the compressibility factor (unitless), and
M is the average molecular weight of the discharge material.

The constant χ is represented by Equation 10-7. It is conveniently calculated using the following fixed-unit expression:

$$\chi = 519.5\sqrt{\gamma\left(\frac{2}{\gamma+1}\right)^{(\gamma+1)/(\gamma-1)}}. \tag{10-10}$$

If Equation 10-9 is used, Equation 10-9 must have the following fixed units: Q_m in lb_m/hr, P in psia, T in °R, and M in lb_m/lb-mol. The area computed is in in^2.

K_b is the backpressure correction and depends on the type of relief used. Values are given in Figure 10-5 for conventional spring reliefs and in Figure 10-6 for balanced-bellows reliefs.

The pressure used in Equation 10-9 is the maximum absolute relieving pressure. It is given for the fixed-unit case by

$$P = P_{max} + 14.7, \tag{10-11}$$

where P_{max} is the maximum gauge pressure in psig. For vapor reliefs the following guidelines are recommended:[3]

$$\boxed{\begin{aligned} P_{max} &= 1.1P_s \text{ for unfired pressure vessels,} \\ P_{max} &= 1.2P_s \text{ for vessels exposed to fire,} \\ P_{max} &= 1.33P_s \text{ for piping.} \end{aligned}} \tag{10-12}$$

For vapor flows that are not choked by sonic flow the area is determined using Equation 4-48. The downstream pressure P is now required, and the discharge coefficient C_o must be estimated. The API Pressure Vessel Code[4] provides working equations that are equivalent to Equation 4-48.

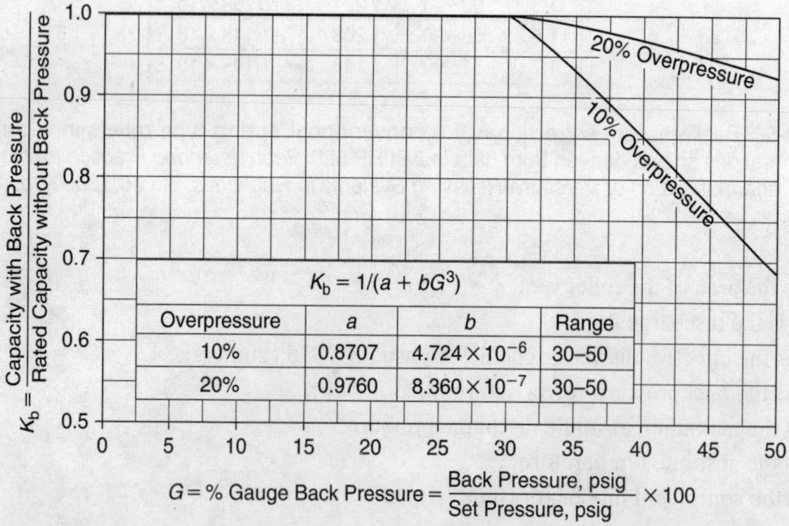

Figure 10-6 Backpressure correction K_b for **balanced-bellows reliefs** in vapor or gas service. This is drawn using the equations provided. Data from API RP 520, *Recommended Practice for the Sizing, Selection, and Installation of Pressure-Relieving Systems in Refineries*, 7th ed. (2000), p. 37.

[3] *ASME Boiler and Pressure Vessel Code* (New York: American Society of Mechanical Engineers, 1998).
[4] API RP 520, *Recommended Practice.*

Example 10-2

A nitrogen regulator fails and allows nitrogen to enter a reactor through a 6-in-diameter line. The source of the nitrogen is at 70°F and 150 psig. The reactor relief is set at 50 psig. Determine the diameter of a balanced-bellows spring-type vapor relief required to protect the reactor from this incident. Assume a relief backpressure of 20 psig.

Solution

The nitrogen source is at 150 psig. If the regulator fails, the nitrogen will flood the reactor, increasing the pressure to a point where the vessel will fail. A relief vent must be installed to vent the nitrogen as fast as it is supplied through the 6-in line. Because no other information on the piping system is provided, the flow from the pipe is initially assumed to be represented by critical flow through an orifice. Equation 4-50 describes this:

$$(Q_m)_{\text{choked}} = C_o A P \sqrt{\frac{\gamma g_c M}{R_g T}\left(\frac{2}{\gamma + 1}\right)^{(\gamma+1)/(\gamma-1)}}.$$

First, however, the choked pressure across the pipe must be determined to ensure critical flow. For diatomic gases the choked pressure is given as (see Chapter 4)

$$P_{\text{choked}} = 0.528P = (0.528)(150 + 14.7) = 87.0 \text{ psia}.$$

The maximum relief design pressure within the reactor during the relief venting is, from Equation 10-12,

$$P_{\max} = 1.1P_s = (1.1)(50 \text{ psig}) = 55.0 \text{ psig} = 69.7 \text{ psia}.$$

This is a 10% overpressure. Thus the pressure in the reactor is less than the choked pressure, and the flow from the 6-in line will be critical. The required quantities for Equation 4-50 are

$$A = \frac{\pi d^2}{4} = \frac{(3.14)(6 \text{ in})^2}{4} = 28.3 \text{ in}^2,$$

$$P = 150 + 14.7 = 164.7 \text{ psia},$$

$$\gamma = 1.40 \text{ for diatomic gases},$$

$$T = 70°\text{F} + 460 = 530°\text{R},$$

$$M = 28 \text{ lb}_m/\text{lb-mol},$$

$$C_o = 1.0,$$

$$\left(\frac{2}{\gamma + 1}\right)^{(\gamma+1)/(\gamma-1)} = \left(\frac{2}{1.4 + 1}\right)^{(2.4/0.4)} = 0.335.$$

Substituting into Equation 4-50, we obtain

$$(Q_m)_{\text{choked}} = (1.0)(28.3 \text{ in}^2)(164.7 \text{ lb}_f/\text{in}^2) \times \sqrt{\frac{(1.4)(32.17 \text{ ft lb}_m/\text{lb}_f \text{s}^2)(28 \text{ lb}_m/\text{lb-mol})(0.335)}{(1545 \text{ ft lb}_f/\text{lb-mol°R})(530°\text{R})}}$$

$$= 106 \text{ lb}_m/\text{s}$$

$$= 3.82 \times 10^5 \text{ lb}_m/\text{ hr}.$$

The area of the relief vent is computed using Equations 10-9 and 10-10 with a backpressure correction K_b determined from Figure 10-6. The backpressure is 20 psig. Thus

$$\left(\frac{\text{backpressure, psig}}{\text{set pressure, psig}}\right) \times 100 = \left(\frac{20 \text{ psig}}{50 \text{ psig}}\right) \times 100 = 40\%.$$

From Figure 10-6, $K_b = 0.86$ for an overpressure of 10%. The effective discharge coefficient is assumed to be 0.975. The gas compressibility factor z is approximately 1 at these pressures. The pressure P is the maximum absolute pressure. Thus $P = 69.7$ psia. The constant χ is computed from Equation 10-10:

$$\chi = 519.5\sqrt{\gamma\left(\frac{2}{\gamma+1}\right)^{(\gamma+1)/(\gamma-1)}} = 519.5\sqrt{(1.4)(0.335)} = 356.$$

The required vent area is computed using Equation 10-9:

$$A = \frac{Q_m}{C_o \chi K_b P}\sqrt{\frac{Tz}{M}}$$

$$= \frac{3.82 \times 10^5 \text{ lb}_m/\text{hr}}{(0.975)(356)(0.86)(69.7 \text{ psia})}\sqrt{\frac{(530°\text{R})(1.0)}{(28 \text{ lb}_m/\text{lb-mol})}}$$

$$= 79.9 \text{ in}^2.$$

The required vent diameter is

$$d = \sqrt{\frac{4A}{\pi}} = \sqrt{\frac{(4)(79.9 \text{ in}^2)}{(3.14)}} = 10.1 \text{ in}.$$

Manufacturers provide relief devices only at convenient sizes. The next largest diameter closest to the one required is selected. This would likely be $10\frac{1}{8}$ in (10.125 in).

10-3 Rupture Disc Reliefs in Liquid Service

For liquid reliefs through rupture discs without significant lengths of downstream piping the flow is represented by Equation 10-2 or by Equation 10-3 for flow through a sharp-edged orifice. No corrections are suggested.

$$A = \left[\frac{in^2(psi)^{1/2}}{38.0gpm}\right]\frac{Q_v}{C_o}\sqrt{\frac{(\rho/\rho_{ref})}{\Delta P}} \tag{10-3}$$

Equations 10-2 and 10-3 apply to rupture discs discharging directly to the atmosphere. For rupture discs discharging into a relief system (which might include knockout drums, scrubbers, or flares), the rupture disc is considered a flow restriction, and the flow through the entire pipe system must be considered. The calculation is performed identically to regular pipe flow (see Chapter 4). The calculation to determine the rupture disc area is iterative for this case. Isaacs[5] recommended assuming that the rupture disc is equivalent to 50 pipe diameters in the calculation.

10-4 Rupture Disc Reliefs in Vapor or Gas Service

Flow of vapor through rupture discs is described using an orifice equation similar to Equation 10-9 but without the additional correction factors. The result is

$$\boxed{A = \frac{Q_m}{\chi P}\sqrt{\frac{Tz}{M}}.} \tag{10-13}$$

Equation 10-13 assumes a discharge coefficient C_o of 1.0.

If appreciable backpressures exist from downstream relief systems, a procedure similar to the procedure used for liquid reliefs through rupture discs is required. The procedure is iterative.

Example 10-3

Determine the diameter of a rupture disc required to relieve the pump of Example 10-1, part a.

Solution

The pressure drop across the rupture disc is

$$\Delta P = P_{max} - P_b = 220 \text{ psig} - 20 \text{ psig} = 200 \text{ psig}.$$

The specific gravity of the water (ρ/ρ_{ref}) is 1.0. A conservative discharge coefficient of 0.61 is assumed. Substituting into Equation 10-3, we obtain

$$A = \left[\frac{\text{in}^2(\text{psi})^{1/2}}{38.0 \text{ gpm}}\right]\frac{Q_v}{C_o}\sqrt{\frac{(\rho/\rho_{ref})}{\Delta P}}$$

$$= \left[\frac{\text{in}^2(\text{psi})^{1/2}}{38.0 \text{ gpm}}\right]\frac{200 \text{ gpm}}{0.61}\sqrt{\frac{1.0}{200 \text{ psia}}} = 0.610 \text{ in}^2.$$

[5]Marx Isaacs, "Pressure Relief Systems," *Chemical Engineering* (Feb. 22, 1971), p. 113.

The relief vent diameter is

$$d = \sqrt{\frac{4A}{\pi}} = \sqrt{\frac{(4)(0.610\ \text{in}^2)}{(3.14)}} = 0.881\ \text{in.}$$

This compares to a spring relief vent area of 1.10 in.

Example 10-4

Compute the rupture disc vent diameter required to relieve the process of Example 10-2.

Solution

The solution is provided by Equation 10-9. The solution is identical to Example 10-2, with the exception of a deletion of the correction factor K_b. The area is therefore

$$A = (79.9\ \text{in}^2)(0.86) = 68.7\ \text{in}^2.$$

The rupture disc diameter is

$$d = \sqrt{\frac{4A}{\pi}} = \sqrt{\frac{(4)(68.7\ \text{in}^2)}{(3.14)}} = 9.35\ \text{in.}$$

This compares to a spring relief diameter of 9.32 in.

10-5 Two-Phase Flow during Runaway Reaction Relief

When a runaway reaction occurs within a reactor vessel, two-phase flow should be expected during the relief process. The vent sizing package (VSP) laboratory apparatus described in Chapter 8 provides the much needed temperature and pressure rise data for relief area sizing.

Figure 10-7 shows the most common type of reactor system, called a tempered reactor. It is called "tempered" because the reactor contains a volatile liquid that vaporizes or flashes during the relieving process. This vaporization removes energy by means of the heat of vaporization and *tempers* the rate of temperature rise resulting from the exothermic reaction.

The runaway reactor is treated as entirely adiabatic. The energy terms include (1) energy accumulation resulting from the sensible heat of the reactor fluid as a result of its increased temperature due to overpressure and (2) the energy removal resulting from the vaporization of liquid in the reactor and subsequent discharge through the relief vent.

The first step in the relief sizing calculation for two-phase vents is to determine the mass flux through the relief. This is computed using Equation 4-105, representing choked two-phase flow through a hole:

$$Q_m = \frac{\Delta H_V A}{v_{fg}} \sqrt{\frac{g_c}{T_s C_P}}, \qquad (4\text{-}105)$$

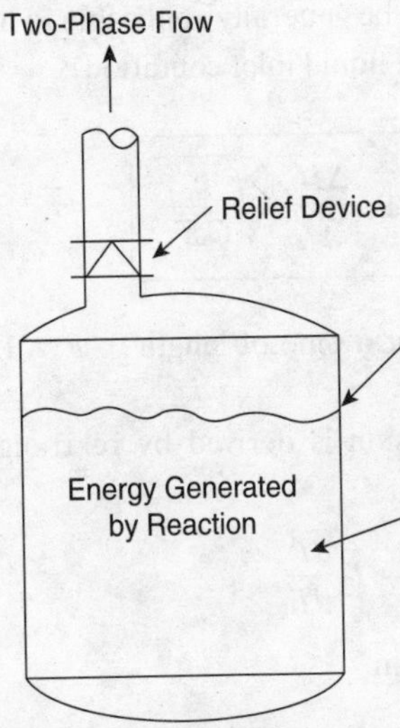

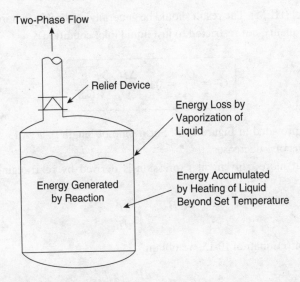

Figure 10-7 A tempered reaction system showing the important energy terms. The heat losses through the reactor walls are assumed negligible.

where, for this case,

Q_m is the mass flow through the relief,
ΔH_V is the heat of vaporization of the fluid,
A is the area of the hole,
v_{fg} is the change of specific volume of the flashing liquid,
C_P is the heat capacity of the fluid, and
T_s is the absolute saturation temperature of the fluid at the set pressure.

The mass flux G_T is given by

$$G_T = \frac{Q_m}{A} = \frac{\Delta H_V}{v_{fg}} \sqrt{\frac{g_c}{C_P T_s}}. \tag{10-14}$$

Equation 10-14 applies to two-phase relief through a hole. For two-phase flow through pipes an overall dimensionless discharge coefficient ψ is applied. Equation 10-14 is the so-called equilibrium rate model (ERM) for low-quality choked flow.[6] Leung[7] showed that Equation 10-14 must be multiplied by a factor 0.9 to bring the value in line with the classic homogeneous

[6]H. K. Fauske, "Flashing Flows or: Some Practical Guidelines for Emergency Releases," *Plant Operations Progress* (July 1985), 4(3).

[7]J. C. Leung, "Simplified Vent Sizing Equations for Emergency Relief Requirements in Reactors and Storage Vessels," *AIChE Journal* (1986), 32(10): 1622.

equilibrium model (HEM). The result should be generally applicable to homogeneous venting of a reactor (low quality, not restricted to just liquid inlet condition):

$$G_T = \frac{Q_m}{A} = 0.9\psi \frac{\Delta H_V}{v_{fg}} \sqrt{\frac{g_c}{C_P T_s}}. \tag{10-15}$$

Values for ψ are provided in Figure 10-8. For a pipe of length 0, $\psi = 1$. As the pipe length increases, the value of ψ decreases.

A somewhat more convenient expression is derived by rearranging Equation 4-103 to yield

$$\frac{\Delta H_V}{v_{fg}} = T_s \frac{dP}{dT}, \tag{10-16}$$

and substituting into Equation 10-15, we obtain

$$G_T = 0.9\psi \frac{dP}{dT} \sqrt{\frac{g_c T_s}{C_P}}. \tag{10-17}$$

The exact derivative is approximated by a finite-difference derivative to yield

$$G_T \cong 0.9\psi \frac{\Delta P}{\Delta T} \sqrt{\frac{g_c T_s}{C_P}}, \tag{10-18}$$

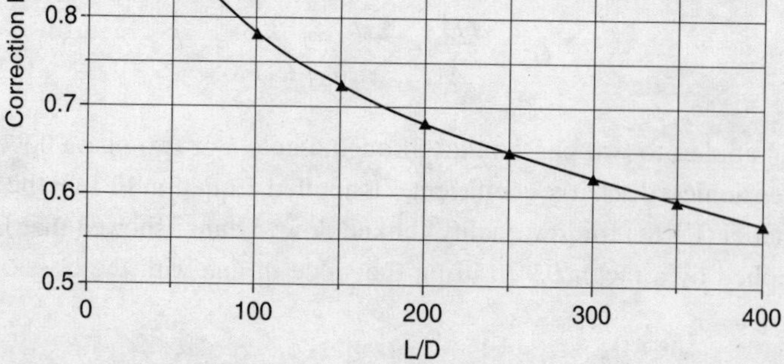

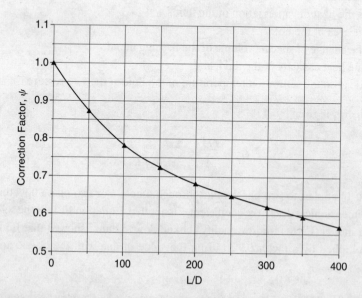

Figure 10-8 Correction factor ψ correcting for two-phase flashing flow through pipes. Data from J. C. Leung and M. A. Grolmes, "The Discharge of Two-Phase Flashing Flow in a Horizontal Duct," *AIChE Journal* (1987), 33(3): 524–527.

where

ΔP is the overpressure and
ΔT is temperature rise corresponding to the overpressure.

The required vent area is computed by solving a particular form of the dynamic energy balance. Details are provided elsewhere.[8] The result is

$$A = \frac{m_o q}{G_T\left(\sqrt{\frac{V}{m_o}\frac{\Delta H_V}{v_{fg}}} + \sqrt{C_V \Delta T}\right)^2}, \tag{10-19}$$

An alternative form is derived by applying Equation 4-103:

$$A = \frac{m_o q}{G_T\left(\sqrt{\frac{V}{m_o}T_s\frac{dP}{dT}} + \sqrt{C_V \Delta T}\right)^2}. \tag{10-20}$$

For Equations 10-19 and 10-20 the following additional variables are defined:

m_o is the total mass contained within the reactor vessel before relief,
q is the exothermic heat release rate per unit mass,
V is the volume of the vessel, and
C_V is the liquid heat capacity at constant volume.

For both Equations 10-19 and 10-20 the relief area is based on the total heat added to the system (numerator) and the heat removed or absorbed (denominator). The first term in the denominator corresponds to the net heat removed by the liquid and vapor leaving the system; the second term corresponds to the heat absorbed as a result of increasing the temperature of the liquid because of the overpressure.

The heat input q resulting from an exothermic reaction is determined using fundamental kinetic information or from the DIERS VSP (see Chapter 8). For data obtained using the VSP, the equation

$$q = \frac{1}{2}C_V\left[\left(\frac{dT}{dt}\right)_s + \left(\frac{dT}{dt}\right)_m\right]. \tag{10-21}$$

is applied, where the derivative denoted by the subscript s corresponds to the heating rate at the set pressure and the derivative denoted by the subscript m corresponds to the temperature rise

[8]J. C. Leung, "Simplified Vent Sizing."

at the maximum turnaround pressure. Both derivatives are determined experimentally using the VSP.

The equations assume that

1. Uniform froth or homogeneous vessel venting occurs
2. The mass flux G_T varies little during the relief
3. The reaction energy per unit mass q is treated as a constant
4. Physical properties C_V, ΔH_V, and v_{fg} are constant
5. The system is a tempered reactor system. This applies to most reaction systems

Units are a particular problem when using the two-phase equations. The best procedure is to convert all energy units to their mechanical equivalents before solving for the relief area, particularly when English engineering units are used.

Example 10-5

Leung[9] reported on the data of Huff[10] involving a 3500-gal reactor with styrene monomer undergoing adiabatic polymerization after being heated inadvertently to 70°C. The maximum allowable working pressure (MAWP) of the vessel is 5 bar. Given the following data, determine the relief vent diameter required. Assume a set pressure of 4.5 bar and a maximum pressure of 5.4 bar absolute:

Data

Volume (V): 3500 gal = 13.16 m^3

Reaction mass (m_o): 9500 kg

Set temperature (T_s): 209.4°C = 482.5 K

Data from VSP

Maximum temperature (T_m): 219.5°C = 492.7 K

$(dT/dt)_s$ = 29.6°C/min = 0.493 K/s

$(dT/dt)_m$ = 39.7°C/min = 0.662 K/s

Physical Property Data

	4.5-bar set	5.4-bar peak
v_f (m^3/kg)	0.001388	0.001414
v_g (m^3/kg)	0.08553	0.07278
C_P (kJ/kg K)	2.470	2.514
ΔH_V (kJ/kg)	310.6	302.3

Solution

The heating rate q is determined using Equation 10-21:

$$q = \frac{1}{2}C_V\left[\left(\frac{dT}{dt}\right)_s + \left(\frac{dT}{dt}\right)_m\right]. \qquad (10\text{-}21)$$

[9]Leung, "Simplified Vent Sizing."

[10]J. E. Huff, "Emergency Venting Requirements," *Plant/Operations Progress* (1982), 1(4): 211.

Assuming that $C_V = C_P$, we have

$$q = \frac{1}{2}(2.470 \text{ kJ/kg K})(0.493 + 0.662)(\text{K/s})$$

$$= 1.426 \text{ kJ/kg s}.$$

The mass flux is given by Equation 10-15. Assuming $L/D = 0$, $\psi = 1.0$:

$$G_T = 0.9\psi \frac{\Delta H_V}{v_{fg}} \sqrt{\frac{g_c}{T_s C_P}}$$

$$= (0.9)(1.0)\frac{(310{,}600 \text{ J/kg})[1 \text{ (N m)/J}]}{(0.08553 - 0.001388) \text{ m}^3\text{/kg}} \times \sqrt{\frac{[1 \text{ (kg m/s}^2\text{)/N}]}{(2470 \text{ J/kg K})(482.5 \text{ K})[1 \text{ (N m)/J}]}}$$

$$= 3043 \text{ kg/m}^2 \text{ s}.$$

The relief vent area is determined from Equation 10-19. The change in temperature ΔT is $T_m - T_s = 492.7 - 482.5 = 10.2$ K:

$$A = \frac{m_o q}{G_T\left(\sqrt{\dfrac{V}{m_o}\dfrac{\Delta H_V}{v_{fg}}} + \sqrt{C_V \Delta T}\right)^2}$$

$$= \frac{(9500 \text{ kg})(1426 \text{ J/kg s})[1 \text{ (N m)/J}]}{(3043 \text{ kg/m}^2 \text{ s})}$$

$$\times \left(\sqrt{\left(\frac{13.16 \text{ m}^3}{9500 \text{ kg}}\right)\left\{\frac{(310{,}600 \text{ J/kg})[1 \text{ (N m)/J}]}{(0.08414 \text{ m}^3\text{/kg})}\right\}} + \sqrt{(2470 \text{ J/kg K})(10.2 \text{ K})[1 \text{ (N m)/J}]}\right)^{-2}$$

$$= 0.084 \text{ m}^2.$$

The required relief diameter is

$$d = \sqrt{\frac{4A}{\pi}} = \sqrt{\frac{(4)(0.084 \text{ m}^2)}{3.14}} = 0.327 \text{ m}.$$

Suppose that all vapor relief was assumed. The size of the required vapor phase rupture disc is determined by assuming that all the heat energy is absorbed by the vaporization of the liquid. At the set temperature the heat release rate q is

$$q = C_V\left(\frac{dT}{dt}\right)_s = (2.470 \text{ kJ/kg K})(0.493 \text{ K/s}) = 1.218 \text{ kJ/kg s}.$$

The vapor mass flow through the relief is then

$$Q_m = \frac{q m_o}{\Delta H_V}$$

$$= \frac{(1218 \text{ J/kg s})(9500 \text{ kg})}{(310{,}600 \text{ J/kg})}$$

$$= 37.2 \text{ kg/s}.$$

Equation 10-6 provides the required relief area. The molecular weight of styrene is 104. Assume that $\gamma = 1.32$ and $C_o = 1.0$. Then

$$A = \frac{Q_m}{C_o P}\sqrt{\frac{R_g T}{\gamma g_c M}\left(\frac{2}{\gamma + 1}\right)^{(\gamma+1)/(1-\gamma)}}$$

$$= \frac{(37.2 \text{ kg/s})}{(1.0)(4.5 \text{ bar})(100{,}000 \text{ Pa/bar})[1 \text{ (N/m}^2\text{)/Pa}]}$$

$$\times \sqrt{\frac{(8314 \text{ Pa m}^3\text{/kg-mol K})(482.5 \text{ K})[1 \text{ (N/m}^2\text{)/Pa})}{(1.32)[1 \text{ (kgm/s}^2\text{)/N}](104 \text{ kg/kg-mol})}} \times \sqrt{\left(\frac{2}{2.32}\right)^{2.32/(-0.32)}}$$

$$= 0.0242 \text{ m}^2.$$

This requires a relief device with a diameter of 0.176 m, a significantly smaller diameter than for two-phase flow. Thus, if the relief were sized assuming all vapor relief, the result would be physically incorrect and the reactor would be severely tested during this runaway event.

Simplified Nomograph Method

Fauske[11] developed a simplified chart-driven approach to the two-phase reactor relief problem. He suggested the following equation for determining the relief area:

$$A = \frac{V\rho}{G_T \Delta t_v}, \tag{10-22}$$

where

A is the relief vent area,
V is the reactor volume,
ρ is the density of the reactants,
G_T is the mass flux through the relief, and
Δt_v is the venting time.

Equation 10-22 was developed by Boyle[12] by defining the required vent area as the size that would empty the reactor before the pressure could rise above some allowable overpressure for a given vessel.

[11] Hans K. Fauske, "A Quick Approach to Reactor Vent Sizing," *Plant/Operations Progress* (1984), 3(3), and "Generalized Vent Sizing Nomogram for Runaway Chemical Reactions," *Plant/Operations Progress* (1984), 3(4).

[12] W. J. Boyle Jr., "Sizing Relief Area for Polymerization Reactors," *Chemical Engineering Progress* (Aug. 1967), 63(8): 61.

The mass flux G_T is given by Equation 10-15 or 10-18, and the venting time is given approximately by

$$\Delta t_c \cong \frac{\Delta T C_P}{q_s}, \tag{10-23}$$

where

ΔT is the temperature increase corresponding to the overpressure ΔP,
T is the temperature,
C_P is the heat capacity, and
q_s is the energy release rate per unit mass at the set pressure of the relief system.

Combining Equations 10-22, 10-14, and 10-23 yields

$$\boxed{A = V\rho(g_c T_s C_P)^{-1/2}\frac{q_s}{\Delta P}.} \tag{10-24}$$

Equation 10-24 provides a conservative estimate of the required vent area. By considering the case of 20% absolute overpressure, assuming a typical liquid heat capacity of 2510 J/kg K for most organic materials, and assuming a saturated water relationship, we can obtain the following equation:[13]

$$A = (\text{m}^2/1000\text{ kg}) = \frac{0.00208\left(\dfrac{dT}{dt}\right)(°\text{C/min})}{P_s(\text{bar})}. \tag{10-25}$$

A simple nomograph of the results can be plotted and is shown in Figure 10-9. The required vent area is determined simply from the heating rate, the set pressure, and the mass of reactants.

The Fauske nomograph is useful for performing quick estimates and for checking the results of the more rigorous computation.

Recent studies[14] suggest that the nomograph data of Figure 10-9 apply for a discharge coefficient of $\psi = 0.5$, representing a discharge (L/D) of 400. Use of the nomograph at other discharge pipe lengths and different ψ requires a suitable correction, as shown in the following example.

[13] J. C. Leung and H. K. Fauske, "Runaway System Characterization and Vent Sizing Based on DIERS Methodology," *Plant/Operations Progress* (Apr. 1987), 6(2).

[14] H. G. Fisher and J. C. Leung, personal communication, January 1989.

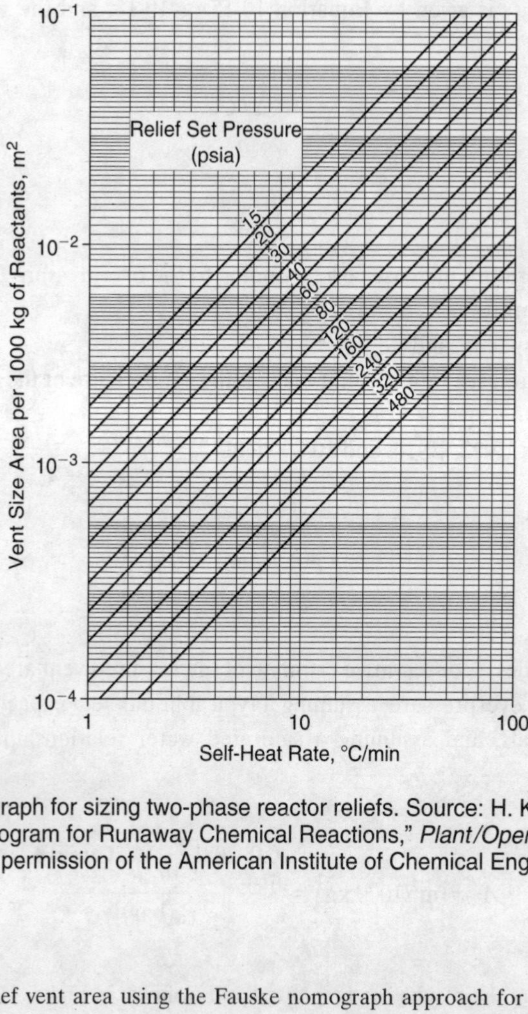

Figure 10-9 Nomograph for sizing two-phase reactor reliefs. Source: H. K. Fauske, "Generalized Vent Sizing Nomogram for Runaway Chemical Reactions," *Plant/Operations Progress* (1984), 3(4). Used by permission of the American Institute of Chemical Engineers.

Example 10-6

Estimate the relief vent area using the Fauske nomograph approach for the reaction system of Example 10-5.

Solution

The heating rate at the set temperature is specified as 29.6°C/min. The set pressure is 4.5 bar absolute, so

$$P_s = (4.5 \text{ bar})(0.9869 \text{ bar/atm})(14.7 \text{ psia/atm}) = 65.3 \text{ psia}.$$

From Figure 10-9 the vent area required per 1000 kg of reactant is about 1.03×10^{-2} m². Thus the total relief area is

$$A = (1.03 \times 10^{-2} \text{ m}^2/1000 \text{ kg})(9500 \text{ kg})$$

$$= 0.098 \text{ m}^2.$$

Figure 10-9 is applicable for $\psi = 0.5$. For $\psi = 1.0$ the area is adjusted linearly:

$$A = (0.098 \text{ m}^2)\left(\frac{0.5}{1.0}\right)$$

$$= 0.049 \text{ m}^2.$$

This assumes a 20% absolute overpressure. The result can be adjusted for other overpressures by multiplying the area by a ratio of 20/(new absolute percentage of overpressure).

This result compares to a more rigorously computed area of 0.084 m^2.

Two-phase flow through reliefs is much more complex than the introduction provided here. Furthermore, the technology is still undergoing substantial development. The equations presented here are not universally applicable; however, they do represent the most accepted method available today.

10-6 Pilot-Operated and Buckling-Pin Reliefs

Pilot-operated and buckling-pin reliefs have significant advantages over other reliefs (see Table 9-2). Calculation methods for the pilot-operated reliefs are similar to those used for spring-operated reliefs.[15, 16] The calculation methods for buckling-pin reliefs are not in the open literature. Those interested in sizing buckling-pin reliefs should contact relief vendors[17, 18] or companies that specialize in sizing reliefs.[19]

10-7 Deflagration Venting for Dust and Vapor Explosions

Loss prevention means preventing the existence of hazards. However, for some situations hazards are unavoidable. For example, during the milling process to make flour from wheat, substantial quantities of flammable dust are produced. An uncontrolled dust explosion in a warehouse, storage bin, or processing unit can eject high-velocity structural debris over a considerable area, propagating the accident and resulting in increased injuries. Deflagration venting reduces the impact of dust and vapor cloud explosions by controlling the release of the explosion energy. The energy of the explosion is directed away from plant personnel and equipment.

[15] Crosby Engineering Handbook, *www.tycoflowcontrol-na.com/ld/CROMC-0296-US.pdf*.

[16] "Sizing, Selection, and Installation of Pressure-Relieving Devices in Refineries, Part 1, Sizing and Selection," *API Recommended Practice 520*, 7th ed. (2000).

[17] Buckling Pin Relief Valve, *www.bucklingpin.com/*.

[18] Rupture Pin Technology, *www.rupturepin.com/*.

[19] Lloyd's Register Celerity3 Inc., *www.lrenergy.org/celerity_3.aspx*.

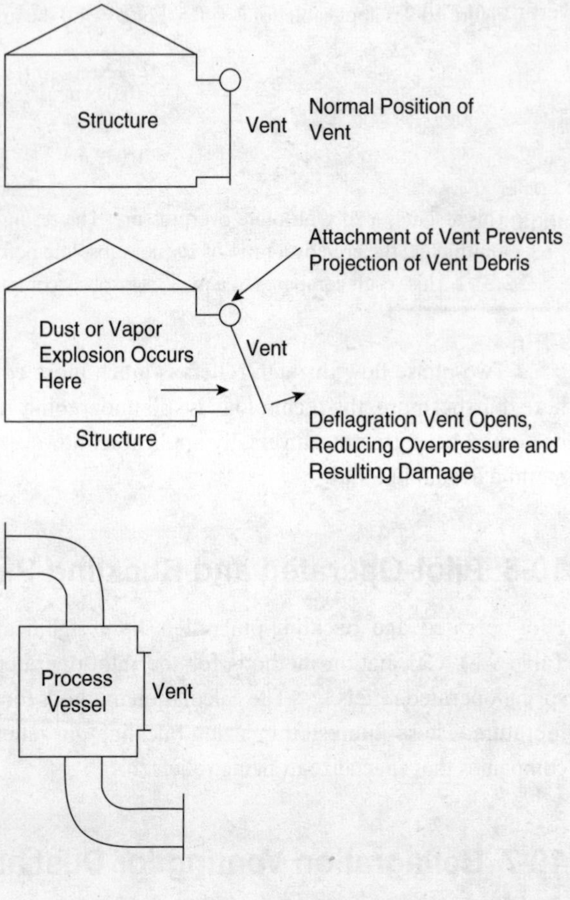

Figure 10-10 Deflagration vents for structures and process vessels.

Deflagration venting in buildings and process vessels is usually achieved by using blowout panels, as shown in Figure 10-10. The blowout panel is designed to have less strength than the walls of the structure. Thus, during an explosion, the blowout panels are preferentially detached and the explosive energy is vented. Damage to the remaining structure and equipment is minimized. For particularly explosive dusts or vapors, it is not unusual for the walls (and perhaps roof) of the entire structure to be constructed of blowout panels.

The actual construction details of blowout panels are beyond the scope of the text. A detached blowout panel moving at high velocity can cause considerable damage. Therefore a mechanism must be provided to retain the panel during the deflagration process. Furthermore, thermal insulation of panels is also required. Construction details are available in manufacturers' literature.

Blowout panels are designed to provide the proper relief area, depending on a number of design factors. These include the explosive behavior of the dust or vapor, the maximum overpressure allowable in the structure, and the volume of the structure. Design standards are available.[20]

Deflagration design is segregated into two categories: low-pressure and high-pressure structures. Low-pressure structures include structures with sheet metal sides and other low-strength building materials. These structures are capable of withstanding not more than 1.5 psig (0.1 bar gauge). High-pressure structures include steel process vessels, concrete buildings, and so forth that are capable of withstanding pressures greater than 1.5 psig (0.1 bar gauge).

Vents for Low-Pressure Structures

For low-pressure structures that are capable of withstanding pressures of not more than 1.5 psi (0.1 bar gauge), original design techniques were based on the Runes (pronounced Roo-ness) equation:[21]

$$A = \frac{C^*_{\text{vent}} L_1 L_2}{\sqrt{P}}, \tag{10-26}$$

where

A is the required vent area,
C^*_{vent} is a constant that depends on the nature of the combustible material,
L_1 is the smallest dimension of the rectangular building structure to be vented,
L_2 is the second smallest dimension of the enclosure to be vented, and
P is the maximum internal pressure that can be withstood by the weakest member of the enclosure.

Swift and Epstein[22] presented a more detailed equation, including many important combustion features:

$$A = \frac{\dfrac{A_s}{C_o} \dfrac{\lambda S_u \rho_u}{G} \left[\left(\dfrac{P_{\max}}{P_o} \right)^{1/\gamma} - 1 \right]}{\sqrt{\dfrac{P_f}{P_o} - 1}}, \tag{10-27}$$

[20]NFPA 68, *Guide for Venting of Deflagrations* (Quincy, MA: National Fire Protection Association, 1998).

[21]Richard R. Schwab, "Recent Developments in Deflagration Venting Design," in *Proceedings of the International Symposium on Preventing Major Chemical Accidents,* John L. Woodward, ed. (New York: American Institute of Chemical Engineers, 1987), p. 3.101.

[22]Ian Swift and Mike Epstein, "Performance of Low Pressure Explosion Vents," *Plant/Operations Progress* (Apr. 1987), 6(2).

where

A is the required vent area,
A_s is the inside surface area of the enclosure,
C_o is the discharge coefficient,
λ is the turbulent augmentation factor,
S_u is the laminar burning velocity,
ρ_u is the density of the unburned gas,
G is the mass flux,
P_{max} is the maximum unvented explosion pressure,
P_o is the initial pressure,
P_f is the final peak pressure during the vent, and
γ is the heat capacity ratio.

Many of the variables in Equation 10-27 can be estimated or assumed. These variables are regrouped to result in the following form:

$$\boxed{A = \frac{C_{vent} A_s}{\sqrt{P}}}, \tag{10-28}$$

where P is the maximum internal overpressure that can be withstood by the weakest structural element. Equation 10-28 is remarkably similar to the Runes equation (Equation 10-26).

Values for the constant C_{vent} are given in Table 10-1.

Table 10-1 Combustible Characteristic Constant for the Swift-Epstein Equation[a]

Combustible material	C_{vent} ($\sqrt{\text{psi}}$)	C_{vent} ($\sqrt{\text{kPa}}$)
Anhydrous ammonia	0.05	0.13
Methane	0.14	0.37
Aliphatic gases (excluding methane) or gases with a fundamental burning velocity less than 1.3 times that of propane	0.17	0.45
St-1 dusts	0.10	0.26
St-2 dusts	0.12	0.30
St-3 dusts	0.20	0.51

[a]NFPA, *Venting of Deflagrations* (Quincy, MA: National Fire Protection Association, 1998).

Example 10-7

A room is used for dispensing flammable liquids. The liquids are expected to have fundamental burning velocities less than 1.3 times that of propane. The room is 9 m long by 6 m wide by 6 m in height. Three of the walls are shared with an adjoining structure. The fourth and larger wall of the room is on the outer surface of the structure. The three inside walls are capable of withstanding a pressure of 0.05 bar. Estimate the vent area required for this operation.

Solution

The vent must be installed on the larger outer wall to vent the combustion away from the adjoining structure. The venting constant for this flammable vapor is provided in Table 10-1 and has a value of 0.45 $\sqrt{\text{kPa}}$. Equation 10-28 is used to estimate the required vent area. The total surface area of the room (including floor and ceiling) is

$$A_s = (2)(9\text{ m})(6\text{ m}) + (2)(6\text{ m})(6\text{ m}) + (2)(6\text{ m})(9\text{ m}) = 288\text{ m}^2.$$

The required vent area is

$$A = \frac{C_{\text{vent}} A_s}{\sqrt{P}} = \frac{(0.45\sqrt{\text{kPa}})(288\text{ m}^2)}{\sqrt{(0.05\text{ bar})(100\text{ kPa/bar})}} = 183\text{ m}^2.$$

This is larger than the area of the outer wall. One option is to strengthen the three inner walls to withstand a higher pressure. This would reduce the vent area required.

Vents for High-Pressure Structures

High-pressure structures are capable of withstanding pressures of more than 1.5 psig (0.1 bar gauge). The vent design is based on the definition of a deflagration index for gases or dusts:

$$K_G \text{ or } K_{St} = \left(\frac{dP}{dt}\right)_{\max} V^{1/3}, \tag{10-29}$$

where

K_G is the deflagration index for gases and vapors,
K_{St} is the deflagration index for dusts,
$(dP/dt)_{\max}$ is the maximum pressure increase, determined experimentally, and
V is the volume of the vessel.

We discussed the experimental procedure used to determine the deflagration indexes for gases and dusts in Chapter 6. Tables of typical values were also provided.

Extensive testing with dusts and vapors has resulted in a detailed set of empirical equations for the relief vent area (published as NFPA 68).[23] The length-to-diameter ratio L/D of the

[23]NFPA 68, *Guide for Venting of Deflagrations* (Quincy, MA: National Fire Protection Association, 1998).

enclosure determines the equation(s) used for calculating the necessary vent area. For noncircular enclosures the value used for the diameter is the equivalent diameter given by $D = 2\sqrt{A/\pi}$, where A is the cross-sectional area normal to the longitudinal axis of the space.

For combusting vapors discharging through a low inertial vent and an enclosure L/D of less than 2, the following equation from NFPA 68 applies:

$$A_v = [(0.127 \log K_G - 0.0567)P_{red}^{-0.582} + 0.175P_{red}^{-0.572}(P_{stat} - 0.1)]V^{2/3}, \qquad (10\text{-}30)$$

where

A_v is the vent area (m^2),
K_G is the vapor deflagration index (bar-m/s),
P_{red} is the maximum pressure during venting (bar gauge), and
P_{stat} is the vent release pressure (bar gauge).

Equation 10-30 has the following restrictions on its use:

- K_G is less than 550 bar-m/s.
- P_{stat} is less than 0.5 bar gauge.
- P_{red} is less than 2 bars gauge.
- V is less than 1000 m^3.

The experimental conditions under which Equation 10-30 was developed are as follows:

- vessel volumes of 2.4, 10, 25, and 250 m^3 with an L/D for all test vessels of approximately 1,
- initial pressure atmospheric,
- ignition energy of 10 J,
- quiescent gas mixture at time of ignition with no turbulence inducers, and
- P_{stat} ranging from 0.1 bar gauge to 0.5 bar gauge.

For enclosures with L/D ranging from 2 to 5 the area calculated using Equation 10-30 is adjusted using

$$\Delta A = \frac{A_v K_G \left(\frac{L}{D} - 2\right)^2}{750}, \qquad (10\text{-}31)$$

where

ΔA is the adjustment to the vent area of Equation 10-30 (m^2),
K_G is the deflagration index for the combusting gas (bar-m/s), and
L/D is the length to diameter ratio of the enclosure (unitless).

For L/D values greater than 5, NFPA 68 must be consulted.

For venting of combustible dusts through a low inertial vent and an enclosure L/D of less than 2, the following equation from NFPA 68 applies:

$$A_v = [(3.264 \times 10^{-5})(P_{max} K_{St} P_{red}^{-0.569}) + 0.27(P_{stat} - 0.1)P_{red}^{-0.5}]V^{0.753}, \qquad (10\text{-}32)$$

where

A_v is the vent area (m^2),
P_{max} is the maximum pressure reached during deflagration of an optimum mixture of combustible dust and air in a closed vessel (bar gauge),
K_{St} is the dust deflagration index (bar-m/s),
P_{red} is the maximum pressure during venting (bar gauge),
P_{stat} is the vent release pressure (bar gauge), and
V is the volume of the enclosure (m^3).

The following limitations apply to Equation 10-32:

- For K_{St} between 10 and 300 bar-m/s, P_{max} must be between 5 and 10 bars gauge.
- For K_{St} between 300 and 800 bar-m/s, P_{max} must be between 5 and 12 bars gauge.
- P_{stat} must be between 0.1 and 1 bar gauge.
- P_{red} must be between 0.1 and 2 bars gauge.
- The enclosure volume must be between 0.1 and 10,000 m^3.

For L/D values equal to or greater than 2 but less than 6 and for P_{red} less than 1.5 bars gauge (22 psi), the vent area of Equation 10-32 is increased by

$$\Delta A = A_v(-4.305 \log P_{red} + 0.758)\log \frac{L}{D}. \qquad (10\text{-}33)$$

The adjusted vent area (Equation 10-33) is sensitive to P_{red}. For low values of P_{red} the additional vent area is large. For P_{red} values of 1.5 bars gauge and higher Equation 10-32 should be used alone. For long pipes and ducts where L/D is greater than 6, NFPA 68 must be consulted.

Example 10-8

Consider again the flammable liquid dispensing room of Example 10-7. In this case the walls have been reinforced to withstand a pressure of 0.4 bar (P_{red}). Assume that the vent will operate at 0.2 bar (P_{stat}) and that the K_G of the vapor is 100 bar-m/s. Estimate the vent area required to protect this enclosure.

Solution

The L/D ratio must first be determined for this enclosure. The longitudinal axis runs the 9 m length of the room. The cross-sectional area normal to this axis is (6 m)(6 m) = 36 m^2. Thus

$D = 2\sqrt{(36\ \text{m}^2)/\pi} = 6.77$ m. Then $L/D = 9\ \text{m}/6.77\ \text{m} = 1.3$, and it follows that Equation 10-30 applies without further correction. The volume of the enclosure is (9 m)(6 m)(6 m) = 324 m^3. Substituting into Equation 10-30, we obtain

$$A_v = [(0.127 \log 100 - 0.0567)(0.4)^{-0.582} + 0.175(0.4)^{-0.572}(0.2 - 0.1)](324)^{2/3}$$

$$= 17.3\ \text{m}^2.$$

More than adequate area exists on the outer wall of the enclosure to accommodate this vent.

Both vent sizing methods for gases and dusts require values for the deflagration indexes, K_G or K_{St}. We discussed the experimental procedure to determine these values and also provided tables of typical values for gases and dusts in Chapter 6.

10-8 Venting for Fires External to Process Vessels

Fires external to process vessels can result in heating and boiling of process liquids, as shown in Figure 10-11. Venting is required to prevent explosion of these vessels.

Two-phase flow during these reliefs is possible but not likely. For runaway reactor reliefs the energy is generated by reaction throughout the entire reactor liquid contents. For heating caused by external fire the heating occurs only at the surface of the vessel. Thus liquid boiling will occur only next to the wall, and the resulting two-phase foam or froth at the liquid surface will not have a substantial thickness. Two-phase flow during fire relief can therefore be prevented by providing a suitable vapor space above the liquid within the vessel.

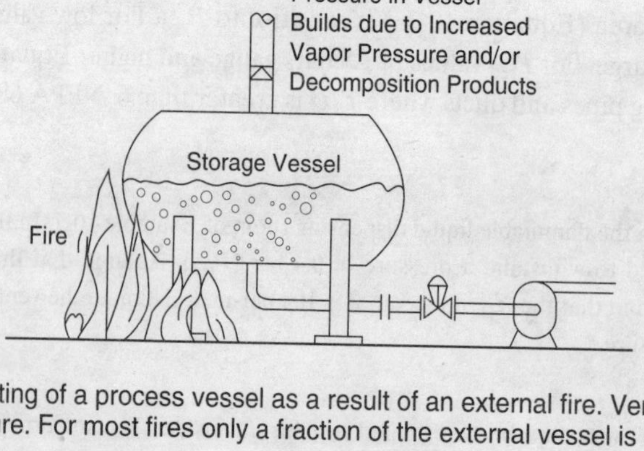

Figure 10-11 Heating of a process vessel as a result of an external fire. Venting is required to prevent vessel rupture. For most fires only a fraction of the external vessel is exposed to fire.

Two-phase fire relief equations are available for conservative design. Leung[24] presented an equation for the maximum temperature based on an energy balance around the heated vessel. This assumes a constant heat input rate Q:

$$T_m - T_s = \frac{Q}{G_T A C_V}\left[\ln\left(\frac{m_o}{V}\frac{Q}{G_T A}\frac{v_{fg}}{\Delta H_V}\right) - 1\right] + \frac{V \Delta H_v}{m_o C_V v_{fg}}, \tag{10-34}$$

where

T_m is the maximum temperature in the vessel,
T_s is the set temperature corresponding to the set pressure,
Q is the constant heat input rate,
G_T is the mass flux through the relief,
A is the area of the relief,
C_V is the heat capacity at constant volume,
m_o is the liquid mass in the vessel,
V is the volume of the vessel,
v_{fg} is the volume difference between the vapor and liquid phases, and
ΔH_v is the heat of vaporization of the liquid.

The solution to Equation 10-34 for $G_T A$ is done by an iterative or trial-and-error technique. Equation 10-34 is likely to produce multiple roots. In this case the correct solution is the minimum mass flux G_T. For the special case of no overpressure, $T_m = T_s$, and Equation 10-34 reduces to

$$\boxed{A = \frac{Q m_o v_{fg}}{G_T V \Delta H_v}.} \tag{10-35}$$

Various relationships have been recommended for computing the heat added to a vessel that is engulfed in fire. For regulated materials the OSHA 1910.106 criterion[25] is mandatory. Other standards are also available.[26] Crozier,[27] after analysis of the various standards, recommended the following equations for determining the total heat input Q:

$$Q = 20{,}000A \qquad \text{for } 20 < A < 200,$$

$$Q = 199{,}300A^{0.566} \qquad \text{for } 200 < A < 1000,$$

[24]Leung, "Simplified Vent Sizing Equations."

[25]OSHA 1910.106, *Flammable and Combustible Liquids* (Washington, DC: US Department of Labor, 1996).

[26]API Standard 2000, *Venting Atmospheric and Low-Pressure Storage Tanks (Nonrefrigerated and Refrigerated),* 5th ed. (Washington, DC: American Petroleum Institute, 1998); and NFPA 30, *Flammable and Combustible Liquids Code* (Quincy, MA: National Fire Protection Association, 2000).

[27]R. A. Crozier, "Sizing Relief Valves for Fire Emergencies," *Chemical Engineering* (Oct. 28, 1985).

$$Q = 936{,}400A^{0.338} \quad \text{for } 1000 < A < 2800,$$
$$Q = 21{,}000A^{0.82} \quad \text{for } A > 2800, \tag{10-36}$$

where

A is the area absorbing heat (in ft^2) for the following geometries:
for spheres, 55% of total exposed area;
for horizontal tanks, 75% of total exposed area;
for vertical tanks, 100% of total exposed area for first 30 ft, and
Q is the total heat input to the vessel (in Btu/hr).

The mass flux G_T is determined using Equation 10-15 or 10-18.

API 520[28] suggests a slightly different approach to estimate the heat flux to process equipment as a result of a fire. If prompt fire fighting is available and if the flammable material is drained away from the vessel, then the heat flux is estimated using

$$Q = 21{,}000FA^{0.82}. \tag{10-37}$$

If adequate fire fighting and drainage do not exist, then the following equation is used:

$$Q = 34{,}500FA^{0.82}, \tag{10-38}$$

where

Q is the total heat input through the surface of the vessel (Btu/hr),
F is an environment factor (unitless), and
A is the total wetted surface of the vessel (ft^2).

The environment factor F is used to account for vessel protection from insulation. A number of values for various insulation thicknesses are shown in Table 10-2.

Table 10-2 Environment Factors *F* for Equations 10-37 and 10-38

Insulation thickness (in)	Environment factor *F*
0	1.0
1	0.30
2	0.15
4	0.075

[28]API RP 520, *Sizing, Selection, and Installation of Pressure-Relieving Devices in Refineries,* 6th ed. (Washington, DC: American Petroleum Institute, 1993).

The surface area A is the area of the vessel wetted by its internal liquid with a height less than 25 ft above the flame source. Wong[29] provided considerably more detail on how to determine this and provided a number of equations for various vessel geometries.

Example 10-9

Leung[30] reported on the computation of the required relief area for a spherical propane vessel exposed to fire. The vessel has a volume of 100 m^3 and contains 50,700 kg of propane. A set pressure of 4.5 bars absolute is required. This corresponds to a set temperature, based on the saturation pressure, of 271.5 K. At these conditions the following physical property data are reported:

$$C_P = C_V = 2.41 \times 10^3 \text{ J/kg K},$$

$$\Delta H_v = 3.74 \times 10^5 \text{ J/kg},$$

$$v_{fg} = 0.1015 \text{ m}^3/\text{kg}.$$

The molecular weight of propane is 44.

Solution

The problem is solved by assuming no overpressure during the relief. The relief vent area calculated is larger than the actual area required for a real relief device with overpressure.

The diameter of the sphere is

$$d = \left(\frac{6A}{\pi}\right)^{1/3} = \left[\frac{(6)(100 \text{ m}^3)}{(3.14)}\right]^{1/3} = 5.76 \text{ m}.$$

The surface area of the sphere is

$$\pi d^2 = (3.14)(5.76 \text{ m})^2 = 104.2 \text{ m}^2 = 1121 \text{ ft}^2.$$

The area exposed to heat is given by the geometry factors provided with Equation 10-36:

$$A = (0.55)(1121 \text{ ft}^2) = 616 \text{ ft}^2.$$

The total heat input is found using Equation 10-36:

$$Q = 199{,}300A^{0.566} = (199{,}300)(616 \text{ ft}^2)^{0.566} = 7.56 \times 10^6 \text{ Btu/hr}$$
$$= 2100 \text{ Btu/s} = 2.22 \times 10^6 \text{ J/s}.$$

If we use Equation 10-37 and assume that the vessel is full of liquid, then the entire vessel surface area is exposed to the fire. If we also assume that no insulation is present, then $F = 1.0$. Then

$$Q = 21{,}000FA^{0.82} = (21{,}000)(1.0)(1121 \text{ ft}^2)^{0.82} = 6.65 \times 10^6 \text{ Btu/hr},$$

which is close to the value estimated using Equation 10-36.

[29] W. Y. Wong, "Fires, Vessels, and the Pressure Relief Valve," *Chemical Engineering* (May 2000).
[30] Leung, "Simplified Vent Sizing Equations."

From Equation 10-15 and assuming $\psi = 1.0$, we obtain

$$G_T = \frac{Q_m}{A} = 0.9\psi \frac{\Delta H_V}{v_{fg}} \sqrt{\frac{g_c}{C_P T_s}}$$

$$= (0.9)(1.0)\left(\frac{3.74 \times 10^5 \text{ J/kg}}{0.1015 \text{ m}^3/\text{ kg}}\right)\left(\frac{1 \text{ N m}}{\text{J}}\right) \times \sqrt{\frac{1 \text{ (kg m/s}^2)/\text{ N}}{(2.41 \times 10^3 \text{ J/kg K})(271.5 \text{ K})(1 \text{ N m/J})}}$$

$$= 4.10 \times 10^3 \text{ kg/m}^2 \text{ s.}$$

The required vent area is determined from Equation 10-35:

$$A = \frac{Qm_o v_{fg}}{G_T V \Delta H_v}$$

$$= \frac{(2.22 \times 10^6 \text{ J/s})(50{,}700 \text{ kg})(0.1015 \text{ m}^3/\text{kg})}{(4.10 \times 10^3 \text{ kg/m}^2 \text{ s})(100 \text{ m}^3)(3.74 \times 10^5 \text{ J/kg})}$$

$$= 0.0745 \text{ m}^2.$$

The required diameter is

$$d = \sqrt{\frac{4A}{\pi}} = \sqrt{\frac{(4)(0.0745 \text{ m}^2)}{(3.14)}}$$

$$= 0.308 \text{ m} = 12.1 \text{ in.}$$

An alternative way to look at the problem might be to ask the question, What initial fill fraction should be specified in the tank to avoid two-phase flow during a fire exposure incident? No tested correlations are presently available to compute the height of a foam layer above the boiling liquid.

For fire reliefs with single-phase vapor flow the equations provided in Sections 10-2 and 10-4 are used to determine the size of the relief.

As mentioned previously, two-phase flow discharges for fire scenarios are possible but not likely. To size the relief for fire and a single-vapor phase, use the heat input determined from Equations 10-36 to 10-38, and determine the vapor mass flow rate through the relief by dividing the heat input by the heat of vaporization of the liquid. This assumes that all the heat input from the fire is used to vaporize the liquid. The relief area is then determined using Equations 10-3 to 10-12.

10-9 Reliefs for Thermal Expansion of Process Fluids

Liquids contained within process vessels and piping will normally expand when heated. The expansion will damage pipes and vessels if the pipe or vessel is filled completely with fluid and the liquid is blocked in.

A typical situation is thermal expansion of water in cooling coils in a reactor, shown in Figure 10-12. If the coils are filled with water and are accidentally blocked in, the water will expand when heated by the reactor contents, leading to damage to the cooling coils.

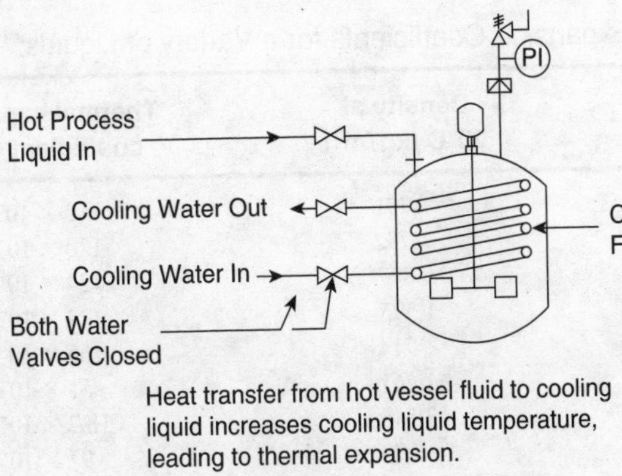

Figure 10-12 Damage to cooling coils as a result of external heating of blocked-in cooling fluid.

Relief vents are installed in these systems to prevent damage resulting from liquid expansion. Although this may appear to be a minor problem, damage to heat exchange systems can result in (1) contamination of product or intermediate substances, (2) subsequent corrosion problems, (3) substantial plant outages, and (4) large repair expenses. Failure in heat exchange equipment is also difficult to identify, and repairs are time consuming.

A thermal expansion coefficient for liquids, β, is defined as

$$\beta = \frac{1}{V}\left(\frac{dV}{dT}\right), \tag{10-39}$$

where

V is the volume of the fluid and
T is the temperature.

Table 10-3 lists thermal expansion coefficients for a number of substances. Water behaves in an unusual fashion. The thermal expansion coefficient decreases with increasing temperature up to about 4°C, after which the thermal expansion coefficient increases with temperature. Coefficients for water are readily determined from the steam tables.

The volumetric expansion rate Q_v through the relief resulting from thermal expansion is

$$Q_v = \frac{dV}{dt} = \frac{dV}{dT}\frac{dT}{dt}. \tag{10-40}$$

By applying the definition of the thermal expansion coefficient, given by Equation 10-39, we obtain

$$Q_v = \beta V \frac{dT}{dt}. \tag{10-41}$$

Table 10-3 Thermal Expansion Coefficients for a Variety of Liquids[a]

Liquid	Density at 20°C (kg/m^3)	Thermal expansion coefficient (°C^{-1})
Alcohol, ethyl	791	112×10^{-5}
Alcohol, methyl	792	120×10^{-5}
Benzene	877	124×10^{-5}
Carbon tetrachloride	1,595	124×10^{-5}
Ether, ethyl	714	166×10^{-5}
Glycerin	1,261	51×10^{-5}
Mercury	13,546	18.2×10^{-5}
Turpentine	873	97×10^{-5}

[a]G. Shortley and D. Williams, *Elements of Physics,* 4th ed. (Englewood Cliffs, NJ: Prentice Hall, 1965), p. 302.

For a pipe or process vessel heated externally by a hot fluid, an energy balance on the fluid is given by

$$mC_P \frac{dT}{dt} = UA(T - T_a), \tag{10-42}$$

where

T is the temperature of the fluid,
C_P is the heat capacity of the liquid,
UA is an overall heat transfer coefficient, and
T_a is the ambient temperature.

It follows that

$$\frac{dT}{dt} = \frac{UA}{mC_P}(T - T_a). \tag{10-43}$$

Substituting into Equation 10-41, we obtain

$$Q_v = \frac{\beta V}{mC_P} UA(T - T_a), \tag{10-44}$$

and, invoking the definition of the liquid density ρ,

$$\boxed{Q_v = \frac{\beta}{\rho C_P} UA(T - T_a).} \tag{10-45}$$

Equation 10-45 describes the fluid expansion only at the beginning of heat transfer, when the fluid is initially exposed to the external temperature T_a. The heat transfer will increase the temperature of the liquid, changing the value of T. However, it is apparent that Equation 10-45 provides the maximum thermal expansion rate, sufficient for sizing a relief device.

The volumetric expansion rate Q_v is subsequently used in an appropriate equation to determine the relief vent size.

Example 10-10

The cooling coil in a reactor has a surface area of 10,000 ft². Under the most severe conditions the coils can contain water at 32°F and can be exposed to superheated steam at 400°F. Given a heat transfer coefficient of 50 Btu/hr-ft²-°F, estimate the volumetric expansion rate of the water in the cooling coils in gpm.

Solution

The expansion coefficient β for water at 32°F should be used. This is estimated using liquid volumetric data from the steam tables over a short range of temperatures around 32°F. However, the steam tables do not provide liquid water specific volume data below 32°F. A value between 32°F and some appropriate higher temperature will suffice. From the steam tables:

Temperature (°F)	Specific volume (ft³/lb$_m$)
32	0.01602
50	0.01603

The expansion coefficient is computed using Equation 10-39:

$$\beta = \frac{1}{v}\frac{dv}{dT} = \frac{1}{0.016025 \text{ ft}^3/\text{lb}_m}\left(\frac{0.01602 - 0.01603}{32 - 50}\right)\left(\frac{\text{ft}^3/\text{lb}_m}{°\text{F}}\right)$$

$$= 3.47 \times 10^{-5}\,°\text{F}^{-1}.$$

The volumetric expansion rate is given by Equation 10-45:

$$Q_v = \frac{\beta}{\rho C_P} UA(T - T_a)$$

$$= \frac{(3.47 \times 10^{-5}/°\text{F})(50 \text{ Btu/hr-ft}^2\text{-}°\text{F})(10{,}000 \text{ ft}^2)(400 - 32)°\text{F}}{(62.4 \text{ lb}_m/\text{ft}^3)(1 \text{ Btu/lb}_m°\text{F})}$$

$$= 102 \text{ ft}^3/\text{hr} = 12.7 \text{ gpm}.$$

The relief device vent area must be designed to accommodate this volumetric flow.

Suggested Reading

Deflagration Vents

W. Bartknecht, "Pressure Venting of Dust Explosions in Large Vessels," *Plant/Operations Progress* (Oct. 1986), 5(4): 196.

Frank T. Bodurtha, *Industrial Explosion Prevention and Protection* (New York: McGraw-Hill, 1980).

Ian Swift and Mike Epstein, "Performance of Low Pressure Explosion Vents," *Plant/Operations Progress* (Apr. 1987), 6(2).

Relief Codes

API RP 520, *Recommended Practice for the Sizing, Selection, and Installation of Pressure-Relieving Systems in Refineries,* 6th ed. (Washington, DC: American Petroleum Institute, 1993).

API RP 521, *Guide for Pressure-Relieving and Depressurizing Systems,* 3rd ed. (Washington, DC: American Petroleum Institute, 1990).

API Standard 2000, *Venting Atmospheric and Low-Pressure Storage Tanks (Nonrefrigerated and Refrigerated),* 5th ed. (Washington, DC: American Petroleum Institute, 1998).

ASME Boiler and Pressure Vessel Code (New York: American Society of Mechanical Engineers, 1998).

NFPA 68, *Guide for Venting of Deflagrations* (Quincy, MA: National Fire Protection Association, 1998).

Two-Phase Flow

G. W. Boicourt, "Emergency Relief System (ERS) Design: An Integrated Approach Using DIERS Methodology," *Process Safety Progress* (Apr. 1995), 14(2).

R. D'Alessandro, "Thrust Force Calculations for Pressure Safety Valves," *Process Safety Progress* (Sept. 2006), 25(3): 203.

R. Darby, "Relief Sizing for Deflagrations," *Process Safety Progress* (June 2006), 25(2): 130.

H. K. Fauske, "Determine Two-Phase Flows During Release," *Chemical Engineering Progress* (Feb. 1999).

H. K. Fauske, "Emergency Relief System (ERS) Design," *Chemical Engineering Progress* (Aug. 1985).

H. K. Fauske, "Flashing Flows or Some Practical Guidelines for Emergency Releases," *Plant/Operations Progress* (July 1985).

H. K. Fauske, "Generalized Vent Sizing Nomogram for Runaway Chemical Reactions," *Plant/Operations Progress* (Oct. 1984), 3(4).

H. Fauske, "Managing Chemical Reactivity—Minimum Best Practice," *Process Safety Progress* (June 2006), 25(2): 120.

H. K. Fauske, "Properly Sized Vents for Nonreactive and Reactive Chemicals," *Chemical Engineering Progress* (Feb. 2000).

H. Fauske, "Revisiting DIERS' Two-Phase Methodology for Reactive Systems Twenty Years Later," *Process Safety Progress* (Sept. 2006), 25(3): 180.

H. K. Fauske and J. C. Leung, "New Experimental Technique for Characterizing Runaway Chemical Reactions," *Chemical Engineering Progress* (Aug. 1985).

K. E. First and J. E. Huff, "Design Charts for Two-Phase Flashing Flow in Emergency Pressure Relief Systems," paper presented at 1988 AIChE Spring National Meeting.

Harold G. Fisher, "DIERS Research Program on Emergency Relief Systems," *Chemical Engineering Progress* (Aug. 1985), p. 33.

H. G. Fisher, H. S. Forrest, S. S. Grossel, J. E. Huff, A. R. Muller, J. A. Noronha, D. A. Shaw, and R. J. Tilley, *Emergency Relief System Design Using DIERS Technology* (New York: American Institute of Chemical Engineers, 1992).

J. C. Leung, "A Generalized Correlation for One-Component Homogeneous Equilibrium Flashing Choked Flow," *AIChE Journal* (Oct. 1986), 32(10): 1743.

J. C. Leung, "Simplified Vent Sizing Equations for Emergency Relief Requirements in Reactors and Storage Vessels," *AIChE Journal* (Oct. 1986), 32(10): 1622.

J. C. Leung and H. G. Fisher, "Two-Phase Flow Venting from Reactor Vessels," *Journal of Loss Prevention* (Apr. 1989), 2(2): 78.

J. C. Leung and M. A. Grolmes, "The Discharge of Two-Phase Flashing Flows in a Horizontal Duct," *AIChE Journal* (Mar. 1987), 33(3): 524.

J. C. Leung and M. A. Grolmes, "A Generalized Correlation for Flashing Choked Flow of Initially Subcooled Liquid," *AIChE Journal* (Apr. 1988), 34(4): 688.

S. Waldram, R. McIntosh, and J. Etchells, "Thrust Force Calculations for Pressure Safety Valves," *Process Safety Progress* (Sept. 2006), 25(3): 214.

Problems

10-1. Estimate the diameter of spring-type liquid reliefs for the following conditions:

Pump capacity at ΔP (gpm)	Set pressure (psig)	Over-pressure (%)	Back-pressure (%)	Valve type	(ρ/ρ_{ref})
a. 100	50	20	10	Conventional	1.0
b. 200	100	20	30	Balanced-bellows	1.3
c. 50	50	10	40	Balanced-bellows	1.2

10-2. Determine the diameter of a spring-type vapor relief for the following conditions. Assume for each case that $\gamma = 1.3$, the set pressure is 100 psia, and the temperature is 100°F.

Compressibility, z	Molecular weight	Mass flow (lb/hr)	Over-pressure (%)	Back-pressure (%)
a. 1.0	28	50	10	10
b. 0.8	28	50	30	10
c. 1.0	44	50	10	10
d. 0.8	44	50	30	10
e. 1.0	28	100	10	30
f. 0.8	28	100	30	30

10-3. Determine the required diameter for rupture discs for the following conditions. Assume a specific gravity of 1.2 for all cases.

Liquid flow (gpm)	Pressure drop (psi)
a. 1000	100
b. 100	100
c. 1000	50
d. 100	50

10-4. Determine the required diameter for rupture discs in vapor service for the following conditions. Assume that nitrogen is the vent gas and that the temperature is 100°F.

Gas flow (lb/hr)	Pressure (psia)
a. 100	100
b. 200	100
c. 100	50
d. 200	50

10-5. Determine the proper relief diameter for the following two-phase flow conditions. Assume in all cases that $L/D = 0.0$.

	a	b	c	d
Reaction mass, lb	10,000	10,000	10,000	10,000
Volume, ft^3	200	500	500	500
Set pressure, psia	100	100	100	100
Set temperature, °F	500	500	500	500
$(dT/dt)_s$, °F/s	0.5	0.5	2.0	2.0
Maximum pressure, psia	120	120	120	140
Maximum temperature, °F	520	520	520	550
$(dT/dt)_m$, °F/s	0.66	0.66	2.4	2.6
Liquid specific volume, ft^3/lb	0.02	0.2	0.02	0.02
Vapor specific volume, ft^3/lb	1.4	1.4	1.4	1.4
Heat capacity, Btu/lb °F	1.1	1.1	1.1	1.1
Heat of vaporization, Btu/lb	130	130	130	130

10-6. How is the overpressure included in the design of two-phase reliefs?

10-7. Determine the relief vent areas for the following two-phase fire scenarios. Assume a spherical vessel in each case.

	a	b	c	d
Molecular weight	72	72	86	86
Volume, ft^3	5000	5000	5000	5000
Initial mass, lb	30,000	15,000	15,000	15,000
Set pressure, psia	100	100	100	100
Set temperature, °F	220	220	220	220
Maximum pressure, psia	100	100	130	150
Maximum temperature, °F	220	220	240	275
Heat of vaporization, Btu/lb	130	130	150	150
v_{fg}, ft^3/lb	1.6	1.6	1.6	1.6
C_P, Btu/lb °F	0.40	0.40	0.52	0.52

10-8. Determine the relief size for spray dryers operating under the following conditions:

Vapors	a	b	c	d
Volume, ft^3	1000	1000	1000	1000
Set pressure, psia	16.7	16.7	16.7	16.7
Maximum pressure, psia	17.6	17.6	29.4	29.4
Gas	Methane	Hydrogen	Methane	Hydrogen

Dusts	a	b	c	d
Volume, ft^3	1000	1000	1000	1000
Dust class	1	3	1	3
Set pressure, psia	16.7	16.7	16.7	16.7
Maximum pressure, psia	20.6	20.6	29.4	29.4

Maximum pressure during combustion, P_{max} is 100 psia

10-9. Determine the size of relief required to protect the following cooling coils against thermal expansion. Water is used for each case. Assume that the tubes can withstand a pressure of 1000 psig and that the normal operating pressure is 200 psig. Assume a set pressure of 500 psig, an overpressure of 20%, and no backpressure.

	a	b	c	d
Blocked-in area, ft^2	10,000	10,000	10,000	10,000
Maximum temperature, °F	550	550	800	550
Minimum temperature, °F	70	50	32	70
Heat transfer coefficient, Btu/hr ft^2 °F	75	75	75	125

10-10. Consider Problem 10-9, part a. This time use alcohol as a liquid medium with a thermal expansion coefficient of $1.12 \times 10^{-3}/°C$. The heat capacity of the alcohol is 0.58 kcal/kg°C, and its density is 791 kg/m^3. Determine the relief size required.

10-11. A process vessel is equipped with a 2-in rupture disc set at 100 psig and designed for 10% overpressure. A nitrogen line must be added to the vessel to provide the capability of purging and/or pressure discharging liquids. What size line would you select if the nitrogen is available from a 500-psig source? The temperature is 80°F.

10-12. A cylindrical tank, 4 ft in diameter and 10 ft long, is completely filled with water and blocked in. Estimate the thermal expansion rate of the water if the water is at 50°F and the steel shell of the tank is suddenly heated to 100°F by the sun. Assume a heat transfer coefficient of 50 Btu/hr ft^2 °F and that only the top half of the tank is heated.

If the tank is exposed to fire, what is the required relief area? Assume no overpressure. The tank MAWP is 200 psig.

10-13. A spray dryer is used to dry vitamins in powder form. The dryer consists of a cylindrical Section 12.0 ft high and 5 ft in diameter. Attached to the bottom of the cylindrical section is a cone section for collecting the dried powder. The cone is 5 ft long. If the deflagration index for the vitamin powder is 80 bar m/s, determine the area required for a deflagration vent. Assume that the vent opens at 0.2 bar gauge and the maximum pressure during combustion is 0.5 bar gauge.

10-14. The reactor system in a pilot plant contains stock tanks that are 24 in in diameter and 36 in high. A relief system must be designed to protect the vessel in the event of fire exposure. The vessel contains a flammable polymer material. What rupture disc diameter is required to relieve the vessel properly? Assume a discharge pressure of 10 psig. The molecular weight of the liquid is 162.2, its boiling point is 673°R, the heat of vaporization is 92.4 Btu/lb, and the heat capacity ratio of the vapor is 1.30.

10-15. You have been assigned the task of reviewing the relief scenarios for a specific chemical reactor in your plant. You are currently reviewing the scenario involving the failure of a nitrogen regulator that provides inert padding to the vapor space of the reactor. Your calculations show that the maximum discharge rate of nitrogen through the existing relief system of the vessel is 0.5 kg/s. However, your calculations also show that the flow of nitrogen through the 1-in supply pipe will be much greater than this. Thus under the current configuration a failure of the nitrogen regulator will result in an overpressuring of the reactor.

One way to solve the problem is to install an orifice plate in the nitrogen line, thus limiting the flow to the maximum of 0.5 kg/s. Determine the orifice diameter (in cm) required to achieve this flow. Assume a nitrogen source supply pressure of 15 bar absolute. The ambient temperature is 25°C and the ambient pressure is 1 atm.

10-16. A batch chemical reactor contains 10,000 kg of reacting liquid material. A relief device must be properly sized for a potential runaway reaction.

A laboratory test has shown that the reaction will not result in a two-phase relief. Thus a vapor relief system must be designed. Furthermore, calorimeter tests indicate that the maximum self-heat rate is 40°C/min. The physical properties of the material are also reported:

Heat capacity of liquid: 2.5 kJ/kg K
Heat of vaporization: 300 kJ/kg
Molecular weight: 100
Vapor acts as an ideal triatomic gas.

a. Determine the maximum vaporization rate during a runaway reaction (in kg/s).

b. Determine the relief diameter (in m) required to vent the runaway reaction. Assume a MAWP of 7 bar gauge, 10% backpressure, and a conventional spring-operated relief. Assume a temperature of 200°C at the relief conditions.

10-17. A pole barn with thin metal walls must be fitted with a vent to safely vent a hydrocarbon deflagration from the combustion of a hydrocarbon similar to propane. The maximum pressure that this building can withstand is estimated at 0.5 psi. Determine the vent area required for this structure if the total internal surface area of the structure (including floor and roof) is 24,672 ft^2.

10-18. a. Calculate the mass flux (kg/m^2s) of gaseous material through a leak assuming that the material is stored at its vapor pressure within the vessel (9.5×10^5 Pa abs). Assume that the material is stored at 25°C, that it is discharged to 1 atm pressure, and that its molecular weight is 44.

b. Calculate the mass flux (kg/m^2s) of two-phase material through the same leak under the same conditions of part a. Assume that the discharge length is greater than 10 cm. Additional physical property data are

Heat of vaporization: 3.33×10^5 J/kg
v_{fg}: 0.048 m^3/kg
Heat capacity of liquid: 2.23×10^3 J/kg K
Heat capacity of vapor: 1.70×10^3 J/kg K

c. Comment on the difference in flux rates between parts a and b. In general, relief systems designed for two-phase flow must be larger than those for all-vapor flow. Is this consistent with the results of parts a and b? Why?

d. Calculate the energy discharge rate for the discharge of part a. Assume that the energy content of the vapor is due to the heat of vaporization of the liquid to gas.

e. Calculate the energy discharge rate for the discharge of part b. Assume that the energy is due to the sensible heat increase of the two-phase discharge stream and that the temperature of the discharge is 10 K higher.

f. Compare the results of parts d and e. How many times larger must the area of the two-phase discharge be in order to remove energy at the same rate as the single-phase relief? Comment on the implications for relief systems on reactor vessels.

10-19. A 500-gpm pump is used to provide water to a reactor vessel. If the pump continues to operate, the reactor might be overfilled and overpressurized. Determine the relief diameter (in inches) required to protect the vessel. The MAWP of the vessel is 100 psig. Please state clearly any additional assumptions required for your calculation. Assume a 10% backpressure and a 10% overpressure in the relief system.

10-20. Determine the areas of two relief valves – (a) conventional spring-operated and (b) pilot-operated – for the following conditions:

Liquid:	100 gpm
Set pressure:	100 psig
Overpressure:	10 %
Backpressure:	30 %
Viscosity:	1000 centipoise
Temperature:	60 deg. F
Specific gravity: 1.23	

10-21. A vent must be designed for a room that is 20 ft long, 30 ft wide, and 20 ft high. The room is used for dispensing flammable liquids. The fundamental burning velocities of the liquid vapors are less than 1.3 times that of propane. One wall of the room is located against the wall of another structure and is thus not available for a vent.

a. Determine the vent area required if the maximum pressure that the room can withstand is 0.69 psi. How does this area compare to the wall area available for the vent?

b. Determine the vent area required if the maximum pressure that the room can withstand is 1.04 psi. Is adequate wall area now available for the vent?

CHAPTER 11

Hazards Identification

Hazards are everywhere. Unfortunately, a hazard is not always identified until an accident occurs. It is essential to identify the hazards and reduce the risk well in advance of an accident.

For each process in a chemical plant the following questions must be asked:

1. What are the hazards?
2. What can go wrong and how?
3. What are the chances?
4. What are the consequences?

The first question represents hazard identification. The last three questions are associated with risk assessment, considered in detail in Chapter 12. Risk assessment includes a determination of the events that can produce an accident, the probability of those events, and the consequences. The consequences could include human injury or loss of life, damage to the environment, or loss of production and capital equipment. Question 2 is frequently called scenario identification.

The terminology used varies considerably. Hazard identification and risk assessment are sometimes combined into a general category called hazard evaluation. Risk assessment is sometimes called hazard analysis. A risk assessment procedure that determines probabilities is frequently called probabilistic risk assessment (PRA), whereas a procedure that determines probability and consequences is called quantitative risk analysis (QRA).

Figure 11-1 illustrates the normal procedure for using hazards identification and risk assessment. After a description of the process is available, the hazards are identified. The various scenarios by which an accident can occur are then determined. This is followed by a concurrent

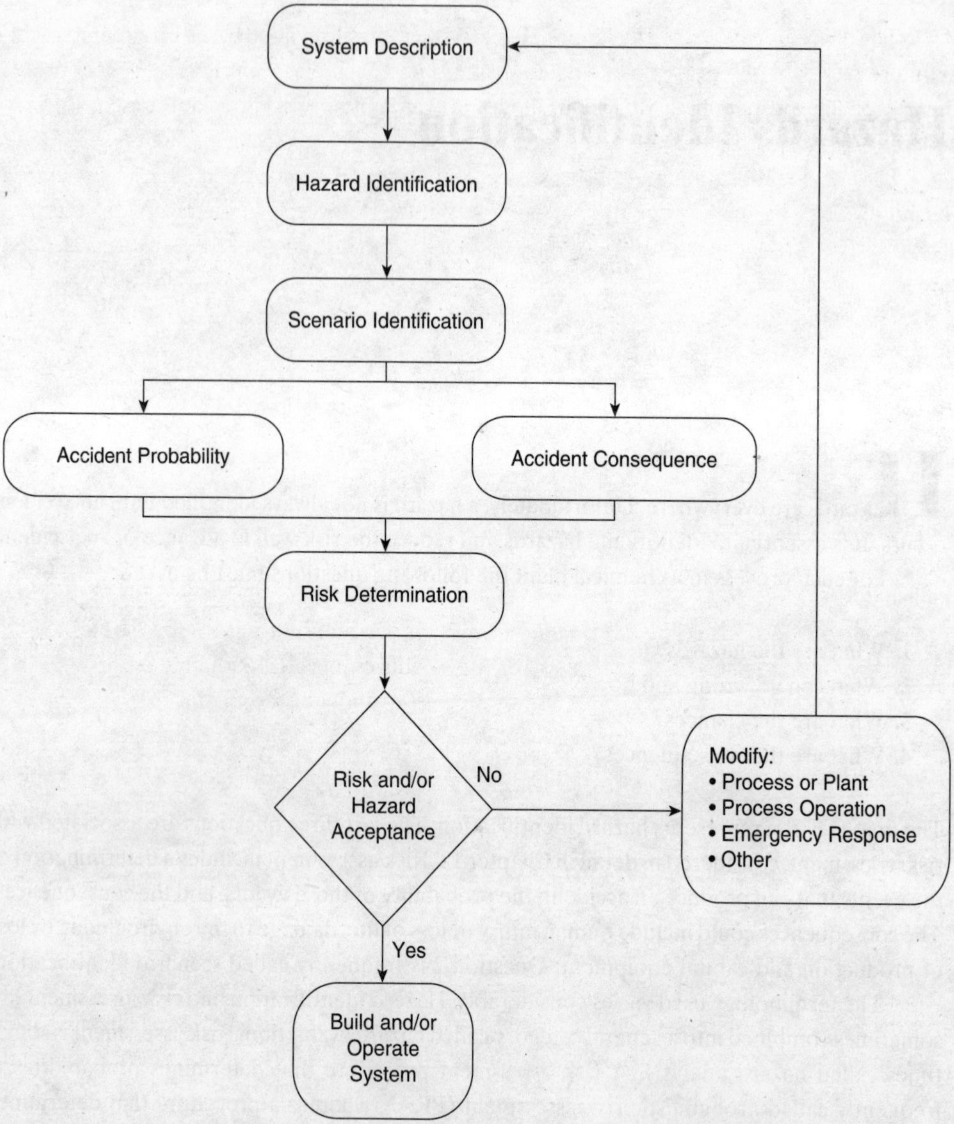

Figure 11-1 Hazards identification and risk assessment procedure. Adapted from *Guidelines for Hazards Evaluation Procedures* (New York: American Institute of Chemical Engineers, 1985), pp. 1–9.

study of both the probability and the consequences of an accident. This information is assembled into a final risk assessment. If the risk is acceptable, then the study is complete and the process is operated. If the risk is unacceptable, then the system must be modified and the procedure is restarted.

The procedure described by Figure 11-1 is frequently abbreviated based on circumstances. If failure rate data on the applicable equipment are not available, then risk assessment procedures cannot be fully applied. Most plant sites (and even subunits within a plant) modify the procedure to fit their particular situation.

Hazards identification and risk assessment studies can be performed at any stage during the initial design or ongoing operation of a process. If the study is performed with the initial design, it should be done as soon as possible. This enables modifications to be easily incorporated into the final design.

Hazard identification can be performed independent of risk assessment. However, the best result is obtained if they are done together. One outcome is that hazards of low probability and minimal consequences are identified and addressed with the result that the process is "gold-plated." This means that potentially unnecessary and expensive safety equipment and procedures are implemented. For instance, flying aircraft and tornadoes are hazards to a chemical plant. What are the chances of their occurrence, and what should be done about them? For most facilities the probability of these hazards is small: No steps are required for prevention. Likewise, hazards with reasonable probability but minimal consequences are sometimes also neglected.

An important part of the hazard identification procedure shown in Figure 11-1 is the risk acceptance step. Each organization using these procedures must have suitable criteria.

Many methods are available for performing hazard identification and risk assessment.[1] Only a few of the more popular approaches are considered here. No single approach is necessarily best suited for any particular application. The selection of the best method requires experience. Most companies use these methods or adaptations to suit their particular operation.

The hazard identification methods described in this chapter include the following:

1. Process hazards checklists: This is a list of items and possible problems in the process that must be checked.
2. Hazards surveys: This can be as simple as an inventory of hazardous materials, or it can be as detailed as the Dow indexes. The Dow indexes are a formal rating system, much like an income tax form, that provides penalties for hazards and credits for safety equipment and procedures.
3. Hazards and operability (HAZOP) studies: This approach allows the mind to go free in a controlled environment. Various events are suggested for a specific piece of equipment with the participants determining whether and how the event could occur and whether the event creates any form of risk.
4. Safety review: An effective but less formal type of HAZOP study. The results are highly dependent on the experience and synergism of the group reviewing the process.

[1] *Guidelines for Hazard Evaluation Procedures,* 3rd ed. (New York: American Institute of Chemical Engineers, 2008).

11-1 Process Hazards Checklists

A process hazards checklist is simply a list of possible problems and areas to be checked. The list reminds the reviewer or operator of the potential problem areas. A checklist can be used during the design of a process to identify design hazards, or it can be used before process operation.

A classic example is an automobile checklist that one might review before driving away on a vacation. This checklist might contain the following items:

- Check oil in engine
- Check air pressure in tires
- Check fluid level in radiator
- Check air filter
- Check fluid level in windshield washer tank
- Check headlights and taillights
- Check exhaust system for leaks
- Check fluid levels in brake system
- Check gasoline level in tank

Checklists for chemical processes can be detailed, involving hundreds or even thousands of items. But, as illustrated in the vacation example, the effort expended in developing and using checklists can yield significant results.

A typical process design safety checklist is shown in Figure 11-2. Note that three checkoff columns are provided. The first column is used to indicate those areas that have been thoroughly investigated. The second column is used for those items that do not apply to the particular process. The last column is used to mark those areas requiring further investigation. Extensive notes on individual areas are kept separate from the checklist.

The design of the checklist depends on the intent. A checklist intended for use during the initial design of the process will be considerably different from a checklist used for a process change. Some companies have checklists for specific pieces of equipment, such as a heat exchanger or a distillation column.

Checklists should be applied only during the preliminary stages of hazard identification and should not be used as a replacement for a more complete hazard identification procedure. Checklists are most effective in identifying hazards arising from process design, plant layout, storage of chemicals, electrical systems, and so forth.

11-2 Hazards Surveys

A hazards survey can be as simple as an inventory of hazardous materials in a facility or as complicated as a rigorous procedure such as the Dow Fire and Explosion Index (F&EI)[2] and the

[2] *Dow's Fire and Explosion Index Hazard Classification Code,* 7th ed. (New York: American Institute of Chemical Engineers, 1994).

	Completed ↓	Does not apply ↓	Further study required ↓
General layout			
1. Areas properly drained?	□	□	□
2. Aisleways provided?	□	□	□
3. Fire walls, dikes and special guardrails needed?	□	□	□
4. Hazardous underground obstructions?	□	□	□
5. Hazardous overhead restrictions?	□	□	□
6. Emergency accesses and exits?	□	□	□
7. Enough headroom?	□	□	□
8. Access for emergency vehicles?	□	□	□
9. Safe storage space for raw materials and finished products?	□	□	□
10. Adequate platforms for safe maintenance operations?	□	□	□
11. Hoists and elevators properly designed and safeguarded?	□	□	□
12. Clearance for overhead power lines?	□	□	□
Buildings			
1. Adequate ladders, stairways and escapeways?	□	□	□
2. Fire doors required?	□	□	□
3. Head obstructions marked?	□	□	□
4. Ventilation adequate?	□	□	□
5. Need for ladder or stairway to roof?	□	□	□
6. Safety glass specified where necessary?	□	□	□
7. Need for fireproofed structural steel?	□	□	□
Process			
1. Consequences of exposure to adjacent operations considered?	□	□	□
2. Special fume or dust hoods required?	□	□	□
3. Unstable materials properly stored?	□	□	□
4. Process laboratory checked for runaway explosive conditions?	□	□	□
5. Provisions for protection from explosions?	□	□	□
6. Hazardous reactions possible due to mistakes or contamination?	□	□	□
7. Chemistry of processes completely understood and reviewed?	□	□	□
8. Provisions for rapid disposal of reactants in an emergency?	□	□	□
9. Failure of mechanical equipment possible cause of hazards?	□	□	□

Figure 11-2 A typical process safety checklist. A list of this type is frequently used before a more complete analysis. Adapted from Henry E. Webb, "What to Do When Disaster Strikes," in *Safe and Efficient Plant Operation and Maintenance,* Richard Greene, ed. (New York: McGraw-Hill, 1980). (*continues*)

	Further study required ↓	Does not apply ↓	Completed ↓
10. Hazards possible from gradual or sudden blockages in piping or equipment?	□	□	□
11. Public liability risks possible from sprays, fumes, mists or noise?	□	□	□
12. Provisions made for disposal of toxic materials?	□	□	□
13. Hazards involved in sewering material?	□	□	□
14. Material safety data sheets available for all chemical species?	□	□	□
15. Hazards possible from simultaneous loss of two or more utilities?	□	□	□
16. Safety factors altered by design revisions?	□	□	□
17. Consequences of reasonably worst incident, or combination of incidents, reviewed?	□	□	□
18. Process diagrams correct and up-to-date?	□	□	□
Piping			
1. Safety showers and eye baths required?	□	□	□
2. Sprinkler systems required?	□	□	□
3. Provisions for thermal expansion?	□	□	□
4. All overflow lines directed to safe areas?	□	□	□
5. Vent lines directed safely?	□	□	□
6. Piping specifications followed?	□	□	□
7. Washing-down hoses needed?	□	□	□
8. Check valves provided as needed?	□	□	□
9. Protection and identification of fragile pipe considered?	□	□	□
10. Possible deterioration of exterior of piping by chemicals?	□	□	□
11. Emergency valves readily accessible?	□	□	□
12. Long and large vent lines supported?	□	□	□
13. Steam condensate piping safely designed?	□	□	□
14. Relief valve piping designed to prevent plugging?	□	□	□
15. Drains to relieve pressure on suction and discharge of all process pumps?	□	□	□
16. City water lines not connected to process pipes?	□	□	□
17. Flammable fluids feeding production units shut off from a safe distance in case of fire or other emergency?	□	□	□
18. Personnel protective insulation provided?	□	□	□
19. Hot steam lines insulated?	□	□	□
Equipment			
1. Designs correct for maximum operating pressure?	□	□	□
2. Corrosion allowance considered?	□	□	□

Figure 11-2 (*continues*)

	Completed ↓	Does not apply ↓	Further study required ↓
3. Special isolation for hazardous equipment?	☐	☐	☐
4. Guards for belts, pulleys, sheaves and gears?	☐	☐	☐
5. Schedule for checking protective devices?	☐	☐	☐
6. Dikes for any storage tanks?	☐	☐	☐
7. Guard rails for storage tanks?	☐	☐	☐
8. Construction materials compatible with process chemicals?	☐	☐	☐
9. Reclaimed and replacement equipment checked structurally and for process pressures?	☐	☐	☐
10. Pipelines independently supported to relieve pumps and other equipment, as necessary?	☐	☐	☐
11. Automatic lubrication of critical machinery?	☐	☐	☐
12. Emergency standby equipment needed?	☐	☐	☐
Venting			
1. Relief valves or rupture disks required?	☐	☐	☐
2. Materials of construction corrosion resistant?	☐	☐	☐
3. Vents properly designed? (Size, direction, configuration?)	☐	☐	☐
4. Flame arrestors required on vent lines?	☐	☐	☐
5. Relief valves protected from plugging by rupture disks?	☐	☐	☐
6. Telltale pressure gauges installed between rupture disks and relief valve?	☐	☐	☐
Instrument and Electrical			
1. All controls fail safe?	☐	☐	☐
2. Dual indication of process variables necessary?	☐	☐	☐
3. All equipment properly labelled?	☐	☐	☐
4. Tubing runs protected?	☐	☐	☐
5. Safeguards provided for process control when an instrument must be taken out of service?	☐	☐	☐
6. Process safety affected by response lag?	☐	☐	☐
7. Labels for all start-stop switches?	☐	☐	☐
8. Equipment designed to permit lockout protection?	☐	☐	☐
9. Electrical failures cause unsafe conditions?	☐	☐	☐
10. Sufficient lighting for both outside and inside operations?	☐	☐	☐
11. Lights provided for all sight glasses, showers and eyebaths?	☐	☐	☐
12. Breakers adequated for circuit protection?	☐	☐	☐
13. All equipment grounded?	☐	☐	☐

Figure 11-2 *(continues)*

	Further study required ↓	Does not apply ↓	Completed ↓
14. Special interlocks needed for safe operation?	☐	☐	☐
15. Emergency standby power on lighting equipment required?	☐	☐	☐
16. Emergency escape lighting required during power failure?	☐	☐	☐
17. All necessary communications equipment provided?	☐	☐	☐
18. Emergency disconnect switches properly marked?	☐	☐	☐
19. Special explosion proof electrical fixtures required?	☐	☐	☐
Safety Equipment			
1. Fire extinguishers required?	☐	☐	☐
2. Special respiratory equipment required?	☐	☐	☐
3. Diking material required?	☐	☐	☐
4. Colorimetric indicator tubes required?	☐	☐	☐
5. Flammable vapor detection apparatus required?	☐	☐	☐
6. Fire extinguishing materials compatible with process materials?	☐	☐	☐
7. Special emergency procedures and alarms required?	☐	☐	☐
Raw Materials			
1. Any materials and products require special handling equipment?	☐	☐	☐
2. Any raw materials and products affected by extreme weather conditions?	☐	☐	☐
3. Any products hazardous from a toxic or fire standpoint?	☐	☐	☐
4. Proper containers being used?	☐	☐	☐
5. Containers properly labelled for toxicity, flammability, stability, etc?	☐	☐	☐
6. Consequences of bad spills considered?	☐	☐	☐
7. Special instructions needed for containers or for storage and warehousing by distributors?	☐	☐	☐
8. Does warehouse have operating instructions covering each product regarded as critical?	☐	☐	☐

Figure 11-2 (*continued*)

Dow-Chemical Exposure Index (CEI)[3], which are two popular forms of hazards survey. These are formal systematized approaches using a rating form, similar to an income tax form. The final rating number provides a relative ranking of the hazard. The F&EI also contains a mechanism for estimating the dollar loss in the event of an accident.

The Dow F&EI is designed for rating the relative hazards with the storage, handling, and processing of explosive and flammable materials. The main idea of this procedure is to provide a purely systematic approach, mostly independent of judgmental factors, for determining the relative magnitude of flammable hazards in a chemical plant. The main forms used for the computations are shown in Figures 11-3 and 11-4.

The procedure begins with a material factor that is a function only of the type of chemical or chemicals used. This factor is adjusted for general and special process hazards. These adjustments or penalties are based on conditions such as storage above the flash or boiling point, endo- or exothermic reactions, and fired heaters. Credits for various safety systems and procedures are used for estimating the consequences of the hazard, after the fire and explosion index has been determined.

The form shown in Figure 11-3 consists of three columns of numbers. The first column is the penalty column. Penalties for various unsafe situations are placed in this column. The second column contains the penalty actually used. This allows for a reduction or increase in the penalty based on extenuating circumstances not completely covered by the form. In the event of uncertainty here, the complete penalty value from the first column is used. The final column is used for computation.

The first step in the procedure is to conceptually divide the process into separate process units. A process unit is a single pump, a reactor, or a storage tank. A large process results in hundreds of individual units. It is not practical to apply the fire and explosion index to all these units. The usual approach is to select only the units that experience shows to have the highest likelihood of a hazard. A process safety checklist or hazards survey is frequently used to select the most hazardous units for further analysis.

The next step is to determine the material factor (MF) for use in the form shown in Figure 11-3. Table 11-1 lists MFs for a number of important compounds. This list also includes data on heat of combustion and flash and boiling point temperatures. The additional data are also used in the computation of the Dow F&EI. A procedure is provided in the complete index for computing the material factor for other compounds not listed in Table 11-1 or provided in the Dow reference.

In general, the higher the value of the MF, the more flammable and/or explosive the material. If mixtures of materials are used, the MF is determined from the properties of the mixture. The highest value of the MF under the complete range of operating conditions is suggested. The resulting MF value for the process is written in the space provided at the top of the form in Figure 11-3.

[3]*Dow's Chemical Exposure Index Guide,* 1st ed. (New York: American Institute of Chemical Engineers, 1998).

FIRE & EXPLOSION INDEX

AREA / COUNTRY	DIVISION	LOCATION	DATE
SITE	MANUFACTURING UNIT	PROCESS UNIT	
PREPARED BY:	APPROVED BY: (Superintendent)	BUILDING	
REVIEWED BY: (Management)	REVIEWED BY: (Technology Center)	REVIEWED BY: (Safety & Loss Prevention)	
MATERIALS IN PROCESS UNIT			
STATE OF OPERATION __ DESIGN __ START UP __ NORMAL OPERATION __ SHUTDOWN		BASIC MATERIAL(S) FOR MATERIAL FACTOR	
MATERIAL FACTOR (See Table 1 or Appendices A or B) Note requirements when unit temperature over 140 °F (60 °C)			

1. General Process Hazards	Penalty Factor Range	Penalty Factor Used(1)
Base Factor	1.00	1.00
A. Exothermic Chemical Reactions	0.30 to 1.25	
B. Endothermic Processes	0.20 to 0.40	
C. Material Handling and Transfer	0.25 to 1.05	
D. Enclosed or Indoor Process Units	0.25 to 0.90	
E. Access	0.20 to 0.35	
F. Drainage and Spill Control ______ gal or cu.m.	0.25 to 0.50	
General Process Hazards Factor (F_1)		
2. Special Process Hazards		
Base Factor	1.00	1.00
A. Toxic Material(s)	0.20 to 0.80	
B. Sub-Atmospheric Pressure (< 500 mm Hg)	0.50	
C. Operation In or Near Flammable Range ___ Inerted ___ Not Inerted		
1. Tank Farms Storage Flammable Liquids	0.50	
2. Process Upset or Purge Failure	0.30	
3. Always in Flammable Range	0.80	
D. Dust Explosion (See Table 3)	0.25 to 2.00	
E. Pressure (See Figure 2) Operating Pressure ______ psig or kPa gauge Relief Setting ______ psig or kPa gauge		
F. Low Temperature	0.20 to 0.30	
G. Quantity of Flammable/Unstable Material: Quantity ____ lb or kg H_C = _____BTU/lb or kcal/kg		
1. Liquids or Gases in Process (See Figure 3)		
2. Liquids or Gases in Storage (See Figure 4)		
3. Combustible Solids in Storage, Dust in Process (See Figure 5)		
H. Corrosion and Erosion	0.10 to 0.75	
I. Leakage – Joints and Packing	0.10 to 1.50	
J. Use of Fired Equipment (See Figure 6)		
K. Hot Oil Heat Exchange System (See Table 5)	0.15 to 1.15	
L. Rotating Equipment	0.50	
Special Process Hazards Factor (F_2)		
Process Unit Hazards Factor ($F_1 \times F_2$) = F_3		
Fire and Explosion Index ($F_3 \times MF$ = F&EI)		

(1) For no penalty use 0.00.

5

Rev/01-94

Figure 11-3 Form used in the Dow Fire and Explosion Index. The figures and tables referenced in the form are provided in the index booklet. Source: *Dow's Fire and Explosion Index Hazard Classification Guide,* 7th ed. (1994). Reproduced by permission of the American Institute of Chemical Engineers.

LOSS CONTROL CREDIT FACTORS

1. Process Control Credit Factor (C_1)

Feature	Credit Factor Range	Credit Factor Used(2)	Feature	Credit Factor Range	Credit Factor Used(2)
a. Emergency Power	0.98		f. Inert Gas	0.94 to 0.96	
b. Cooling	0.97 to 0.99		g. Operating Instructions/Procedures	0.91 to 0.99	
c. Explosion Control	0.84 to 0.98		h. Reactive Chemical Review	0.91 to 0.98	
d. Emergency Shutdown	0.96 to 0.99		i. Other Process Hazard Analysis	0.91 to 0.98	
e. Computer Control	0.93 to 0.99				

C_1 Value(3) ☐

2. Material Isolation Credit Factor (C_2)

Feature	Credit Factor Range	Credit Factor Used(2)	Feature	Credit Factor Range	Credit Factor Used(2)
a. Remote Control Valves	0.96 to 0.98		c. Drainage	0.91 to 0.97	
b. Dump/Blowdown	0.96 to 0.98		d. Interlock	0.98	

C_2 Value(3) ☐

3. Fire Protection Credit Factor (C_3)

Feature	Credit Factor Range	Credit Factor Used(2)	Feature	Credit Factor Range	Credit Factor Used(2)
a. Leak Detection	0.94 to 0.98		f. Water Curtains	0.97 to 0.98	
b. Structural Steel	0.95 to 0.98		g. Foam	0.92 to 0.97	
c. Fire Water Supply	0.94 to 0.97		h. Hand Extinguishers/Monitors	0.93 to 0.98	
d. Special Systems	0.91		i. Cable Protection	0.94 to 0.98	
e. Sprinkler Systems	0.74 to 0.97				

C_3 Value(3) ☐

Loss Control Credit Factor = C_1 X C_2 X C_3(3) = ☐ (Enter on line 7 below)

PROCESS UNIT RISK ANALYSIS SUMMARY

1. Fire & Explosion Index (F&EI)........................ (See Front)		
2. Radius of Exposure..(Figure 7)	ft or m	
3. Area of Exposure...	ft² or m²	
4. Value of Area of Exposure..		$MM
5. Damage Factor ....(Figure 8)		
6. Base Maximum Probable Property Damage – (Base MPPD) [4 x 5]		$MM
7. Loss Control Credit Factor...............................(See Above)		
8. Actual Maximum Probable Property Damage – (Actual MPPD) [6 x 7]		$MM
9. Maximum Probable Days Outage – (MPDO)......(Figure 9)	days	
10. Business Interruption – (BI)..		$MM

(2) For no credit factor enter 1.00. (3) Product of all factors used.
Refer to *Fire & Explosion Index Hazard Classification Guide* for details.

Rev/01-94

Figure 11-4 Form used for consequences analysis. Source: *Dow's Fire and Explosion Index Hazard Classification Guide,* 7th ed. (1994). Reproduced by permission of the American Institute of Chemical Engineers.

Table 11-1 Selected Data for the Dow Fire and Explosion Index[a]

Compound	Material factor	Heat of combustion (Btu/lb × 10^{-3})	Flash point (°F)	Boiling point (°F)
Acetone	16	12.3	−4	133
Acetylene	29	20.7	Gas	−118
Benzene	16	17.3	12	176
Bromine	1	0.0	–	–
1,3-Butadiene	24	19.2	−105	24
Butane	21	19.7	Gas	31
Calcium carbide	24	9.1	–	–
Carbon monoxide	21	4.3	Gas	−313
Chlorine	1	0.0	Gas	−29
Cyclohexane	16	18.7	−4	179
Cyclohexanol	10	15.0	154	322
Diesel fuel	10	18.7	100–130	315
Ethane	21	20.4	Gas	−128
Ethylene	24	20.8	Gas	−155
Fuel oil #1	10	18.7	100–162	304–574
Fuel oil #6	10	18.7	100–270	–
Gasoline	16	18.8	−45	100–400
Hydrogen	21	51.6	Gas	−423
Methane	21	21.5	Gas	−258
Methanol	16	8.6	52	147
Mineral oil	4	17.0	380	680
Nitroglycerine	40	7.8	–	–
Octane	16	20.5	56	258
Pentane	21	19.4	<−40	97
Petroleum (crude)	16	21.3	20–90	–
Propylene	21	19.7	−162	−54
Styrene	24	17.4	88	293
Toluene	16	17.4	40	232
Vinyl chloride	24	8.0	−108	7
Xylene	16	17.6	77	279

[a]Selected from *Dow's Fire and Explosion Index Hazard Classification Guide,* 7th ed. (New York: American Institute of Chemical Engineers, 1994).

The next step is to determine the general process hazards. Penalties are applied for the following factors:

1. Exothermic reactions that might self-heat
2. Endothermic reactions that could react because of an external heat source such as a fire
3. Material handling and transfer, including pumping and connection of transfer lines
4. Enclosed process units preventing dispersion of escaped vapors

5. Limited access for emergency equipment
6. Poor drainage of flammable materials away from the process unit

Penalties for special process hazards are determined next:

1. Toxic materials, which could impede fire fighting
2. Less than atmospheric pressure operation with a risk of outside air entering
3. Operation in or near the flammable limits
4. Dust explosion risks
5. Higher than atmospheric pressure
6. Low-temperature operation with potential embrittlement of carbon steel vessels
7. Quantity of flammable material
8. Corrosion and erosion of process unit structures
9. Leakage around joints and packings
10. Use of fired heaters, providing a ready ignition source
11. Hot oil heat exchange systems where the hot oil is above its ignition temperature
12. Large rotating equipment, including pumps and compressors

Detailed instructions and correlations for determining the general and special process hazards are provided in the complete Dow F&EI.

The general process hazard factor (F_1) and special process hazard factor (F_2) are multiplied together to produce a unit hazard factor (F_3). The Dow F&EI is computed by multiplying the unit hazard factor by the MF. Table 11-2 provides the degree of hazard based on the index value.

The Dow F&EI can be used to determine the consequences of an accident. This includes the maximum probable property damage (MPPD) and the maximum probable days outage (MPDO).

The consequences analysis is completed using the worksheet form shown in Figure 11-4. The computations are completed in the Risk Analysis Summary table at the bottom of the form.

Table 11-2 Determining the Degree of Hazard from the Dow Fire and Explosion Index

Dow Fire and Explosion Index	Degree of hazard
1–60	Light
61–96	Moderate
97–127	Intermediate
128–158	Heavy
159 and above	Severe

The damage radius is first estimated using a correlation published in the complete Dow index. This correlation is based on the previously determined F&EI. The dollar value of the equipment within this radius is determined. Next, a damage factor (based on a correlation provided) is applied to the fraction of the equipment actually damaged by the explosion or fire. Finally, a credit factor is applied based on safety systems. The final number, in dollars, is the MPPD value. This number is used to estimate the MPDO using a correlation. Details on the procedure are available in the complete Dow reference.

The Dow indexes are useful for determining equipment spacing requirements. The F&EI uses an empirical correlation based entirely on the F&EI value to estimate the radius of exposure. It is assumed that any equipment located outside this distance would not be damaged by a fire or explosion. The CEI estimates the hazard distance for chemical exposure based on the emergency response planning guideline (ERPG) values for the particular material released.

Example 11-1

Your plant is considering the installation of a new railcar tank unloading facility. The facility will unload nominal 25,000-gal tank cars containing either pure butadiene or cyclohexane. The unloading system will be equipped with an emergency shutdown system with remotely operated block valves. The unloading operation will be done by computer control. The railcars are inerted with nitrogen to a pressure of 40 psig, and the railcar relief system has a set pressure of 75 psig. The unloading operating instructions are written and have been reviewed by the corporate technical staff. A reactive chemicals review has already been completed on the proposed facility. Combustible gas detectors will be located at the unloading station. A deluge system will be installed at the unloading site with an excellent water supply. A diking system will surround three sides of the facility, with any spills directed to a covered impounding area.

Determine the Dow F&EI for this operation, and determine the minimum spacing from adjacent units.

Solution

The Dow Index contains most of the data required to complete the evaluation. The data for the chemical species used in this facility are

Species	Material factor	NFPA health rating	Heat of combustion (Btu/lb)	Flash point (°F)
Butadiene	24	2	19.2×10^3	−105
Cyclohexane	16	1	18.7×10^3	−4

Because the butadiene has the higher MF, it is the material we need to evaluate using the Dow F&EI.

The completed F&EI form is shown in Figure 11-5. Each nonzero item on the form is discussed in what follows.

FIRE & EXPLOSION INDEX

AREA / COUNTRY North America	DIVISION North Central	LOCATION Arkansas	DATE 03/04/94
SITE No Loss	MANUFACTURING UNIT Dow Polymer	PROCESS UNIT Rail Car Unloading	
PREPARED BY: John Smith	APPROVED BY: (Superintendent) Alvin Doe		BUILDING A-103
REVIEWED BY: (Management) Robert Big	REVIEWED BY: (Technology Center) Bill Wright		REVIEWED BY: (Safety & Loss Prevention)
MATERIALS IN PROCESS UNIT Butadiene, Cyclohexane			
STATE OF OPERATION __ DESIGN __ START UP _X_ NORMAL OPERATION __ SHUTDOWN		BASIC MATERIAL(S) FOR MATERIAL FACTOR Butadiene	
MATERIAL FACTOR (See Table 1 or Appendices A or B) Note requirements when unit temperature over 140 °F (60 °C)			24

	Penalty Factor Range	Penalty Factor Used(1)
1. General Process Hazards		
Base Factor	1.00	1.00
A. Exothermic Chemical Reactions	0.30 to 1.25	–
B. Endothermic Processes	0.20 to 0.40	–
C. Material Handling and Transfer	0.25 to 1.05	.5
D. Enclosed or Indoor Process Units	0.25 to 0.90	–
E. Access	0.20 to 0.35	–
F. Drainage and Spill Control ______ gal or cu.m.	0.25 to 0.50	–
General Process Hazards Factor (F_1)		1.5
2. Special Process Hazards		
Base Factor	1.00	1.00
A. Toxic Material(s) Nh=2	0.20 to 0.80	.4
B. Sub-Atmospheric Pressure (< 500 mm Hg)	0.50	–
C. Operation In or Near Flammable Range _X_ Inerted __ Not Inerted		–
1. Tank Farms Storage Flammable Liquids	0.50	–
2. Process Upset or Purge Failure	0.30	.30
3. Always in Flammable Range	0.80	–
D. Dust Explosion (See Table 3)	0.25 to 2.00	–
E. Pressure (See Figure 2) Operating Pressure __40__ psig ~~or kPa gauge~~; Relief Setting __75__ psig ~~or kPa gauge~~		.28
F. Low Temperature	0.20 to 0.30	–
G. Quantity of Flammable/Unstable Material: Quantity _130K_ lb ~~or kg~~; H_C = _19.2K_ BTU/lb or kcal/kg		
1. Liquids or Gases in Process (See Figure 3)		–
2. Liquids or Gases in Storage (See Figure 4)		.76
3. Combustible Solids in Storage, Dust in Process (See Figure 5)		–
H. Corrosion and Erosion	0.10 to 0.75	.1
I. Leakage – Joints and Packing	0.10 to 1.50	.1
J. Use of Fired Equipment (See Figure 6)		–
K. Hot Oil Heat Exchange System (See Table 5)	0.15 to 1.15	–
L. Rotating Equipment	0.50	–
Special Process Hazards Factor (F_2)		2.94
Process Unit Hazards Factor ($F_1 \times F_2$) = F_3		4.41
Fire and Explosion Index ($F_3 \times MF$ = F&EI)		106.00

(1) For no penalty use 0.00.

FORM C-22380 Rev/01-94

Figure 11-5 The Dow Fire and Explosion Index applied to the railcar unloading facility of Example 11-1.

1.A. Exothermic chemical reactions: The reactive chemical review has determined that an exothermic chemical reaction here is not possible. The penalty is zero.

1.B. Endothermic chemical reactions: This penalty applies only to reactors, so the penalty is zero.

1.C. Material handling and transfer: The index documentation states: "Any loading and unloading operation involving Class I flammables or LPG-type materials where transfer lines are connected and disconnected receives a penalty of 0.50."

1.D. Enclosed or indoor process units: The unit is outdoors, so the penalty is zero.

1.E. Access: The unit will have emergency access from all sides, so the penalty is zero.

1.F. Drainage and spill control: No penalty is applied because the dike and impounding system is present.

2.A. Toxic materials: The index suggests using a penalty value of 0.20 × NFPA Health Rating. Because the rating is 2, the penalty value is 0.4.

2.B. Subatmospheric pressure: The operation is pressurized, so no penalty is applied here.

2.C. Operation in or near flammable range

1. Tank farms storage flammable liquids: The tanks are inerted with a closed vapor recovery system, so the penalty here is zero.
2. Process upset or purge failure: The unit relies on inert purging to keep it out of the flammable range, so a penalty of 0.30 is applied.
3. Always in flammable range: The process is not in the flammable range during normal operation, so the penalty is zero.

2.D. Dust explosion: No dusts are involved, so the penalty is zero.

2.E. Pressure: The Dow index provides a detailed procedure for determining this penalty. The operating pressure penalty is determined from Figure 2 in the Dow index booklet using the operating pressure. In this case the operating pressure of 40 psig results in a penalty of 0.24. Second, a penalty is determined at the relief set pressure (75 psig), again using Figure 2 in the Dow index booklet. This value is 0.27. The operating pressure penalty is then divided by the set pressure penalty to get a final pressure penalty adjustment. In this case the adjustment is 0.24/0.27 = 0.8889. This is multiplied by the operating pressure penalty to obtain 0.24(0.8889) = 0.2133. Finally, this is multiplied by a correction factor of 1.3 because this is a liquefied flammable gas. The final penalty is 0.2133(1.3) = 0.28.

2.F. Low temperature: Low-temperature operating is not expected, so the penalty is zero.

2.G. Quantity of flammable/unstable material

1. Liquids or gases in process: This is not part of the process, so the penalty is zero.
2. Liquids or gases in storage: The total energy contained within the storage inventory is estimated in order to determine the penalty. This requires the specific gravity of butadiene, which can be found on the MSDS sheet or other reference. This value is 0.6263. Thus the total energy is

$$(25{,}000\ \text{GAL})(8.345\ \text{lb/GAL})(0.6263) = 130{,}662\ \text{lb},$$

$$(1.30 \times 10^5\ lb)(19.2 \times 10^3\ Btu/lb) = 2.51 \times 10^9\ Btu.$$

   From Figure 4, curve B, in the Dow index booklet, the penalty is 0.76.

3. Combustible solids in storage, dust in process: No solids are present here, so the penalty is zero.

2.H. Corrosion and erosion: Corrosion and erosion are expected to be less than 0.5 mil/yr. Thus the penalty is 0.10.

2.I. Leakage – joints and packing: The pump and gland seals are expected to have some small but minor leakage. Thus the penalty here is 0.10.

2.J. Use of fired equipment: No fired equipment is present, so the penalty is zero.

2.K. Hot oil heat exchange system: Not present, so the penalty is zero.

2.L. Rotating equipment: No large rotating equipment is present, so the penalty is zero.

These penalties and factors are summarized in Figure 11-5. The resulting calculation shows an F&EI value of 106, which means that this unloading station is an intermediate hazard.

Figure 7 in the Dow index booklet provides the radius of exposure based on the F&EI value. For this case the radius is 90 ft. Thus the unloading station must be located a minimum of 90 ft from any other equipment or processes.

The Dow CEI is a simple method of rating the relative acute health hazard potential for people in neighboring plants or communities arising from possible chemical release incidents.

To use the CEI, the following items are required:

- An accurate plot plan of the plant and the surrounding area
- A simplified process flow sheet showing the containment vessels, major piping, and chemical inventories
- Physical and chemical properties of the materials investigated
- ERPG values, from Table 5-6
- The CEI guide
- The CEI form shown in Figure 11-6

A flowchart of the CEI procedure is shown in Figure 11-7. The procedure begins with a definition of possible release incidents. These include releases from pipes, hoses, pressure relief devices relieving directly to the atmosphere, vessels, and tank overflows and spills. The CEI guide has detailed guidelines for these incidents, as shown in Table 4-6. The incidents are used with a number of simplified source models provided in the Dow guide[4] to estimate the release rate of material. The ERPGs are then used with a simplified dispersion model to determine the CEI value and downwind hazard distances resulting from the release.

Hazards surveys are suitable for identifying hazards associated with equipment design, layout, material storage, and so forth. They are not suitable for identifying hazards resulting from improper operation or upset conditions. On the other hand, this approach is fairly rigorous, requires little experience, is easy to apply, and provides a quick result.

[4] *Dow's Chemical Exposure Index Guide.*

CHEMICAL EXPOSURE INDEX SUMMARY

Plant ______________________ Location ______________

Chemical ______________________ Total Quantity In Plant ________

Largest Single Containment ______________________

Pressure Of Containment __________ Temperature Of Containment ________

1. Scenario Being Evaluated ______________________

2. Airborne Release Rate from Scenario ________ kg/sec
   ________ lb/min

3. **Chemical Exposure Index** ________

4.

	Concentration		Hazard Distance	
	mg/m³	**PPM**	**meters**	**feet**
ERPG-1/EEPG-1	____	____	____	____
ERPG-2/EEPG-2	____	____	____	____
ERPG-3/EEPG-3	____	____	____	____

5. Distances to:

	meters	**feet**
Public (generally considered property line)	____	____
Other in-company facility	____	____
Non-company plant or business	____	____

6. The CEI and the Hazard Distance establish the level of review needed.

7. If further review is required, complete Containment and Mitigation Checklist (*Chemical Exposure Index Guide*, 2nd Edition – Appendix 2, page 26) and prepare Review Package.

8. List any sights, odors or sounds that might come from your facility and cause public concern or inquiries (e.g., smoke, large relief valves, odors below hazardous levels such as mercaptans or amines, etc.)
   ____
   ____
   ____

Prepared by: ______________________

Reviewed by: ______________________

		Date
Plant Superintendent or Manager	____	____
Site Review Representative	____	____
Additional Management Review (if required)	____	____

Figure 11-6 Form used for the Dow Chemical Exposure Index. Source: *Dow's Chemical Exposure Index Guide* (New York: American Institute of Chemical Engineers, 1998). Reproduced by permission of the American Institute of Chemical Engineers.

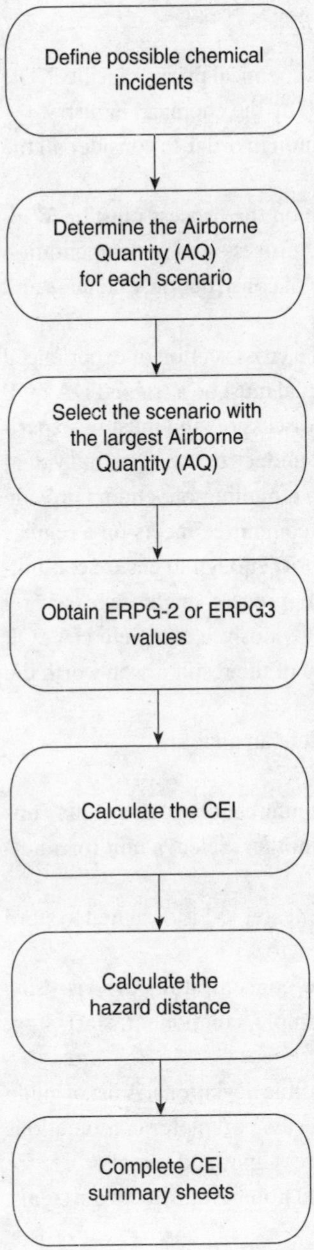
Define possible chemical incidents
Determine the Airborne Quantity (AQ) for each scenario
Select the scenario with the largest Airborne Quantity (AQ)
Obtain ERPG-2 or ERPG3 values
Calculate the CEI
Calculate the hazard distance
Complete CEI summary sheets

Figure 11-7 Procedure for calculating the Chemical Exposure Index (CEI). Source: *Dow's Chemical Exposure Index Guide* (New York: American Institute of Chemical Engineers, 1998).

11-3 Hazards and Operability Studies

The HAZOP study is a formal procedure to identify hazards in a chemical process facility.[5] The procedure is effective in identifying hazards and is well accepted by the chemical industry.

The basic idea is to let the mind go free in a controlled fashion in order to consider all the possible ways that process and operational failures can occur.

Before the HAZOP study is started, detailed information on the process must be available. This includes up-to-date process flow diagrams (PFDs), process and instrumentation diagrams (P&IDs), detailed equipment specifications, materials of construction, and mass and energy balances.

The full HAZOP study requires a committee composed of a cross-section of experienced plant, laboratory, technical, and safety professionals. One individual must be a trained HAZOP leader and serves as the committee chair. This person leads the discussion and must be experienced with the HAZOP procedure and the chemical process under review. One individual must also be assigned the task of recording the results, although a number of vendors provide software to perform this function on a personal computer. The committee meets on a regular basis for a few hours each time. The meeting duration must be short enough to ensure continuing interest and input from all committee members. A large process might take several months of biweekly meetings to complete the HAZOP study. Obviously, a complete HAZOP study requires a large investment in time and effort, but the value of the result is well worth the effort.

The HAZOP procedure uses the following steps to complete an analysis:

1. Begin with a detailed flow sheet. Break the flow sheet into a number of process units. Thus the reactor area might be one unit, and the storage tank another. Select a unit for study.
2. Choose a study node (vessel, line, operating instruction).
3. Describe the design intent of the study node. For example, vessel V-1 is designed to store the benzene feedstock and provide it on demand to the reactor.
4. Pick a process parameter: flow, level, temperature, pressure, concentration, pH, viscosity, state (solid, liquid, or gas), agitation, volume, reaction, sample, component, start, stop, stability, power, inert.
5. Apply a guide word to the process parameter to suggest possible deviations. A list of guide words is shown in Table 11-3. Some of the guide word process parameter combinations are meaningless, as shown in Tables 11-4 and 11-5 for process lines and vessels.
6. If the deviation is applicable, determine possible causes and note any protective systems.
7. Evaluate the consequences of the deviation (if any).
8. Recommend action (what? by whom? by when?).
9. Record all information.

[5]*Guidelines for Hazard Evaluation Procedures,* 3rd ed. (New York: American Institute of Chemical Engineers, 2008).

Table 11-3 Guide Words Used for the HAZOP Procedure

Guide words	Meaning	Comments
NO, NOT, NONE	The complete negation of the intention	No part of the design intention is achieved, but nothing else happens.
MORE, HIGHER, GREATER	Quantitative increase	Applies to quantities such as flow rate and temperature and to activities such as heating and reaction.
LESS, LOWER	Quantitative decrease	Applies to quantities such as flow rate and temperature and to activities such as heating and reaction.
AS WELL AS	Qualitative increase	All the design and operating intentions are achieved along with some additional activity, such as contamination of process streams.
PART OF	Qualitative decrease	Only some of the design intentions are achieved, some are not.
REVERSE	The logical opposite of	Most applicable to activities such as flow or chemical reaction. Also applicable to substances, for example, poison instead of antidote.
OTHER THAN	Complete substitution	No part of the original intention is achieved—the original intention is replaced by something else.
SOONER THAN	Too early or in the wrong order	Applies to process steps or actions.
LATER THAN	Too late or in the wrong order	Applies to process steps or actions.
WHERE ELSE	In additional locations	Applies to process locations, or locations in operating procedures.

Table 11-4 Valid Guide Word and Process Parameter Combinations for Process Lines (x's represent valid combinations)

Process parameters	No, not, none	More, higher, greater	Less, lower	As well as	Part of	Reverse	Other than	Sooner, faster	Later, slower	Where else
Flow	x	x	x	x	x	x	x	x	x	
Temperature		x	x					x	x	
Pressure		x	x	x				x	x	
Concentration	x	x	x	x	x		x	x	x	
pH		x	x					x	x	
Viscosity		x	x					x	x	
State				x				x	x	

Table 11-5 Valid Guide Word and Process Parameter Combinations for Process Vessels (x's represent valid combinations)

Process Parameters	No, not, none	More, higher, greater	Less, lower	As well as	Part of	Reverse	Other than	Sooner, faster	Later, slower	Where else
Level	x	x	x	x	x		x	x	x	x
Temperature		x	x					x	x	
Pressure		x	x	x				x	x	
Concentration	x	x	x	x	x		x	x	x	
pH		x	x					x	x	
Viscosity		x	x					x	x	
Agitation	x	x	x		x	x		x	x	
Volume	x	x	x	x	x			x	x	x
Reaction	x	x	x				x	x	x	
State				x			x	x	x	
Sample	x			x	x		x	x	x	

10. Repeat steps 5 through 9 until all applicable guide words have been applied to the chosen process parameter.
11. Repeat steps 4 through 10 until all applicable process parameters have been considered for the given study node.
12. Repeat steps 2 through 11 until all study nodes have been considered for the given section and proceed to the next section on the flow sheet.

The guide words AS WELL AS, PART OF, and OTHER THAN can sometimes be conceptually difficult to apply. AS WELL AS means that something else happens in addition to the intended design intention. This could be boiling of a liquid, transfer of some additional component, or the transfer of some fluid somewhere else than expected. PART OF means that one of the components is missing or the stream is being preferentially pumped to only part of the process. OTHER THAN applies to situations in which a material is substituted for the expected material, is transferred somewhere else, or the material solidifies and cannot be transported. The guide words SOONER THAN, LATER THAN, and WHERE ELSE are applicable to batch processing.

An important part of the HAZOP procedure is the organization required to record and use the results. There are many methods to accomplish this and most companies customize their approach to fit their particular way of doing things.

Table 11-6 presents one type of basic HAZOP form. The first column, denoted "Item," is used to provide a unique identifier for each case considered. The numbering system used is a number-letter combination. Thus the designation "1A" would designate the first study node and the first guide word. The second column lists the study node considered. The third column lists the process parameter, and the fourth column lists the deviations or guide words. The next three columns are the most important results of the analysis. The first column lists the possible

Table 11-6 HAZOP Form for Recording Data

Hazards and Operability Review

Project name:				Date:	Page of		Completed:
Process:							No action:
Section:				Reference drawing:			Reply date:
Item	Study node	Process parameters	Deviations (guide words)	Possible causes	Possible consequences	Action required	Assigned to:

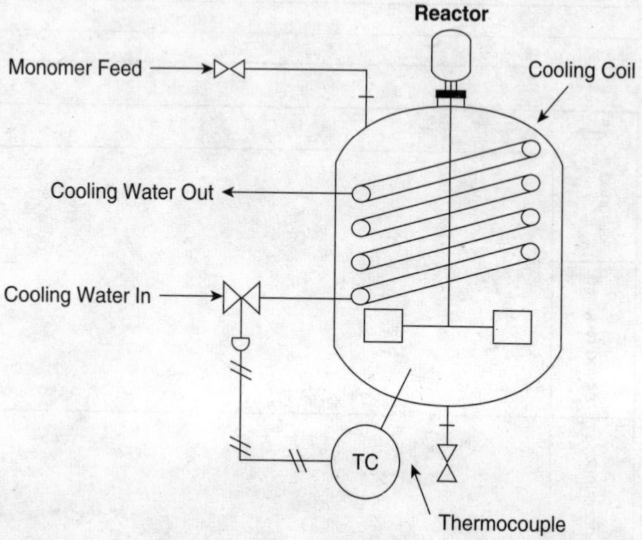

Figure 11-8 An exothermic reaction controlled by cooling water.

causes. These causes are determined by the committee and are based on the specific deviation–guide word combination. The next column lists the possible consequences of the deviation. The last column lists the action required to prevent the hazard from resulting in an accident. Notice that the items listed in these three columns are numbered consecutively. The last several columns are used to track the work responsibility and completion of the work.

Example 11-2

Consider the reactor system shown in Figure 11-8. The reaction is exothermic, so a cooling system is provided to remove the excess energy of reaction. In the event that the cooling function is lost, the temperature of the reactor would increase. This would lead to an increase in reaction rate, leading to additional energy release. The result would be a runaway reaction with pressures exceeding the bursting pressure of the reactor vessel.

The temperature within the reactor is measured and is used to control the cooling water flow rate by a valve.

Perform a HAZOP study on this unit to improve the safety of the process. Use as study nodes the cooling coil (process parameters: flow and temperature) and the stirrer (process parameter: agitation).

Solution

The guide words are applied to the study node of the cooling coils and the stirrer with the designated process parameters.

The HAZOP results are shown in Table 11-7, which is only a small part of the complete analysis.

Table 11-7 HAZOP Study Applied to the Exothermic Reactor of Example 11-2.

Hazards and Operability Review

Project name: Example 11-2	Date: 1/1/93	Page 1 of 2	Completed:
Process: Reactor of Example 11-2			No action:
Section: Reactor shown in Example 11-2	Reference drawing:		Reply date:

Item	Study node	Process parameters	Deviations (guide words)	Possible causes	Possible consequences	Action required	Assigned to:	Reply date	No action	Completed
1A	Cooling coils	Flow	No	1. Control valve fails closed	1. Loss of cooling, possible runaway	1. Select valve to fail open	DAC	1/93		
				2. Plugged cooling coils	2. "	2. Install filter with maintenance procedure Install cooling water flow meter and low flow alarm Install high temperature alarm to alert operator	DAC DAC DAC	1/93 2/93 2/93		
				3. Cooling water service failure	3. "	3. Check and monitor reliability of water service	DAC	2/93		
				4. Controller fails and closes valve	4. "	4. Place controller on critical instrumentation list	DAC	1/93		
				5. Air pressure fails, closing valve	5. "	5. See 1A.1				
1B			High	1. Control valve fails open	1. Reactor cools, reactant conc. builds, possible runaway on heating	1. Instruct operators and update procedures	JFL	1/93		
				2. Controller fails and opens valve	2. "	2. See 1A.4				
1C			Low	1. Partially plugged cooling line	1. Diminished cooling, possible runaway	1. See 1A.2				
				2. Partial water source failure	2. "	2. See 1A.2				
				3. Control valve fails to respond	3. "	3. Place valve on critical instrumentation list	JFL	1/93		
1D			As well as,	1. Contamination of water supply	1. Not possible here	1. None			X	
1E			part of,	1. Covered under 1C					X	
1F			reverse	1. Failure of water source resulting in backflow	1. Loss of cooling, possible runaway	1. See 1A.2				
				2. Backflow due to high backpressure	2. "	2. Install check valve	JFL	2/93		
1G			Other than,	1. Not considered possible					X	
1H			sooner than,	1. Cooling normally started early	1. None				X	
1I			later than	1. Operator error	1. Temperature rises, possible runaway	1. Interlock between cooling flow and reactor feed	JW	1/93		
1J			Where else	1. Not considered possible					X	
1K		Temp.	Low	1. Low water supply temperature	1. None—controller handles	1. None			X	
1L			High	1. High water supply temperature	1. Cooling system capacity limited, temp. increases	1. Install high flow alarm and/or cooling water high temp. alarm	JW	1/93		
2A	Stirrer	Agitation	No	1. Stirrer motor malfunction	1. No mixing, possible accumulation of unreacted materials	1. Interlock with feed line	JW	1/93		
				2. Power failure	2. Monomer feed continues, possible accumulation of unreacted materials	2. Monomer feed valve must fail closed on power loss	JW	2/93		
2B			More	1. Stirrer motor controller fails, resulting in high motor speed	1. None				X	

The potential process modifications resulting from this study (Example 11-2) are the following:

- Install a high-temperature alarm to alert the operator in the event of cooling function loss
- Install a high-temperature shutdown system (this system would automatically shut down the process in the event of a high reactor temperature; the shutdown temperature would be higher than the alarm temperature to provide the operator with the opportunity to restore cooling before the reactor is shut down)
- Install a check valve in the cooling line to prevent reverse flow (a check valve could be installed both before and after the reactor to prevent the reactor contents from flowing upstream and to prevent the backflow in the event of a leak in the coils)
- Periodically inspect the cooling coil to ensure its integrity
- Study the cooling water source to consider possible contamination and interruption of supply
- Install a cooling water flow meter and low-flow alarm (which will provide an immediate indication of cooling loss)

In the event that the cooling water system fails (regardless of the source of the failure), the high-temperature alarm and emergency shutdown system prevents a runaway reaction. The review committee performing the HAZOP study decided that the installation of a backup controller and control valve was not essential. The high-temperature alarm and shutdown system prevents a runaway reaction in this event. Similarly, a loss of coolant water source or a plugged cooling line would be detected by either the alarm or the emergency shutdown system. The review committee suggested that all coolant water failures be properly reported and that if a particular cause occurred repeatedly, then additional process modifications were warranted.

Example 11-2 demonstrates that the number of suggested process changes is great, although only a single process intention is considered.

The advantage to this approach is that it provides a more complete identification of the hazards, including information on how hazards can develop as a result of operating procedures and operational upsets in the process. Companies that perform detailed HAZOPs studies find that their processes operate better and have less downtime, that their product quality is improved, that less waste is produced, and that their employees are more confident in the safety of the process. The disadvantages are that the HAZOP approach is tedious to apply, requires considerable staff time, and can potentially identify hazards independent of the risk.

11-4 Safety Reviews

Another method that is commonly used to identify safety problems in laboratory and process areas and to develop solutions is the safety review. A "safety review" brings together a diverse group of people to review a project or operation with a broad safety perspective. The review team identifies and eliminates hazards in the design and procedures. The review process includes finding initiating events or upset conditions that can cause an accident. The team subsequently develops recommendations including new, modified, and improved equipment, controls, and procedures (operating, emergency, maintenance, etc.). The focus should be on developing a high-quality review that prevents personnel injuries, equipment damage or failures, and business interruptions.

Safety reviews include a review of previous accidents and incidents in similar plants or processes. Some incidents are referred to as "near-misses," meaning that a serious consequence did not occur but could have. Incident investigations or case histories contain actions to prevent a recurrence of similar incidents.[6] They identify the underlying causes of incidents and outline steps to be implemented to prevent similar events. The study of previous accident and incident reports helps the reviewers avoid repeating past mistakes; that is, learn from history or you're doomed to repeat it.

The review should be conducted periodically during the entire life of a project. The first review (before the detailed design) is the most important, because changes in the original design are less expensive compared to changes in an operating plant. Often an informal safety review will identify the need for a more detailed review, such as a formal safety review described in Section 11-3, or other PHA methods described in Section 11-5.[7,8] After startup, the periodic reviews should be conducted about every year or whenever the process adds new equipment, new chemicals, new reactions, and new procedures.

A safety review is a cooperative, constructive, and creative process that improves the safety and performance of the process. Safety reviews are positive experiences, and good reviews prevent the dreadful experiences associated with accidents and accident investigations. An especially high-quality review is not limited to environmental and safety consequences but is expanded to include operability and product quality concerns.[9]

In all of the methods mentioned above, checklists are recommended to facilitate the review process. A typical checklist is shown in Figure 11-2. The reviewers should develop checklists specifically tailored to the plant and personnel conducting the review. An adaptation of Figure 11-2 is shown in Table 11-8.

The first review uses a checklist for each of the six phases of a project's life (see Table 11-8, that is, design construction, startup, operation, cleaning, and shutdown.[7] The periodic and follow-up reviews include the last four items: startup, operation, cleaning, and shutdown.

[6]"Compliance Guidelines and Recommendations for Process Safety Management (Nonmandatory)," Code of Federal Regulations, OSHA 29 CFR 1926.64 App C, 127–138.

[7]Guidelines for Hazard Evaluation Procedures, Third Edition, *Center for Chemical Process Safety of the Guidelines for Hazard Evaluation Procedures,* 3rd ed. (Center for Chemical Process Safety of the American Institute of Chemical Engineers, 2008).

[8]"Process Safety Management of Highly Hazardous Chemicals," Code of Federal Regulations, OSHA 29 CFR 1910.119, *Federal Register,* (1993), 364–385.

[9]R. Collins, "Process Hazard Analysis Quality," *Process Safety Progress*, Vol 29 (2), June 2004, 113–117.

Table 11-8 Checklist for Informal and Formal Safety Reviews

Design: Design features to prevent accidents	Materials: a. Flammability – AIT, LFL/UFL, flash point b. Explosivity – conditions to prevent c. Toxicity – TLV-TWA, IDLH, required protection d. Corrosivity and compatibility – correct materials of construction e. Waste disposal – equipment, personnel, and legal constraints f. Storage – constraints including stability in storage g. Static electricity – bonding and grounding h. Reactivity – reactivity alone or with other components in the process, effect of impurities, temperatures for auto-reactions Equipment: a. Safety margins – temperature, pressure, flow, level, etc. b. Pressure relief – scenarios, worst cases, correct type and size c. Plant arrangement – spacing adequate, flame arrestors, remotely operated safety control valves, containment of chemicals d. Electrical equipment – electrical classifications e. Controls – redundancy and fail-safe designs Procedures: Operating and maintenance procedures for construction, startup, operation, cleaning, and shutdown, including emergency situations and normal operation
Construction: Construction practices to prevent accidents in specific area and adjacent areas	Materials: Authorized individuals check materials received in relationship to specifications, spare parts Equipment: Hydrostatic tests, mechanical integrity of equipment and controls Procedures: Craftsmen trained, permits used appropriately, house-keeping, maintenance defined and scheduled
Startups: Thought and actions that are dedicated to this critical and hectic period to prevent problems	Materials: All raw materials in place, and disposal methods for off-specification materials Equipment: a. Actual equipment, pipes and controls as specified in the design documents (after including the recommendations of the safety review) b. Equipment purged, blinds removed, instrument and interlock checks completed Procedures: Procedures and training completed, detailed plans communicated
Operation: Procedures to help plant personnel to remain diligent to minimize operating hazards	Conduct periodic audits to be sure materials, equipment, procedures, training (operators and maintenance), and permit systems are appropriate and current
Cleaning: Procedures for routine and emergency situations	Procedures must be in place for cleaning equipment, and for disposing of cleaning materials
Shutdown: Procedures for systematic and safe shutdowns	Procedures for handling all chemicals, cleaning equipment, disposing of chemicals and materials, inerting equipment and pipe systems, and a system to keep the system in a safe shutdown mode, and a procedure in place for the transition from shutdown to startup

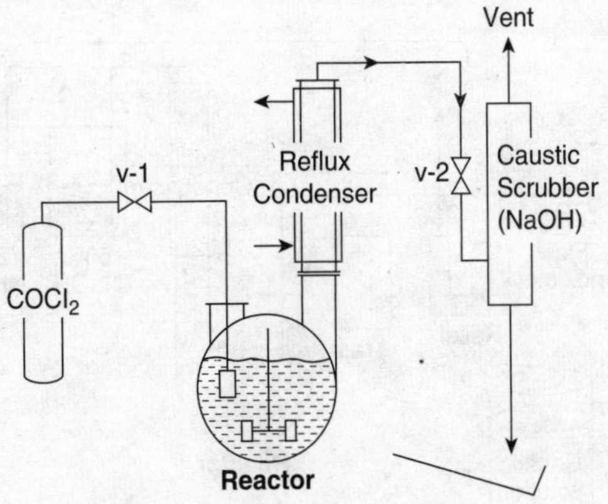

Figure 11-9 Original design of phosgene reactor before informal safety review.

There are two types of safety reviews: the informal and the formal.

Informal Review

The *informal safety review* is used for small changes to existing processes and for small bench-scale or laboratory processes. The informal safety review procedure usually involves just two or three people. It includes the individual responsible for the process and one or two others not directly associated with the process but experienced with proper safety procedures. The idea is to provide a lively dialogue where ideas can be exchanged and safety improvements can be developed.

The reviewers simply meet in an informal fashion to examine the process equipment and operating procedures and to offer suggestions on how the safety of the process might be improved. Significant improvements should be summarized in a memo for others to reference in the future. The improvements must be implemented before the process is operated.

Example 11-3

Consider the laboratory reactor system shown in Figure 11-9. This system is designed to react phosgene ($COCl_2$) with aniline to produce isocyanate and HCl. The reaction is shown in Figure 11-10. The isocyanate is used for the production of foams and plastics.

Phosgene is a colorless vapor with a boiling point of 46.8°F. Thus it is normally stored as a liquid in a container under pressure above its normal boiling point temperature. The TLV for phosgene is 0.1 ppm, and its odor threshold is 0.5–1 ppm, well above the TLV.

Aniline is a liquid with a boiling point of 364°F. Its TLV is 2 ppm. It is absorbed through the skin.

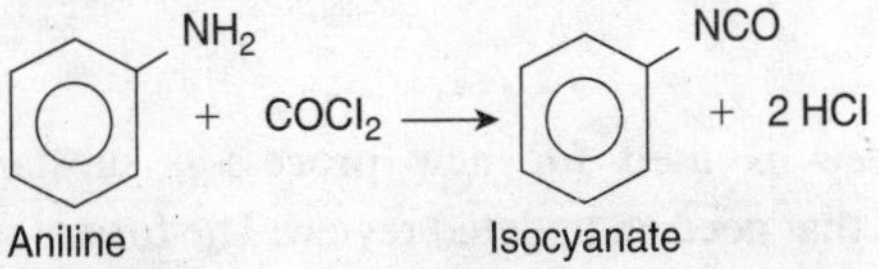

Figure 11-10 Reaction stoichiometry for phosgene reactor.

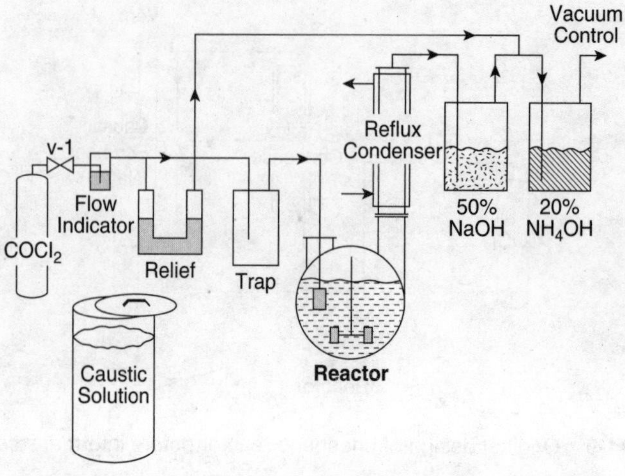

Figure 11-11 Final design of phosgene reactor after informal safety review.

In the process shown in Figure 11-9 the phosgene is fed from the container through a valve into a fritted glass bubbler in the reactor. The reflux condenser condenses aniline vapors and returns them to the reactor. A caustic scrubber is used to remove the phosgene and HCl vapors from the exit vent stream. The complete process is contained in a hood.

Conduct an informal safety review of this process.

Solution

The safety review was completed by two individuals. The final process design is shown in Figure 11-11. The changes and additions to the process are as follows:

1. Vacuum is added to reduce boiling temperature
2. Relief system is added with an outlet to a scrubber to prevent hazards resulting from a plugged fritted glass bubbler
3. Flow indicator provides visual indication of flow
4. Bubblers are used instead of scrubbers because they are more effective
5. Ammonium hydroxide bubbler is more effective for absorbing phosgene
6. Trap catches liquid phosgene
7. Pail of caustic is added (the phosgene cylinder would be dumped into this pail in the event of a cylinder or valve leak; the caustic would absorb the phosgene)

In addition, the reviewers recommended the following: (1) Hang phosgene indicator paper around the hood, room, and operating areas (this paper is normally white but turns brown when exposed to 0.1 ppm of phosgene), (2) use a safety checklist, daily, before the process is started, and (3) post an up-to-date process sketch near the process.

Formal Review

The *formal safety review* is used for new processes, substantial changes in existing processes, and processes that need an updated review. The formal safety review is a three-step procedure. This consists of preparing a detailed formal safety review report, having a committee review the report and inspect the process, developing improvements in the design and operating procedures, and implementing the recommendations. The formal safety review report includes the following sections:

I. Introduction
  A. Overview or summary: Provides a brief summary of the results of the formal safety review. This is done after the formal safety review is complete.
  B. Process overview or summary: Provides a brief description of the process with an emphasis on the major hazards in the operation.
  C. Reactions and stoichiometry: Provides the chemical reaction equations and stoichiometry.
  D. Engineering data: Provides operating temperatures, pressures, and relevant physical property data for the materials used.

II. Raw materials and products: Refers to specific hazards and handling problems associated with the raw materials and products. Discusses procedures to minimize these hazards.

III. Equipment setup
  A. Equipment description: Describes the configuration of the equipment. Sketches of the equipment are provided.
  B. Equipment specifications: Identifies the equipment by manufacturer name and model number. Provides the physical data and design information associated with the equipment.

IV. Procedures
  A. Normal operating procedures: Describes how the process is operated.
  B. Safety procedures: Provides a description of the unique concerns associated with the equipment and materials and specific procedures used to minimize the risk. This includes:
    1. Emergency shutdown: Describes the procedure used to shut down the equipment if an emergency should occur. This includes major leaks, reactor runaway, and loss of electricity, water, and air pressure.
    2. Fail-safe procedures: Examines the consequences of utility failures, such as loss of steam, electricity, water, air pressure, or inert padding. Describes what to do for each case so that the system fails safely.
    3. Major release procedures: Describes what to do in the event of a major spill of toxic or flammable material.
  C. Waste disposal procedure: Describes how toxic or hazardous materials are collected, handled, and disposed.
  D. Cleanup procedures: Describes how to clean the process after use.

V. Safety checklist: Provides the complete safety checklist for the operator to complete before operation of the process. This checklist is used before every startup.

VI. Material safety data sheets: Provided for each hazardous material used.

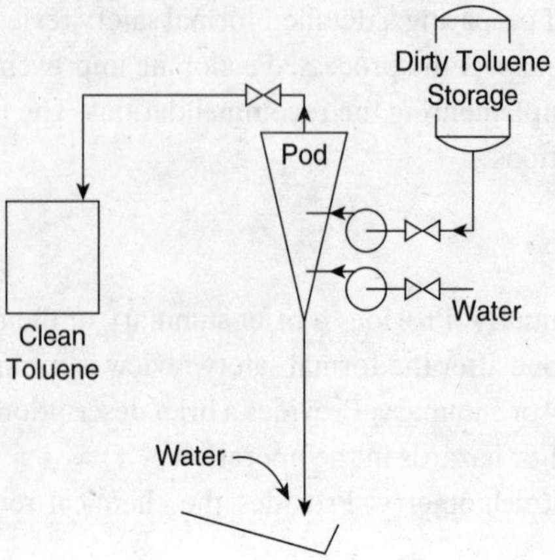

Figure 11-12 Toluene water wash process before formal safety review.

Example 11-4

A toluene water wash process is shown in Figure 11-12. This process is used to clean water-soluble impurities from contaminated toluene. The separation is achieved with a Podbielniak centrifuge, or Pod, because of a difference in densities. The light phase (contaminated toluene) is fed to the periphery of the centrifuge and travels to the center. The heavy phase (water) is fed to the center and travels countercurrent to the toluene to the periphery of the centrifuge. Both phases are mixed within the centrifuge and separated countercurrently. The extraction is conducted at 190°F.

The contaminated toluene is fed from a storage tank into the Pod. The heavy liquid out (contaminated water) is sent to waste treatment and the light liquid out (clean toluene) is collected in a 55-gal drum.

Perform a formal safety review of this process.

Solution

The complete safety review report is provided in Appendix D. Figure 11-13 shows the modified process after the formal safety review has been completed. The significant changes or additions added as a result of the review are as follows:

1. Add grounding and bonding to all collection and storage drums and process vessels
2. Add inerting and purging to all drums
3. Add elephant trunks at all drums to provide ventilation
4. Provide dip legs in all drums to prevent the free fall of solvent resulting in the generation and accumulation of static charge
5. Add a charge drum with grounding, bonding, inerting, and ventilation
6. Provide a vacuum connection to the dirty toluene storage for charging
7. Add a relief valve to the dirty toluene storage tank
8. Add heat exchangers to all outlet streams to cool the exit solvents below their flash point (this must include temperature gauges to ensure proper operation)

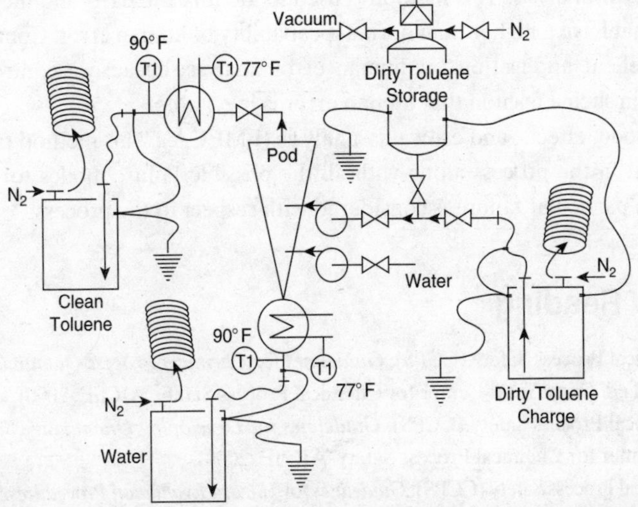

Figure 11-13 Toluene water wash process after formal safety review.

9. Provide a waste water collection drum to collect all waste water that might contain substantial amounts of toluene from upset conditions

Additional changes were made in the operating and emergency procedure. They included

1. Checking the room air periodically with colorimetric tubes to determine whether any toluene vapors are present
2. Changing the emergency procedure for spills to include (a) activating the spill alarm, (b) increasing the ventilation to high speed, and (c) throwing the sewer isolation switch to prevent solvent from entering the main sewer lines

The formal safety review can be used almost immediately, is relatively easy to apply, and is known to provide good results. However, the committee participants must be experienced in identifying safety problems. For less experienced committees, a more formal HAZOP study may be more effective in identifying the hazards.

11-5 Other Methods

Other methods that are available for identifying hazards are the following:

1. "What if" analysis: This less formal method of identifying hazards applies the words "what if" to a number of areas of investigation. For instance, the question might be, What if the flow stops? The analysis team then decides what the potential consequences might be and how to solve any problems.

2. Human error analysis: This method is used to identify the parts and the procedures of a process that have a higher than normal probability of human error. Control panel layout is an excellent application for human error analysis because a control panel can be designed in such a fashion that human error is inevitable.
3. Failure mode, effects, and criticality analysis (FMECA): This method tabulates a list of equipment in the process along with all the possible failure modes for each item. The effect of a particular failure is considered with respect to the process.

Suggested Reading

Center for Chemical Process Safety (CCPS), *Guidelines for Chemical Process Quantitative Risk Analysis,* (CPQRA), 2nd ed. (New York: Center for Chemical Process Safety, AIChE, 2000).

Center for Chemical Process Safety (CCPS), *Guidelines for Developing Quantitative Safety Risk Criteria* (New York: Center for Chemical Process Safety, AIChE, 2009).

Center for Chemical Process Safety (CCPS), *Guidelines for Hazard Evaluation Procedures*, 3rd ed. (Hoboken, NJ: John Wiley & Sons, 2008).

Center for Chemical Process Safety (CCPS), *Guidelines for Risk-Based Process Safety* (New York: Center for Chemical Process Safety, AIChE, 2008).

Dow's Fire and Explosion Index Hazard Classification Guide, 7th ed. (New York: American Institute of Chemical Engineers, 1994).

Trevor A. Kletz, *HAZOP and HAZAN,* 3d ed. (Warwickshire, England: Institution of Chemical Engineers, 1992).

S. Mannan, ed., *Lees' Loss Prevention in the Process Industries,* 3rd ed. (London: Butterworth Heinemann, 2005).

Problems

11-1. The hydrolysis of acetic anhydride is being studied in a laboratory-scale continuously stirred tank reactor (CSTR). In this reaction acetic anhydride [$(CH_3CO)_2O$] reacts with water to produce acetic acid (CH_3COOH).

The concentration of acetic anhydride at any time in the CSTR is determined by titration with sodium hydroxide. Because the titration procedure requires time (relative to the hydrolysis reaction time), it is necessary to quench the hydrolysis reaction as soon as the sample is taken. The quenching is achieved by adding an excess of aniline to the sample. The quench reaction is

$$(CH_3CO)_2 + C_6H_5NH_2 \rightarrow CH_3COOH + C_6H_5NHCOCH_3.$$

The quenching reaction also forms acetic acid, but in a different stoichiometric ratio from the hydrolysis reaction. Thus it is possible to determine the acetic anhydride concentration at the time the sample was taken.

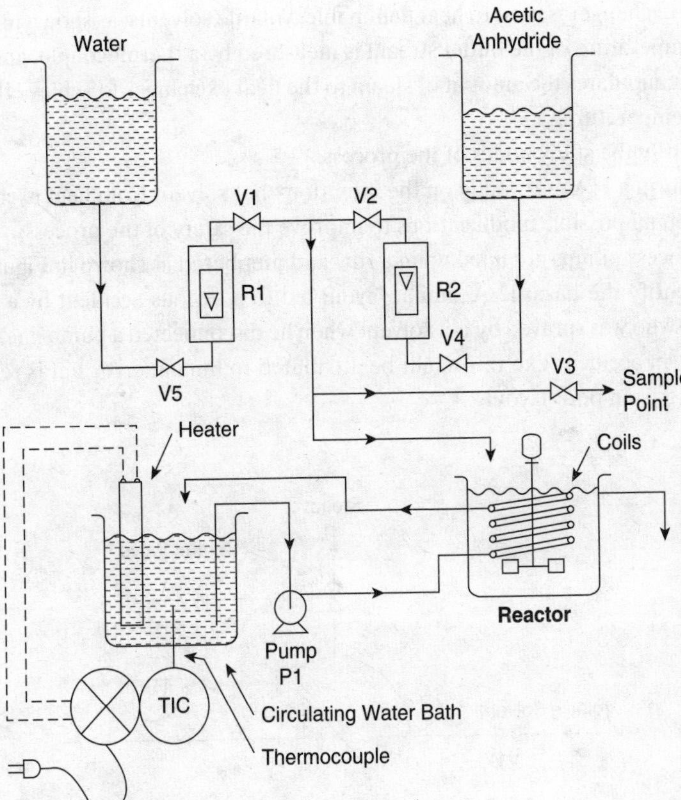

Figure 11-14 Acetic anhydride reactor system.

The initial experimental design is shown in Figure 11-14. Water and acetic anhydride are gravity-fed from reservoirs and through a set of rotameters. The water is mixed with the acetic anhydride just before it enters the reactor. Water is also circulated by a centrifugal pump from the temperature bath through coils in the reactor vessel. This maintains the reactor temperature at a fixed value. A temperature controller in the water bath maintains the temperature to within 1°F of the desired temperature.

Samples are withdrawn from the point shown and titrated manually in a hood.

a. Develop a safety checklist for use before operation of this experiment.

b. What safety equipment must be available?

c. Perform an informal safety review of the experiment. Suggest modifications to improve the safety.

11-2. Perform a HAZOP study on the laboratory process of Problem 11-1. Consider the intention "reactant flow to reactor" for your analysis. What specific recommendations can you make to improve the safety of this experiment?

11-3. A heat exchanger is used to heat flammable, volatile solvents, as shown in Figure 11-15. The temperature of the outlet stream is measured by a thermocouple, and a controller valve manipulates the amount of steam to the heat exchanger to achieve the desired set point temperature.

a. Identify the study nodes of the process.

b. Perform a HAZOP study on the intention "hot solvent from heat exchanger." Recommend possible modifications to improve the safety of the process.

11-4. Five process pumps are lined up in a row and numbered as shown in Figure 11-16. Can you identify the hazard? A similar layout led to a serious accident by a maintenance worker who was sprayed by hot solvent when he disconnected a pump line on the wrong pump. An accident like this might be attributed to human error but is really a hazard resulting from poor layout.

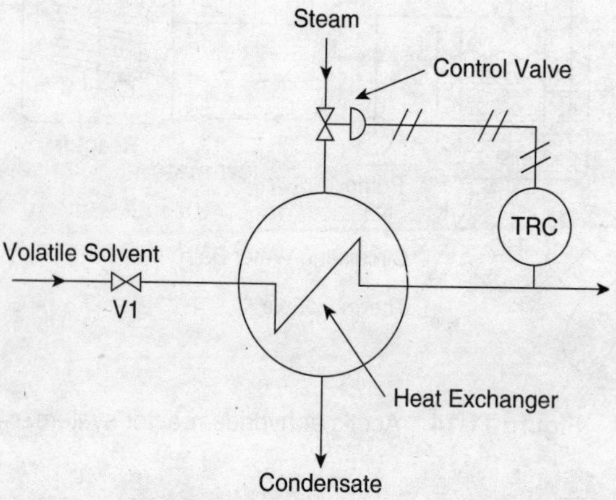

Figure 11-15 Volatile solvent heating system.

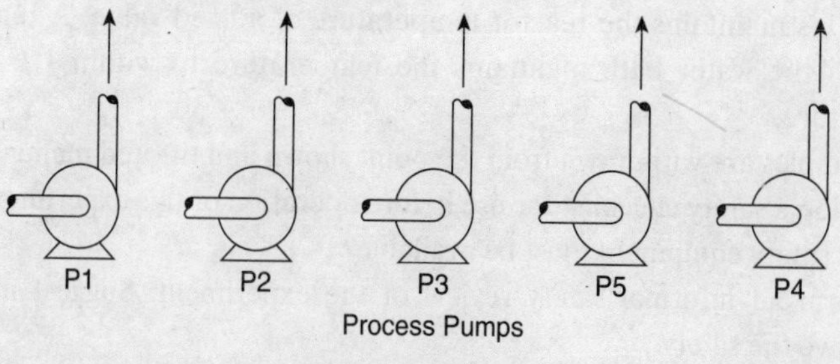

Figure 11-16 Pump layout.

11-5. A good acronym in chemical plant design is KISS – Keep It Simple, Stupid! This also applies to hazards. Complicated designs are almost always more hazardous than simple ones.

Figure 11-17 shows a sump designed to collect process fluids. The level controller and pump ensure that the sump level is maintained below a maximum height. Can you suggest a much simpler system?

11-6. Storage tanks typically are not capable of withstanding much pressure or vacuum. Standard storage tanks are designed for a maximum of 2.5 in of water gauge vacuum (0.1 psi) and about 6 in of water gauge pressure (0.2 psi).

A welding operation was to occur on the roof of a storage vessel. The tank contained a flammable, volatile liquid. The roof was equipped with a vent pipe with a flame arrestor.

The foreman recognized a possible hazard from flammable vapor escaping from the vent pipe and igniting on the sparks from the welding operation. He connected a hose to the vent at the top of the tank and ran the hose down to the ground. Because the flammable vapors were water soluble, he stuck the end of the hose in a drum full of water. During a subsequent operation that involved emptying the tank, an accident occurred. Can you explain what happened and how?

11-7. Figure 11-18 shows a storage tank blanketed with nitrogen. This configuration resulted in an explosion and fire because of loss of inert material. Can you explain why?

11-8. Figure 11-19 shows two tanks in series, both with independent level controllers. This configuration will result in the lower tank inevitably overflowing. Can you explain why?

11-9. Describe an informal safety review process for using a cylinder of phosgene to charge gaseous phosgene to a reactor. Review up to the reactor only.

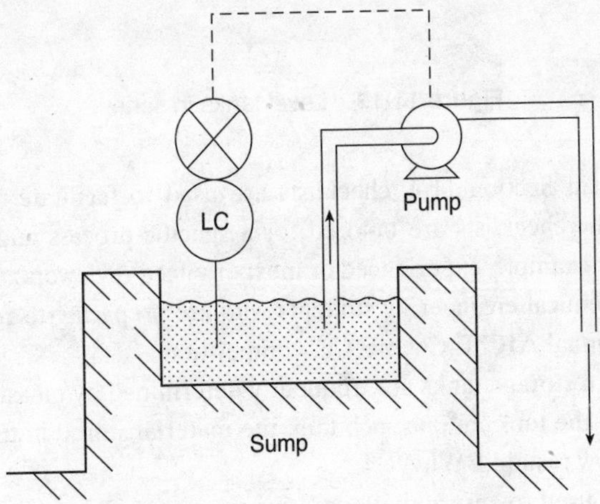

Figure 11-17 Sump level control system.

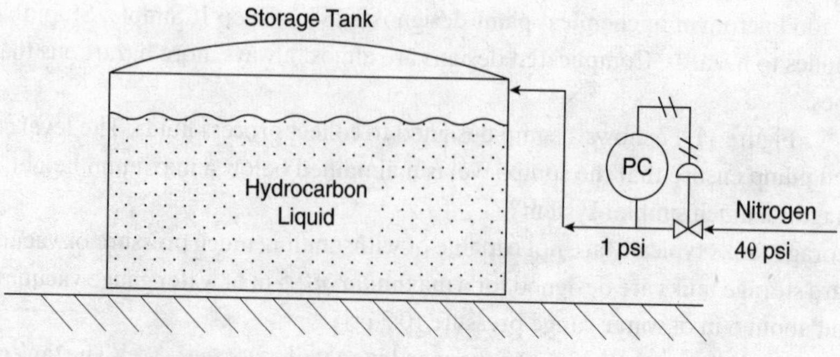

Figure 11-18 Nitrogen padding system for a storage tank.

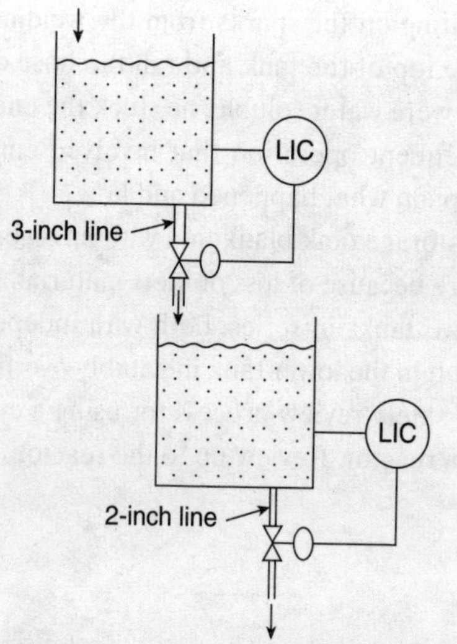

Figure 11-19 Level tanks in series.

11-10. As described in Section 11-4, checklists are used to facilitate a high-quality safety review, and the checklists are tailored for a specific process and a specific group of reviewers (for example, experienced or inexperienced reviewers). Tailor a checklist for a group of chemical engineering students who are preparing to review a new ChemE Car for the annual AIChE ChemE Car competition.

11-11. Liquid levels in storage tanks are frequently determined by measuring the pressure at the bottom of the tank. In one such tank the material stored in the tank was changed and an overflow resulted. Why?

11-12. Interlocks are used to ensure that operations in a chemical plant are performed in the proper sequence. Interlocks can be mechanical or electronic. In many cases they can be as simple as a lock and key.

Specify the simplest mechanical interlock capable of achieving the following functions:

a. A valve cannot be closed until a furnace is shut down.

b. Two valves cannot both be closed at the same time.

c. A valve must be closed before a pump is started.

d. Feed to a reactor cannot be started until the reactor vessel stirring motor is activated.

11-13. Exothermic chemical reactions are frequently dangerous because of the potential for a runaway reaction. Cooling coils are provided in batch reactors to remove the energy of reaction. In the event of a cooling water failure, the reactor temperature rises, resulting in a higher reaction rate and higher energy generation. The result is a runaway reaction. During a runaway reaction, the temperature can rise quickly, resulting in dangerous pressures within the reactor and a possible explosion.

Loss of cooling can be detected by measuring the temperature within the reactor and sounding an alarm. Frequently, by the time the alarm sounds, it is too late. Design a better instrumentation and alarm configuration to detect loss of cooling more directly. Draw the instrumentation diagram.

11-14. La La Pharmaceuticals has recently discovered a new drug, Lalone, in their chemical laboratories. Lalone is expected to be a blockbuster drug, raking in billions of dollars each year. For the next stage of clinical studies over 50 kg of Lalone is required, and La La Pharmaceuticals has decided to produce this in their existing pilot plant operations in Lala Land. As the safety director for the pilot plant operations, you are in charge of ensuring the safety of all operations.[10]

During a meeting with the chemist who synthesized Lalone in the laboratory, you have learned the following: (1) Lalone is a fine, white powder; (2) Lalone is synthesized by a batch process through a series of four major steps – three sets of reactions to produce intermediates, followed by drying to produce Lalone (all reactions are carried out in the liquid phase and require acetone as a solvent); (3) the chemical reactions are not fully understood, and most physical and chemical properties are not known; (4) so far, Lalone has been manufactured only in the laboratory and in small quantities (less than 50 g); (5) management wants the pilot plant operations to be started as soon as possible; and (6) the Engineering Division has already started writing the operating procedures for the eventual process.

As the safety director of the pilot plant:

a. Based on your safety knowledge and experience, identify the major hazards in this process that you would be concerned about.

b. Describe how you would structure a hazard study for the Lalone manufacturing process.

c. What additional information will you need to conduct the hazard analysis study?

[10]Problem provided courtesy of Rajagopalan Srinivasan of the University of Singapore.

11-15. Your manufacturing plant has purchased a number of robots to facilitate production. What are the main hazards associated with robots? What are some effective safeguards against these hazards?[11]

11-16. An operator was told to control the temperature of a reactor at 60°C. He set the set point of the temperature controller at 60. The scale actually indicated 0–100% of a temperature range of 0–200°C. This caused a runaway reaction that overpressured the vessel. Liquid was discharged and injured the operator. What was the set point temperature the operator actually set?

11-17. (This problem requires student access to the *Dow Fire and Explosion Index* manual.) In a devolatilizer, a solvent (60% cyclohexane and 40% pentane) is removed from a polymer and sent to the solvent recycle section of the plant for treatment and recovery. The devolatilizer is located in an open structure with good access for fire fighting. The process area has a 1% sloping concrete surface with a remote impounding area capable of handling all of a spill and 30 min of fire water. The process is run above the flash point of the solvent at 300 mm Hg. The vessel has a relief device set at 50 psig. Assume a potential spill of 8000 lb of flammable material with a heat of combustion of 19.4×10^3 Btu/lb.

The process unit has many loss control features. The plant has a diesel emergency power generator with an emergency cooling system. The plant is also under computer control with emergency shutdown based on redundant inputs. Vacuum is always broken with nitrogen. The process has complete, written, and up-to-date operating instructions. A reactive chemicals review was completed recently. The process has several interlocks to prevent polymerization.

The process area has combustible gas detectors, fireproofing, and a water deluge system. Cable trays are protected with deluge, and portable dry chemical extinguishers are in the process area. Diesel-powered fire water pumps can provide a maximum fire water demand for 4 hr.

a. Determine the Dow F&EI value for this process to estimate the relative degree of hazard.

b. Assuming an equipment value within the radius of exposure of $1 million, estimate the maximum probable property damage.

c. Assuming a product value of $1.50 per pound and an annual plant production rate of 35 million lb, estimate the business interruption loss.

11-18. A light in the control room of a chemical plant indicated whether a valve was closed or not. In reality it indicated only the status of the signal being sent to the valve. The valve did not close when it should have, and the plant exploded. Why? How would you prevent this problem?

11-19. A flammable liquid is to be stored in a large storage vessel. Two vessels are available. One vessel is called a weak seam roof tank, with the weakest part of the vessel being the

[11]Problem provided courtesy of Alvin Yee of the University of Singapore.

welded seam between the roof and the vertical wall of the tank. The other vessel is a domed roof tank, with the weakest part being the seam along the bottom of the tank. Which tank is the better choice for storing this material?

11-20. In Figure 11-8, identify the study nodes of the reactor process, as shown.

11-21. A process operator is given the following instructions: "Charge 10 lb of catalyst into batch reactor A at 3 hr into the cycle." Determine at least 15 ways in which the operator might fail to perform the instructions correctly.

11-22. "Fail-safe" is a concept used to specify the position of process instrumentation in the event of power, air pressure, or other utility failures. For instance, the valve supplying cooling water to a chemical reactor would fail in the open position ("fail open") in the event of a power failure. This would provide maximum cooling to the reactor and prevent dangerous high temperatures in the vessel.

Specify the proper fail-safe positions for the valves in the following equipment. Specify either fail open or fail close.

a. A flammable solvent is heated by steam in a heat exchanger. The valve controls the flow of steam to the exchanger.

b. A valve controls the flow rate of reactant to a reactor vessel. The reaction is exothermic.

c. A valve controls the flow rate of reactant to a reactor vessel. The reaction is endothermic.

d. A valve controls the flow of natural gas to a utility furnace in a power station.

e. A remotely operated valve is connected to a drain on a storage tank.

f. A remotely operated valve is used to fill a tank from a supply line.

g. A valve controls combustion air to a furnace.

h. A valve controls the pressure in a steam header.

11-23. Thermocouples in chemical plants are usually found in sheaths. These sheaths protect the thermocouple and also allow the thermocouple to be removed and replaced without shutting down the process. One chemical plant had some thermocouples that did not have sheaths, although they looked like the sheathed type. This led to an accidental release of toxic and flammable material. Can you explain why?

CHAPTER 12

Risk Assessment

Risk assessment includes incident identification and consequence analysis. Incident identification describes how an accident occurs. It frequently includes an analysis of the probabilities. Consequence analysis describes the expected damage. This includes loss of life, damage to the environment or capital equipment, and days outage.

The hazards identification procedures presented in Chapter 11 include some aspects of risk assessment. The Dow F&EI includes a calculation of the maximum probable property damage (MPPD) and the maximum probable days outage (MPDO). This is a form of consequences analysis. However, these numbers are obtained by some rather simple calculations involving published correlations. Hazard and operability (HAZOP) studies provide information on how a particular accident occurs. This is a form of incident identification. No probabilities or numbers are used with the typical HAZOP study, although the experience of the review committee is used to decide on an appropriate course of action.

In this chapter we will

- Review probability mathematics, including the mathematics of equipment failure,
- Show how the failure probabilities of individual hardware components contribute to the failure of a process,
- Describe two probabilistic methods (event trees and fault trees),
- Describe the concepts of layer of protection analysis (LOPA), and
- Describe the relationship between quantitative risk analysis (QRA) and LOPA.

We focus on determining the frequency of accident scenarios. The last two sections show how the frequencies are used in QRA and LOPA studies; LOPA is a simplified QRA. It should be emphasized that the teachings of this chapter are all easy to use and to apply, and the results are often the basis for significantly improving the design and operation of chemical and petrochemical plants.

12-1 Review of Probability Theory

Equipment failures or faults in a process occur as a result of a complex interaction of the individual components. The overall probability of a failure in a process depends highly on the nature of this interaction. In this section we define the various types of interactions and describe how to perform failure probability computations.

Data are collected on the failure rate of a particular hardware component. With adequate data it can be shown that, on average, the component fails after a certain period of time. This is called the average failure rate and is represented by μ with units of faults/time. The probability that the component will not fail during the time interval $(0, t)$ is given by a Poisson distribution:[1]

$$R(t) = e^{-\mu t}, \tag{12-1}$$

where R is the reliability. Equation 12-1 assumes a constant failure rate μ. As $t \to \infty$, the reliability goes to 0. The speed at which this occurs depends on the value of the failure rate μ. The higher the failure rate, the faster the reliability decreases. Other and more complex distributions are available. This simple exponential distribution is the one that is used most commonly because it requires only a single parameter, μ. The complement of the reliability is called the failure probability (or sometimes the unreliability), P, and it is given by

$$P(t) = 1 - R(t) = 1 - e^{-\mu t}. \tag{12-2}$$

The failure density function is defined as the derivative of the failure probability:

$$f(t) = \frac{dP(t)}{dt} = \mu e^{-\mu t}. \tag{12-3}$$

The area under the complete failure density function is 1.

The failure density function is used to determine the probability P of at least one failure in the time period t_o to t_1:

$$P(t_o \to t_1) = \int_{t_o}^{t_1} f(t)\,dt = \mu \int_{t_o}^{t_1} e^{-\mu t}\,dt = e^{-\mu t_o} - e^{-\mu t_1}. \tag{12-4}$$

[1] B. Roffel and J. E. Rijnsdorp, *Process Dynamics, Control, and Protection* (Ann Arbor, MI: Ann Arbor Science, 1982), p. 381.

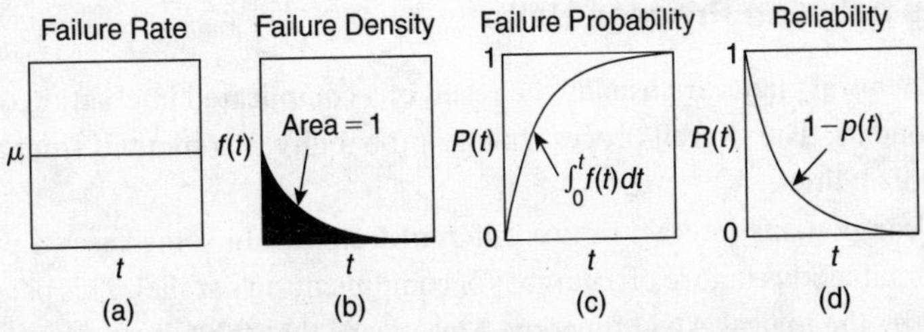

Figure 12-1 Typical plots of (a) the failure rate μ, (b) the failure density $f(t)$, (c) the failure probability $P(t)$, and (d) the reliability $R(t)$.

The integral represents the fraction of the total area under the failure density function between time t_o and t_1.

The time interval between two failures of the component is called the mean time between failures (MTBF) and is given by the first moment of the failure density function:

$$E(t) = \text{MTBF} = \int_0^\infty t f(t)\, dt = \frac{1}{\mu}. \tag{12-5}$$

Typical plots of the functions μ, f, P, and R are shown in Figure 12-1.

Equations 12-1 through 12-5 are valid only for a constant failure rate μ. Many components exhibit a typical bathtub failure rate, shown in Figure 12-2. The failure rate is highest when the component is new (infant mortality) and when it is old (old age). Between these two periods (denoted by the lines in Figure 12-2), the failure rate is reasonably constant and Equations 12-1 through 12-5 are valid.

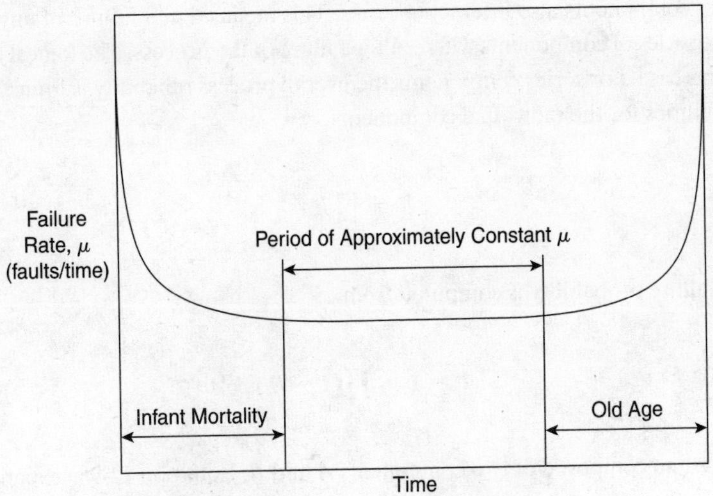

Figure 12-2 A typical bathtub failure rate curve for process hardware. The failure rate is approximately constant over the midlife of the component.

Interactions between Process Units

Accidents in chemical plants are usually the result of a complicated interaction of a number of process components. The overall process failure probability is computed from the individual component probabilities.

Process components interact in two different fashions. In some cases a process failure requires the simultaneous failure of a number of components in parallel. This parallel structure is represented by the logical AND function. This means that the failure probabilities for the individual components must be multiplied:

$$P = \prod_{i=1}^{n} P_i, \tag{12-6}$$

where

n is the total number of components and
P_i is the failure probability of each component.

This rule is easily memorized because for *p*arallel components the *p*robabilities are multiplied.

The total reliability for parallel units is given by

$$R = 1 - \prod_{i=1}^{n}(1 - R_i), \tag{12-7}$$

where R_i is the reliability of an individual process component.

Process components also interact in series. This means that a failure of any single component in the series of components will result in failure of the process. The logical OR function represents this case. For series components the overall process reliability is found by multiplying the reliabilities for the individual components:

$$R = \prod_{i=1}^{n} R_i. \tag{12-8}$$

The overall failure probability is computed from

$$P = 1 - \prod_{i=1}^{n}(1 - P_i). \tag{12-9}$$

For a system composed of two components A and B, Equation 12-9 is expanded to

$$P(A \text{ or } B) = P(A) + P(B) - P(A)P(B). \tag{12-10}$$

The cross-product term $P(A)P(B)$ compensates for counting the overlapping cases twice. Consider the example of tossing a single die and determining the probability that the number of points is even *or* divisible by 3. In this case

$$P(\text{even } or \text{ divisible by 3}) = P(\text{even}) + P(\text{divisible by 3}) - P(\text{even } and \text{ divisible by 3}).$$

The last term subtracts the cases in which both conditions are satisfied.

If the failure probabilities are small (a common situation), the term $P(A)P(B)$ is negligible, and Equation 12-10 reduces to

$$P(A \text{ or } B) = P(A) + P(B). \quad (12\text{-}11)$$

This result is generalized for any number of components. For this special case Equation 12-9 reduces to

$$P = \sum_{i=1}^{n} P_i.$$

Table 12-1 Failure Rate Data for Various Selected Process Components[a]

Instrument	Faults/year
Controller	0.29
Control valve	0.60
Flow measurement (fluids)	1.14
Flow measurement (solids)	3.75
Flow switch	1.12
Gas-liquid chromatograph	30.6
Hand valve	0.13
Indicator lamp	0.044
Level measurement (liquids)	1.70
Level measurement (solids)	6.86
Oxygen analyzer	5.65
pH meter	5.88
Pressure measurement	1.41
Pressure relief valve	0.022
Pressure switch	0.14
Solenoid valve	0.42
Stepper motor	0.044
Strip chart recorder	0.22
Thermocouple temperature measurement	0.52
Thermometer temperature measurement	0.027
Valve positioner	0.44

[a]Selected from Frank P. Lees, *Loss Prevention in the Process Industries* (London: Butterworths, 1986), p. 343.

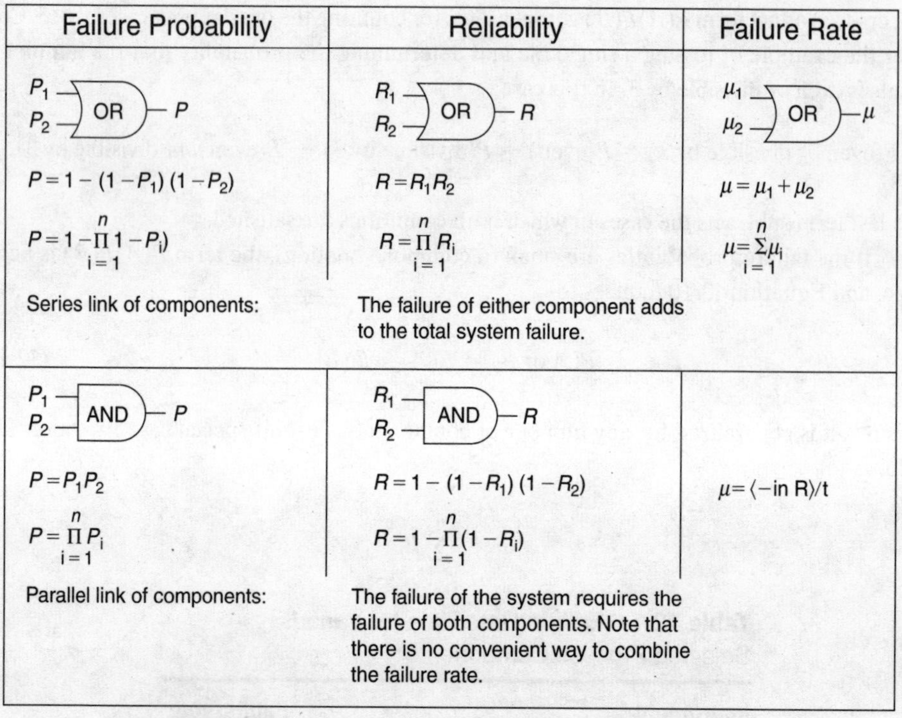

Figure 12-3 Computations for various types of component linkages.

Failure rate data for a number of typical process components are provided in Table 12-1. These are average values determined at a typical chemical process facility. Actual values would depend on the manufacturer, materials of construction, the design, the environment, and other factors. The assumptions in this analysis are that the failures are independent, hard, and not intermittent and that the failure of one device does not stress adjacent devices to the point that the failure probability is increased.

A summary of computations for parallel and series process components is shown in Figure 12-3.

Example 12-1

The water flow to a chemical reactor cooling coil is controlled by the system shown in Figure 12-4. The flow is measured by a differential pressure (DP) device, the controller decides on an appropriate control strategy, and the control valve manipulates the flow of coolant. Determine the overall failure rate, the unreliability, the reliability, and the MTBF for this system. Assume a 1-yr period of operation.

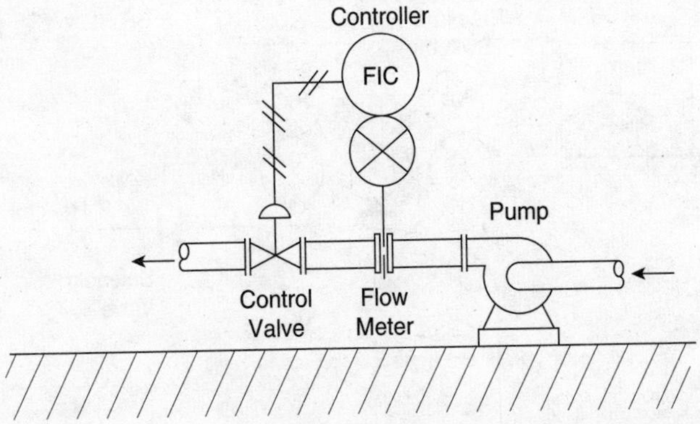

Figure 12-4 Flow control system. The components of the control system are linked in series.

Solution

These process components are related in series. Thus, if any one of the components fails, the entire system fails. The reliability and failure probability are computed for each component using Equations 12-1 and 12-2. The results are shown in the following table. The failure rates are from Table 12-1.

Component	Failure rate μ (faults/yr)	Reliability $R = e^{-\mu t}$	Failure probability $P = 1 - R$
Control valve	0.60	0.55	0.45
Controller	0.29	0.75	0.25
DP cell	1.41	0.24	0.76

The overall reliability for components in series is computed using Equation 12-8. The result is

$$R = \prod_{i=1}^{3} R_i = (0.55)(0.75)(0.24) = 0.10.$$

The failure probability is computed from

$$P = 1 - R = 1 - 0.10 = 0.90/\text{yr}.$$

The overall failure rate is computed using the definition of the reliability (Equation 12-1):

$$0.10 = e^{-\mu}$$

$$\mu = -\ln(0.10) = 2.30 \text{ failures/yr}.$$

The MTBF is computed using Equation 12-5:

$$\text{MTBF} = \frac{1}{\mu} = 0.43 \text{ yr}.$$

This system is expected to fail, on average, once every 0.43 yr.

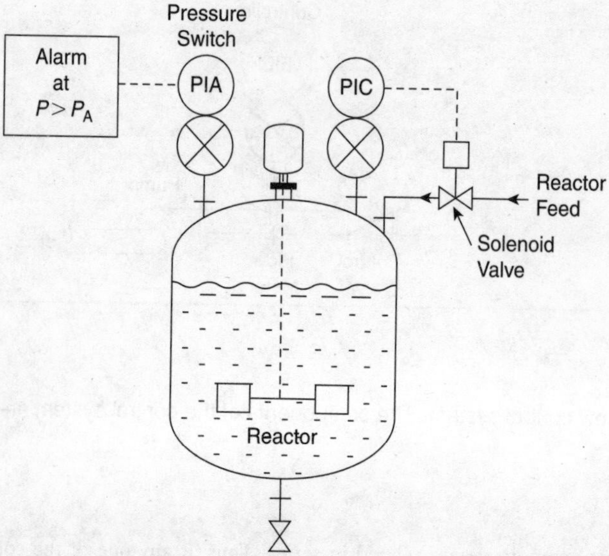

Figure 12-5 A chemical reactor with an alarm and an inlet feed solenoid. The alarm and feed shutdown systems are linked in parallel.

Example 12-2

A diagram of the safety systems in a certain chemical reactor is shown in Figure 12-5. This reactor contains a high-pressure alarm to alert the operator in the event of dangerous reactor pressures. It consists of a pressure switch within the reactor connected to an alarm light indicator. For additional safety an automatic high-pressure reactor shutdown system is installed. This system is activated at a pressure somewhat higher than the alarm system and consists of a pressure switch connected to a solenoid valve in the reactor feed line. The automatic system stops the flow of reactant in the event of dangerous pressures. Compute the overall failure rate, the failure probability, the reliability, and the MTBF for a high-pressure condition. Assume a 1-yr period of operation. Also, develop an expression for the overall failure probability based on the component failure probabilities.

Solution

Failure rate data are available from Table 12-1. The reliability and failure probabilities of each component are computed using Equations 12-1 and 12-2:

Component	Failure rate μ (faults/yr)	Reliability $R = e^{-\mu t}$	Failure probability $P = 1 - R$
1. Pressure switch 1	0.14	0.87	0.13
2. Alarm indicator	0.044	0.96	0.04
3. Pressure switch 2	0.14	0.87	0.13
4. Solenoid valve	0.42	0.66	0.34

A dangerous high-pressure reactor situation occurs only when both the alarm system and the shutdown system fail. These two components are in parallel. For the alarm system the components are in series:

$$R = \prod_{i=1}^{2} R_i = (0.87)(0.96) = 0.835,$$

$$P = 1 - R = 1 - 0.835 = 0.165,$$

$$\mu = -\ln R = -\ln(0.835) = 0.180 \text{ faults/yr},$$

$$\text{MTBF} = \frac{1}{\mu} = 5.56 \text{ yr}.$$

For the shutdown system the components are also in series:

$$R = \prod_{i=1}^{2} R_i = (0.87)(0.66) = 0.574,$$

$$P = 1 - R = 1 - 0.574 = 0.426,$$

$$\mu = -\ln R = -\ln(0.574) = 0.555 \text{ faults/yr},$$

$$\text{MTBF} = \frac{1}{\mu} = 1.80 \text{ yr}.$$

The two systems are combined using Equation 12-6:

$$P = \prod_{i=1}^{2} P_i = (0.165)(0.426) = 0.070,$$

$$R = 1 - P = 0.930,$$

$$\mu = -\ln R = -\ln(0.930) = 0.073 \text{ faults/yr},$$

$$\text{MTBF} = \frac{1}{\mu} = 13.7 \text{ yr}.$$

For the alarm system alone a failure is expected once every 5.5 yr. Similarly, for a reactor with a high-pressure shutdown system alone, a failure is expected once every 1.80 yr. However, with both systems in parallel the MTBF is significantly improved and a combined failure is expected every 13.7 yr.

The overall failure probability is given by

$$P = P(A)P(S),$$

where $P(A)$ is the failure probability of the alarm system and $P(S)$ is the failure probability of the emergency shutdown system. An alternative procedure is to invoke Equation 12-9 directly. For the alarm system

$$P(A) = P_1 + P_2 - P_1 P_2.$$

For the shutdown system

$$P(S) = P_3 + P_4 - P_3P_4.$$

The overall failure probability is then

$$P = P(A)P(S) = (P_1 + P_2 - P_1P_2)(P_3 + P_4 - P_3P_4).$$

Substituting the numbers provided in the example, we obtain

$$P = [0.13 + 0.04 - (0.13)(0.04)][0.34 + 0.13 - (0.34)(0.13)]$$

$$= (0.165)(0.426) = 0.070.$$

This is the same answer as before.

If the products P_1P_2 and P_3P_4 are assumed to be small, then

$$P(A) = P_1 + P_2,$$

$$P(S) = P_3 + P_4,$$

and

$$P = P(A)P(S) = (P_1 + P_2)(P_3 + P_4)$$

$$= 0.080.$$

The difference between this answer and the answer obtained previously is 14.3%. The component probabilities are not small enough in this example to assume that the cross-products are negligible.

Revealed and Unrevealed Failures

Example 12-2 assumes that all failures in either the alarm or the shutdown system are immediately obvious to the operator and are fixed in a negligible amount of time. Emergency alarms and shutdown systems are used only when a dangerous situation occurs. It is possible for the equipment to fail without the operator being aware of the situation. This is called an unrevealed failure. Without regular and reliable equipment testing, alarm and emergency systems can fail without notice. Failures that are immediately obvious are called revealed failures.

A flat tire on a car is immediately obvious to the driver. However, the spare tire in the trunk might also be flat without the driver being aware of the problem until the spare is needed.

Figure 12-6 shows the nomenclature for revealed failures. The time that the component is operational is called the period of operation and is denoted by τ_o. After a failure occurs, a period of time, called the period of inactivity or downtime (τ_r), is required to repair the component. The MTBF is the sum of the period of operation and the downtime, as shown.

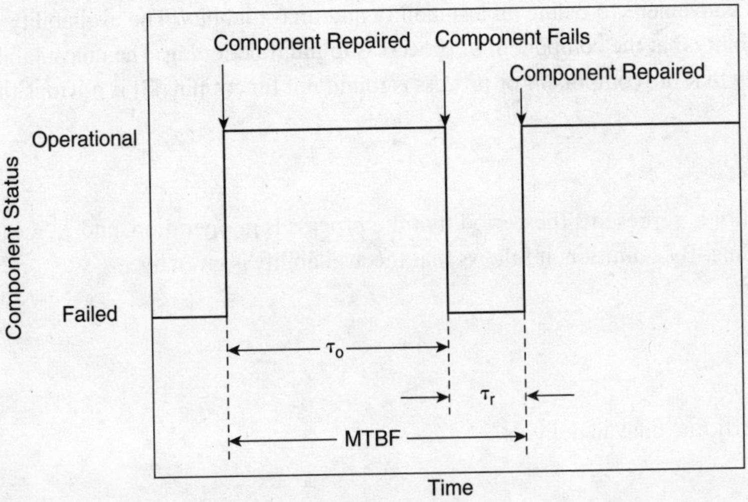

Figure 12-6 Component cycles for revealed failures. A failure requires a period of time for repair.

For revealed failures the period of inactivity or downtime for a particular component is computed by averaging the inactive period for a number of failures:

$$\tau_r \cong \frac{1}{n} \sum_{i=1}^{n} \tau_{r_i}, \tag{12-12}$$

where

n is the number of times the failure or inactivity occurred and
τ_{r_i} is the period for repair for a particular failure.

Similarly, the time before failure or period of operation is given by

$$\tau_o \cong \frac{1}{n} \sum_{i=1}^{n} \tau_{o_i}, \tag{12-13}$$

where τ_{o_i} is the period of operation between a particular set of failures.

The MTBF is the sum of the period of operation and the repair period:

$$\text{MTBF} = \frac{1}{\mu} = \tau_r + \tau_o. \tag{12-14}$$

It is convenient to define an availability and unavailability. The availability A is simply the probability that the component or process is found functioning. The unavailability U is the probability that the component or process is found not functioning. It is obvious that

$$A + U = 1. \tag{12-15}$$

The quantity τ_o represents the period that the process is in operation, and $\tau_r + \tau_o$ represents the total time. By definition, it follows that the availability is given by

$$A = \frac{\tau_o}{\tau_r + \tau_o}, \tag{12-16}$$

and, similarly, the unavailability is

$$U = \frac{\tau_r}{\tau_r + \tau_o}. \tag{12-17}$$

By combining Equations 12-16 and 12-17 with the result of Equation 12-14, we can write the equations for the availability and unavailability for revealed failures:

$$\boxed{\begin{aligned} U &= \mu\tau_r, \\ A &= \mu\tau_o. \end{aligned}} \tag{12-18}$$

For unrevealed failures the failure becomes obvious only after regular inspection. This situation is shown in Figure 12-7. If τ_u is the average period of unavailability during the inspection interval and if τ_i is the inspection interval, then

$$U = \frac{\tau_u}{\tau_i}. \tag{12-19}$$

The average period of unavailability is computed from the failure probability:

$$\tau_u = \int_0^{\tau_i} P(t)\, dt. \tag{12-20}$$

Combining with Equation 12-19, we obtain

$$U = \frac{1}{\tau_i} \int_0^{\tau_i} P(t)\, dt. \tag{12-21}$$

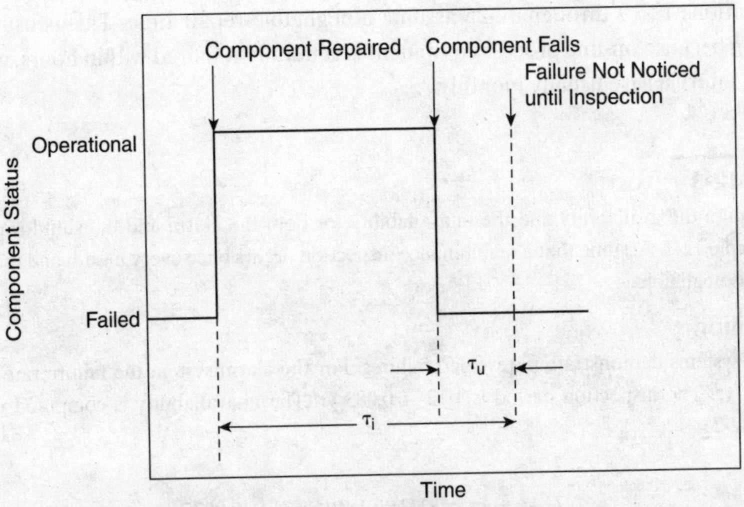

Figure 12-7 Component cycles for unrevealed failures.

The failure probability $P(t)$ is given by Equation 12-2. This is substituted into Equation 12-21 and integrated. The result is

$$U = 1 - \frac{1}{\mu\tau_i}(1 - e^{-\mu\tau_i}). \tag{12-22}$$

An expression for the availability is

$$A = \frac{1}{\mu\tau_i}(1 - e^{-\mu\tau_i}). \tag{12-23}$$

If the term $\mu\tau_i \ll 1$, then the failure probability is approximated by

$$P(t) \approx \mu t, \tag{12-24}$$

and Equation 12-21 is integrated to give, for unrevealed failures,

$$\boxed{U = \frac{1}{2}\mu\tau_i.} \tag{12-25}$$

This is a useful and convenient result. It demonstrates that, on average, for unrevealed failures the process or component is unavailable during a period equal to half the inspection interval. A decrease in the inspection interval is shown to increase the availability of an unrevealed failure.

Equations 12-19 through 12-25 assume a negligible repair time. This is usually a valid assumption because on-line process equipment is generally repaired within hours, whereas the inspection intervals are usually monthly.

Example 12-3

Compute the availability and the unavailability for both the alarm and the shutdown systems of Example 12-2. Assume that a maintenance inspection occurs once every month and that the repair time is negligible.

Solution

Both systems demonstrate unrevealed failures. For the alarm system the failure rate is $\mu = 0.18$ faults/yr. The inspection period is $1/12 = 0.083$ yr. The unavailability is computed using Equation 12-25:

$$U = \frac{1}{2}\mu\tau_i = (1/2)(0.18)(0.083) = 0.0075,$$

$$A = 1 - U = 0.992.$$

The alarm system is available 99.2% of the time. For the shutdown system $\mu = 0.55$ faults/yr. Thus

$$U = \frac{1}{2}\mu\tau_i = (1/2)(0.55)(0.083) = 0.023,$$

$$A = 1 - 0.023 = 0.977.$$

The shutdown system is available 97.7% of the time.

Probability of Coincidence

All process components demonstrate unavailability as a result of a failure. For alarms and emergency systems it is unlikely that these systems will be unavailable when a dangerous process episode occurs. The danger results only when a process upset occurs and the emergency system is unavailable. This requires a coincidence of events.

Assume that a dangerous process episode occurs p_d times in a time interval T_i. The frequency of this episode is given by

$$\lambda = \frac{p_d}{T_i}. \tag{12-26}$$

For an emergency system with unavailability U, a dangerous situation will occur only when the process episode occurs and the emergency system is unavailable. This is every $p_d U$ episodes.

The average frequency of dangerous episodes λ_d is the number of dangerous coincidences divided by the time period:

$$\lambda_d = \frac{p_d U}{T_i} = \lambda U. \tag{12-27}$$

For small failure rates $U = \frac{1}{2}\mu\tau_i$ and $p_d = \lambda T_i$. Substituting into Equation 12-27 yields

$$\lambda_d = \frac{1}{2}\lambda\mu\tau_i. \tag{12-28}$$

The mean time between coincidences (MTBC) is the reciprocal of the average frequency of dangerous coincidences:

$$\text{MTBC} = \frac{1}{\lambda_d} = \frac{2}{\lambda\mu\tau_i}. \tag{12-29}$$

Example 12-4

For the reactor of Example 12-3 a high-pressure incident is expected once every 14 months. Compute the MTBC for a high-pressure excursion and a failure in the emergency shutdown device. Assume that a maintenance inspection occurs every month.

Solution

The frequency of process episodes is given by Equation 12-26:

$$\lambda = 1 \text{ episode}/[(14 \text{ months})(1 \text{ yr}/12 \text{ months})] = 0.857/\text{yr}.$$

The unavailability is computed from Equation 12-25:

$$U = \frac{1}{2}\mu\tau_i = (1/2)(0.55)(0.083) = 0.023.$$

The average frequency of dangerous coincidences is given by Equation 12-27:

$$\lambda_d = \lambda U = (0.857)(0.023) = 0.020.$$

The MTBC is (from Equation 12-29)

$$\text{MTBC} = \frac{1}{\lambda_d} = \frac{1}{0.020} = 50 \text{ yr}.$$

It is expected that a simultaneous high-pressure incident and failure of the emergency shutdown device will occur once every 50 yr.

If the inspection interval τ_i is halved, then $U = 0.023$, $\lambda_d = 0.010$, and the resulting MTBC is 100 yr. This is a significant improvement and shows why a proper and timely maintenance program is important.

Redundancy[2]

Systems are designed to function normally even when a single instrument or control function fails. This is achieved with redundant controls, including two or more measurements, processing paths, and actuators that ensure that the system operates safely and reliably. The degree of redundancy depends on the hazards of the process and on the potential for economic losses. An example of a redundant temperature measurement is an additional temperature probe. An example of a redundant temperature control loop is an additional temperature probe, controller, and actuator (for example, cooling water control valve).

Common Mode Failures

Occasionally an incident occurs that results in a common mode failure. This is a single event that affects a number of pieces of hardware simultaneously. For example, consider several flow control loops similar to Figure 12-4. A common mode failure is the loss of electrical power or a loss of instrument air. A utility failure of this type can cause all the control loops to fail at the same time. The utility is connected to these systems via OR gates. This increases the failure rate substantially. When working with control systems, one needs to deliberately design the systems to minimize common cause failures.

12-2 Event Trees

Event trees begin with an initiating event and work toward a final result. This approach is inductive. The method provides information on how a failure can occur and the probability of occurrence.

When an accident occurs in a plant, various safety systems come into play to prevent the accident from propagating. These safety systems either fail or succeed. The event tree approach includes the effects of an event initiation followed by the impact of the safety systems.

The typical steps in an event tree analysis are[3]

1. Identify an initiating event of interest,
2. Identify the safety functions designed to deal with the initiating event,
3. Construct the event tree, and
4. Describe the resulting accident event sequences.

If appropriate data are available, the procedure is used to assign numerical values to the various events. This is used effectively to determine the probability of a certain sequence of events and to decide what improvements are required.

[2]S. S. Grossel and D. A. Crowl, eds. *Handbook of Highly Toxic Materials Handling and Management* (New York: Marcel Dekker, 1995), p. 264.

[3]Center for Chemical Process Safety (CCPS), *Guidelines for Hazard Evaluation Procedures*, 3rd ed., (New York: American Institute of Chemical Engineers, 2009).

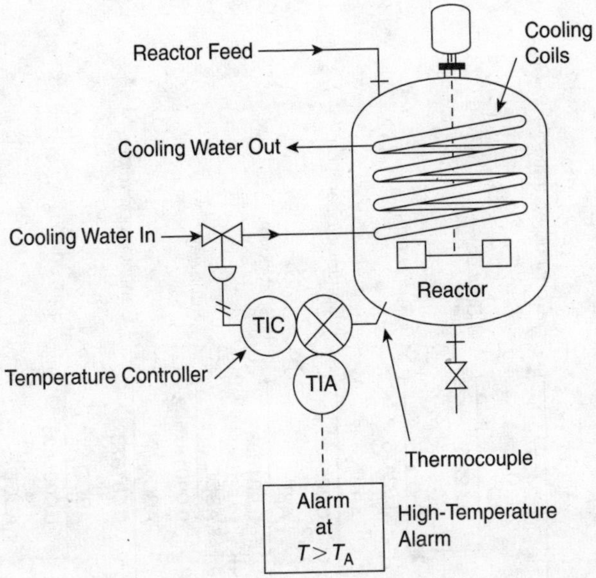

Figure 12-8 Reactor with high-temperature alarm and temperature controller.

Consider the chemical reactor system shown in Figure 12-8. A high-temperature alarm has been installed to warn the operator of a high temperature within the reactor. The event tree for a loss-of-coolant initiating event is shown in Figure 12-9. Four safety functions are identified. These are written across the top of the sheet. The first safety function is the high-temperature alarm. The second safety function is the operator noticing the high reactor temperature during normal inspection. The third safety function is the operator reestablishing the coolant flow by correcting the problem in time. The final safety function is invoked by the operator performing an emergency shutdown of the reactor. These safety functions are written across the page in the order in which they logically occur.

The event tree is written from left to right. The initiating event is written first in the center of the page on the left. A line is drawn from the initiating event to the first safety function. At this point the safety function can either succeed or fail. By convention, a successful operation is drawn by a straight line upward and a failure is drawn downward. Horizontal lines are drawn from these two states to the next safety function.

If a safety function does not apply, the horizontal line is continued through the safety function without branching. For this example, the upper branch continues through the second function, where the operator notices the high temperature. If the high-temperature alarm operates properly, the operator will already be aware of the high-temperature condition. The sequence description and consequences are indicated on the extreme right-hand side of the event tree. The open circles indicate safe conditions, and the circles with the crosses represent unsafe conditions.

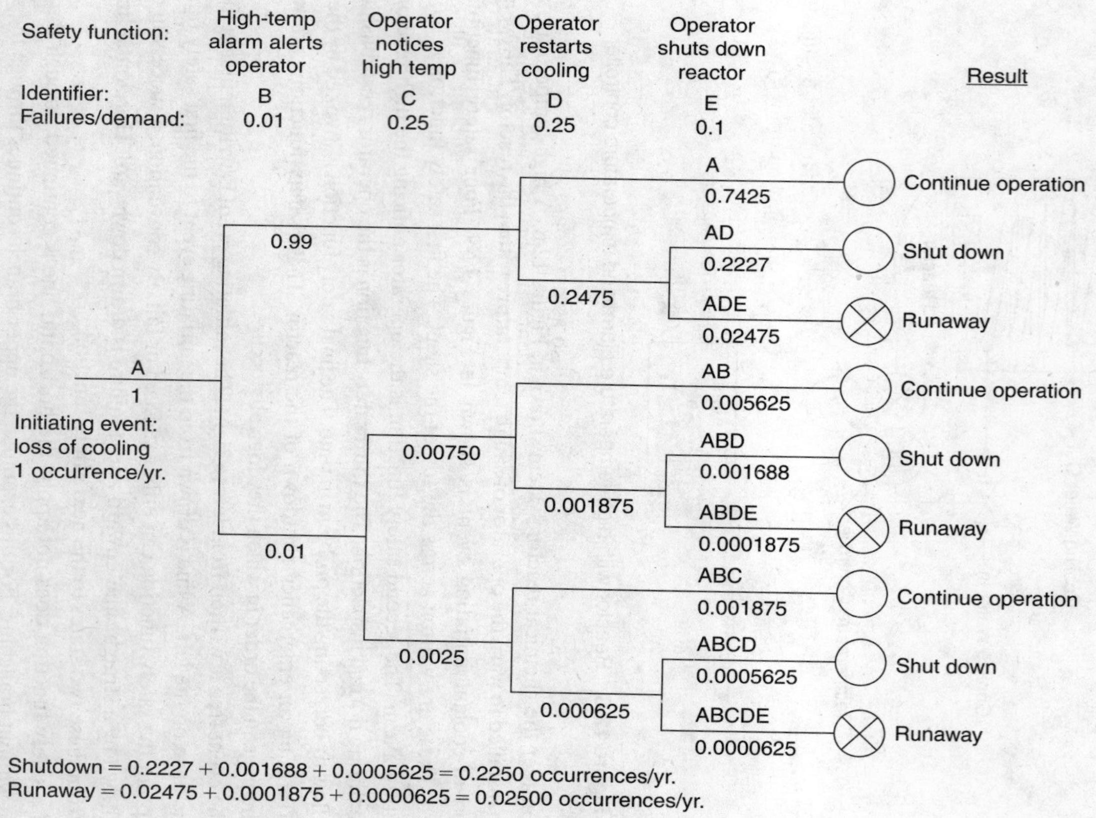

Figure 12-9 Event tree for a loss-of-coolant accident for the reactor of Figure 12-8.

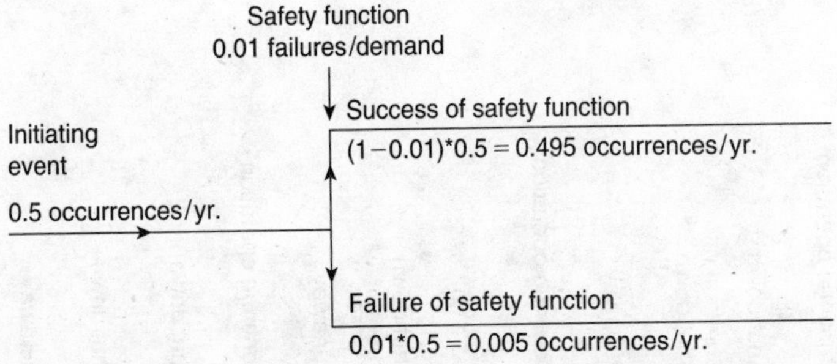

Figure 12-10 The computational sequence across a safety function in an event tree.

The lettering notation in the sequence description column is useful for identifying the particular event. The letters indicate the sequence of failures of the safety systems. The initiating event is always included as the first letter in the notation. An event tree for a different initiating event in this study would use a different letter. For the example here, the lettering sequence ADE represents initiating event A followed by failure of safety functions D and E.

The event tree can be used quantitatively if data are available on the failure rates of the safety functions and the occurrence rate of the initiation event. For this example assume that a loss-of-cooling event occurs once a year. Let us also assume that the hardware safety functions fail 1% of the time they are placed in demand. This is a failure rate of 0.01 failure/demand. Also assume that the operator will notice the high reactor temperature 3 out of 4 times and that 3 out of 4 times the operator will be successful at reestablishing the coolant flow. Both of these cases represent a failure rate of 1 time out of 4, or 0.25 failure/demand. Finally, it is estimated that the operator successfully shuts down the system 9 out of 10 times. This is a failure rate of 0.10 failure/demand.

The failure rates for the safety functions are written below the column headings. The occurrence frequency for the initiating event is written below the line originating from the initiating event.

The computational sequence performed at each junction is shown in Figure 12-10. Again, the upper branch, by convention, represents a successful safety function and the lower branch represents a failure. The frequency associated with the lower branch is computed by multiplying the failure rate of the safety function times the frequency of the incoming branch. The frequency associated with the upper branch is computed by subtracting the failure rate of the safety function from 1 (giving the success rate of the safety function) and then multiplying by the frequency of the incoming branch.

The net frequency associated with the event tree shown in Figure 12-9 is the sum of the frequencies of the unsafe states (the states with the circles and x's). For this example the net frequency is estimated at 0.025 failure per year (sum of failures ADE, ABDE, and ABCDE).

This event tree analysis shows that a dangerous runaway reaction will occur on average 0.025 time per year, or once every 40 years. This is considered too high for this installation. A possible solution is the inclusion of a high-temperature reactor shutdown system. This control

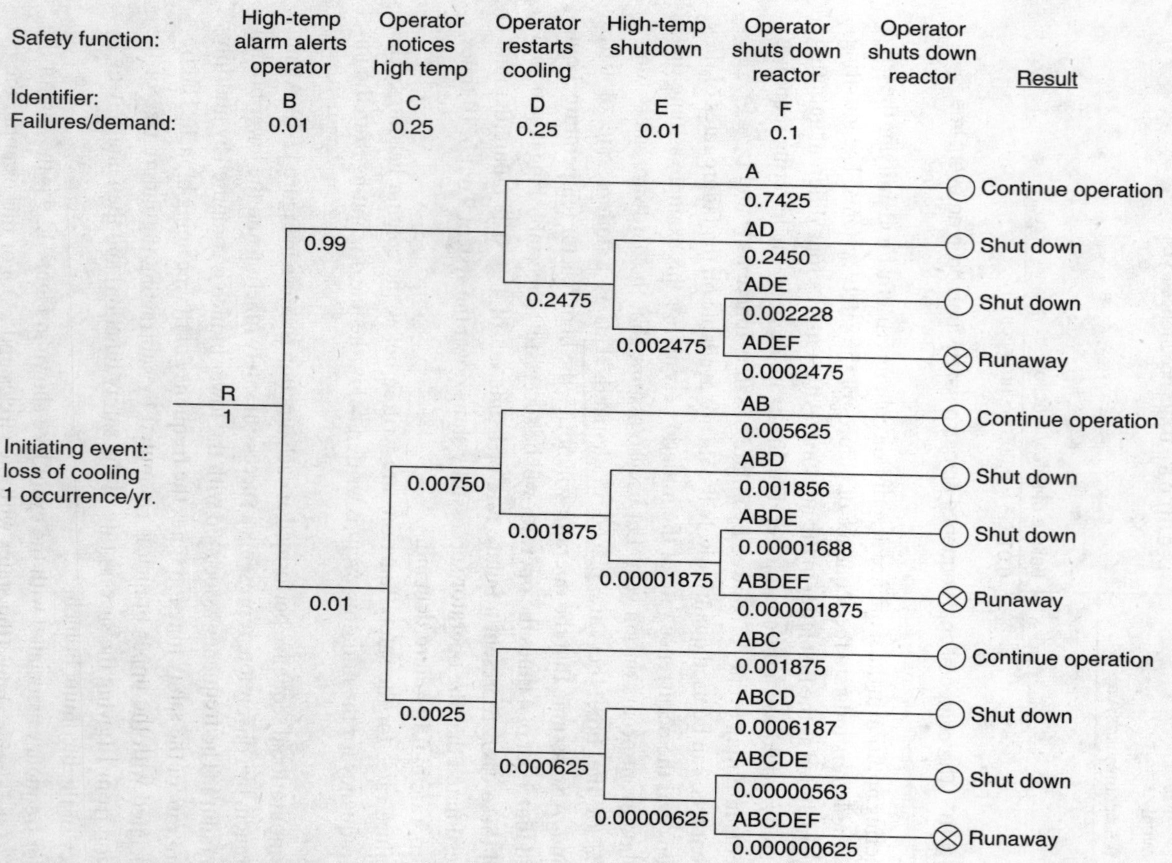

Shutdown = 0.2450 + 0.001856 + 0.00001688 + 0.0006187 = 0.2475 occurrences/yr.
Runaway = 0.0002475 + 0.000001875 + 0.000000625 = 0.0002500 occurrences/yr.

Figure 12-11 Event tree for the reactor of Figure 12-8. This includes a high-temperature shutdown system.

system would automatically shut down the reactor in the event that the reactor temperature exceeds a fixed value. The emergency shutdown temperature would be higher than the alarm value to provide an opportunity for the operator to restore the coolant flow.

The event tree for the modified process is shown in Figure 12-11. The additional safety function provides a backup in the event that the high-temperature alarm fails or the operator fails to notice the high temperature. The runaway reaction is now estimated to occur 0.00025 time per year, or once every 400 years. This is a substantial improvement obtained by the addition of a simple redundant shutdown system.

The event tree is useful for providing scenarios of possible failure modes. If quantitative data are available, an estimate can be made of the failure frequency. This is used most successfully to modify the design to improve the safety. The difficulty is that for most real processes the method can be extremely detailed, resulting in a huge event tree. If a probabilistic computation is attempted, data must be available for every safety function in the event tree.

An event tree begins with a specified failure and terminates with a number of resulting consequences. If an engineer is concerned about a particular consequence, there is no certainty that the consequence of interest will actually result from the selected failure. This is perhaps the major disadvantage of event trees.

12-3 Fault Trees

Fault trees originated in the aerospace industry and have been used extensively by the nuclear power industry to qualify and quantify the hazards and risks associated with nuclear power plants. This approach is becoming more popular in the chemical process industries, mostly as a result of the successful experiences demonstrated by the nuclear industry.

A fault tree for anything but the simplest of plants can be large, involving thousands of process events. Fortunately, this approach lends itself to computerization, with a variety of computer programs commercially available to draw fault trees based on an interactive session.

Fault trees are a deductive method for identifying ways in which hazards can lead to accidents. The approach starts with a well-defined accident, or top event, and works backward toward the various scenarios that can cause the accident.

For instance, a flat tire on an automobile is caused by two possible events. In one case the flat is due to driving over debris on the road, such as a nail. The other possible cause is tire failure. The flat tire is identified as the top event. The two contributing causes are either basic or intermediate events. The basic events are events that cannot be defined further, and intermediate events are events that can. For this example, driving over the road debris is a basic event because no further definition is possible. The tire failure is an intermediate event because it results from either a defective tire or a worn tire.

The flat tire example is pictured using a fault tree logic diagram, shown in Figure 12-12. The circles denote basic events and the rectangles denote intermediate events. The fishlike symbol represents the OR logic function. It means that either of the input events will cause the output state to occur. As shown in Figure 12-12, the flat tire is caused by either debris on the road or tire failure. Similarly, the tire failure is caused by either a defective tire or a worn tire.

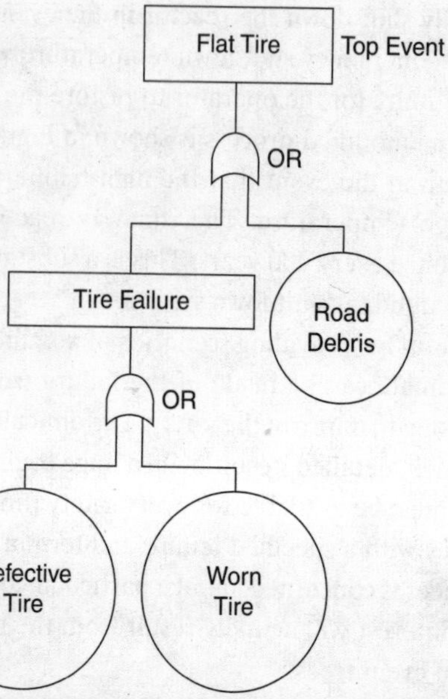

Figure 12-12 A fault tree describing the various events contributing to a flat tire.

Events in a fault tree are not restricted to hardware failures. They can also include software, human, and environmental factors.

For reasonably complex chemical processes a number of additional logic functions are needed to construct a fault tree. A detailed list is given in Figure 12-13. The AND logic function is important for describing processes that interact in parallel. This means that the output state of the AND logic function is active only when both of the input states are active. The INHIBIT function is useful for events that lead to a failure only part of the time. For instance, driving over debris in the road does not always lead to a flat tire. The INHIBIT gate could be used in the fault tree of Figure 12-12 to represent this situation.

Before the actual fault tree is drawn, a number of preliminary steps must be taken:

1. Define precisely the top event. Events such as "high reactor temperature" or "liquid level too high" are precise and appropriate. Events such as "explosion of reactor" or "fire in process" are too vague, whereas an event such as "leak in valve" is too specific.
2. Define the existing event. What conditions are sure to be present when the top event occurs?
3. Define the unallowed events. These are events that are unlikely or are not under consideration at the present. This could include wiring failures, lightning, tornadoes, and hurricanes.
4. Define the physical bounds of the process. What components are to be considered in the fault tree?

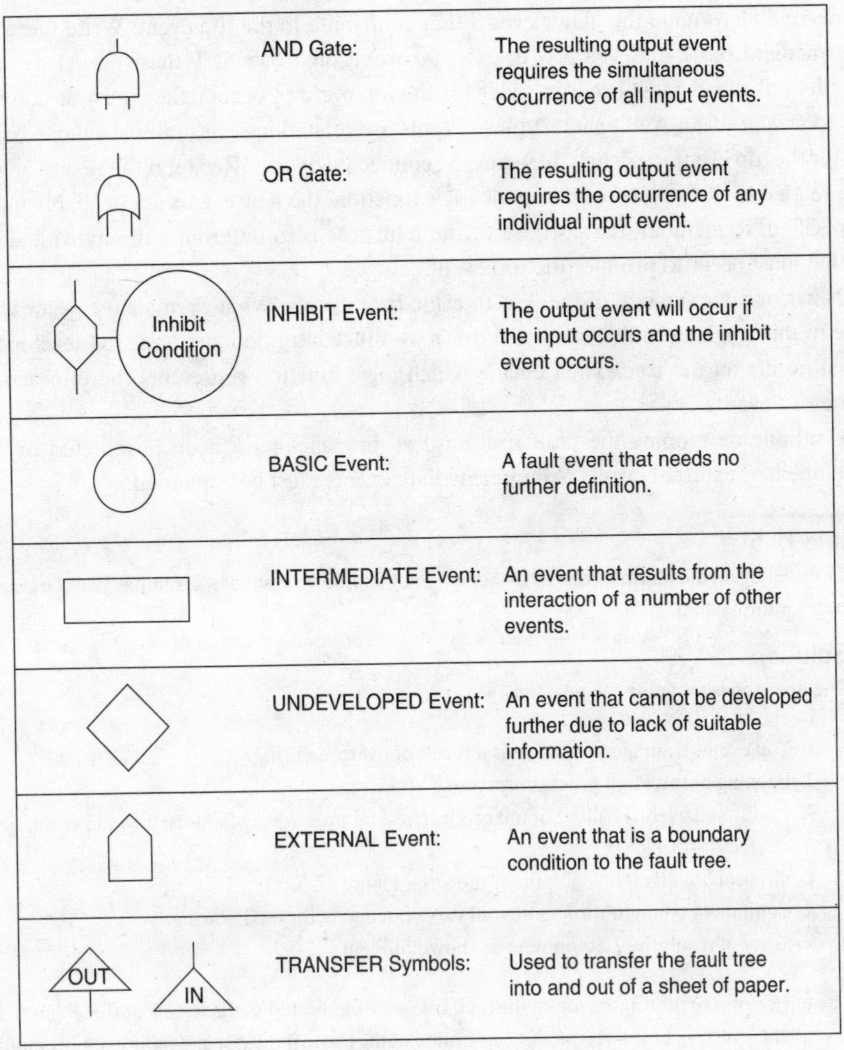
AND Gate:
The resulting output event requires the simultaneous occurrence of all input events.
OR Gate:
The resulting output event requires the occurrence of any individual input event.
Inhibit Condition
INHIBIT Event:
The output event will occur if the input occurs and the inhibit event occurs.
BASIC Event:
A fault event that needs no further definition.
INTERMEDIATE Event:
An event that results from the interaction of a number of other events.
UNDEVELOPED Event:
An event that cannot be developed further due to lack of suitable information.
EXTERNAL Event:
An event that is a boundary condition to the fault tree.
OUT
IN
TRANSFER Symbols:
Used to transfer the fault tree into and out of a sheet of paper.

Figure 12-13 The logic transfer components used in a fault tree.

5. Define the equipment configuration. What valves are open or closed? What are the liquid levels? Is this a normal operation state?
6. Define the level of resolution. Will the analysis consider just a valve, or will it be necessary to consider the valve components?

The next step in the procedure is to draw the fault tree. First, draw the top event at the top of the page. Label it as the top event to avoid confusion later when the fault tree has spread out to several sheets of paper.

Second, determine the major events that contribute to the top event. Write these down as intermediate, basic, undeveloped, or external events on the sheet. If these events are related in parallel (all events must occur in order for the top event to occur), they must be connected to the top event by an AND gate. If these events are related in series (any event can occur in order for the top event to occur), they must be connected by an OR gate. If the new events cannot be related to the top event by a single logic function, the new events are probably improperly specified. Remember, the purpose of the fault tree is to determine the individual event steps that must occur to produce the top event.

Now consider any one of the new intermediate events. What events must occur to contribute to this single event? Write these down as either intermediate, basic, undeveloped, or external events on the tree. Then decide which logic function represents the interaction of these newest events.

Continue developing the fault tree until all branches have been terminated by basic, undeveloped, or external events. All intermediate events must be expanded.

Example 12-5

Consider again the alarm indicator and emergency shutdown system of Example 12-5. Draw a fault tree for this system.

Solution

The first step is to define the problem.

1. Top event: Damage to reactor as a result of overpressuring.
2. Existing event: High process pressure.
3. Unallowed events: Failure of mixer, electrical failures, wiring failures, tornadoes, hurricanes, electrical storms.
4. Physical bounds: The equipment shown in Figure 12-5.
5. Equipment configuration: Solenoid valve open, reactor feed flowing.
6. Level of resolution: Equipment as shown in Figure 12-5.

The top event is written at the top of the fault tree and is indicated as the top event (see Figure 12-14). Two events must occur for overpressuring: failure of the alarm indicator and failure of the emergency shutdown system. These events must occur together so they must be connected by an AND function. The alarm indicator can fail by a failure of either pressure switch 1 or the alarm indicator light. These must be connected by OR functions. The emergency shutdown system can fail by a failure of either pressure switch 2 or the solenoid valve. These must also be connected by an OR function. The complete fault tree is shown in Figure 12-14.

Determining the Minimal Cut Sets

Once the fault tree has been fully drawn, a number of computations can be performed. The first computation determines the minimal cut sets (or min cut sets). The minimal cut sets are the

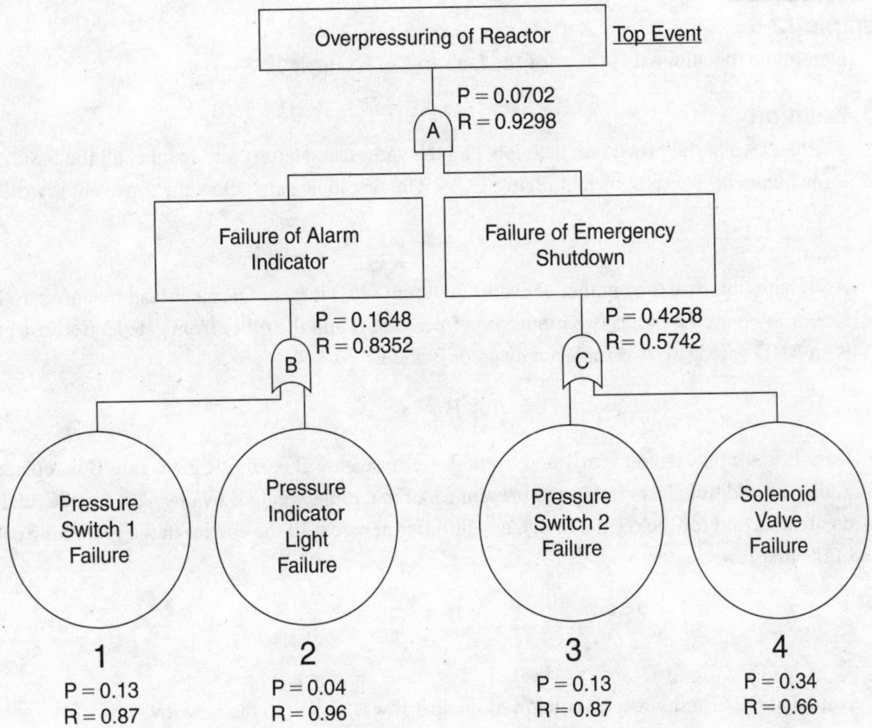

Figure 12-14 Fault tree for Example 12-5.

various sets of events that could lead to the top event. In general, the top event could occur through a variety of different combinations of events. The different unique sets of events leading to the top event are the minimal cut sets.

The minimal cut sets are useful for determining the various ways in which a top event could occur. Some of the mimimal cut sets have a higher probability than others. For instance, a set involving just two events is more likely than a set involving three. Similarly, a set involving human interaction is more likely to fail than one involving hardware alone. Based on these simple rules, the minimal cut sets are ordered with respect to failure probability. The higher probability sets are examined carefully to determine whether additional safety systems are required.

The minimal cut sets are determined using a procedure developed by Fussell and Vesely.[4] The procedure is best described using an example.

[4] J. B. Fussell and W. E. Vesely, "A New Methodology for Obtaining Cut Sets for Fault Trees," *Transactions of the American Nuclear Society* (1972), 15.

Example 12-6

Determine the minimal cut sets for the fault tree of Example 12-5.

Solution

The first step in the procedure is to label all the gates using letters and to label all the basic events using numbers. This is shown in Figure 12-14. The first logic gate below the top event is written:

A

AND gates increase the number of events in the cut sets, whereas OR gates lead to more sets. Logic gate A in Figure 12-14 has two inputs: one from gate B and the other from gate C. Because gate A is an AND gate, gate A is replaced by gates B and C:

~~A~~B C

Gate B has inputs from event 1 and event 2. Because gate B is an OR gate, gate B is replaced by adding an additional row below the present row. First, replace gate B by one of the inputs, and then create a second row below the first. Copy into this new row all the entries in the remaining column of the first row:

~~A~~ ~~B~~ 1 C
2 C

Note that the C in the second column of the first row is copied to the new row.

Next, replace gate C in the first row by its inputs. Because gate C is also an OR gate, replace C by basic event 3 and then create a third row with the other event. Be sure to copy the 1 from the other column of the first row:

~~A~~ ~~B~~ 1 ~~C~~ 3
2 C
1 4

Finally, replace gate C in the second row by its inputs. This generates a fourth row:

~~A~~ ~~B~~ 1 ~~C~~ 3
2 ~~C~~ 3
1 4
2 4

The cut sets are then

1, 3
2, 3
1, 4
2, 4

This means that the top event occurs as a result of any one of these sets of basic events.

The procedure does not always deliver the minimal cut sets. Sometimes a set might be of the following form:

1, 2, 2

This is reduced to simply 1, 2. On other occasions the sets might include supersets. For instance, consider

1, 2
1, 2, 4
1, 2, 3

The second and third sets are supersets of the first basic set because events 1 and 2 are in common. The supersets are eliminated to produce the minimal cut sets.

For this example there are no supersets.

Quantitative Calculations Using the Fault Tree

The fault tree can be used to perform quantitative calculations to determine the probability of the top event. This is accomplished in two ways.

With the first approach the computations are performed using the fault tree diagram itself. The failure probabilities of all the basic, external, and undeveloped events are written on the fault tree. Then the necessary computations are performed across the various logic gates. Remember that probabilities are multiplied across an AND gate and that reliabilities are multiplied across an OR gate. The computations are continued in this fashion until the top event is reached. INHIBIT gates are considered a special case of an AND gate.

The results of this procedure are shown in Figure 12-14. The symbol P represents the probability and R represents the reliability. The failure probabilities for the basic events were obtained from Example 12-2.

The other procedure is to use the minimal cut sets. This procedure approaches the exact result only if the probabilities of all the events are small. In general, this result provides a number that is larger than the actual probability. This approach assumes that the probability cross-product terms shown in Equation 12-10 are negligible.

The minimal cut sets represent the various failure modes. For Example 12-6 events 1, 3 or 2, 3 or 1, 4 or 2, 4 could cause the top event. To estimate the overall failure probability, the probabilities from the cut sets are added together. For this case

$$
\begin{aligned}
P(1 \text{ AND } 3) &= (0.13)(0.13) = 0.0169\\
P(2 \text{ AND } 3) &= (0.04)(0.13) = 0.0052\\
P(1 \text{ AND } 4) &= (0.13)(0.34) = 0.0442\\
P(2 \text{ AND } 4) &= (0.04)(0.34) = \underline{0.0136}\\
\text{Total} &\quad 0.0799
\end{aligned}
$$

This compares to the exact result of 0.0702 obtained using the actual fault tree. The cut sets are related to each other by the OR function. For Example 12-6 all the cut set probabilities were added. This is an approximate result, as shown by Equation 12-10, because the cross-product terms were neglected. For small probabilities the cross-product terms are negligible and the addition will approach the true result.

Advantages and Disadvantages of Fault Trees

The main disadvantage of using fault trees is that for any reasonably complicated process the fault tree will be enormous. Fault trees involving thousands of gates and intermediate events are not unusual. Fault trees of this size require a considerable amount of time, measured in years, to complete.

Furthermore, the developer of a fault tree can never be certain that all the failure modes have been considered. More complete fault trees are usually developed by more experienced engineers.

Fault trees also assume that failures are "hard," that a particular item of hardware does not fail partially. A leaking valve is a good example of a partial failure. Also, the approach assumes that a failure of one component does not stress the other components, resulting in a change in the component failure probabilities.

Fault trees developed by different individuals are usually different in structure. The different trees generally predict different failure probabilities. This inexact nature of fault trees is a considerable problem.

If the fault tree is used to compute a failure probability for the top event, then failure probabilities are needed for all the events in the fault tree. These probabilities are not usually known or are not known accurately.

A major advantage of the fault tree approach is that it begins with a top event. This top event is selected by the user to be specific to the failure of interest. This is opposed to the event tree approach, where the events resulting from a single failure might not be the events of specific interest to the user.

Fault trees are also used to determine the minimal cut sets. The minimal cut sets provide enormous insight into the various ways for top events to occur. Some companies adopt a control strategy to have all their minimal cut sets be a product of four or more independent failures. This, of course, increases the reliability of the system significantly.

Finally, the entire fault tree procedure enables the application of computers. Software is available for graphically constructing fault trees, determining the minimal cut sets, and calculating failure probabilities. Reference libraries containing failure probabilities for various types of process equipment can also be included.

Relationship between Fault Trees and Event Trees

Event trees begin with an initiating event and work toward the top event (induction). Fault trees begin with a top event and work backward toward the initiating event (deduction).

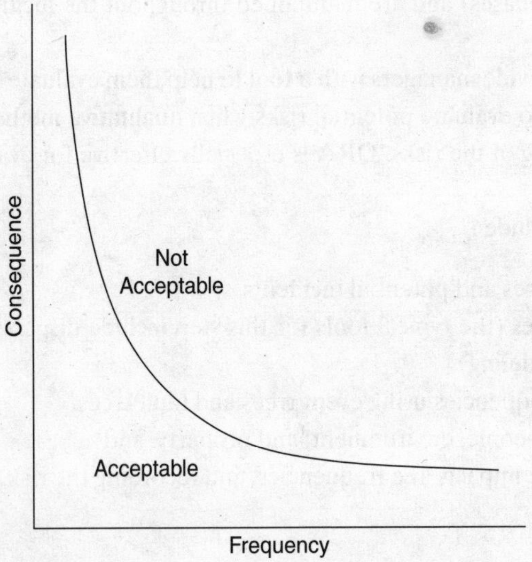

Figure 12-15 General description of risk.

The initiating events are the causes of the incident, and the top events are the final outcomes. The two methods are related in that the top events for fault trees are the initiating events for the event trees. Both are used together to produce a complete picture of an incident, from its initiating causes all the way to its final outcome. Probabilities and frequencies are attached to these diagrams.

12-4 QRA and LOPA

Risk is the product of the probability of a release, the probability of exposure, and the consequences of the exposure. Risk is usually described graphically, as shown in Figure 12-15. All companies decide their levels of acceptable risk and unacceptable risk. The actual risk of a process or plant is usually determined using quantitative risk analysis (QRA) or a layer of protection analysis (LOPA). Other methods are sometimes used; however, QRA and LOPA are the methods that are most commonly used. In both methods the frequency of the release is determined using a combination of event trees, fault trees, or an appropriate adaptation.

Quantitative Risk Analysis[5]

QRA is a method that identifies where operations, engineering, or management systems can be modified to reduce risk. The complexity of a QRA depends on the objectives of the study and the available information. Maximum benefits result when QRAs are used at the beginning of

[5]Center for Chemical Process Safety (CCPS), *Guidelines for Chemical Process Quantitative Risk Analysis,* 2nd ed. (New York: American Institute of Chemical Engineers, 2000).

a project (conceptual review and design phases) and are maintained throughout the facility's life cycle.

The QRA method is designed to provide managers with a tool to help them evaluate the overall risk of a process. QRAs are used to evaluate potential risks when qualitative methods cannot provide an adequate understanding of the risks. QRA is especially effective for evaluating alternative risk reduction strategies.

The major steps of a QRA study include

1. Defining the potential event sequences and potential incidents,
2. Evaluating the incident consequences (the typical tools for this step include dispersion modeling and fire and explosion modeling),
3. Estimating the potential incident frequencies using event trees and fault trees,
4. Estimating the incident impacts on people, environment, and property, and
5. Estimating the risk by combining the impacts and frequencies, and recording the risk using a graph similar to Figure 12-15.

In general, QRA is a relatively complex procedure that requires expertise and a substantial commitment of resources and time. In some instances this complexity may not be warranted; then the application of LOPA methods may be more appropriate.

Layer of Protection Analysis[6]

LOPA is a semi-quantitative tool for analyzing and assessing risk. This method includes simplified methods to characterize the consequences and estimate the frequencies. Various layers of protection are added to a process, for example, to lower the frequency of the undesired consequences. The protection layers may include inherently safer concepts; the basic process control system; safety instrumented functions; passive devices, such as dikes or blast walls; active devices, such as relief valves; and human intervention. This concept of layers of protection is illustrated in Figure 12-16. The combined effects of the protection layers and the consequences are then compared against some risk tolerance criteria.

In LOPA the consequences and effects are approximated by categories, the frequencies are estimated, and the effectiveness of the protection layers is also approximated. The approximate values and categories are selected to provide conservative results. Thus the results of a LOPA should always be more conservative than those from a QRA. If the LOPA results are unsatisfactory or if there is any uncertainty in the results, then a full QRA may be justified. The results of both methods need to be used cautiously. However, the results of QRA and LOPA studies are especially satisfactory when comparing alternatives.

Individual companies use different criteria to establish the boundary between acceptable and unacceptable risk. The criteria may include frequency of fatalities, frequency of fires, maximum frequency of a specific category of a consequence, and required number of independent layers of protection for a specific consequence category.

[6] Center for Chemical Process Safety (CCPS), *Layer of Protection Analysis: Simplified Process Risk Assessment,* D. A. Crowl, ed. (New York: American Institute of Chemical Engineers, 2001).

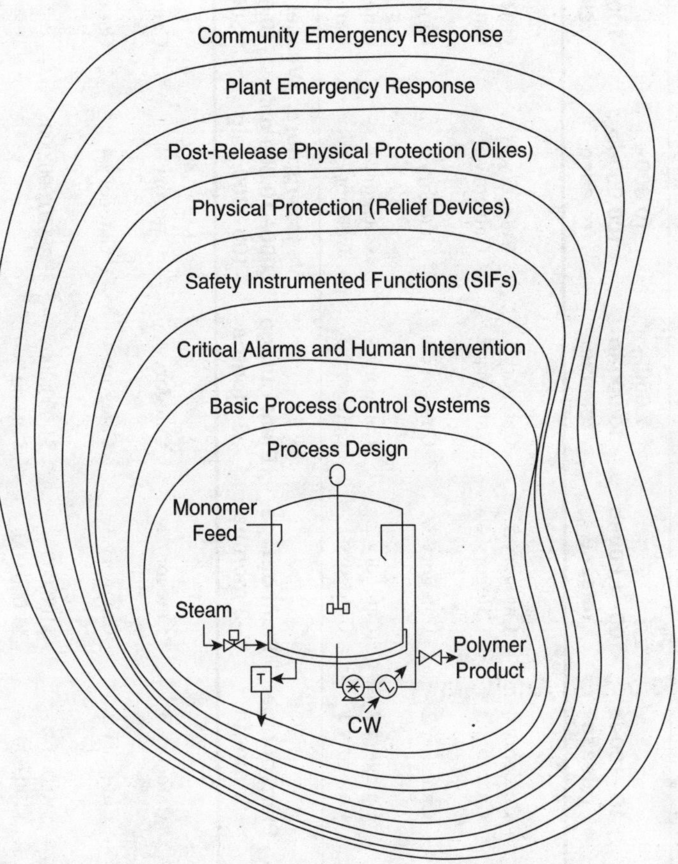

Figure 12-16 Layers of protection to lower the frequency of a specific accident scenario.

The primary purpose of LOPA is to determine whether there are sufficient layers of protection against a specific accident scenario. As illustrated in Figure 12-16, many types of protective layers are possible. Figure 12-16 does not include all possible layers of protection. A scenario may require one or many layers of protection, depending on the process complexity and potential severity of an accident. Note that for a given scenario only one layer must work successfully for the consequence to be prevented. Because no layer is perfectly effective, however, sufficient layers must be added to the process to reduce the risk to an acceptable level.

The major steps of a LOPA study include

1. Identifying a single consequence (a simple method to determine consequence categories is described later)
2. Identifying an accident scenario and cause associated with the consequence (the scenario consists of a single cause-consequence pair)
3. Identifying the initiating event for the scenario and estimating the initiating event frequency (a simple method is described later)

Table 12-2 Semi-Quantitative Consequences Categorization

	Consequence size					
	1–10-lb release	**10–100-lb release**	**100–1,000-lb release**	**1,000–10,000-lb release**	**10,000–100,000-lb release**	**>100,000-lb release**
Release characteristic						
Extremely toxic above BP[a]	Category 3	Category 4	Category 5	Category 5	Category 5	Category 5
Extremely toxic below BP or highly toxic above BP	Category 2	Category 3	Category 4	Category 5	Category 5	Category 5
Highly toxic below BP or flammable above BP	Category 2	Category 2	Category 3	Category 4	Category 5	Category 5
Flammable below BP	Category 1	Category 2	Category 2	Category 3	Category 4	Category 5
Combustible liquid	Category 1	Category 1	Category 1	Category 2	Category 2	Category 3
	Spared or nonessential equipment	**Plant outage <1 month**	**Plant outage 1–3 months**	**Plant outage >3 months**	**Vessel rupture, 3,000–10,000 gal, 100–300 psig**	**Vessel rupture, >10,000 gal, >300 psig**
Consequence characteristic						
Mechanical damage to large main product plant	Category 2	Category 3	Category 4	Category 4	Category 4	Category 5
Mechanical damage to small by-product plant	Category 2	Category 2	Category 3	Category 4	Category 4	Category 5
Consequence cost (U.S. dollars)	\$0–\$10,000	\$10,000–\$100,000	\$100,000–\$1,000,000	\$1,000,000–\$10,000,000	>\$10,000,000	
Categories	Category 1	Category 2	Category 3	Category 4	Category 5	

[a]BP, atmospheric boiling point.

4. Identifying the protection layers available for this particular consequence and estimating the probability of failure on demand for each protection layer
5. Combining the initiating event frequency with the probabilities of failure on demand for the independent protection layers to estimate a mitigated consequence frequency for this initiating event
6. Plotting the consequence versus the consequence frequency to estimate the risk (the risk is usually shown in a figure similar to Figure 12-15)
7. Evaluating the risk for acceptability (if unacceptable, additional layers of protection are required)

This procedure is repeated for other consequences and scenarios. A number of variations on this procedure are used.

Consequence

The most common scenario of interest for LOPA in the chemical process industry is loss of containment of hazardous material. This can occur through a variety of incidents, such as a leak from a vessel, a ruptured pipeline, a gasket failure, or release from a relief valve.

In a QRA study the consequences of these releases are quantified using dispersion modeling and a detailed analysis to determine the downwind consequences as a result of fires, explosions, or toxicity. In a LOPA study the consequences are estimated using one of the following methods: (1) semi-quantitative approach without the direct reference to human harm, (2) qualitative estimates with human harm, and (3) quantitative estimates with human harm. See the reference mentioned in footnote 6 for the detailed methods.

When using the semi-quantitative method, the quantity of the release is estimated using source models, and the consequences are characterized with a category, as shown in Table 12-2. This is an easy method to use compared with QRA.

Although the method is easy to use, it clearly identifies problems that may need additional work, such as a QRA. It also identifies problems that may be deemphasized because the consequences are insignificant.

Frequency

When conducting a LOPA study, several methods can be used to determine the frequency. One of the less rigorous methods includes the following steps:

1. Determine the failure frequency of the initiating event.
2. Adjust this frequency to include the demand; for example, a reactor failure frequency is divided by 12 if the reactor is used only 1 month during the entire year. The frequencies are also adjusted (reduced) to include the benefits of preventive maintenance. If, for example, a control system is given preventive maintenance 4 times each year, then its failure frequency is divided by 4.
3. Adjust the failure frequency to include the probabilities of failure on demand (PFDs) for each independent layer of protection.

Table 12-3 Typical Frequency Values Assigned to Initiating Events[a]

Initiating event	Frequency range from literature (per yr)	Example of a value chosen by a company for use in LOPA (per yr)
Pressure vessel residual failure	10^{-5} to 10^{-7}	1×10^{-6}
Piping residual failure, 100 m, full breach	10^{-5} to 10^{-6}	1×10^{-5}
Piping leak (10% section), 100 m	10^{-3} to 10^{-4}	1×10^{-3}
Atmospheric tank failure	10^{-3} to 10^{-5}	1×10^{-3}
Gasket/packing blowout	10^{-2} to 10^{-6}	1×10^{-2}
Turbine/diesel engine overspeed with casing breach	10^{-3} to 10^{-4}	1×10^{-4}
Third-party intervention (external impact by backhoe, vehicle, etc.)	10^{-2} to 10^{-4}	1×10^{-2}
Crane load drop	10^{-3} to 10^{-4}/lift	1×10^{-4}(/lift)
Lightning strike	10^{-3} to 10^{-4}	1×10^{-3}
Safety valve opens spuriously	10^{-2} to 10^{-4}	1×10^{-2}
Cooling water failure	1 to 10^{-2}	1×10^{-1}
Pump seal failure	10^{-1} to 10^{-2}	1×10^{-1}
Unloading/loading hose failure	1 to 10^{-2}	1×10^{-1}
BPCS instrument loop failure	1 to 10^{-2}	1×10^{-1}
Regulator failure	1 to 10^{-1}	1×10^{-1}
Small external fire (aggregate causes)	10^{-1} to 10^{-2}	1×10^{-1}
Large external fire (aggregate causes)	10^{-2} to 10^{-3}	1×10^{-2}
LOTO (lock-out tag-out) procedure failure (overall failure of a multiple element process)	10^{-3} to 10^{-4}/ opportunity	1×10^{-3} (/opportunity)
Operator failure (to execute routine procedure; well trained, unstressed, not fatigued)	10^{-1} to 10^{-3}/ opportunity	1×10^{-2} (/opportunity)

[a]Individual companies choose their own values, consistent with the degree of conservatism or the company's risk tolerance criteria. Failure rates can also be greatly affected by preventive maintenance routines.

The failure frequencies for the common initiating events of an accident scenario are shown in Table 12-3.

The PFD for each independent protection layer (IPL) varies from 10^{-1} to 10^{-5} for a weak IPL and a strong IPL, respectively. The common practice is to use a PFD of 10^{-2} unless experience shows it to be higher or lower. Some PFDs recommended by CCPS (see footnote 6) for screening are given in Tables 12-4 and 12-5. There are three rules for classifying a specific system or action of an IPL:

1. The IPL is *effective* in preventing the consequence when it functions as designed.
2. The IPL functions *independently* of the initiating event and the components of all other IPLs that are used for the same scenario.
3. The IPL is *auditable,* that is, the PFD of the IPL must be capable of validation including review, testing, and documentation.

Table 12-4 PFDs for Passive IPLs

Passive IPLs	Comments (assuming an adequate design basis, inspections, and maintenance procedures)	PFDs from industry[a]	PFDs from CCPS[a]
Dike	Reduces the frequency of large consequences (widespread spill) of a tank overfill, rupture, spill, etc.	1×10^{-2} to 1×10^{-3}	1×10^{-2}
Underground drainage system	Reduces the frequency of large consequences (widespread spill) of a tank overfill, rupture, spill, etc.	1×10^{-2} to 1×10^{-3}	1×10^{-2}
Open vent (no valve)	Prevents overpressure	1×10^{-2} to 1×10^{-3}	1×10^{-2}
Fireproofing	Reduces rate of heat input and provides additional time for depressurizing, fire fighting, etc.	1×10^{-2} to 1×10^{-3}	1×10^{-2}
Blast wall or bunker	Reduces the frequency of large consequences of an explosion by confining blast and by protecting equipment, buildings, etc.	1×10^{-2} to 1×10^{-3}	1×10^{-3}
Inherently safer design	If properly implemented, can eliminate scenarios or significantly reduce the consequences associated with a scenario	1×10^{-1} to 1×10^{-6}	1×10^{-2}
Flame or detonation arrestors	If properly designed, installed, and maintained, can eliminate the potential for flashback through a piping system or into a vessel or tank	1×10^{-1} to 1×10^{-3}	1×10^{-2}

[a]Center for Chemical Process Safety (CCPS), *Layer of Protection Analysis, Simplified Process Risk Assessment,* D. A. Crowl, ed. (New York: American Institute of Chemical Engineers, 2001).

The frequency of a consequence of a specific scenario endpoint is computed using

$$f_i^C = f_i^I \times \prod_{j=1}^{i} \text{PFD}_{ij}, \tag{12-30}$$

where

f_i^C is the mitigated consequence frequency for a specific consequence C for an initiating event i,

f_i^I is the initiating event frequency for the initiating event i, and

PFD_{ij} is the probability of failure of the jth IPL that protects against the specific consequence and the specific initiating event i. The PFD is usually 10^{-2}, as described previously.

When there are multiple scenarios with the same consequence, each scenario is evaluated individually using Equation 12-30. The frequency of the consequence is subsequently determined using

$$f^C = \sum_{i=1}^{I} f_i^C, \tag{12-31}$$

Table 12-5 PFDs for Active IPLs and Human Actions

Active IPL or human action	Comments [assuming an adequate design basis, inspections, and maintenance procedures (active IPLs) and adequate documentation, training, and testing procedures (human action)]	PFDs from industry[a]	PFDs from CCPS[a]
Relief valve	Prevents system from exceeding specified overpressure. Effectiveness of this device is sensitive to service and experience.	1×10^{-1} to 1×10^{-5}	1×10^{-2}
Rupture disc	Prevents system from exceeding specified overpressure. Effectiveness of this device can be sensitive to service and experience.	1×10^{-1} to 1×10^{-5}	1×10^{-2}
Basic process control system (BPCS)	Can be credited as an IPL if not associated with the initiating event being considered. See IEC (1998, 2001).[b,c]	1×10^{-1} to 1×10^{-2}	1×10^{-1}
Safety instrumented functions (interlocks)	See IEC 61508 (IEC, 1998) and IEC 61511 (IEC, 2001) for life-cycle requirements and additional discussion.[b,c]		
Human action with 10 min response time	Simple well-documented action with clear and reliable indications that the action is required.	1 to 1×10^{-1}	1×10^{-1}
Human action with 40 min response time	Simple well-documented action with clear and reliable indications that the action is required.	1×10^{-1} to 1×10^{-2}	1×10^{-2}

[a]Center for Chemical Process Safety (CCPS), *Layer of Protection Analysis, Simplified Process Risk Assessment,* D. A. Crowl, ed. (New York: American Institute of Chemical Engineers, 2001).
[b]IEC, IEC 61508, *Functional Safety of Electrical/Electronic/Programmable Electronic Safety-Related Systems, Parts 1–7* (Geneva: International Electrotechnical Commission, 1998).
[c]IEC, IEC 61511, *Functional Safety Instrumented Systems for the Process Industry Sector, Parts 1–3* (2004).

where

f_i^C is the frequency of the Cth consequence for the ith initiating event and
I is the total number of initiating events for the same consequence.

Example 12-7

Determine the consequence frequency for a cooling water failure if the system is designed with two IPLs. The IPLs are human interaction with 10-min response time and a basic process control system (BPCS).

Solution

The frequency of a cooling water failure is taken from Table 12-3; that is, $f_1^I = 10^{-1}$. The PFDs are estimated from Tables 12-4 and 12-5. The human response PFD is 10^{-1} and the PFD for the BPCS is 10^{-1}. The consequence frequency is found using Equation 12-30:

$$f_1^C = f_1^I \times \prod_{j=1}^{2} \mathrm{PFD}_{1j}$$

$$= 10^{-1} \times (10^{-1})(10^{-1}) = 10^{-3} \text{ failure/yr.}$$

As illustrated in Example 12-7, the failure frequency is determined easily by using LOPA methods.

The concept of PFD is also used when designing emergency shutdown systems called safety instrumented functions (SIFs). A SIF achieves low PFD figures by

- Using redundant sensors and final redundant control elements
- Using multiple sensors with voting systems and redundant final control elements
- Testing the system components at specific intervals to reduce the probability of failures on demand by detecting hidden failures
- Using a deenergized trip system (i.e., a relayed shutdown system)

There are three safety integrity levels (SILs) that are generally accepted in the chemical process industry for emergency shutdown systems:

1. SIL1 (PFD = 10^{-1} to 10^{-2}): These SIFs are normally implemented with a single sensor, a single logic solver, and a single final control element, and they require periodic proof testing.
2. SIL2 (PFD = 10^{-2} to 10^{-3}): These SIFs are typically fully redundant, including the sensor, logic solver, and final control element, and they require periodic proof testing.
3. SIL3 (PFD = 10^{-3} to 10^{-4}): SIL3 systems are typically fully redundant, including the sensor, logic solver, and final control element; and the system requires careful design and frequent validation tests to achieve the low PFD figures. Many companies find that they have a limited number of SIL3 systems because of the high cost normally associated with this architecture.

Typical LOPA

A typical LOPA study addresses about 2% to 5% of the significant issues defined in a PHA. To do this, each company develops limits for LOPA studies, for example, major consequences with a Category 4 and accidents with one or more fatalities. Effective LOPA studies should focus on areas that are associated with major accidents based on historical data, especially startups and shutdowns. It is generally accepted that 70% of accidents occur during startup and shutdown; therefore it is recommended that significant effort be devoted to these areas.[7] Less time on LOPAs leaves more time for PHAs to identify other undiscovered and significant accident scenarios.

Each identified independent protection layer (IPL), or safeguard, is evaluated for two characteristics: (1) Is the IPL effective in preventing the scenario from reaching the consequences? and (2) Is the safeguard independent? All IPLs, in addition to being independent, have three characteristics:[8]

- Detect or sense the initiating event in the specific scenario
- Decide to take action or not
- Deflect and eliminate the undesired consequences

Some of the benefits of LOPAs are that they (1) focus attention on the major issues, (2) eliminate unnecessary safeguards, (3) establish valid safeguards to improve the PHA process, (4) require fewer resources and are faster than fault tree analysis or QRAs, and (5) provide a basis for managing layers of protection, such as spare parts and maintenance.

The general format for an LOPA is shown in Example 12-8.

Example 12-8

A PHA team has identified several major consequences with different initiating events and frequencies. Develop a table to document the LOPA results for two of the major scenarios. The first scenario is for a fire due to a tank rupture, and the second scenario is for a release from a reactor because of a control loop failure. Both scenarios have a vessel volume of 50,000 lb of a flammable above the BP, and the failures result in a six-month outage. The reactor is operated 100 days in a year.

Solution

The LOPA results are shown in Table 12-6. A typical LOPA team develops a table with many columns for all significant events.

The batch reactor initiating event (IE) frequency is adjusted for the 100 days of operation; that is, the initiating frequency is 10^{-1} failures per year times 100/300 or a frequency of 3.0×10^{-2}.

Table 12-6 General Format of LOPA

Items of LOPA	Results for scenario 1	Results for scenario 2
Description of event (Table 12-3)	Fire due to tank rupture	Reactor – major release
Initiating event (cause) (Table 12-3 and PHA)	Loss of cooling	BPCS failure
Consequence and severity (Table 12-2 and PHA results)	Failure causing > 3 mo. outage or Category 4	Failure causing > 3 mo. outage or Category 4

[7] W. Bridges and T. Clark, "Key Issues with Implementing LOPA (Layer of Protection Analysis): Perspective from One of the Originators of LOPA," *Proceedings from the AIChE Plant Process Safety Symposium*, Paper 19a (2009).

[8] A. Dowell and D. Hendershot, "Simplified Risk Analysis – LOPA," *Proceedings from the AIChE Loss Prevention Symposium*, Paper 281a (2002).

Table 12-6 General Format of LOPA *(continued)*

Items of LOPA	Results for scenario 1		Results for scenario 2	
Initiating event frequency (per year) (Table 12-3)	1×10^{-1}		Adjusted to 3×10^{-2}	
Risk tolerance criteria – company chooses tolerance levels				
a. category	Category 4		Category 4	
b. risk of damage (per year)	$<10^{-5}$		$<10^{-5}$	
c. risk of fatality (per year)	$<10^{-9}$		$<10^{-9}$	
Layers of protection – existing (type and PFD) List the existing layers with the PFD frequencies (Tables 12-4 and 12-5)	Process design	10^{-1}	New BPCS	10^{-1}
	Relief	10^{-2}	Relief	10^{-2}
	Dike	10^{-2}	Dike	10^{-2}
	Etc.		Etc.	
Intermediate likelihood (PFD) (product of the existing layers and IE frequency)	10^{-6}		3×10^{-7}	
Layers of protection – new (type and PFD) (add new layers to reach the tolerance criteria, and add redundancy if relatively inexpensive)	SIL1	10^{-1}	SIL1	10^{-1}
	SIL2	10^{-2}	SIL2	10^{-2}
Mitigated IE likelihood (failures/yr) (the product of all layers of protection and IE frequency)	10^{-9}		3×10^{-10} (the LOPA team decided that the redundancy is justified)	
Notes regarding process design: includes an LIC, alarm, and maintenance				

As illustrated above, the resulting table contains information for characterizing risk (consequence and frequency). In each case the mitigated event frequencies are compared to the tolerable risk, and additional IPLs are added to reach these criteria. The results are an order of magnitude approximation of the risk, but the numbers in the tables give conservative estimates of failure probabilities. So the absolute risk may be off, but the comparisons of conservative risks identify the areas needing attention.

This method, therefore, identifies controls for reducing the frequency. However, the LOPA and PHA team members should also consider inherently safe design alternatives (see Section 1-7). Additional LOPA details, methods, examples, and references are in the CCPS books.[9,10]

[9]Center for Chemical Process Safety (CCPS), *Simplified Process Risk Assessment: Layer of Protection Analysis*, D. A. Crowl, ed. (New York: American Institute of Chemical Engineers, 2001).

[10]Center for Chemical Process Safety (CCPS), *Initiating Events and Independent Protection Layers for LOPA*, J. Murphy, ed. (New York: American Institute of Chemical Engineers, 2010).

Suggested Reading

Center for Chemical Process Safety (CCPS), *Guidelines for Chemical Process Quantitative Risk Analysis* 2nd ed. (New York: American Institute of Chemical Engineers 2000).

Center for Chemical Process Safety (CCPS), *Guidelines for Consequence Analysis of Chemical Releases* (New York: American Institute of Chemical Engineers, 1999).

Center for Chemical Process Safety (CCPS), *Guidelines for Developing Quantitative Safety Risk Criteria* (New York: American Institute of Chemical Engineers 2009).

Center for Chemical Process Safety (CCPS), *Guidelines for Hazard Evaluation Procedures*, 3rd ed. (New York: American Institute of Chemical Engineers, 2009).

Center for Chemical Process Safety (CCPS), *Guidelines for Risk-Based Process Safety* (New York: American Institute for Chemical Engineers, 2008).

Center for Chemical Process Safety (CCPS), *Initiating Events and Independent Protection Layers for LOPA* (New York: American Institute of Chemical Engineers, 2010).

Center for Chemical Process Safety (CCPS), *Layer of Protection Analysis: Simplified Process Risk Assessment*, D. A. Crowl, ed. (New York: American Institute of Chemical Engineers, 2001).

Arthur M. Dowell III, "Layer of Protection Analysis and Inherently Safer processes," *Process Safety Progress* (1999), 18(4): 214–220.

Raymond Freeman, "Using Layer of Protection Analysis to Define Safety Integrity Level Requirements," *Process Safety Progress* (Sept. 2007), 26(3): 185–194.

J. B. Fussell and W. E. Vesely, "A New Methodology for Obtaining Cut Sets for Fault Trees," *Transactions of the American Nuclear Society* (1972), 15.

J. F. Louvar and B. D. Louvar, *Health and Environmental Risk Analysis: Fundamentals with Applications* (Upper Saddle River, NJ: Prentice Hall PTR, 1998).

S. Mannan, ed., *Lees' Loss Prevention in the Process Industries*, 3rd ed. (London: Butterworth Heinemann, 2005).

J. Murphy and W. Chastain, "Initiating Events and Independent Protection Layers for LOPA – A New CCPS Guideline Book," *Loss Prevention Symposium Proceedings* (2009), pp. 206–222.

B. Roffel and J. E. Rijnsdorp, *Process Dynamics, Control, and Protection* (Ann Arbor, MI: Ann Arbor Science, 1982), ch. 19.

A. E. Summers, "Introduction to Layers of Protection Analysis," *J. Hazard. Mater* (2003), 104(1–3): 163–168.

Problems

12-1. Given the fault tree gates shown in Figure 12-17 and the following set of failure probabilities:

Component	Failure probability
1	0.1
2	0.2
3	0.3
4	0.4

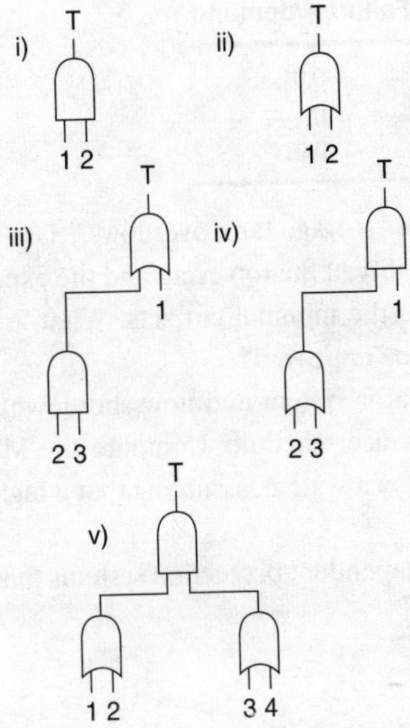

Figure 12-17 Fault tree gates.

a. Determine an expression for the probability of the top event in terms of the component failure probabilities.

b. Determine the minimal cut sets.

c. Compute a value for the failure probability of the top event. Use both the expression of part a and the fault tree itself.

12-2. The storage tank system shown in Figure 12-18 is used to store process feedstock. Overfilling of storage tanks is a common problem in the process industries. To prevent overfilling, the storage tank is equipped with a high-level alarm and a high-level shutdown system. The high-level shutdown system is connected to a solenoid valve that stops the flow of input stock.

a. Develop an event tree for this system using the "failure of level indicator" as the initiating event. Given that the level indicator fails 4 times/yr, estimate the number of overflows expected per year. Use the following data:

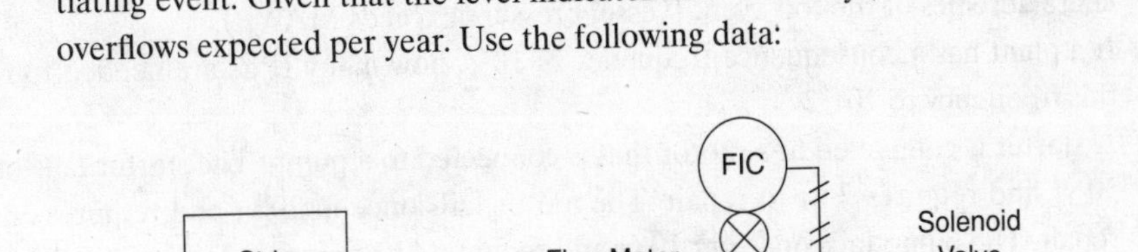

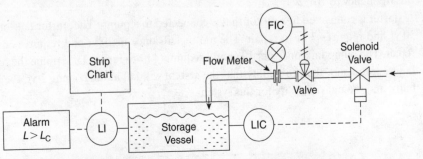

Figure 12-18 Level control system with alarm.

System	Failures/demand
High-level alarm	0.01
Operator stops flow	0.1
High-level switch system	0.01

b. Develop a fault tree for the top event of "storage tank overflows." Use the data in Table 12-1 to estimate the failure probability of the top event and the expected number of occurrences per year. Determine the minimal cut sets. What are the most likely failure modes? Should the design be improved?

12-3. Compute the availability of the level indicator system and flow shutdown system for Problem 12-2. Assume a 1-month maintenance schedule. Compute the MTBC for a high-level episode and a failure in the shutdown system, assuming that a high-level episode occurs once every 6 months.

12-4. Show that for a process protected by two independent protection systems the frequency of dangerous coincidences is given by

$$\lambda_d = \frac{1}{4}\lambda\mu^2\tau_i^2.$$

12-5. Assume that a company decides to characterize an acceptable risk as a Category 1 failure every 2 years and a Category 5 failure every 1000 years. Are the following scenarios acceptable or not?

a. Category 4 every 100 years.
b. Category 2 every 50 years.

12-6. Using the results of Problem 12-5,

a. What would you do to move the unacceptable scenarios into the acceptable region?
b. Was the analysis of Problem 12-5 acceptable?

12-7. Using the rules for IPLs, list four protective layers that are clearly IPLs.

12-8. Determine the MTBF for SIL1–3 systems, if they have PFDs of 10^{-1}, 10^{-2}, and 10^{-3}, respectively. (Note: This is not the same as Problem 12-22.)

12-9. Using the system shown in Figure 12-19, draw the fault tree and determine the failure characteristics of the top event (vessel pressure exceeds MAWP).

12-10. If a plant has a consequence frequency of 10^{-2}, how many IPLs are needed to reduce this frequency to 10^{-6}?

12-11. A starter is connected to a motor that is connected to a pump. The starter fails once in 50 yr and requires 2 hr to repair. The motor fails once in 20 yr and requires 36 hr to repair. The pump fails once per 10 yr and requires 4 hr to repair. Determine the overall failure frequency, the probability that the system will fail in the coming 2 yr, the reliability, and the unavailability for this system.

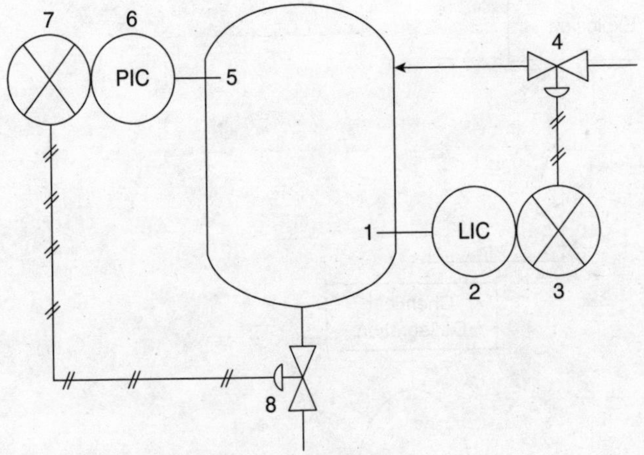

Figure 12-19 A control system to prevent the pressure from exceeding the MAWP.

12-12. If your lockout/tagout procedure has a failure frequency of 10^{-3} per opportunity, what measures could be taken to reduce this frequency?

12-13. A reactor experiences trouble once every 16 months. The protection device fails once every 25 yr. Inspection takes place once every month. Calculate the unavailability, the frequency of dangerous coincidences, and the MTBC.

12-14. What consequence categories do the following scenarios have?

a. Release of 1000 pounds of phosgene.

b. Release of 1000 pounds of isopropanol at 75°F.

c. Potential facility damage of $1,000,000.

12-15. If a specific consequence has two initiating events that give the same consequence, describe the process for determining the frequency of this specific event.

12-16. Determine the MTBF of the top event (explosion) of the system shown in Figure 12-20.

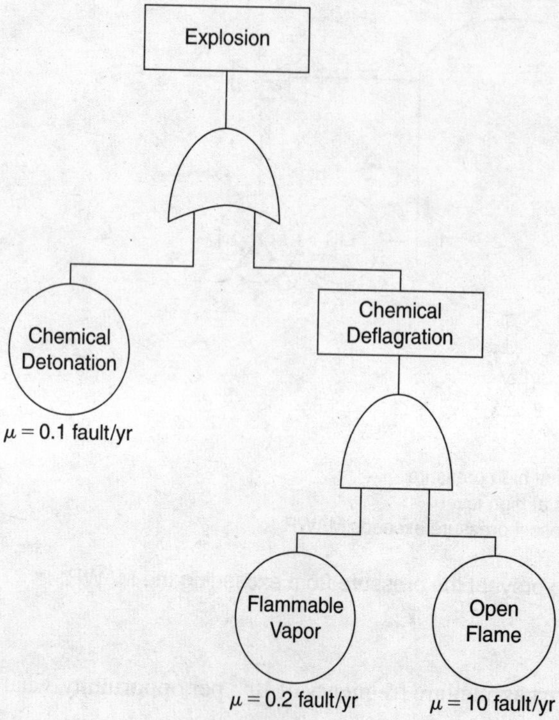

Figure 12-20 Determine the MTBF of the top event.

12-17. Determine the failure characteristics and the minimal cut sets for the system shown in Figure 12-21.

12-18. Compute the MTBF, failure rate, reliability, and probability of failure of the top event of the system shown in Figure 12-22. Also show the minimal cut sets.

12-19. Determine P, R, μ, and the MTBF for the top event of the system shown in Figure 12-23. Also list the minimal cut sets.

12-20. Determine the consequence frequency for a regular failure if the system is designed with three IPLs.

12-21. Using the system shown in Figure 12-24, draw the fault tree and determine the failure characteristics of the top event (vessel overflows). In this problem you have human intervention; that is, when the alarm sounds, someone turns off valve 7.

12-22. Determine the expected failure rates and MTBFs for control systems with SIL1, SIL2, and SIL3 ratings with PFDs of 10^{-2}, 10^{-3}, and 10^{-4}, respectively.

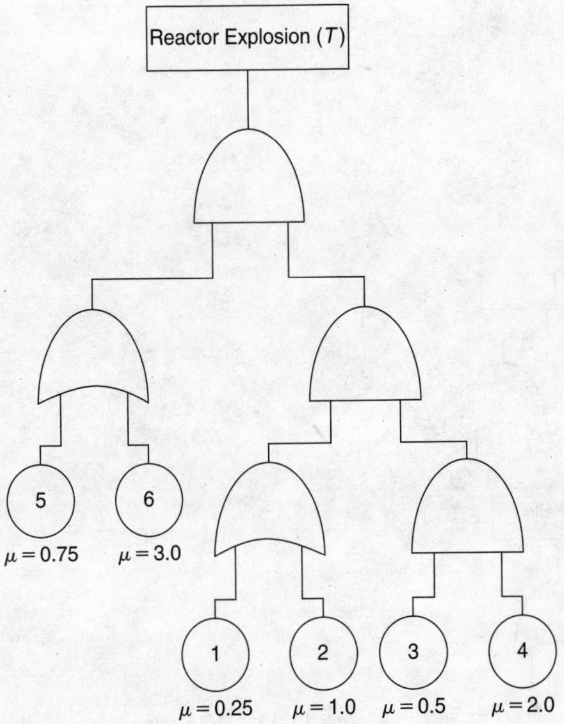

Figure 12-21 Determine the failure characteristics of a reactor explosion.

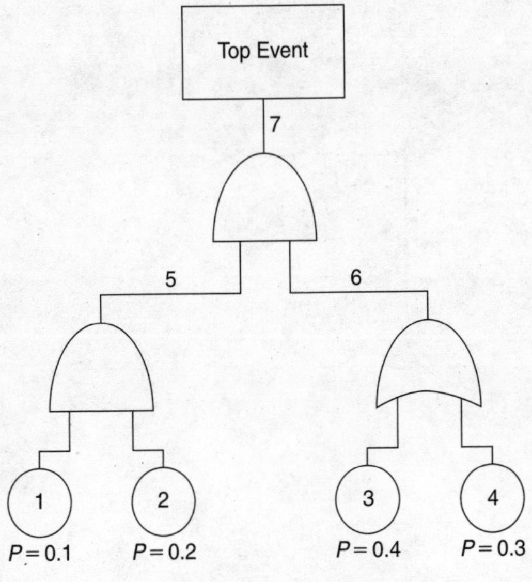

Figure 12-22 Determine the failure characteristics of the top event.

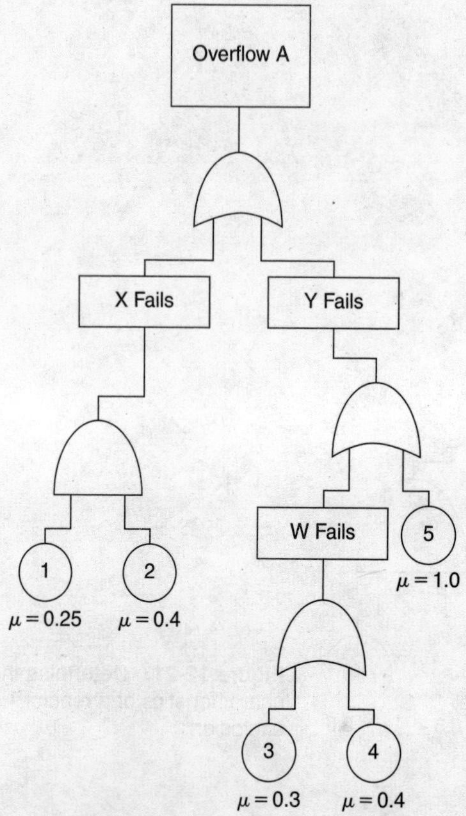

Figure 12-23 Determine the failure characteristics of the top event.

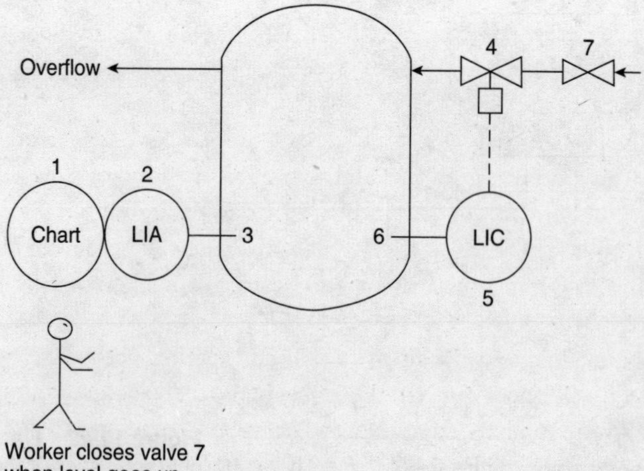

Figure 12-24 Control system to prevent vessel overflow.

CHAPTER 13

Safety Procedures and Designs

Process accidents are prevented by managing the development and maintenance of important process activities. This chapter covers the details of this management process by focusing on the following topics:

- Process safety hierarchy
- Managing safety
- Best practices
- Procedures—operating
- Procedures—permits
- Procedures—safety reviews and accident investigations
- Designs for process safety
- Miscellaneous designs for fires and explosions
- Designs for runaway reactions
- Designs for handling dusts

The knowledge gained by focusing on these topics will help students, engineers, and managers prevent accidents. The motivation for including many of these topics is based on four well-known paraphrased quotations: (1) The causes of accidents are visible the day before the accident; (2) we are not inventing new ways to have accidents; (3) learn from history or you're doomed to repeat it; and (4) sometimes doing your best is not enough—sometimes you need to do what is required.

The content of this chapter will help to identify and eliminate causes before the accident, but more important, it will help to prevent the causes in the first place. Additionally, this chapter is intended to motivate students, engineers, and managers to understand that safety is a very important subject and responsibility.

13-1 Process Safety Hierarchy

Process Safety Strategies

There are four categories of process safety strategies, in order of preference: (1) inherent, (2) passive, (3) active, and (4) procedural.[1,2]

- Inherent: Identify and implement ways to completely eliminate or significantly reduce hazards, rather than to develop add-on protective systems and procedures. Inherently safer design includes identifying technology that operates in less severe conditions rather than devoting extensive resources to safety systems and procedures to manage the risks associated with the hazards.
- Passive: Add safety features that do not require action by any device. Passive devices perform their intended functions without personnel or control actions. Passive systems include dikes, passive flame arrestors, and the use of welded fittings versus flanges and threaded connections.
- Active: Add safety shutdown systems to prevent accidents. Active systems include process control systems, safety interlocks, automatic shutdown systems, and automated mitigation systems.
- Procedural: Include standard operating procedures, safety rules, operator training, emergency response procedures, and management techniques in general.

Inherent and passive strategies are the most robust and reliable, but elements of all strategies are required to minimize safety problems.

Layers of Protection

The application of these safety strategies is often described as a series of layers of protection surrounding a process, as shown in Figure 12-16. These layers are necessary because it is unlikely that inherently safer design features alone will eliminate all hazards. Each layer reduces the process risk.

Active and procedural layers of protection require constant maintenance and management to ensure that they continue to function as designed. If they are not managed correctly, the protection systems will degrade and increase the hazards to an unacceptable level. Inherently safer designs make these layers of protection more reliable and robust.

[1] Center for Chemical Process Safety (CCPS), *Inherently Safer Processes: A Life Cycle Approach* (New York: American Institute of Chemical Engineers, 2008).

[2] D. Hendershot, "An Overview of Inherently Safer Design," *Process Safety Progress* (June 2009), 25(2): 98.

13-2 Managing Safety

A simple and general description of a good management process includes deciding what needs to be done, doing it, documenting that it has been done, and studying these results and improving the process. In the area of safety, this simple process is adapted to include

- Documentation: Describe what needs to be done to eliminate hazards and accidents.
- Communication: Motivate everyone influenced by this document to do what needs to be done.
- Delegation: Delegate portions (manageable parts) of the responsibilities to those involved.
- Follow-up: Check to be sure that the documentation (procedures, etc.) is used as intended. Also use this follow-up process to make improvements.

Documentation

The safety documentation may be a procedure for conducting a safety review, designing a plant, operating procedures for normal and emergency conditions, and training procedures.

The documentation should, in general, be clear, readily available, and easy to follow.[3] Additionally, the documents should be controlled; that is, the documents should include a cover page containing the revisions made, including dates and the responsible person's signature. Notice that revisions should be expected, because the follow-up process encourages improvements.

Communications

After procedures are developed, they should not be idle documents on a shelf but should be used appropriately and enthusiastically. This communication step motivates all personnel about the documents or procedures, including the importance of the documents, the importance of everyone taking the time to use them appropriately, and the consequences of non-conformance that may seriously affect them, their coworkers, and their families. It also emphasizes the importance of preventing the existence of hazards.

Delegation

It is important to have employee participation with regard to safety responsibilities. Therefore, as many people as possible should be delegated the responsibility for developing and modifying specific documents or procedures. This participation improves the quality of the documents and it motivates compliance.

[3]Center for Chemical Process Safety (CCPS), *Guidelines for Process Safety Documentation* (New York: American Institute of Chemical Engineers, 1995).

Follow-up

Responsibilities will only be completed satisfactorily if authorities follow up to check on progress. Trevor Kletz preaches, "It isn't what you expect, but it is what you inspect." In this safety case, the facility management must take the responsibility for inspecting. In an industrial production plant, this manager will probably be the plant manager. As stated previously, this follow-up process should also include making improvements to the documented procedures.

13-3 Best Practices

Engineers have the responsibility to use best practices when designing and operating plants. The Engineering Code of Ethics requires that their designs meet standards and established practices.[4] The AIChE Code of Ethics states that engineers must perform professional services only in areas of their competence.[5] Also see Table 1-1.

Some engineers neglect this responsibility with grave consequences. Many accidents investigated by CSB[6] were due to the failure to use the codes, standards, and other Recognized and Generally Accepted Good Engineering Practices (RAGAGEP).

Sources of RAGAGEP include

- Government laws
- American Petroleum Institute (API) standards
- AIChE's Center for Chemical Process Safety (CCPS) guidelines
- National Fire Protection Association (NFPA) fire codes and standards
- Methods and rules in engineering texts
- Industrial experience acquired by sharing information within industry

Some of the most widely used best practices documents include those by CCPS,[7,8] NFPA,[9,10] API,[11] and OSHA.[12]

13-4 Procedures—Operating

Operating procedures are designed and managed to help operators run a plant or facility with no problems or mishaps. They should include steps for each operating phase and operating

[4]M. W. Mike and S. Roland, *Ethics in Engineering,* 3rd ed. (New York: McGraw-Hill, 1996).

[5]"AIChE Code of Ethics", *www.aiche.org/About/Code.aspx, 2003*.

[6]A. S. Blair, "RAGAGEP Beyond Regulation: Good Engineering Practices for the Design and Operation of Plants," *Process Safety Progress*, (Dec. 2007), 26(4): 330.

[7]Center for Chemical Process Safety (CCPS), *Guidelines for Design Solutions for Process Equipment Failures* (New York: American Institute of Chemical Engineers, 1998).

[8]Center for Chemical Process Safety (CCPS), *Guidelines for Engineering Design for Process Safety* (New York: American Institute of Chemical Engineers, 1993).

[9]NFPA 68, *Venting of Deflagrations* (Quincy, MA: National Fire Protection Association, 1997).

[10]NFPA 30, *Flammable and Combustible Liquids Code* (Quincy, MA: National Fire Protection Association, 1996).

[11]API 750, *Management of Process Hazards* (Washington DC: American Petroleum Institute, 1990).

[12]"Process Safety Management of Highly Hazardous Chemicals," *Code of Federal Regulations, 29CFR 1910.119* (57FR23061, June 1, 1992).

limits for the startup, shutdown, normal, temporary, and emergency procedures. The operating limits should be highlighted with the consequences of exceeding these limits, and with steps to correct or avoid deviations from normal conditions. Additionally, they should (1) contain engineering and administrative controls for preventing exposures, (2) include a description of the controls that are needed for safe operation, and (3) highlight the permits that are used to control the environment.[12]

13-5 Procedures—Permits

Permits are used to control nonroutine activities that are conducted in potentially hazardous environments. The permit includes a description of the hazards and actions taken to prevent accidents. The formal permit communicates relevant information between the people doing the work and the operating personnel who are affected by the work. The required permit actions include those by the workers and the operators; they include actions before the work is permitted and actions after the work is completed to transition from the permitted environment to the normal operating mode. The following examples give the key features of a few permits; but they do not include all of the requirements, because the detailed requirements may be uniquely designed for different environments.[13]

Hot Work Permit

This permit prevents the ignition of flammable or combustible gases or liquids in a work environment. Hot work operations include welding, grinding, torch cutting or soldering, and any other ignition sources. These permits are valid for only one shift at a time. The procedure includes the following:

1. Check for flammable materials in areas and trenches with a flammable gas detection meter. If there are flammable vapors in the area, then a permit is not allowed.
2. Remove all containers of flammable and combustible materials within a 35-foot radius of the hot work. If they can't be removed, then cover them with a flame-retardant tarp and post the area with a fire watch.
3. Place a fire extinguisher in the area, and check to be sure that smoke detection, sprinkler, and alarm systems are working.
4. Inform operations and everyone in the area and then post the signed permit. Also, maintain a file of past permits.

Lock-Tag-Try Permit

This permit prevents injuries or damage due to the accidental release of stored energy from equipment. The stored energy includes electrical, gravitational, mechanical, and thermal. This permit is intended to prevent equipment from unexpectedly being set into motion and

[13]"Iowa State University Permits," *www.ehs.iastate.edu/cms/default.asp?action=article&ID=300.*

endangering workers. Typical activities that require this permit include an employee going into a danger zone (rotating equipment or in a vessel with an agitator), repairing electrical circuits, maintaining machinery with moving parts, cleaning jammed mechanisms, and removing guards or safety devices. The lock-tag-try procedure starts with a de-energize process:

- De-energize the equipment by unplugging electrical connections; releasing pressured lines such as hydraulic, air, steam, gas and water; and releasing spring-loaded devices.
- Lock the equipment or electrical device to prevent reactivation. A gang lock device is used to allow the device to be locked out by several maintenance trades and operations personnel.
- Tag the equipment or device to warn against re-energizing the equipment. Tags alone can be used only when the equipment cannot be physically locked, for example, some valves.
- Try to re-energize the equipment to verify that the locking process works.

Prior to going back to the normal operation, the operations supervisor is the last one to remove the lock, after being certain that the device or equipment is safe to re-energize.

Vessel Entry Permit

This permit is sometimes called the confined space permit. It is used to prevent someone from being injured in a confined space. The confined space could be a vessel, a diked area, or even reaching into a large pipe opening. The potential injuries include being overcome by a gas (nitrogen, carbon monoxide, etc.), being entangled with moving equipment, and being engulfed by entering gases or liquids. The permit includes the following steps:

1. Have an area supervisor take complete control of the vessel entry according to the permit details.
2. Isolate the equipment by disconnecting all process lines going into the vessel, which may include activating double block and bleed systems.
3. Clean the equipment.
4. Manage all other permits on this system, including lock-tag-try and hot work permits, to prevent inadvertent activation.
5. Have a second attendant in the area to help with emergencies.
6. Place emergency equipment in the area, such as a fire extinguisher.
7. Place safety cuffs around the entering person's wrists with a chain and pulley to enable removal of the person under emergency situations.
8. Continuously monitor the oxygen concentration to be sure that it is at least 19.5%.
9. Add ventilation in the vessel or confined space to be sure the concentration of oxygen is maintained.
10. Have a ground fault interrupting light to assist the person's visibility in the vessel.

11. Have a two-way radio at the vessel to summon help if required.
12. Use a ladder to enter the vessel, unless step-down distance is small compared to the height of the person entering.
13. Have the manager in charge sign the permit and post it in the area.

13-6 Procedures—Safety Reviews and Accident Investigations

Safety Reviews

This section expands the safety reviews described in Chapter 11, because a major focus of a review is to improve procedures and designs. In this regard, some of the features of safety reviews include the following:

1. Develop and review detailed process descriptions. This description should include (a) a process flow diagram (PFD) that contains the major equipment, pipes, and controls, and material and energy balances; (b) a piping and instrumentation diagram (P&ID) that contains all of the equipment, pipes, valves, controls, and design specifications relevant to safety; and (c) a layout to show the relationship of the equipment.
2. Accumulate and review the chemical, physical, and reactive properties of all chemicals in the plant. The list of chemicals should include all combinations of the chemicals being used in the process, and the chemicals plus possible contaminants.
3. Develop and review operating procedures, including startup, shutdown, normal, and emergency procedures. The operating procedures should highlight the limitations of the process (e.g., temperature and pressure) and give the consequences when the limitations are exceeded.
4. Accumulate and review accident investigations of previous and relevant incidents that are shared throughout the company and between companies.
5. Develop recommendations to improve the design and operating procedures to eliminate hazards and prevent accidents.
6. Develop and review the management system to ensure that all of the safety review recommendations are implemented and documented before the startup.

The plant descriptions and procedures may be adapted for specific situations; for example, laboratory descriptions will be informal sketches.

Incident Investigations

The objectives of investigations are to identify the causes of incidents, understand the interrelationship between causes, and develop actions to prevent the recurrence of similar incidents. Paraphrasing Kletz:[14] "We do not invent new ways to have accidents—we only continue to make

[14]Trevor Kletz, *Learning from Accidents*, 3rd ed. (Boston: Butterworth-Heinemann, 2001).

Table 13-1 Typical Accident Report

Accident title:
Major damage:
Date:
Location:

<u>Events</u>

1. Major accident scenario:
2. Pre-accident conditions:
3. Events that precipitated the accident:

<u>Causes of accident</u>

1. Design problems
2. Control problems
3. Problems in the operating procedures
4. Management problems, including maintenance and bad decisions

<u>Recommendations for prevention/mitigation</u>

1. 1st layer: Immediate technical recommendation: specific changes to the design, operating procedures, maintenance, etc.
2. 2nd layer: Recommendations for avoiding the hazard: clearly specifying process limitations and the consequences of deviations.
3. 3rd layer: Recommendation for improving the management systems; add annual audits to be sure the new designs and operating procedures are used as specified, and add periodic training.

the same mistakes." Therefore the review of accident investigations is particularly important before designing a new plant.

A typical accident investigation report format is shown in Table 13-1. This table is an adaptation of a report recommended by Kletz. As illustrated, a typical report includes recommendations that can and should be used in similar plants to prevent accidents. The Center for Chemical Process Safety also has a book covering incident investigations.[15] The safety review procedure outlined above includes the review and use of accident investigations.

13-7 Designs for Process Safety

The following safe design features are only samples to illustrate some key safety features. There are many more safety designs that are described in many books and standards.[16]

[15]Center for Chemical Process Safety (CCPS), *Guidelines for Investigation of Chemical Process Incidents*, 2nd ed. (New York: American Institute of Chemical Engineers, 2003).

[16]See the sources cited in footnotes 6–11 as well as NFPA 654, *Standard for the Prevention of Fire and Dust Explosions from the Manufacturing, Processing, and Handling of Combustible Particulates Solids* (Quincy, MA: National Fire Protection Association, 2000).

Inherently Safer Designs

Inherently safer technology (IST) permanently *eliminates* and *reduces* hazards in order to avoid or reduce the consequences of incidents, rather than using add-on protection measures to control the risks arising from hazards. Inherent safety is a relative characteristic, and it is appropriate to describe one process as inherently safer than another. It is possible that a modification in one area may increase or decrease a hazard in another area. An engineer, therefore, should evaluate alternative inherently safer designs, in order to choose the best inherently safer design.

In these cases a decision tool is used to evaluate the options to identify the best designs. The tools include voting methods, weighted scoring methods, cost-benefit analysis, and decision analysis.[17] Inherently safer technology can result in lower capital cost in new plant design and typically produces lower operating costs, greater reliability, and quicker startup times. Plants with inherently safer technologies tend to be simpler, easier and friendlier to operate, and more tolerant of errors.

Incidentally, this search for inherently safer technology applies to all stages of a process. The best opportunities for implementing inherently safer designs are in the early stages of development. But the concepts should be periodically reviewed for any process, from startup to shutdown. For example, some years ago, the CFC refrigeration technology was an inherently safer design compared to ammonia refrigeration, but the subsequent identification of the environmental ozone depletion problems required another review and IST.

Given a choice, the preferred designs are inherently safer designs. The concept of inherent safety is to design a system that fails safely even when operators make mistakes or equipment fails.[18]

Inherent safety is introduced in Chapter 1. A simple summary description of inherent safety includes four alternatives:

1. Moderate: Use milder conditions.
2. Substitute: Replace hazardous with nonhazardous chemicals.
3. Minimize: Use smaller vessels (reactors or storage) and quantities.
4. Simplify: Design systems to be easy to understand, including the mechanical designs and computer screens.

A simple design includes the mechanical configurations of vessels, pumps, pipelines, and so forth. A simple versus a complex design is illustrated in Figure 13-1. Other inherently safe designs are described in Table 1-9.

[17]D. Hendershot, "Conflicts and Decisions in the Search for Inherently Safer Process Options," *Process Safety Progress* (Jan. 1995), 14(1): 52.

[18]Trevor Kletz, *Plant Design for Safety: A User-Friendly Approach* (New York: Hemisphere Publishing Corporation, 1990).

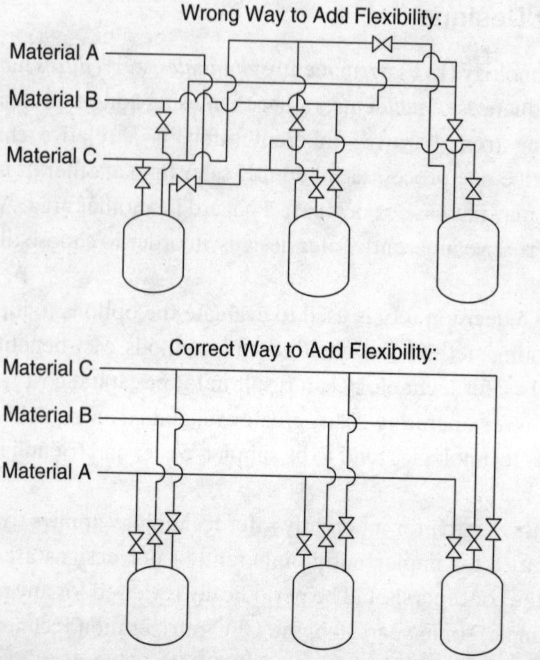

Figure 13-1 Sketch of a simple versus a complex design.

Controls—Double Block and Bleed

Double block and bleed systems are installed, for example, in monomer lines between the reactor and the monomer feed tanks as shown in Figure 13-2. This prevents the reactor contents,

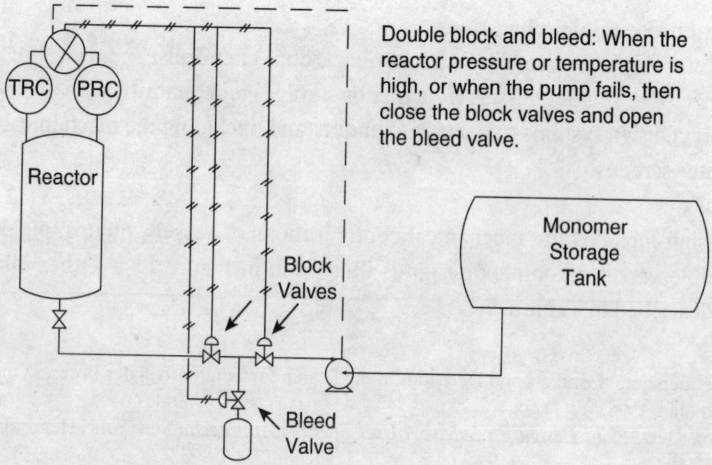

Figure 13-2 Double block and bleed system.

including catalysts, from inadvertently backing up into the monomer tank. To put this in perspective, polyether polymerization reactions require the addition of a monomer from a storage vessel at about 30 psig into a reactor. As a result of the exothermic reaction the reactor is at higher temperatures and pressures; polyether reactors are run at about 130 psig. Under this condition, if the monomer pump fails, then the reactor contents with the catalyst will back up through the pump and system into the monomer tank. This results in a catalyzed reaction with prohibitively very high monomer concentrations—a classical runaway reaction that will give high temperatures, pressures, and usually a large explosion and fire. In this case the problem is eliminated by placing this double block and bleed system in all monomer lines. When the pump fails, the double block and bleed is activated, and it is virtually impossible to transfer reactor contents to the monomer tank. Notice that the monomer lines may also include check valves, but they are not as reliable; check valves can leak through their seals.

Controls—Safeguards or Redundancy

Safeguards or redundant controls are a special set of controls that are added to a system to reduce the possibility of an accident. For example, a reactor that controls a rapid and exothermic reaction should have a group of safeguards to prevent the hazardous runaway as shown in Figure 13-3. Redundancy increases the reliability of a control system; the quantitative effects of redundancy are computed using fault tree analysis as discussed in Chapter 12.

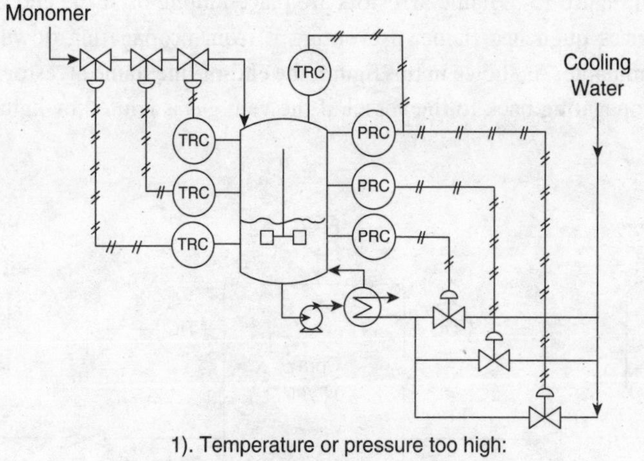

1). Temperature or pressure too high: open cooling valves and close monomer valves.
2). Motor or agitation fails: the same.
3). Heat balance off: the same.
4). In all cases, the double block and bleed valves in the monomer lines would be activated.

Figure 13-3 Safeguards or redundancy.

Controls—Block Valves

Block valves are installed throughout plants to shut a system down during unusual circumstances. Block valves can be manually operated or operated by a control system or field analyzer. Block valves typically are installed in lines at all vessels containing hazardous materials, and activated when an adjoining line or hose develops a leak; installed in sewer lines to prevent major leaks from contaminating a treatment facility; and sometimes installed in plants so that materials can be transferred from a hazardous environment to a safe one; for example, when a fire is around a vessel, a normally closed block valve would be opened to transfer the material to a safe location.

Controls—Explosion Suppression

As illustrated in Figure 13-4, an explosion suppression system detects a flame or pressure at the incipient phase of an explosion or fire. This detection system sets off quick-acting valves to inject a flame-quenching substance into the burning region. The one illustrated in this figure would prevent the explosion of the spray dryer. This type of system can be installed in pipelines, to prevent a fire from going from one vessel to another, and it can also be used outside equipment to detect and quench fires or explosions.

Flame Arrestors

As illustrated in Figure 13-5, flame arrestors are placed inline or at the end of a line. In both cases these devices quench a flame, preventing it from propagating down a pipe or duct containing a flammable. As shown in this figure, the end-of-line flame arrestor prevents a burning gas from propagating back to the vessel, if the vent gas is ignited by lightning. The inline

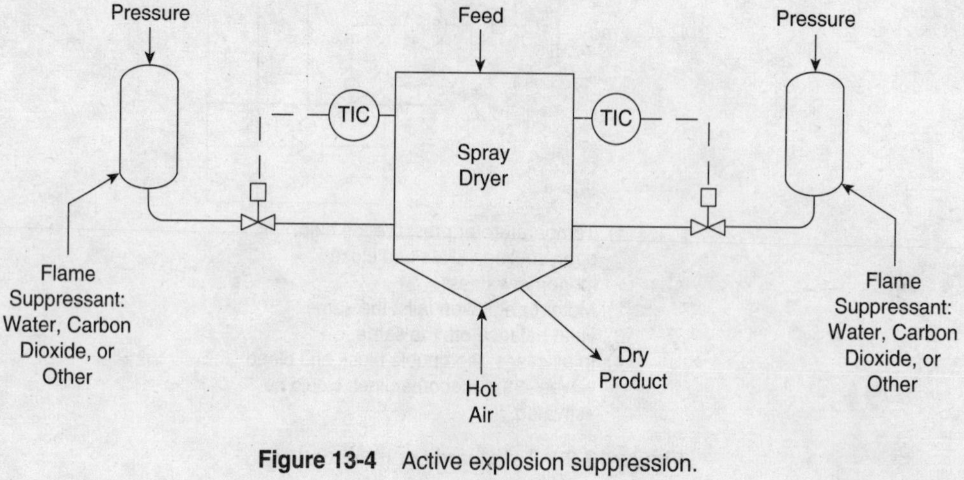

Figure 13-4 Active explosion suppression.

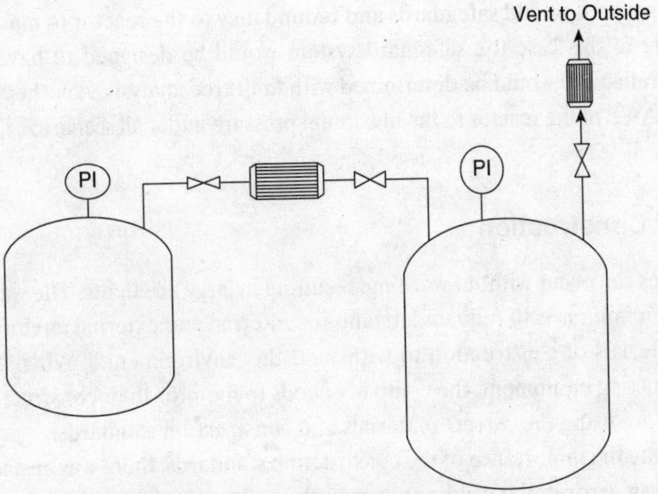

Figure 13-5 Passive flame arrestors.

arrestor prevents a fire or explosion from occurring in one vessel and propagating to the other vessel.

Containment

With a chemical that is especially hazardous, the exits of a relief system should go to a containment system, as shown in Figure 13-6. When containment is used, however, it is very important that a detailed management system be used to ensure it is always maintained and operational. The Bhopal plant had a containment system similar to the one shown, but due to their poor management, including poor mechanical integrity, the system didn't work when it was needed, with catastrophic results.

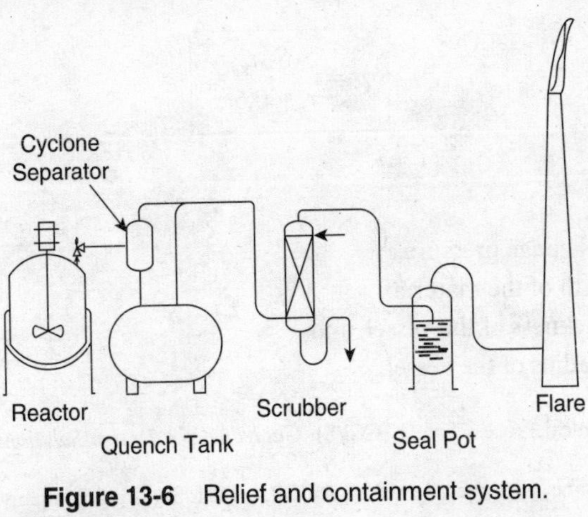

Figure 13-6 Relief and containment system.

An alternative is to add safeguards and redundancy to the reactor to make a relief virtually impossible. In this case the safeguard system would be designed to have an acceptable reliability; the reliability would be determined with fault tree analysis. Another alternative is to increase the MAWP of the reactor to the maximum pressure under all scenarios, that is, operating and accidental.

Materials of Construction

Material failures can occur without warning, resulting in large accidents. The way to reduce the risk of corrosion failures is to fully understand the internal and external environments, and to specify the materials of construction to withstand this environment.[19] When a company has vendors constructing equipment, the company needs to monitor their construction techniques to be sure they are using the correct materials and construction standards.

To illustrate the importance of the construction standards, there was an accident in an oil refinery due to an error in the welding process; the welder used a weld material that was less noble then the tower's material of construction. Therefore, corrosion transferred the less noble weld material to the tower. The weld seam around the entire tower failed, and the tower fell with major adverse consequences[20]–17 fatalities and $100 million loss.

Process Vessels

Process vessels are designed to withstand the temperatures, pressures, and corrosion environments of the process. Normally, the thickness of the vessel is chosen to withstand the pressure, and the thickness is increased for a corrosion allowance. The corrosion allowance is based on laboratory determinations of the corrosion rate and the desired life of the vessel.

The pressure necessary to produce a specific stress in a vessel depends on the thickness of the vessel, the vessel diameter, and the mechanical properties of the vessel wall.[21] For cylindrical vessels with the pressure p not exceeding 0.385 times the mechanical strength of the material S_M,

$$p = \frac{S_M t_v}{r + 0.6 t_v}, \tag{13-1}$$

where

p is the internal gauge pressure,
S_M is the strength of the material,
t_v is the wall thickness of the vessel, and
r is the inside radius of the vessel.

[19] Center for Chemical Process Safety (CCPS), *Guidelines for Design Solutions for Process Equipment Failures*.

[20] "Union Oil Amine Absorber Tower–Accident," TWI Services Company, *www.twi.co.uk/content/oilgas_casedown29.html*.

[21] Samuel Strelzoff and L. C. Pan, "Designing Pressure Vessels," *Chemical Engineering* (Nov. 4, 1968), p. 191.

For cylindrical vessels and pressures exceeding $0.385S_M$, the following equation applies:

$$p = \frac{S_M\left(\frac{t_v}{r}+1\right)^2 - S_M}{\left(\frac{t_v}{r}+1\right)^2 + 1}. \tag{13-2}$$

For spherical vessels with pressures not exceeding $0.665S_M$ the equation is

$$p = \frac{2t_v S_M}{r + 0.2t_v}. \tag{13-3}$$

For spherical vessels and pressures exceeding $0.665S_M$ the equation is

$$p = \frac{2S_M\left(\frac{t_v}{r}+1\right)^2 - 2S_M}{\left(\frac{t_v}{r}+1\right)^2 + 2}. \tag{13-4}$$

These formulas are also used to determine the pressure required to produce elastic deformations by using yield strengths for S_M. They are also used to determine the pressures required to produce failures by using tensile strengths for S_M. Strength of material data are provided in Table 13-2.

Table 13-2 Strength of Materials[a]

Material	Tensile strength (psi)	Yield point (psi)
Borosilicate glass	10,000	
Carbon	660	
Duriron	60,000	30,000
Hastelloy C	72,000	48,000
Nickel	65,000	48,000
Stainless 304	80,000	35,000
Stainless 316	85,000	40,000
Stainless 420	105,000	55,000

[a]Robert H. Perry and Cecil H. Chilton, eds., *Chemical Engineers' Handbook* (New York: McGraw-Hill, 1973), pp. 6–96 and 6–97.

High-pressure failures are as likely to occur in a pipe or pipe system as in vessels. The maximum internal pressure for pipes is calculated using Equations 13-1 and 13-2.

All process vessels that are designed to withstand a pressure should also be designed for full vacuum. This vacuum constraint allows for vacuum puring and accidental process vacuums, for example, steam cleaning a vessel that is entirely blocked (no vents).

Deflagrations

Breaks in pipes or vessels resulting from deflagrations or simple overpressurizations are usually tears with lengths no longer than a few pipe diameters.

The pressure increases during deflagrations are approximately[22]

$$\frac{p_2}{p_1} \approx 8 \text{ for hydrocarbon-air mixtures,} \tag{13-5}$$

$$\frac{p_2}{p_1} \approx 16 \text{ for hydrocarbon-oxygen mixtures.} \tag{13-6}$$

Detonations

As described in Chapter 6, detonations have a rapidly moving flame and/or pressure front. Detonation failures usually occur in pipelines or vessels with large length-to-diameter ratios.

In a single vessel detonations increase pressures significantly:[23]

$$\frac{p_2}{p_1} \approx 20. \tag{13-7}$$

When a pipe network is involved, the downstream p_1 increases because of pressure piling; therefore p_2 may increase by as much as another factor of 20.

Detonation failures in pipe networks are always downstream from the ignition source. They usually occur at pipe elbows or other pipe constrictions, such as valves. Blast pressures can shatter an elbow into many small fragments. A detonation in light-gauge ductwork can tear the duct along seams and can also produce a large amount of structural distortion in the torn ducts.

In pipe systems explosions can initiate as deflagrations and the flame front may accelerate to detonation speeds.

Example 13-1

Determine the pressure required to rupture a cylindrical vessel if the vessel is stainless 316, has a radius of 3 ft, and has a wall thickness of 0.5 in.

Solution

Because the pressure is unknown, Equation 13-1 or 13-2 is used by trial and error until the correct equation is identified. Equation 13-1 is applicable for pressures below $0.385S_M$. Because S_M (from

[22]Frank P. Lees, *Loss Prevention in the Process Industries* (Boston: Butterworths, 1983), p. 567.
[23]Lees, *Loss Prevention*, p. 569.

Table 13-2) is 85,000 psi, $0.385S_M = 32{,}700$ psi, and $r = 3$ ft $= 36$ in and $t_v = 0.5$ in. By substituting into Equation 13-1 for cylindrical vessels, we obtain

$$p = \frac{S_M t_v}{r + 0.6t_v} = \frac{(85{,}000 \text{ psi})(0.5 \text{ in})}{(36 \text{ in}) + 0.6(0.5 \text{ in})} = 1170 \text{ psi.}$$

Therefore Equation 13-1 is applicable, and a pressure of 1170 psi is required to rupture this vessel.

Example 13-2

Determine the pressure required to rupture a spherical vessel if the vessel is stainless 304, has a radius of 5 ft, and has a wall thickness of 0.75 in.

Solution

This problem is similar to Example 13-1; Equation 13-3 is applicable if the pressure is less than $0.665S_M$ or $0.665(80{,}000) = 53{,}200$ psi. Using Equation 13-3 for spherical vessels, we obtain

$$p = \frac{2t_v S_M}{r + 0.2t_v} = \frac{2(0.75 \text{ in})(80{,}000 \text{ psi})}{(5 \text{ ft})(12 \text{ in/ft}) + 0.2(0.75 \text{ in})} = 1990 \text{ psi.}$$

The pressure criterion is met for this equation. The pressure required to rupture this vessel is 1990 psi.

Example 13-3

During an accident investigation, it is found that the source of the accident was an explosion that ruptured a 4-in-diameter stainless 316 schedule 40 pipe. It is hypothesized that a hydrogen and oxygen deflagration or a detonation was the cause of the accident. Deflagration tests in a small spherical vessel indicate a deflagration pressure of 500 psi. What pressure ruptured the pipe, and was it a deflagration or a detonation that caused this rupture?

Solution

A 4-in schedule 40 pipe has an outside diameter of 4.5 in, a wall thickness of 0.237 in, and an inside diameter of 4.026 in. From Table 13-2 the tensile strength S_M for stainless 316 is 85,000 psi. Equation 13-1 for cylinders is used to compute the pressure necessary to rupture this pipe:

$$p = \frac{S_M t_v}{r + 0.6t_v} = \frac{(85{,}000 \text{ psi})(0.237 \text{ in})}{(2.013 \text{ in}) + 0.6(0.237 \text{ in})} = 9348 \text{ psi.}$$

Equation 13-1 is applicable because the pressure is less than $0.385S_M = 32{,}700$ psi. The pressure required to rupture this pipe, therefore, is 9348 psi. Using the deflagration test data, which gave a p_2 of 500 psi, and assuming pressure piling, we can estimate the deflagration pressure in the pipe using Equation 13-6:

$$p_2 = 500 \times 16 = 8000 \text{ psi.}$$

To estimate pressures resulting from a detonation and pressure piling, we estimate the original deflagration test pressure p_1 using Equation 13-6:

$$p_1 = 500/16 = 31.3 \text{ psi}.$$

A detonation with pressure piling is now computed using Equation 13-7:

$$p_2 = 31.3 \times 20 \times 20 = 12{,}500 \text{ psi}.$$

This pipe rupture was therefore due to a detonation. The next step in the investigation would include searching for a chemical reaction that would give a detonation. A small vessel could be used as a test.

Example 13-4

An explosion rips through a chemical plant. A 1000-ft^3 tank containing compressed air at 100 atm is suspected. Site damage indicates that the windows in a structure 100 yd away are shattered. Is the mechanical explosion of this compressed air tank consistent with the damage reported, or is the explosion the result of some other process?

Solution

From Equation 6-29, representing the energy contained in a compressed gas,

$$W_e = \left(\frac{P_1 V_1}{\gamma - 1}\right)\left[1 - \left(\frac{P_2}{P_1}\right)^{(\gamma-1)/\gamma}\right].$$

For air, $\gamma = 1.4$. Substituting the known quantities, we obtain

$$W_e = \frac{(101 \text{ atm})\left(14.7\,\dfrac{\text{lb}_f/\text{in}^2}{\text{atm}}\right)\left(144\,\dfrac{\text{in}^2}{\text{ft}^2}\right)(1000 \text{ ft}^3)}{1.4 - 1}\left[1 - \left(\frac{1 \text{ atm}}{101 \text{ atm}}\right)^{(1.4-1)/1.4}\right]$$

$$= 3.91 \times 10^8 \text{ ft-lb}_f = 1.27 \times 10^8 \text{ cal}.$$

The equivalent amount of TNT is

$$m_{\text{TNT}} = 1.27 \times 10^8 \text{ cal}/(1120 \text{ cal/g TNT}) = 1.13 \times 10^5 \text{ g TNT}$$

$$= 249 \text{ lb of TNT}.$$

From Equation 6-21 the scaling factor is

$$z_e = \frac{r}{(m_{\text{TNT}})^{1/3}}.$$

Substituting, we obtain

$$z_e = \frac{300 \text{ ft}}{(249 \text{ lb})^{1/3}} = 47.66 \text{ ft/lb}^{1/3} = 18.9 \text{ m/kg}^{1/3}.$$

From Figure 6-23 the overpressure is estimated at 1.3 psia. From the data provided in Table 6-9 the estimated damage is consistent with the observed damage.

13-8 Miscellaneous Designs for Fires and Explosions

There are many other design features that prevent fires and explosions, as shown in Table 7-8 and CCPS books.[24,25,26,27]

13-9 Designs for Runaway Reactions

The essential requirements to prevent runaway reactions include

- understanding the concepts and hazards of runaway reactions (see Section 8-1),
- characterizing all possible runaway reactions in the specific system being designed (see Section 8-2), and
- using this knowledge to design the equipment and controls to avoid runaways. The equipment features may include a semi-batch reactor versus a batch, and the controls may include redundancy and double block and bleeds in the monomer feed lines (see Section 8-3).

Some of the other design features[28] that are used to prevent runaways include the following:

1. Design to consume the reactants rapidly to avoid the accumulation of reactants.
2. Design the system to remove the heat and gaseous products generated by the reactions.
3. Use semi-batch reactors instead of batch and add the reactants at rates to control monomer concentrations, that is, lower concentrations that prevent excessive pressures and releases with the accidental loss of cooling.
4. Add safeguards to prevent runaways due to equipment and control failures. The equipment failures may be pumps, agitators, and so on and the control failures may be temperature and pressure controls. In cases like these, redundant control loops would catch the failure and activate a safe shutdown of the reactor system.

[24]Center for Chemical Process Safety (CCPS), *Guidelines for Chemical Reactivity Evaluation and Application to Process Design* (New York: American Institute of Chemical Engineers, 1995).

[25]Center for Chemical Process Safety (CCPS), *Guidelines for Facility Siting and Layout* (New York: American Institute of Chemical Engineers, 2003).

[26]Center for Chemical Process Safety (CCPS), *Guidelines for Performing Effective Pre-Startup Reviews* (New York: American Institute of Chemical Engineers, 2007).

[27]Center for Chemical Process Safety (CCPS), *Guidelines for Safe and Reliable Instrumented Protective Systems* (New York: American Institute of Chemical Engineers, 2007).

[28]R. Johnson, "Chemical Reactivity Hazards," Safety and Chemical Engineering Education Committee of AIChE's Center for Chemical Process Safety (*www.SACHE.org*, 2005).

As mentioned above, knowledge of the potential problems with runaway reactions is essential. In addition to the key design features listed, this knowledge would help designers recognize the value of other potential problems; for example, recognizing that heat removal is more difficult with larger reactors, avoiding adding materials at temperatures above the reactor contents, and knowing that reliefs for runaway reactions need to be designed for two-phase flow.

The key design features mentioned above are for reactors, and these are sometimes called intended reactions with reactive chemicals. Runaways also occur in storage vessels, tank trucks, and tank cars; these would be classified as unintended reactions with reactive chemicals. There is a different set of design features to prevent these accidents,[29] including training personnel to be sure they are aware of these potential problems; cooling the materials to safe margins below the self-accelerating decomposition temperature; including redundant controls to monitor temperatures and activate alarms; designing to separate incompatible materials; storing materials in areas remote from the process areas; and labeling reactive materials, including limiting conditions.

13-10 Designs for Handling Dusts

The safe handling of solids is important because many chemicals are produced as solids to eliminate the transportation of hazardous solvent diluents. Although engineers and chemists usually understand the hazards of flammable liquids and gases, they often don't recognize the hazards of handling dusts. Dusts, for example, have flammability regions similar to gases, and they can burn and explode as deflagrations and detonations. The added problem with dusts, however, is that primary explosions can, and usually do, initiate secondary explosions as the explosion forces and turbulence disperse dusts that may have accumulated on floors, inducts, or above false ceilings. Dust hazards are eliminated with special design features and management practices as described below.

Flammable gases have a three-sided fire triangle that illustrates the three necessary conditions for fires; that is, to burn a flammable gas you need fuel (flammable gas) and an ignition source, and oxygen. Flammable dusts have the five-sided fire pentagon that includes fuel, an ignition source, oxygen, low moisture, and suspension in air. In this regard, dusts burn relatively slowly when ignited on a surface, but they explode when they are ignited as suspensions. Many of the design and management practices[30] mentioned below are focused on this pentagon.

The essential requirements to prevent dust explosions include

- understanding the concepts and hazards of dusts (see Chapter 6),
- characterizing the properties of dusts for the specific system being designed (see Chapters 6 and 7), and
- using this knowledge to design the equipment and management practices to avoid dust explosions; see the next two sections.

[29] R. Johnson, "Chemical Reactivity Hazards."

[30] Louvar and Schoeff, "Dust Explosion Control," Safety and Chemical Engineering Education Committee of AIChE's Center for Chemical Process Safety *www.SACHE.org*, 2006).

Designs for Preventing Dust Explosions

Some of the key design features[31] that are used to prevent dust explosions include the following:

1. When transferring dusts to flammable liquids, use containment and inerting as described in Chapter 7.
2. Eliminate ignition sources due to tramp metal, mechanical failure, overheating, electrical sparks, high dust concentrations, and static electricity. The tramp metal problem is solved by adding magnetic traps that collect metal parts; the mechanical failure problems are solved by adding detectors to detect failures and initiate a safe shutown; overheating problems are solved by monitoring the temperature of bearings and belts (e.g., slipping); electrical sparks are eliminated by using all explosion-proof electrical fittings (Class III and appropriate division; see Chapter 7); the high dust concentrations in equipment and in vents from equipment are reduced by using pneumatic dust collection systems (sometimes called bag houses), and high dust concentrations outside of equipment due to leaks from flanges or equivalent are prevented by adding gaskets and tightening the gasket flanges; and static electricity problems are solved using the teachings of Chapter 7, including grounding and bonding.
3. Mitigate dust explosions using vent panels and explosion suppression as described in Chapter 7.

Management Practices for Preventing Dust Explosions

There are two especially important management practices that should be used to prevent dust explosions: (1) schedule periodic cleaning to remove accumulated dusts from floors, ducts, and even above false ceilings (see Chapter 14), and (2) control welding and cutting operations using the hot work permits discussed previously. Additional recommended practices include scheduling the periodic cleaning of the magnetic tramp metal traps and mechanical integrity checks to be sure all controls and alarms are working as specified.

Suggested Reading

API 750, *Management of Process Hazards* (Washington DC: American Petroleum Institute, 1990).

L. Britton, *Avoiding Static Ignition Hazards in Chemical Operations* (New York: American Institute of Chemical Engineers, Center for Chemical Process Safety, 1999).

Center for Chemical Process Safety, *Guidelines for Design Solutions for Process Equipment Failures* (New York: American Institute of Chemical Engineers, 1998).

Center for Chemical Process Safety, *Guidelines for Engineering Design for Process Safety* (New York: American Institute of Chemical Engineers, 1993).

[31] Louvar and Schoeff, "Dust Explosion Control."

Code of Federal Regulations, "Process Safety Management of Highly Hazardous Chemicals," *29CFR 1910.119* (57FR23061), June 1, 1992.

R. K. Eckhoff, *Dust Explosion in the Process Industries*, 3rd ed. (Houston: Gulf Publishing, 2003).

M. Glor, *Electrostatic Hazards in Powder Handling* (New York: John Wiley & Sons, 1988).

Trevor Kletz, *Plant Design for Safety: A User-Friendly Approach* (New York: Hemisphere Publishing Corporation, 1990).

T. Kletz, *Process Plants: A Handbook for Inherently Safer Design*, 2nd ed. (New York: Taylor & Francis Group, 2010).

J. F. Louvar, B. Maurer, G. W. Boicourt, "Fundamentals of Static Electricity," *Chem. Engr. Prog.* (Nov. 1994), pp. 75–81.

Problems

13-1. What facts should a near-miss accident report include? Compare your answer to CCPS's (1992, p. 240).

13-2. Redundant instrumentation is an important design concept for improving the safety of a system. Give examples where redundant instrumentation would have prevented major accidents.

13-3. In the 1930s there were many accidents in homes because of the explosion of hot water heaters. Describe what features are added to water heaters to eliminate accidents.

13-4. The double block and bleed system shown in Figure 13-2 bleeds chemicals into a small vessel. This method, however, creates a new hazard: It adds another vessel that contains a hazardous chemical. Design an inherently safer system.

13-5. Nitrogen is used most frequently to inert systems; that is, nitrogen is added to keep the flammable vapor concentration below the LFL. What precautions are taken when handling nitrogen?

13-6. Describe why accident investigation recommendations must include recommendations to improve the management system.

13-7. The accident investigation at Lodi, New Jersey, included previous industrial accidents with sodium hydrosulfite and aluminum. Summarize the findings of these accidents and develop a few management system recommendations for these industries. See *www.epa.gov/ceppo/pubs/lodirecc.htm.*

13-8. Determine the pressure required for a pipe to swell and the pressure required for a pipe failure. The pipe is 3-in stainless 316 schedule 40 pipeline for transporting a gas mixture that is sometimes within the explosive composition range.

13-9. A management system for accident investigations includes good communications. What are the tangible benefits of a good communications system? Compare your answer to CCPS's (1992, p. 238).

13-10. Near-miss (close-call) accident investigation reports are also important. Define near-miss accidents. Compare your answer to CCPS's (1992, p. 239).

13-11. It is recommended that process vessels be designed for full vacuum. Describe several ways to cave in vessels that are not designed for full vacuum.

13-12. Design a system for pouring a powder into a flammable liquid.

13-13. Metal sheathing on the outside of insulated pipe is known to accumulate static charges. What two methods are used to prevent this hazard and which is better?

13-14. The U.S. Chemical Safety and Hazard Investigation Board investigated an accident at the Morton Specialty Chemical Company in 1998. Evaluate the board's recommendations, and break them down into three layers of recommendations. See *www.chemsafety.gov/*.

13-15. The concept of using checklists is very important. Give several examples of useful checklists.

13-16. Determine the required thickness of a reactor with cylindrical walls that must be designed to safely contain a deflagration (hydrocarbon plus air). The vessel has a diameter of 4 ft and is constructed with stainless steel 304. The normal operating pressure is 2 atm.

13-17. Compute the theoretical maximum pressure obtained after igniting a stoichiometric quantity of methane and oxygen in a spherical vessel that is 1.5 ft in diameter. Assume an initial pressure of 1 atm.

13-18. Compute the theoretical maximum pressure obtained after igniting a stoichiometric quantity of methane and air in a spherical vessel that is 1.5 ft in diameter. Assume that the initial pressure is 1 atm.

13-19. Using the results of Problem 13-17, determine the required vessel wall thickness to contain this explosion if the vessel is made of stainless 316.

13-20. Using the results of Problem 13-19, determine the vessel wall thickness required to contain an explosion in another vessel that is physically connected to the first vessel with a 1-in pipe. Describe why the second vessel requires a greater wall thickness.

13-21. An accident occurs that ruptures a high-pressure spherical vessel. The vessel is 1.5 ft in diameter, is made of stainless 304, and the walls are 0.25 in thick. Determine the pressure required to cause this failure. Develop some hypotheses regarding the causes of this accident.

13-22. Using the data and results of Example 13-3, determine the wall thickness required to eliminate future failures. Assume that the vessel's cylindrical wall height is equal to the vessel's diameter.

CHAPTER 14

Case Histories

Case histories are written descriptions of accidents, including the causes, consequences, and methods required to prevent similar events. They are descriptions written by plant managers and operating personnel. These are the people with the hands-on experience, the ones who know and appreciate the accident and accident prevention methods.

The study of case histories is important in the area of safety. To paraphrase G. Santayana, one learns from history or is doomed to repeat it. This is especially true for safety; anyone working in the chemical industry can learn from case histories and avoid hazardous situations or ignore history and be involved in potentially life-threatening accidents.

In this chapter we cover case histories as reported in the literature. References are provided for more thorough studies. The objective of this chapter is to illustrate, through actual case histories, the importance of applying the fundamentals of chemical process safety.

These case histories are categorized into five sections:

- Static electricity
- Chemical reactivity
- System design
- Procedures
- Training

The cause of a specific accident frequently places it in more than one category. Each of these sections includes descriptions of several accidents and a summary of the lessons learned.

The following statements place the case histories into perspective:

1. These accidents actually occurred. Anyone familiar with the specific equipment or procedures will appreciate the lessons learned.

2. Accidents occur rapidly and unexpectedly. There is usually inadequate time to manually return a situation back into control after a significant deviation from the norm is observed. Those who believe that they can successfully control accident deviations manually are doomed to repeat history.

14-1 Static Electricity

A large proportion of the reported fires and explosions are the result of a flammable mixture being ignited by a spark caused by static electricity. Many of these accidents are repeats of previously recorded accidents; engineers are missing some of the important aspects of this subject. The following series of case histories is given to illustrate the complexity of this topic and to give some important design requirements for preventing future accidents involving static electricity.

Tank Car Loading Explosion[1]

Two plant operators were filling a tank car with vinyl acetate. One operator was on the ground, and the other was on top of the car with the nozzle end of a loading hose. A few seconds after the loading operation started, the contents of the tank exploded. The operator on top of the tank was thrown to the ground; he sustained a fractured skull and multiple body burns and died from these injuries.

The accident investigation indicated that the explosion was caused by a static spark that jumped from the steel nozzle to the tank car. The nozzle was not bonded to the tank car to prevent static accumulation. The use of a nonmetallic hose probably also contributed.

Explosion in a Centrifuge[2]

A slurry containing a solvent mixture of 90% methylcyclohexane and 10% toluene was being fed into a basket centrifuge. A foreman was about to look into the centrifuge when it exploded. The lid was lifted and a flame was released between the centrifuge and the lid. The foreman's hand was burned.

The fill line from the reactor to the centrifuge was Teflon-lined steel, running to a point 3 ft from the centrifuge where there was a rubber sleeve connector. The short line from the sleeve to the centrifuge was steel. The centrifuge was lined.

[1] *Case Histories of Accidents in the Chemical Industry,* v. 1 (Washington, DC: Manufacturing Chemists' Association, July 1962), p. 106.

[2] *Case Histories of Accidents in the Chemical Industry,* v. 2 (Washington, DC: Manufacturing Chemists' Association, Jan. 1966), p. 231.

The accident investigation indicated that a flammable atmosphere had developed because of an air leak. The lined centrifuge was the source of ignition as a result of static accumulation and discharge.

Later (and successful) processing was conducted in a grounded stainless steel centrifuge that was inerted with nitrogen.

Duct System Explosion[3]

Two duct systems in the same vicinity contained dust transport lines, dryers, and hoppers. One system was recently repaired and left open. The open system emitted some methanol vapors. The other system was being charged through a funnel with a dry organic intermediate. The charge line consisted of a new glass pipe and a 6-ft section of plastic pipe. The duct system that was being charged exploded violently, and the explosion initiated other fires. Fortunately, no one was seriously injured.

The accident investigation indicated that methanol vapors entered the second charging system. The transportation of the intermediate dust through the glass and plastic line generated a static charge and spark. The ignition source created violent explosions in both systems. Several explosion vents were ruptured, and a building blowout panel also ruptured.

This accident points out the need for carefully reviewing systems before, during, and after modifications are made. Open lines should be blanked off when the discharge of flammable vapors is possible. Also, proper grounding and bonding techniques must be used to prevent static buildup.

Conductor in a Solids Storage Bin[4]

A dry organic powder was collected in a hopper. A piece of tramp metal entered the hopper with the solids. As it rolled down the solids, it accumulated a charge by the charging method called separation. At some point in the operation the tramp metal approached the metal wall of the hopper, which was grounded. A spark jumped from the tramp metal to the grounded wall. The spark was energetic compared to the minimum ignition energy of the dust. Because the storage hopper's atmosphere was air (plus the dust), the dust exploded and the storage hopper ruptured.

This explosion could have been prevented with a tramp metal collector, for example, a magnetic trap or a screen. An additional safeguard would be the addition of an inerting gas.

[3] *Case Histories of Accidents in the Chemical Industry,* v. 3 (Washington, DC: Manufacturing Chemists' Association, Apr. 1970), p. 95.

[4] J. F. Louvar, B. Maurer, and G. W. Boicourt, "Tame Static Electricity," *Chemical Engineering Progress* (Nov. 1994), pp. 75–81.

Pigment and Filter[5]

A low-flash-point solvent containing pigment was pumped through a bag filter into an open drum. The pigment drum was grounded by means of a grounding rod. Although the operation ran successfully for some time, one day there was a fire.

It is hypothesized that one of two scenarios could have created the ignition. Possibly, the grounding rod was placed closer to the filter than previously, giving the conditions for a brush discharge between the filter and the grounding rod. It is also possible that the grounding rod wire was closer to the isolated drum than previously; in this case a spark could have jumped between the drum and the grounding wire.

This system was modified to include an inerting system and a dip pipe charging line, and all metal parts were bonded. Subsequent operations were incident-free.

Pipefitter's Helper[6]

A pipefitter's helper was transporting tools to the boss. The helper walked through a cloud of steam before handing the tool to his boss. Upon each transfer, the boss received a rather large shock.

The problem was the steam; it became charged as it exited a manifold. Then the charge was transferred to the helper and to the tools when the helper passed through the steam cloud. Charge loss was prevented because the helper was wearing insulated shoes. The boss was grounded because he was kneeling on a damp grounded grating.

Using conductive shoes and changing the location of the toolbox solved this problem. This example may have been a disaster if the pipefitter was repairing a flammable gas leak, for example, during an emergency situation.

Lessons Learned Concerning Static Electricity

Case histories involving static electricity emphasize the importance of understanding and using the fundamentals described in Chapter 7. In reviewing approximately 30 additional case histories regarding static electricity, some important lessons were identified: (1) A built-in ground line is rendered nonconductive by the use of a nonconductive pipe dope; (2) a potential is generated between two vessels that are not bonded; (3) leather arch supporters make shoes ineffective against static; (4) free-fall filling generates static charge and discharge; (5) the use of nonmetallic hoses is a source of static buildup; (6) large voltages are generated when crumpling and shaking an empty polyethylene bag; and (7) a weak grounding clamp may not penetrate the paint on a drum adequately to provide a good electrical contact.

A number of recommendations are also developed: (1) Operators must be cautioned against drawing pipes or tubing through their rubber gloves, resulting in static buildup; (2) clothing that generates static electricity must be prohibited; (3) recirculation lines must be extended into the liquid to prevent static buildup; (4) shoes with conductive soles are required when

[5]Louvar et al., "Tame Static Electricity."
[6]Louvar et al., "Tame Static Electricity."

handling flammable materials; (5) bonding, grounding, humidification, ionization, or combinations are recommended when static electricity is a fire hazard; (6) a small water spray will rapidly drain electrical charges during chopping operations; (7) inert gas blankets must be used when handling flammable materials; (8) drums, scoops, and bags should be physically bonded and grounded; (9) ground connections must be verified with a resistance tester; (10) spring-loaded grounding or bonding clips should be replaced with screw type C-clamps; (11) conductive grease should be used in bearing seals that need to conduct static charges; (12) sodium hydride must be handled in static-proof bags; (13) stainless steel centrifuges must be used when handling flammable materials; and (14) flanges in piping and duct systems must be bonded.

Example 14-1

Using the layered accident investigation process discussed in Chapter 13, develop the underlying causes of the tank car loading explosion discussed earlier in this section.

Solution

The facts uncovered by the investigation are

1. Contents at the top of vessel were flammable
2. The charging line was a nonconductive hose
3. A spark probably jumped between the charging nozzle and the tank car
4. The explosion knocked the man off the tank car (the fatal injury was probably the fractured skull sustained in the fall)
5. No inspection or safety review procedure was in place to identify problems of this kind

Layered recommendations are the result of uncovering the underlying causes of the accident.

First-layer recommendations: immediate technical recommendations

1. Use a conductive metal hose for transferring flammable fluids.
2. Bond hose to tank car, and ground tank car and hose.
3. Provide dip pipe design for charging tank cars.
4. Provide a means to nitrogen-pad the tank car during the filling operation.
5. Add guardrails to charging platforms to prevent accidental falls from the top of the tank car to the ground.

Second-layer recommendations: avoiding the hazard

1. Develop tank car loading procedures.
2. Develop and give operators special training so the hazards are understood for every loading and unloading operation.

Third-layer recommendations: improving the management system

1. Initiate an immediate inspection of all loading and unloading operations.
2. Initiate, as a standard practice, a policy to give all new loading and unloading applications a safety review. Include engineers and operators in this review.
3. Initiate a periodic (every six months) audit to ensure that all standards and procedures are effectively utilized.

14-2 Chemical Reactivity

Although accidents attributable to chemical reactivity are less frequent compared to fires and explosions, the consequences are dramatic, destructive, and often injurious to personnel. When working with chemicals, the potential for unwanted, unexpected, and hazardous reactions must always be recognized. The following case histories illustrate the importance of understanding the complete chemistry of a reaction system, including potential side reactions, decomposition reactions, and reactions resulting from the accidental and wrong combination of chemicals or reaction conditions (wrong type, wrong concentrations, or the wrong temperature).

Chapter 8 provides more detailed information on chemical reactivity and related hazards.

Functional Groups

A preliminary indication of the potential hazards can be estimated by knowing something about the chemical structure. Specific functional groups that contribute to the explosive properties of a chemical through rapid combustion or detonation are illustrated in Table 8-3.

Peroxides

Peroxides *and* peroxidizable compounds are dangerous sources of explosions. Structures of peroxidizable compounds are shown in Table 14-1. Some examples of peroxidizable compounds are given in Table 14-2.

When peroxide concentrations increase to 20 ppm or greater, the solution is hazardous. Methods for detecting and controlling peroxides are outlined by H. L. Jackson et al.[7]

Reaction Hazard Index

D. R. Stull[8] developed a rating system to establish the relative potential hazards of specific chemicals; the rating is called the reaction hazard index (RHI). The RHI is related to the maximum adiabatic temperature reached by the products of a decomposition reaction. It is defined as

$$\boxed{\mathrm{RHI} = \frac{10T_\mathrm{d}}{T_\mathrm{d} + 30E_\mathrm{a}},} \tag{14-1}$$

[7]H. L. Jackson et al., "Control of Peroxidizable Compounds," in *Safety in the Chemical Industry,* v. 3, Norman V. Steere, ed. (Easton, PA: Division of Chemical Education, American Chemical Society, 1974), pp. 114–117.

[8]D. R. Stull, "Linking Thermodynamic and Kinetics to Predict Real Chemical Hazards," in *Safety in the Chemical Industry,* pp. 106–110.

Table 14-1 Peroxidizable Compounds[a,b]

Organic material and structure

1. Ethers, acetals:

$$\begin{array}{c} H \\ | \\ -C-O- \\ | \end{array}$$

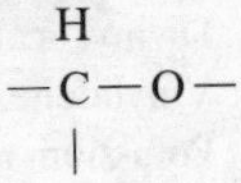

2. Olefins with allylic hydrogen, chloro- and fluoroolefins, terpenes, tetrahydronaphthalene:

$$>C=C<$$

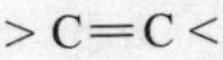

3. Dienes, vinyl acetylenes:

$$\begin{array}{c} | \quad | \\ >C=C-C=C< \end{array}$$

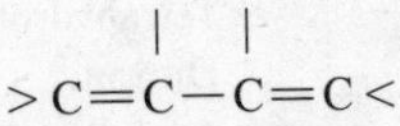

and

$$\begin{array}{c} >C=C-C\equiv CH \\ | \end{array}$$

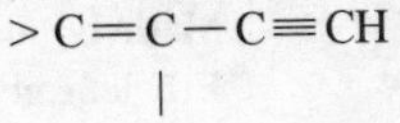

4. Paraffins and alkyl-aromatic hydrocarbons, particularly those with tertiary hydrogen:

$$\begin{array}{c} >C- \\ | \\ H \end{array}$$

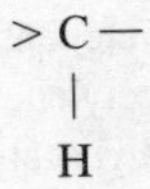

5. Aldehydes:

$$\begin{array}{c} -C=O \\ | \\ H \end{array}$$

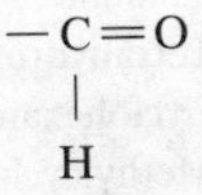

6. Ureas, amides, lactones:

$$\begin{array}{ccc} O & & H \\ \| & | & | \\ -C-N-C \end{array}$$

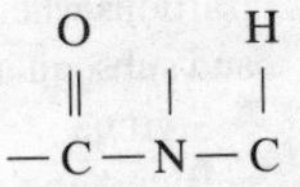

7. Vinyl monomers, including vinyl halides, acrylates, methacrylates, vinyl esters:

$$\begin{array}{c} | \\ >C=C- \end{array}$$

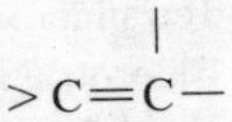

8. Ketones having an alpha-hydrogen:

$$\begin{array}{cc} -C-C< \\ \| & | \\ O & H \end{array}$$

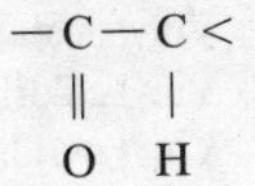

Inorganic materials

1. Alkali metals, particularly potassium
2. Alkali metal alkoxides and amides
3. Organometallics

[a] H. L. Jackson, W. B. McCormack, C. S. Rondestvedt, K. C. Smeltz, and I. E. Viele, "Control of Peroxidizable Compounds," in *Safety in the Chemical Industry*, v. 3, Norman V. Steere, ed. (Easton, PA: Division of Chemical Education, American Chemical Society, 1974), pp. 114–117.
[b] R. J. Kelly, "Review of Safety Guidelines for Peroxidizable Organic Chemicals," *Chemical Health and Safety* (Sept. Oct. 1996), pp. 28–36.

Table 14-2 Examples of Peroxidizable Compounds[a]

Peroxidizable hazard on storage
Isopropyl ether
Divinyl acetylene
Vinylidene chloride
Potassium metal
Sodium amide
Peroxidizable hazard on concentration
Diethyl ether
Tetrahydrofuran
Dioxane
Acetal
Methyl *i*-butyl ketone
Ethylene glycol dimethyl ether (glyme)
Vinyl ethers
Dicyctapentadiene
Diacetylene
Methyl acetylene
Cumene
Tetrahydronaphthalene
Cyclohexane
Methylcyclopentane
Hazardous when exposed to oxygen due to peroxide formation and subsequent peroxide initiation of polymerization
Styrene
Butadiene
Tetrafluoroethylene
Chlorotrifluoroethylene
Vinyl acetylene
Vinyl acetate
Vinyl chloride
Vinyl pyridine
Chloroprene

[a]H. L. Jackson et al., "Control of Peroxidizable Compounds," in *Safety in the Chemical Industry,* v. 3, Norman V. Steere, ed. (Easton, PA: Division of Chemical Education, American Chemical Society, 1974), pp. 114–117.

where

T_d is the decomposition temperature (K) and
E_a is the Arrhenius activation energy (kcal/mol).

The RHI relationship (Equation 14-1) has a low value (1 to 3) for relatively low reactivities and higher values (5 to 8) for high reactivities. Some RHI data for various chemicals are provided in Table 14-3.

Table 14-3 Reaction Hazard Index Data[a]

Number	Formula	Compound	Decomposition temperature (K)	Activation energy (kcal/mol)	RHI
1	$CHCl_3$	chloroform	683	47	3.26
2	C_2H_6	ethane	597	89.5	1.82
3	C_7H_8	toluene	859	85	2.52
4	$C_2H_4O_2$	acetic acid	634	67.5	2.38
5	C_3H_6	propylene	866	78	2.70
6	$C_6H_{14}O$	isopropyl ether	712	63.5	2.72
7	C_2H_4	ethylene	1005	46.5	4.19
8	C_4H_6	1,3-butadiene	991	79.4	2.94
9	C_4H_8O	vinyl ethyl ether	880	44.4	3.98
10	C_8H_8	styrene	993	19.2	6.33
11	N_2H_4	hydrazine	1338	60.5	4.25
12	C_2H_4O	ethylene oxide	1062	57.4	3.81
13	C_4H_4	vinylacetylene	2317	28.0	7.33
14	$C_{12}H_{16}N_4O_{18}$	cellulose nitrate	2213	46.7	6.12
15	C_2H_2	acetylene	2898	40.5	7.05
16	$C_3H_5N_3O_9$	nitroglycerine	2895	40.3	7.05
17	$C_4H_{10}O_2$	diethyl peroxide	968	37.3	4.64

[a]D. R. Stull, "Linking Thermodynamics and Kinetics to Predict Real Chemical Hazards," in *Safety in the Chemical Industry,* v. 3, Norman V. Steere, ed. (Easton, PA: Division of Chemical Education, American Chemical Society, 1974), pp. 106–110.

Example 14-2

Compute the RHI for isopropyl ether, and compare the result to that shown in Table 14-3. Explain why the RHI is relatively low.

Solution

The RHI is computed using Equation 14-1:

$$\text{RHI} = \frac{10T_\text{d}}{T_\text{d} + 30E_\text{a}},$$

where, from Table 14-3, T_d is 712°K and E_a is 63.5 kcal/mol. The units are compatible with Equation 14-1. Substituting, we obtain

$$\text{RHI} = \frac{(10)(712)}{(712) + (30)(63.5)}$$

$$= 2.72,$$

which is the same as the value given in Table 14-3. This RHI indicates a chemical with low reactivity. However, isopropyl ether is a peroxidizable compound, as indicated in Table 14-2. If we assume an RHI equivalent to diethyl peroxide (RHI = 4.64), the hazards of handling isopropyl ether are high even with peroxide concentrations as low as 20 ppm. This example illustrates the importance of understanding the chemistry of the entire system.

Bottle of Isopropyl Ether[9]

A chemist needed isopropyl ether. He found a pint glass bottle. He unsuccessfully tried to open the bottle over a sink. The cap appeared to be stuck tightly, so he grasped the bottle in one hand, pressed it to his stomach and twisted the cap with his other hand. Just as the cap broke loose, the bottle exploded, practically disemboweling the man and tearing off several fingers. The victim remained conscious and, in fact, coherently described how the accident happened. The man was taken to a hospital and died within 2 hr of the accident of massive internal hemorrhage.

An accident investigation identified the cause of the accident to be the rapid decomposition of peroxides, which formed in the ether while the bottle sat in storage. It is hypothesized that some of the peroxides crystallized in the threads of the cap and exploded when the cap was turned.

As ethers age, especially isopropyl ether, they form peroxides. The peroxides react further to form additional hazardous by-products, such as triacetone peroxide. These materials are unstable. Light, air, and heat accelerate the formation of peroxides.

Ethers should be stored in metal containers. Only small quantities should be purchased. Ethers should not be kept over 6 months. Containers should be labeled and dated upon receipt, and opened containers should be discarded after 3 months. All work with ethers should be done behind safety shields. Inhibitors should be used whenever possible.

Nitrobenzene Sulfonic Acid Decomposition[10]

A 300-gal reactor experienced a violent reaction, resulting in the tank being driven through the floor, out the wall of the building, and through the roof of an adjoining building. The reactor was designed to contain 60 gal of sulfuric acid and nitrobenzene sulfonic acid, which was known to decompose at 200°C.

The investigation indicated that the vessel contents were held for 11 hr. A steam leak into the jacket brought the temperature to about 150°C. Although previous tests indicated decomposition at 200°C, subsequent tests showed exothermic decomposition above 145°C.

The underlying cause of this accident was the lack of precise reaction decomposition data. With good data, engineers can design safeguards to absolutely prevent accidental heat-up.

[9] *Case Histories,* v. 2, p. 6.
[10] *Case Histories,* v. 3, p. 111.

Organic Oxidation[11]

Chemical operators were preparing for an organic oxidation. Steam was applied to the reactor jacket to heat the sulfuric acid and an organic material to a temperature of 70°C. The rate of heating was slower than normal. The two operators turned the agitator off and also shut off the steam. One operator went to find a thermometer. Approximately 1 hour later, the operator was ready to take a temperature reading through the manhole. He turned on the agitator. At this point the material in the kettle erupted through the manhole. The two operators were drenched and both died from these injuries.

The accident investigation stated that the agitator should never be turned off for this type of reaction. Without agitation, cooling is no longer efficient; so heat-up occurs. Without agitation, segregation of chemicals also occurs. When the agitator is subsequently activated, the hotter chemicals mix and react violently.

This type of problem is currently preventable through better operator training and installation of electronic safeguards to prevent operators from making this mistake. This is achieved by adding redundant and remote temperature sensors and by adding electronic interlocks to prevent the agitator from being turned off while the reaction is still exothermic.

Lessons Learned Concerning Chemical Reactivity

Case histories regarding reactive chemicals teach the importance of understanding the reactive properties of chemicals before working with them. The best source of data is the open literature. If data are not available, experimental testing is necessary. Data of special interest include decomposition temperatures, rate of reaction or activation energy, impact shock sensitivity, and flash point.

14-3 System Designs

When new plants are constructed or when modifications are needed in existing plants, detailed process designs are required. These designs must include special safety features to protect the system and operating personnel. The following case histories emphasize the importance of these special safety design features.

Ethylene Oxide Explosion[12]

A process storage tank contained 6500 gal of ethylene oxide. It was accidentally contaminated with ammonia. The tank ruptured and dispersed ethylene oxide into the air. A vapor cloud was formed and almost immediately exploded. It created an explosive force equivalent to 18 tons

[11] *Case Histories,* v. 3, p. 121.

[12] J. A. Davenport, "A Survey of Vapor Cloud Incidents," *Chemical Engineering Progress* (Sept. 1977), pp. 54–63.

of TNT, as evidenced by the damage. The events happened so rapidly that personnel could not take appropriate cover. One person was killed and nine were injured; property losses exceeded $16.5 million.

This accident was attributed to the lack of design protection to prevent the backup of ammonia into this storage tank. It also appears that mitigation techniques were not part of the system (deluge systems, dikes, and the like).

Ethylene Explosion[13]

Failure of a 3/8-in compression fitting on a 1000–2500-psi ethylene line in a pipe trench resulted in a spill of 200–500 lb of ethylene. A cloud was formed and ignited, giving an explosion equivalent to 0.12–0.30 ton of TNT. This accident took place in a courtyard, giving a partially confined vapor cloud explosion. Two people were killed and 17 were injured; property loss was $6.5 million.

The probable causes of this accident include (1) use of nonwelded pipe, (2) installation of pipe in trenches, resulting in an accumulation of flammable vapors, and (3) lack of automated vapor detection analyzers and alarms.

Butadiene Explosion[14]

A valve on the bottom of a reactor accidentally opened because of an air failure. The spill generated a vapor cloud that was ignited 50 ft from the source. About 200 gal of butadiene spilled before ignition. Overpressures of 0.5–1 psi were estimated. Three people were killed and two were injured.

Probable causes of this accident include (1) installation of a fail-open valve instead of a fail-closed valve, (2) lack of vapor detectors, (3) lack of a block installed as a mitigating device, and (4) failure to eliminate ignition sources in this operating region.

Light Hydrocarbon Explosion[15]

A pipe failed and resulted in a spill of 16,800 lb of light hydrocarbons. A vapor cloud developed and ignited. The explosion knocked out the deluge systems and electrical supplies to the fire pumps. Significant damage resulted from the subsequent fires. The maximum overpressure was estimated from the damage to be 3.5 psi at 120 ft. An equivalent of 1 ton of TNT was estimated, giving an explosion yield of approximately 1% of the total energy source. This accident had two fatalities and nine injuries. The total damage was estimated to be $15.6 million.

[13]Davenport, "A Survey of Vapor Cloud Incidents."
[14]Davenport, "A Survey of Vapor Cloud Incidents."
[15]Davenport, "A Survey of Vapor Cloud Incidents."

The magnitude of this accident could have been reduced with (1) improved pipe design, (2) improved deluge system design, (3) backup or more secure electrical supply, and (4) installation of detection analyzers and block valves.

Pump Vibration[16]

Vibration from a bad pump bearing caused a pump seal to fail in a cumene section of a phenol acetone unit. The released flammable liquids and vapors ignited. An explosion ruptured other process pipes, adding fuel to the original fire. Damage to the plant exceeded $23 million.

This accident could have been prevented by a good inspection and maintenance program. Potential design improvements include vibration detectors, gas analyzers, block valves, and deluge systems.

Pump Failure[17]

Numerous accidents are unfortunate duplicates of previous accidents, as the following shows.

A pump roller bearing failure in a crude oil refinery initiated the fracture of the motor shaft and the pump bearing bracket. The pump casing then broke, releasing hot oil, which autoignited. Secondary pipe and flange failures contributed fuel to the fire. Plant damage totaled over $15 million.

Because the pump was equipped only with manually operated suction-side valves, the valves could not be reached during the fire.

Automated block valves would have minimized damage in this fire. A good inspection and maintenance program would have prevented the accident.

Second Ethylene Explosion[18]

A drain fitting in a high-pressure (40 kpsi) compressor line broke, allowing ethylene to escape. The ethylene cloud drifted and entered the intake system of an engine that was driving one of the compressors. The ethylene detonated in the engine, and this explosion ignited the rest of the vapors.

The explosions were felt 6 miles away. Twelve buildings were destroyed, and fire and explosion damage occurred throughout the polyethylene plant. The damage was estimated at over $15 million.

Automatic equipment promptly detected the hazardous vapor and operated the automatic high-density water-spray system, which was designed to wash the ethylene from the atmosphere. The leak was too large for the spray system to handle.

[16] William G. Garrison, *One Hundred Largest Losses: A Thirty-Year Review of Property Damage Losses in the Hydrocarbon Chemical Industries,* 9th ed. (Chicago: Marsh & McLennan Protection Consultants, 1986), p. 7.

[17] Garrison, *One Hundred Largest Losses,* p. 7.

[18] Garrison, *One Hundred Largest Losses,* p. 3.

This accident could have been mitigated if the gas detection analyzers alarmed at lower concentrations. Also, in the layout design it should have been noticed that the compressor needed special consideration to eliminate this ignition source.

Third Ethylene Explosion[19]

Ethylene was accidentally released from a 1/8-in stainless steel instrument tubing line leading to a gauge from a main line on a compressor system. The tubing failed as a result of transverse fatigue caused by vibration from the reciprocating compressor. Ignition may have been by static electricity. This accident caused $21.8 million in damage.

The unmanned compressor building was equipped with a combustible gas detection system. However, it failed to sound an alarm because of a faulty relay in the control room. Automatic fail-safe valves functioned properly, blocking in the flow of ethylene, but not before 450–11,000 lb of gas had already escaped.

This accident emphasizes the importance of adding gas detectors that measure flammable gases at low concentrations so that alarms and block valves can be actuated before large quantities of gas are released.

Second Ethylene Oxide Explosion[20]

Ethylene oxide is produced by adding ethylene, oxygen, a methane diluent, and recycled carbon dioxide to a continuous reactor. Gaseous compositions are controlled carefully to keep the concentrations outside the explosion limits.

One plant experienced an emergency situation. The emergency procedures specified: Close the oxygen feed valve. The oxygen control valve was normally closed by bleeding air out of the valve bonnet diaphragm (air to open). The bleed line was opened and was noted on the control panel. The air, however, did not bleed off through the bonnet vent because a mud dauber wasp constructed mud cells over the vent hole. Although the vent valve was open, as indicated on the control panel, the air could not escape.

The gases in the ethylene oxide reactor moved into the explosive region while being above the autoignition temperature. A violent explosion occurred, resulting in several injuries and significant plant damage.

It is now an industrial standard to use positive identification of the valve position on all important safety valves–limit switches that are tripped when the valve is open or shut. In addition, all valve vent lines are now covered with bug screens to prevent blockage.

In this particular case the accident could also have been prevented with appropriate inspection and maintenance procedures.

[19]Garrison, *One Hundred Largest Losses,* p. 8.

[20]W. H. Doyle, "Instrument-Connected Losses in the CPI," *Instrument Technology* (Oct. 1972), pp. 38–42.

Lessons Learned Concerning Designs

The case histories related to system design emphasize that (1) accidents occur rapidly, usually with inadequate time to manually return the system to control once the accident scenario is in progress; (2) the system designs required for preventing accidents or mitigating the consequences of accidents are frequently subtle, requiring only minor process changes; and (3) the time and effort required to develop a safe system design are justified: An engineer is hired for a fraction of the cost of most accidents.

Trevor Kletz[21] and Walter B. Howard[22] have emphasized the special design features for safer plants. The following recommendations also include design features from our own experiences:

- Use the appropriate materials of construction, especially when using old systems for new applications.
- Do not install pipes underground.
- Be sure that the quality of construction (for example, welds) meets the required specifications.
- Check all purchased instruments and equipment for integrity and functionality.
- Do not secure pipes too rigidly. Pipes must be free to expand so that they will not damage other parts of the system.
- Do not install liquid-filled flanges above electrical cables. A flange leak will douse the cables with liquid.
- Provide adequate supports for equipment and pipes. Do not allow spring supports to be completely compressed.
- Design doors and lids so that they cannot be opened under pressure. Add interlocks to decrease pressure before the doors can be opened. Also, add visible pressure gauges at the doors.
- Do not let pipes touch the ground.
- Remove all temporary supports after construction is completed.
- Remove all temporary startup or checkout branches, nipples, and plugs, and replace them with properly designed welded plugs.
- Do not use screwed joints and fittings when handling hazardous chemicals.
- Be sure that all tracing is covered.
- Check to ensure that all equipment is assembled correctly.
- Do not install pipes in pits, trenches, or depressions where water can accumulate.
- Do not install relief tailpipes too close to the ground where ice blockage may make them inoperable.

[21]Trevor Kletz, *Learning from Accidents*, 3rd ed. (Boston: Butterworth-Heinemann, 2001).

[22]Walter B. Howard, "Process Safety Technology and the Responsibilities of Industry," *Chemical Engineering Progress* (Sept. 1988), pp. 25–33.

- Be sure that all lines that can catch water can be appropriately drained.
- When welding reinforcement pads to pipes or vessels, ensure that trapped air can escape through a vent during heating.
- Do not install traps in lines where water can collect and develop a corrosion problem.
- Install bellows carefully and according to manufacturers' specifications. Bellows should be used cautiously. If required, inspect frequently and replace when necessary before they fail.
- Make static and dynamic analyses of pipe systems to avoid excessive stresses or excessive vibrations.
- Design systems for easy operation and easy maintenance; for example, install manual valves within easy reach of the operators, and design pipe networks for easy maintenance or with easy access to equipment requiring maintenance.
- Install bug screens on vent lines.
- Make structural analyses of relief systems to avoid structural damage during emergency reliefs.
- Safety technology must work right the first time. Usually, there is no opportunity to adjust or improve its operation.
- Critical safety instruments must have backups.
- Provide hand-operated or automatic block valves, or equivalent valves, for emergency shutdowns.
- Use electronic or mechanical level gauges, not glass sight glasses.
- Add fail-safe block valves with a positive indication of the valve position (limit switches).

Example 14-3

Analyze the first ethylene explosion example (3/8-in fitting failure) to determine the percentage of fuel that actually exploded compared to the quantity of ethylene released in a vapor cloud.

Solution

The total energy contained in the vapor cloud is estimated by assuming the heat of combustion (Appendix B). The combustion reaction is

$$C_2H_4 + 3O_2 \rightarrow 2CO_2 + 2H_2O.$$

Therefore the theoretical energy is

$$\Delta Hc = 1411.2 \text{ kJ/mol} = 12046 \text{ cal/g}.$$

The tons of TNT based on this heat of combustion are calculated using Equation 6-24:

$$m_{\text{TNT}} = \frac{\eta \text{m}\, \Delta Hc}{\text{E}_{\text{TNT}}}$$

where

$$m = (500 \text{ lb})(454 \text{ g/lb}) = 227000 \text{ g}$$

$$E_{TNT} = (1120 \text{ cal/g})(454 \text{ g/lb})(2000 \text{ lb/ton})$$

$$E_{TNT} = 1.017 \times 10^9 \text{ cal/ton}.$$

Therefore

$$m_{TNT} = \frac{(1)(227{,}000 \text{ g})(12{,}046 \text{ cal/g})}{1.017 \times 10^9 \text{ cal/ton}}$$

$$m_{TNT} = 2.69 \text{ ton of TNT}.$$

Based on the accident investigation, the explosive energy was equivalent to 0.3 ton TNT. Therefore the fraction of energy manifested in the explosion is 0.3/2.69 = 11.2%. This 11.2% is considerably higher than the 2% normally observed (see Section 6-13) for unconfined vapor cloud explosions. The higher energy conversion is a result of the explosion occurring in a partially confined area.

14-4 Procedures

An organization can develop a good safety program if it has personnel who can identify and eliminate safety problems. An even better safety program, however, is developed by implementing management systems to prevent the existence of safety problems in the first place. The management systems commonly used in industry include safety reviews, operating procedures, and maintenance procedures.

The causes of all accidents can ultimately be attributed to a lack of management systems. Case histories that especially demonstrate this problem are illustrated in this section. In the study of these case histories, one must recognize that the existence of procedures is not enough. There must also be a system of checks in place to ensure that the procedures are actually used—and used effectively.

Leak Testing a Vessel[23]

A 2-ft-diameter float was fabricated using stainless steel and welded seam construction. Pipefitters were given the job of checking the welds for leaks. They were instructed to use 5 psi of air pressure and a soap solution to identify the leaks.

They clamped a 100-psi air hose to a nipple on the tank. A busy instrument worker gave them a gauge. The gauge was incorrectly chosen for vacuum service and not pressure because the vacuum identifier was small.

[23] *Case Histories,* v. 2, p. 186.

A short time later, as the fitters were carrying out the tests, the float ruptured violently. Fortunately, there was no fragmentation of the metal, and the two fitters escaped injury.

The accident investigation found that the leak test should have been conducted with a hydraulic procedure and not air and that the vessel should have been protected with a relief device. In addition, the fitters should have taken more time to check out the gauge to ensure that it was correct for this application.

Man Working in Vessel[24]

Two maintenance workers were replacing part of a ribbon in a large ribbon mixer. The main switch was left energized; the mixer was stopped with one of three start-stop buttons.

As one mechanic was completing his work inside the mixer, another operator on an adjoining floor pushed, by mistake, one of the other start-stop buttons. The mixer started, killing the mechanic between the ribbon flight and the shell of the vessel.

Lock-tag-and-try procedures were developed to prevent accidents of this kind. A padlocked switch at the starter box disconnect, with the key in the mechanic's pocket, prevents this type of accident. After the switch gear lockout, the mechanic should also verify the dead circuit by testing the push-button at all switches; this is the "try" part of the lock-tag-and-try procedure.

Vinyl Chloride Explosion[25]

Two vinyl chloride polymerization reactors were being operated by the same team of operators. Reactor 3 was in the cool-down and dump phase of the process, and reactor 4 was nearly full of monomer and in the polymerization phase. The foreman and three employees set to work to discharge the contents of reactor 3, but in error they opened vessel 4 instead. The gaseous vinyl chloride monomer just in the process of polymerization burst out of the vessel, filled the room, and shortly afterward exploded violently, presumably ignited by a spark from an electric motor or by static electricity generated by the escaping gas. This accident resulted in four fatalities and ten injuries in and around the plant.

The accident could have been prevented with better operating procedures and better training to make the operators appreciate the consequences of mistakes. Modern plants use interlocks or sequence controllers and other special safeguards to prevent this type of error.

Dangerous Water Expansion[26]

A hot oil distillation system was being prepared for operation. The temperature was gradually raised to 500°F. A valve at the bottom of the tower was opened to initiate the transfer of heavy hot oil to a process pump.

[24] *Case Histories,* v. 2, p. 225.
[25] *Case Histories,* v. 2, p. 113.
[26] *Hazards of Water,* booklet 1 (Chicago: Amoco Oil Company, 1984), p. 20.

Before this particular startup, a double block valve arrangement was installed in the bottom discharge line. It was not realized, however, that the second valve created a dead space between the two block valves and that water was trapped between them.

When the bottom valve was opened, the pocket of water came in contact with the hot oil. Flashing steam surged upward through the tower. The steam created excessive pressures at the bottom of the tower, and all the trays dropped within the tower. In this case the pressure luckily did not exceed the vessel rupture pressure. Although no injuries were sustained, the tower was destroyed by this accident.

Problems similar to this are usually identified in safety reviews. This accident, for example, could have been prevented if the plant had used a safety review procedure during the design phase of this plant modification. A bleed line and possibly a nitrogen blow-out line would have prevented the accumulation of this water.

Consequences of contaminating hot and high boiling liquids with low boilers can be estimated using thermodynamics. If these scenarios are possible, relief valves should also be installed to mitigate these events, or adequate safeguards should be added to the system to prevent the specific hazard scenario.

Phenol-Formaldehyde Runaway Reaction[27]

A plant had a runaway reaction with a phenol-formaldehyde polymerization reaction. The result was one fatality and seven injuries and environmental damage. The runaway reaction was triggered when, contrary to standard operating procedures, all the raw materials and catalyst were charged to the reactor at once, followed by the addition of heat. The primary reason for this accident was the lack of administrative controls to ensure that the standard operating procedures were used appropriately and that the operators were trained.

The other root causes were (1) the poor understanding of the chemistry, (2) an inadequate risk analysis, and (3) no safeguard controls to prevent runaway reactions. This EPA case history also summarized seven similar accidents with phenol-formaldehyde reactions during a 10-year period (1988–1997).

Conditions and Secondary Reaction Cause Explosion[28]

A plant manufactured a dye by mixing and reacting two chemicals, ortho-nitrochlorobenzene (o-NCB) and 2-ethylhexylamine (2-EHA). A runaway reaction caused an explosion and flash fires that injured nine workers. The runaway reaction was the result of the following factors: (1) The reaction was started at a temperature higher than normal, (2) the steam used to initiate the reaction was left on for too long, and (3) the use of cooling water to control the reaction rate was not initiated soon enough.

[27] EPA, *How to Prevent Runaway Reactions,* Report 550-F99-004 (Aug. 1999). Available at *www.epa.gov/ceppo/.*

[28] CSB, *Chemical Manufacturing Incident,* Report 1998-06-I-NY. Available at *www.chemsafety.gov/reports/2000/morton/index.htm.*

The investigation team found that the reaction accelerated beyond the heat-removal capacity of the reactor. The resulting high temperature led to a secondary runaway decomposition reaction, causing an explosion that blew the hatch off the reactor and allowed the release of the contents from the vessel.

This company's initial research for the process identified and described two exothermic chemical reactions: (1) The desired exothermic reaction is initiated at an onset temperature of 38°C, and it proceeds rapidly at 75°C; (2) an undesirable decomposition (the dye) reaction has an onset temperature of 195°C.

The operating plant was not aware of the decomposition reaction. The plant's operating and process information described the desired exothermic reaction, but they did not include information on the undesirable decomposition reaction. Information on their MSDS was also misleading (mentioning a lower reactivity and a much lower boiling point than the actual values).

The root causes of this accident were poor operating procedures and poor process information. The operating procedure, for example, did not cover the safety consequences of deviations from the normal operating conditions, such as the possibility of a runaway reaction and the specific steps to be taken to avoid or recover from such deviations.

The recommendations from the investigation included (1) revalidating the safety data for all reactive chemicals, (2) evaluating relief requirements using the appropriate technology published by the Design Institute for Emergency Relief Systems (DIERS) (see details in Chapters 8 and 9), (3) installing the appropriate controls and safety features to safely manage these reactive chemicals, (4) revising the operating procedures and training for handling these reactive chemicals to include descriptions of the possible consequences of deviations from normal operating conditions and the steps taken to correct the resulting problems, including emergency response action, (5) implementing a program to investigate and document safety incidents, and (6) revising the MSDSs and distributing them to anyone needing this information.

Fuel-Blending Tank Explosion[29]

An accident occurred in a fuel-blending facility that provided a way to reuse flammable and hazardous wastes. One worker was killed and two others were injured. The explosion and resulting fire caused extensive damage to the facility.

This facility had two 1000-gal blend tanks to blend waste solvents, cleaners, and a small quantity of oxidizers, including perchlorates, nitrites, and chlorates. Before this accident the operating procedures included the following: (1) About 500 gal of solvent were added before starting the agitator; (2) no inert gas blanketing was used to lower the vapor concentration to below the LFL; (3) oxidizers were added only after the vessel was three-quarters full of solvent and the agitator was running, according to an unwritten procedure; (4) it was known that the addition of oxidizers could be hazardous if the oxidizers were added without a large quantity of liquid fuel in the blend tanks.

[29]EPA, *Prevention of Reactive Chemical Explosions,* Report 550-F00-001. Available at *www.epa.gov/ceppo/*.

On the day of the accident, two workers poured four drums of liquid waste into the blending vessel—about half the amount needed to reach the agitator. Then they added solids into the top of the tank: about 2 lb each of chlorates, perchlorates, and nitrites. Thirty to 60 seconds after the oxidizers were added and while a fifth drum of solvent was being dumped into the top of the reactor, liquid suddenly erupted out of the vessel manway. The flammable vapor exploded, engulfing one employee, who died, and injuring two others.

In the EPA's report of the investigation it was stated that strong oxidizers are generally considered incompatible with many organic substances because of the potential for dangerous reactions. Chlorates, perchlorates, and other strong oxidizers are potentially incompatible with alcohols, halogenated hydrocarbons, other organic compounds and solvents, and other flammable and combustible wastes. The potential consequences of mixing such incompatible materials are violent reactions, fires, and explosions.

The EPA's recommendations for the prevention of this type of accident included (1) establishing standard operating procedures that are essential for safe operation, (2) evaluating the chemical and process hazards before starting a process or procedure that has been changed or modified, (3) properly training employees in the processes they work on using the standard operating procedures for the processes and job tasks, (4) ensuring that the chemicals and reaction mechanisms associated with the substances mixed or blended are well understood and documented, (5) ensuring that chemical and process hazards are understood and addressed, and (6) ensuring that all employees understand the hazards of the chemical process.

Lessons Learned Concerning Procedures

Procedures are sometimes incorrectly perceived as bureaucratic regulations that impede progress. When reviewing case histories it is apparent that safety procedures and standard operating procedures are needed to help the chemical industry (1) eliminate injury to personnel, (2) minimize incapacitating damage to facilities, and (3) maintain steady progress.

In the review of case histories relevant to procedures, additional lessons are identified:[30]

- Use a permit procedure for opening vessels that are normally under pressure.
- Never use gas to open plugged lines.
- Communicate operating changes to other operations that may be affected by the change.
- Train operators and maintenance personnel to understand the consequences of deviations from the norm.
- Make periodic and precise audits of procedures and equipment.
- Use procedures effectively (lock-tag-and-try, hot work, vessel entry, emergency, and the like).
- Use safety review procedures during the design phases of projects, including new installations or modifications to existing systems.

[30]T. A. Kletz, *What Went Wrong? Case Histories of Process Plant Disasters* (Houston: Gulf Publishing, 1985), pp. 182–188.

14-5 Training

Weld Failure

An oil refinery had an explosion that killed 17 people and the property damage was over $100 million. The explosion was caused by the ignition of a large cloud of propane and butane which leaked from a ruptured amine-absorber tower.

Ten years before the accident, a cylindrical section of the tower was replaced on-site. The on-site arc welding procedure was not correct. In the investigation, it was also found that the weld material was susceptible to hydrogen cracking corrosion. The leaking and falling of this tower was due to the corrosion of this weld around the entire tower.

The cause of this accident was the welding procedure, and properties of the weld material[31] were not suited to the corrosive environment in the tower. The root cause was poor training: The construction engineers must know the importance of specifying construction methods and manage the process so the construction specifications are followed as required.

Safety Culture

A very large oil refinery had a series of explosions in March of 2005. There were 15 fatalities and 180 injuries. The dollar losses were also significant: $ 1.6 billion to compensate victims, an OSHA fine of $ 87 million, and a $ 50 million fine for violations of environmental regulations.

This accident was due to a major tower leak of light and heavy gasoline components that resulted in a vapor cloud explosion.[32] The discharges from a relief went to a disposal system consisting of a blowdown drum with an atmospheric vent. The discharged material expelled from this vent. An inherently safer design (knockout tank and a flare system) would have prevented this accident. The major root causes identified by CSB included deficiencies with the staff management, working culture, maintenance, inspection, and safety assessments.

CSB recommended an independent panel to assess the safety culture within the company. A panel was formed and it studied the company culture; its findings are reported in the Baker Review.[33] The paraphrased major results included training recommendations that are relevant to all companies. Top management must

1. Provide effective leadership and training in the area of process safety
2. Establish and implement a management system and training that continuously identify, reduce, and manage process safety risks

[31]"Union Oil Amine Absorber Tower—Accident," *TWI Services Company*, *www.twi.co.uk/content/oilgas_casedown29.html.*

[32]"Texas City Refinery," *http://en.wikipedia.org/wiki/Texas_City_Refinery_(BP)#Legal_action.*

[33]"BP Texas City Incident—Baker Review," *www.hse.gov.uk/leadership/bakerreport.pdf.*

3. Train to develop a positive, trusting, and open process safety culture within the company
4. Train to develop an effective system to audit and improve process safety performance

Training within Universities

In December of 2007, there was an explosion of a 2450-gal reactor killing four employees, and injuring 32, including four employees and 28 members of the public who were working in companies in the plant area. The explosion damaged buildings within one-quarter mile of the facility.

The explosion occurred during the production of the 175th batch of methylcyclopentadienyl manganese tricarbonyl (never say never!). This accident was due to a loss of sufficient cooling during the process, resulting in an uncontrolled runaway reaction leading to excessive temperatures and pressures.[34] The pressure burst the reactor; the reactor's contents ignited and created an explosion equivalent to 1400 lb of TNT.

CSB found that the management (including one chemist and one chemical engineer) did not understand the runaway reaction hazards associated with producing MCMT. The major technical deficiencies were dependence on a single point temperature control system and undersized relief. They did not understand and appreciate the importance of redundant controls when controlling potential runaway reactions, nor did they have the knowledge regarding sizing reliefs for runaway reactions (two-phase flow reliefs).

CSB made training recommendations as a result of this accident:

1. The American Institute of Chemical Engineers (AIChE) and the Accreditation Board for Engineering and Technology, Inc. (ABET), should work together to add reactive hazard awareness to baccalaureate chemical engineering curricula requirements.
2. AIChE should inform all student members about the AIChE' SACHE Process Safety Certificate Program and encourage participation.

Training Regarding the Use of Standards

Sugar Refinery. In February 2008 a series of sugar dust explosions in a sugar refining facility killed 14 workers and injured 36 who were treated for serious burns. The refinery converted sugarcane into granulated sugar. A system of conveyors and bucket elevators transported the granulated sugar to storage silos.

CSB[35] found that the first (primary explosion) dust explosion was in an enclosed steel belt conveyor, and this explosion lofted and exploded sugar dust that had accumulated on the floors and elevated horizontal surfaces (secondary explosions). The secondary dust explosions

[34]"T2 Laboratories, Inc. Runaway Reaction," *www.csb.gov/assets/document/T2_Final_Copy_9_17_09.pdf.*

[35]"Sugar Dust Explosion and Fire," *www.csb.gov/assets/document/Imperial_Sugar_Report_Final_updated.pdf.*

propagated throughout the buildings. An overheated bearing was the most likely ignition source of the primary explosion.

The major CSB recommendations for this sugar refinery accident that were especially related to training included the following:

1. Management should train to emphasize the importance of minimizing and controlling dust hazards.
2. The company should recognize the significant hazards when handling sugar dusts.
3. Housekeeping policies and procedures should be developed and implemented through training.

Pharmaceutical Company. In January of 2003 an explosion in a pharmaceutical plant killed 6 employees and injured 38, including 2 fire fighters who responded to the accident. The explosion ignited fires throughout the facility and disabled the building's sprinkler system. Two 7500-gal plastic tanks of mineral oil collapsed from the heat, and this fuel propagated more fires.

The CSB investigation identified the root cause of the accident as a hazard that had developed in the plant over the years;[36] combustible dust from a polyethylene powder raw material had accumulated on hidden surfaces above the production area, creating the fuel for massive explosions and fires. The production product was a rubber belt, and the belt was dipped in the polyethylene-water mixture to add the polymer to the rubber belt to serve as a lubricant. Although the powder was originally in a safe water solution, the process included a belt drying step that removed the moisture and a small quantity of dry polyethylene powder. The small quantities of the dry powder, however, accumulated over time to produce the final hazard.

Because the facility produced supplies for medical use, cleanliness was a high priority, and crews continuously cleaned dust from visible areas. However, due to a poor design of the ventilation system, the dust was drawn into vents that were above a false ceiling; this was the area that accumulated the dust. The dust gradually accumulated to a thickness of about one-half inch on the ceiling tiles; as much as a ton of the powder could have accumulated. This dust was the source of the dust explosions.

The root cause of the accident was poorly trained designers and operators. The designers didn't use the available codes and standards for handling dusts (see Chapter 13), and the operators didn't understand the hazards of handling dusts. The facility deficiencies included (1) the use of general-purpose electrical fixtures instead of fixtures for this hazardous environment; (2) the design of the ventilation system, which allowed the accumulation of dusts on the false ceiling tiles; and (3) the lack of regular training to inform the operators and engineers about the hazards of handling dusts.

[36]"Dust Explosion at West Pharmaceutical Services," *www.csb.gov/assets/document/West_Digest.pdf.*

Lessons Learned Concerning Training

In 2005, CSB issued a report[37] that identified 200 dust fires over a 25-year period, resulting in approximately 100 fatalities and 600 injuries. CSB stated that these disasters continue to occur because the control measures that should be in place are neglected. CSB emphasized that NFPA publishes comprehensive standards on combustible dust hazard minimization, but these standards are not recognized and understood by those needing this information. Clearly, training in this area is neglected.

When reviewing the accidents in this section, the lack of training is a major deficiency. These accidents would have been prevented by using the existing teachings of NFPA, CCPS, and others. To paraphrase Trevor Kletz: (1) We don't invent new ways to have accidents; we continue to make the same mistakes over and over; (2) the causes of accidents are visible the day before the accident; and (3) learn from history or you're doomed to repeat it. Winston Churchill is widely quoted as having said, "Sometimes doing your best is not good enough. Sometimes you must do what is required." Be trained and train!!

14-6 Conclusion

This chapter on case histories is brief and does not include all the lessons relevant to accidents. The references provide excellent information for more studies. There is significant information in the open literature. However, case histories and safety literature are of no value unless they are studied, understood, and used appropriately.

Example 14-4

Using the dangerous water expansion example, compute the approximate pressures that were developed in the bottom of this column. Assume a column diameter of 2 ft, a water slug of 1 gal, and a column pressure of 10 psia.

Solution

The areas of the column trays are 3.14 ft^2. If the tray vapor paths are small openings, the worst-case scenario assumes that all the water vapor collects beneath the bottom tray. Assuming a tray spacing of 1 ft, the volume under the first tray is 3.14 ft^3. Using an equation of state, we obtain

$$PV = \left(10.73 \frac{\text{psia ft}^3}{\text{lb-mol°R}}\right) nT,$$

$$P = \left(10.73 \frac{\text{psia ft}^3}{\text{lb-mol°R}}\right) \frac{(0.464 \text{ lb-mol})(500 + 460)\text{°R}}{3.14 \text{ ft}^3}$$

$$= 1522 \text{ psia if all the water vaporized.}$$

[37] "CSB Reports Chemical Dust Explosions Are a 'Serious Problem,'" *www.csb.gov/newsroom/detail.aspx?nid=272&SID=0&pg=1&F.*

At 500°F the vapor pressure of water is 680 psia. Therefore the maximum pressure is 680 psi if some water remains as liquid water. The force on the bottom tray is

$$F = (680\ \text{lb}_f/\text{in}^2)(3.14\ \text{ft}^2)(144\ \text{in}^2/\text{ft}^2)$$
$$= 307{,}500\ \text{lb}_f.$$

If the tray is bolted to the column with six 1/2-in bolts, the stress on each bolt is

$$S = \left(\frac{307{,}500\ \text{lb}_f}{6\ \text{bolts}}\right)\left[\frac{1\ \text{bolt}}{(3.14)(0.25\ \text{in})^2}\right]$$
$$= 261{,}000\ \text{lb}_f/\text{in}^2.$$

Assuming a tensile strength of 85,000 psi for stainless 316, it is clear that the trays are stressed beyond the point of failure. Evidently the vessel could handle 680 psia; otherwise it would have also ruptured.

This example explains why all the column trays were torn away from the supports and also illustrates the hazards of contaminating a hot oil with a low-boiling component.

Suggested Reading

Case Histories of Accidents in the Chemical Industry, v. 1 (Washington, DC: Manufacturing Chemists' Association, July 1962).

Case Histories of Accidents, v. 2 (Jan. 1966).

Case Histories of Accidents, v. 3 (Apr. 1970).

T. A. Kletz, "Friendly Plants," *Chemical Engineering Progress* (July 1989), pp. 8–26.

T. Kletz, *Learning from Accidents*, 3rd ed. (Boston: Butterworth-Heinemann, 2001).

T. A. Kletz, *Plant Design for Safety* (New York: Hemisphere Publishing, 1991).

T. Kletz, *What Went Wrong? Case Histories of Process Plant Disasters and How They Could Have Been Avoided*, 5th ed. (Boston: Butterworth-Heinemann, 2009).

S. Mannan, ed., *Lees' Loss Prevention in the Process Industries,* 3rd ed. (London: Butterworth-Heinemann, 2005).

R. E. Sanders, *Managing Change in Chemical Plants: Learning from Case Histories* (London: Butterworth-Heinemann, 1993).

Problems

14-1. Using the article by Kelly (see Table 14-2), describe the commonly used methods to remove peroxides.

14-2. Use the paper developed by the EPA (see footnote 27) to describe the lessons learned as a result of the phenol-formaldehyde runaway reactions.

14-3. After reading the article by Kelly on peroxidizables (see Table 14-2 reference), state the minimum hazardous concentrations of peroxides in solution with organic chemicals.

14-4. Using the article by Kelly (see Table 14-2), describe the commonly used peroxide detection methods.

14-5. A hydrogen peroxide still is used to concentrate peroxide by removing water. The still is of high-purity aluminum, a material that is noncatalytic to the decomposition of peroxide vapor. The still is designed to produce 78% hydrogen peroxide. It will explode spontaneously at about 90%. Illustrate some recommended design features for this still.

14-6. A 1000-gal cylindrical vessel (4 ft in diameter) is nearly filled with water. It has a 10% pad of air at 0 psig and 70°F. If this air is completely soluble at 360°F and 154 psia, what will the vessel pressure be at 380°F? Assume a wall thickness of 1/4 in of stainless 316 and flat cylindrical heads.

14-7. Review and analyze the EPA document on reactive chemicals (see footnote 29), and describe the steps required to prevent accidents of this type.

14-8. An operation requires the transfer of 50 gal of toluene from a vessel to a 55-gal drum. Develop a set of operator instructions for this operation.

14-9. Read the article by W. B. Howard [*Chemical Engineering Progress* (Sept. 1988), p. 25]. Describe the correct and incorrect designs for installing flame arrestors.

14-10. From W. B. Howard's article (Problem 14-9), describe his concepts concerning combustion venting and thrust forces.

14-11. Use the paper developed by the EPA (see footnote 27) to state the EPA's recommendations for preventing runaway reactions.

14-12. A square stainless steel pad (5 in × 5 in × 1/8 in) is welded to a vessel that is used for high-temperature service (1200°C). The welder welds continuously around the pad, forgetting to leave an opening for a vent. Compute the pressure change between the pad and the vessel if the temperature changes from 0°C to 1200°C.

14-13. Illustrate the layered accident investigation process, using Example 14-1 as a guide, to develop the underlying causes of the duct system explosion described in Section 14-1.

14-14. Repeat Problem 14-13 for the bottle of isopropyl ether accident described in Section 14-2.

14-15. Repeat Problem 14-13 for the vinyl chloride explosion described in Section 14-4.

14-16. Repeat Problem 14-13 for the nitrobenzene sulfonic acid decomposition accident described in Section 14-2.

14-17. Repeat Problem 14-13 for the butadiene explosion described in Section 14-3.

14-18. Vessels normally have a relief device to prevent damage during thermal expansion. A stainless steel cylindrical vessel has 1/4-in-thick walls and is 4 ft in diameter. It is filled with 400 gal of water, and 0.2 ft^3 of air is trapped at a pressure gauge. Start at 0 psig and 50°F and then heat the vessel. At what temperature will this vessel rupture if it does not have a relief?

14-19. A reactor system is charged accidentally with benzene and chlorosulfonic acid with the agitator off. Under this condition the two highly reactive reactants form two layers in the reactor. Develop a set of operating instructions for safely handling this situation.

14-20. Develop design features to prevent the situation described in Problem 14-19.

14-21. Compute the RHI for acetylene.

14-22. Why are bug screens installed on control valve vents?

APPENDIX A

Unit Conversion Constants[1]

Volume Equivalents

in^3	ft^3	US gal	L	m^3
1	5.787×10^{-4}	4.329×10^{-3}	1.639×10^{-2}	1.639×10^{-5}
1728	1	7.481	28.32	2.832×10^{-2}
231	0.1337	1	3.785	3.785×10^{-3}
61.03	3.531×10^{-2}	0.2642	1	1.000×10^{-3}
6.102×10^4	35.31	264.2	1000	1

Mass Equivalents

avoirdupois oz.	lb_m	grains	g	kg
1	6.25×10^{-2}	437.5	28.35	2.835×10^{-2}
16	1	7000	453.6 -	0.4536
2.286×10^{-3}	1.429×10^{-4}	1	6.48×10^{-2}	6.48×10^{-5}
3.527×10^{-2}	2.20×10^{-3}	15.432	1	0.001
35.27	2.20	15,432	1000	1

[1] Selected from David M. Himmelblau, *Basic Principles and Calculations in Chemical Engineering,* 4th ed. (Englewood Cliffs, NJ: Prentice Hall, 1982).

Linear Measure

m	in	ft	mi
1	39.37	3.2808	6.214×10^{-4}
2.54×10^{-2}	1	8.333×10^{-2}	1.58×10^{-5}
0.3048	12	1	1.8939×10^{-4}
1609	6.336×10^{4}	5280	1

Power Equivalents

HP	kW	ft-lb$_f$/s	Btu/s	J/s
1	0.7457	550	0.7068	745.7
1.341	1	737.56	0.9478	1000
1.818×10^{-3}	1.356×10^{-3}	1	1.285×10^{-3}	1.356
1.415	1.055	778.16	1	1055
1.341×10^{-3}	1.000×10^{-3}	0.7376	9.478×10^{-4}	1

Heat, Energy, or Work Equivalents

ft-lb$_f$	kW hr	HP hr	Btu	cal	J
1	3.766×10^{-7}	5.0505×10^{-7}	1.285×10^{-3}	0.3241	1.356
2.655×10^{6}	1	1.341	3412.8	8.6057×10^{5}	3.6×10^{6}
1.98×10^{6}	0.7455	1	2545	6.4162×10^{5}	2.6845×10^{6}
778.16	2.930×10^{-4}	3.930×10^{-4}	1	252	1055
3.086	1.162×10^{-6}	1.558×10^{-6}	3.97×10^{-3}	1	4.184
0.7376	2.773×10^{-7}	3.725×10^{-7}	9.484×10^{-4}	0.2390	1

Pressure Equivalents

mm Hg	in Hg	bar	atm	kPa	psia
1	3.937×10^{-2}	1.333×10^{-3}	1.316×10^{-3}	0.1333	1.934×10^{-2}
25.40	1	0.03387	3.342×10^{-2}	3.387	0.4912
750.06	29.53	1	0.9869	100.0	14.15
760.0	29.92	1.013	1	101.3	14.696
7.502	0.2954	0.01000	9.872×10^{-3}	1	0.1450
51.71	2.036	6.893×10^{-2}	6.805×10^{-2}	6.893	1

Ideal Gas Constant R_g

1.9872 cal/gm-mole K
1.9872 Btu/lb-mole°R
8.3143 J/mol K
10.731 psia ft^3/lb-mole°R
8.3143 kPa m^3/kg-mole K = 8.314 J/gm-mole K
0.83143 bar m^3/kg-mole
82.057 cm^3 atm/gm-mole K = 8.2057 $\times$ 10^{-5} m^3 atm/mol K
0.082057 L atm/gm-mole K = 0.082057 m^3 atm/kg-mole K
21.9 (in Hg) ft^3/lb-mole°R
0.7302 ft^3 atm/lb-mole°R
1,545.3 ft lb$_f$/lb-mole°R
8.314 $\times$ 10^3 kg m^2/kg-mole s^2 K

Gravitational Constant g_c

32.174 ft-lb$_m$/lb$_f$-s^2
1 (kg m/s^2)/N
1 (g cm/s^2)/dyne

Miscellaneous

1 Poise = 100 centipoise = 0.1 kg/m s = 0.1 Pa s = 0.1 N s/m^2
1 N = 1 kg m/s^2
1 J = 1 N m = 1 kg m^2/s^2
1 centipoise = 1 $\times$ 10^{-3} kg/m s = 2.4191 lb$_m$/ft-hr = 6.7197 $\times$ 10^{-4} lb$_m$/ft-s

Flammability Data for Selected Hydrocarbons

Table AB-1 Flammability Data for Selected Hydrocarbons

Compound	Formula	Heat of combustion (kJ/mol)		Flammability limit[a] vol. % fuel in air		Flash point temperature[a] °C	Autoignition temperature[a] °C
		Lower[a]	Upper[b]	LFL	UFL		
Paraffin hydrocarbons							
Methane	CH_4	−802.3	−890.3	5.0	15.0	−188	600
Ethane	C_2H_6	−1428.6	−1559.8	3.0	12.5	−135	515
Propane	C_3H_8	−2043.1	−2219.9	2.1	9.5	−104	450
Butane	C_4H_{10}	−2657.5	−2877.5	1.8	8.5	−60	405
Isobutane	C_4H_{10}	−2649.0	−2869.0	1.8	8.4	−83	460
Pentane	C_5H_{12}	−3245.0	−3536.6	1.4	7.8	−40	260
Isopentane	C_5H_{12}	−3240.3	−3527.6	1.4	7.6	−57	420
Neopentane	C_5H_{12}	−3250.4	−3514.1	1.4	7.5	−65	450
Hexane	C_6H_{14}	−3855.2	−4194.5	1.2	7.5	−23	234
Heptane	C_7H_{16}	−4464.9	−4780.6	1.0	7.0	−4	223
2,3-Dimethylpentane	C_7H_{16}	−4460.7	−4842.3	1.1	6.7	−15	337
Octane	C_8H_{18}	−5074.1	−5511.6	0.8	6.5	13	220
Nonane	C_9H_{20}	−5685.1	–	0.7	5.6	31	206
Decane	$C_{10}H_{22}$	−6294.2	−6737.0	0.8	5.4	46	208
Olefins							
Ethylene	C_2H_4	−1322.6	−1411.2	2.7	36.0	−136	450
Propylene	C_3H_6	−1925.7	−2057.3	2.0	11.0	−108	455
1-Butene	C_4H_8	−2541.2	−2716.8	1.6	9.3	−79	384
2-Butene	C_4H_8	−2534.4	−2708.2	1.8	9.7	−74	324
1-Pentene	C_5H_{10}	−3129.7	−3361.4	1.5	8.7	−18	273
Acetylenes							
Acetylene	C_2H_2	−1255.6	−1299.6	2.5	80.0	−18	305
Aromatics							
Benzene	C_6H_6	−3135.6	−3301.4	1.4	7.1	−11	562
Toluene	C_7H_8	−3733.9	−3947.9	1.2	7.1	4	536
o-Xylene	C_8H_{10}	−4332.8	−4567.6	1.0	6.0	17	464

Table AB-1 (*continued*)

Compound	Formula	Heat of combustion (kJ/mol)		Flammability limit[a] vol. % fuel in air		Flash point temperature[a] °C	Autoignition temperature[a] °C
		Lower[a]	Upper[b]	LFL	UFL		
Cyclic hydrocarbons							
Cyclopropane	C_3H_6	−1959.3	−2091.3	2.4	10.4	−94	498
Cyclohexane	C_6H_{12}	−3655.8	−3953.0	1.3	8.0	−20	260
Methylcyclohexane	C_7H_{14}	−4257.1	−4600.7	1.2	7.2	−4	285
Phenol	C_6H_6O	−2921.4		1.8	8.6	79	715
Terpenes							
Turpentine	$C_{10}H_{16}$	–	–	0.8	6.8	51	252[2]
Alcohols							
Methyl alcohol	CH_4O	−638.1	−764.0	7.5	36.0	11	463
Ethyl alcohol	C_2H_6O	−1235.5	−1409.2	4.3	19.0	13	422
Allyl alcohol	C_3H_6O	−1731.9	−1912.2	2.5	18.0	21	378
n-Propanol	C_3H_8O	−1843.8	−2068.9	2.0	12.0	15	371
Isopropyl alcohol	C_3H_8O	−1830.0	−2051.0	2.0	12.0	12	399
n-Butyl alcohol	$C_4H_{10}O$	−2456.0	−2728.3	1.4	11.2	29	343
Isoamyl alcohol	$C_5H_{12}O$	−3062.3	–	1.2	9.0	43	350
Aldehydes							
Formaldehyde	CH_2O	−519.4	−570.8	7.0	73	−53	430
Acetaldehyde	C_2H_4O	−1104.6	−764.0	1.6	10.4	−38	185
Acrolein	C_3H_4O	−1553.5		2.8	31.0	−26	234
Methacrolein	C_4H_6O	−2150.0	−2268.1	2.1	14.6	2	234
Furfural	$C_5H_4O_2$	−2249.7	−2340.9	2.1	19.3	60	316
Paraldehyde	$C_6H_{12}O_3$	−3125.2	–	1.3	16.2	36	238
Ethers							
Diethyl ether	$C_4H_{10}O$	−2503.5	−2751.1	1.9	48.0	−45	180
Divinyl ether	C_4H_6O	−2260.0	−2416.2	1.7	27.0	−47	360
Disopropyl ether	$C_6H_{14}O$	−3702.3	−4043.0	1.4	21.0	−28	443

(*continues*)

Table AB-1 *(continued)*

Compound	Formula	Heat of combustion (kJ/mol) Lower[a]	Upper[b]	Flammability limit[a] vol. % fuel in air LFL	UFL	Flash point temperature[a] °C	Autoignition temperature[a] °C
Ketones							
Acetone	C_3H_6O	−1659.2	−1821.4	2.6	12.8	−18	538
Methylethyl ketone	C_4H_8O	−2261.6	−2478.7	1.8	10.0	−6	516
2-Pentanone	$C_5H_{10}O$	−2880.0	−3137.6	1.5	8.2	7	457
2-Hexanone	$C_6H_{12}O$	−3490.0	−3796.3	1.2	8.0	25	424
Acids							
Acetic acid	$C_2H_4O_2$	−786.4	−926.1	5.4	16.0	43	427
Hydrogen cyanide	HCN	–	–	6.0	41.0	−18	538
Esters							
Methyl formate	$C_2H_4O_2$	−920.9	−1003.0	5.9	20.0	−19	456
Ethyl formate	$C_3H_6O_2$	−1507.0	−1638.8	2.7	13.5	−4	455
Methyl acetate	$C_3H_6O_2$	−1461.0	−1628.1	3.1	16.0	−10	502
Ethyl acetate	$C_4H_8O_2$	−2061.0	−2273.6	2.2	11.4	−4	427
Propyl acetate	$C_5H_{10}O_2$	−2672.0	–	2.0	8.0	15	450
Isopropyl acetate	$C_5H_{10}O_2$	−2658.1	−2907.0	1.8	7.2	2	479
Butyl acetate	$C_6H_{12}O_2$	−3283.0	−3587.8	1.7	7.6	22	421
Isopentyl acetate	$C_7H_{14}O_2$	−3889.9	−4361.7	1.0	7.5	25	360
Inorganic							
Hydrogen	H_2	−241.8	−285.8	4.0	75.0	–	400
Ammonia	NH_3	–	−382.6	16.0	25.0	–	651
Oxides							
Carbon monoxide	CO	−283.0	–	12.5	74.0	–	609
Ethylene oxide	C_2H_4O	−1218.0	−1264.0	3.0	–	−55	429
Propylene oxide	C_3H_6O	−1785.3	–	2.1	21.5	−37	465
Dioxane	$C_4H_8O_2$	−2178.8	–	2.0	22.0	12	180

Table AB-1 *(continued)*

Compound	Formula	Heat of combustion (kJ/mol)		Flammability limit[a] vol. % fuel in air		Flash point temperature[a] °C	Autoignition temperature[a] °C
		Lower[a]	Upper[b]	LFL	UFL		
Sulfur containing							
Carbon disulfide	CS_2	−1104.2	−1104.2	1.3	50.0	−30	90
Hydrogen sulfide	H_2S	–	−562.6	4.3	45.0	–	260
Carbon oxysulfide	COS	−548.3	−546.0	12.0	29.0	–	–
Chlorine containing							
Methyl chloride	CH_3Cl	−675.4	−687.0	10.7	17.4	−66	632
Ethyl chloride	C_2H_5Cl	−1284.9	−1325.0	3.8	15.4	−50	519
Propyl chloride	C_3H_7Cl	−1864.6	−2001.3	2.8	10.7	−32	593
Butyl chloride	C_4H_9Cl	−2474.2	–	1.8	10.1	−28	460
sec-Butyl chloride	C_4H_9Cl	−2465.2	–	1.9	9.1	−5	–
Amyl chloride	$C_5H_{11}Cl$	−3085.2	–	1.6	8.6	13	260
Vinyl chloride	C_2H_3Cl	−1158.0	–	3.6	33.0	−78	472
Chlorobenzene	C_6H_5Cl	−2976.1	–	1.3	7.1	32	638
Ethylene dichloride	$C_2H_2C_{l2}$	−994.5	−1133.8	5.6	12.8	4	460
Propylene dichloride	$C_3H_6C_{l2}$	−1704.6	–	3.4	14.5	16	557
Bromides							
Methyl bromide	CH_3Br	−705.4	−768.9	10.0	16.0	−44	537
Ethyl bromide	C_2H_5Br	−1284.4	−1424.6	6.7	11.3	−33	511
Amines							
Methyl amine	CH_5N	−975.1	−1085.1	4.9	20.7	−58	430
Ethyl amine	C_2H_7N	−1587.4	−1739.9	3.5	14.0	−46	384
Dimethyl amine	C_2H_7N	−1614.6	−1768.9	2.8	14.4	−50	400
Propyl amine	C_3H_9N	−2164.8	−2396.6	2.0	10.4	−12	318
Diethyl amine	$C_4H_{11}N$	−2800.3	−3074.3	1.8	10.1	−26	312
Trimethyl amine	C_3H_9N	−2244.9	−2443.0	2.0	11.6	−7	190
Triethyl amine	$C_6H_{15}N$	−4044.5	−4134.5	1.2	8.0	−12	–

(continues)

Table AB-1 *(continued)*

Compound	Formula	Heat of combustion (kJ/mol)		Flammability limit[a] vol. % fuel in air		Flash point temperature[a] °C	Autoignition temperature[a] °C
		Lower[a]	Upper[b]	LFL	UFL		
Miscellaneous							
Acrylonitrile	C_3H_3N	−1690.0	−1789.1	2.4	17.3	0	481
Aniline	C_6H_7N	−3238.5	–	1.3	11	70	617
Diborane	B_2H_6	–	–				
	0.8	98	−90	52			
Methyl methacrylate	$C_5H_8O_2$	−2546.8		2.1	12.5	11	–
Styrene	C_8H_8	−4219.3	−4438.8	1.1	6.1	32	490
Gasoline[c]				1.4	7.6	−43	

[a]Carl L. Yaws, *Chemical Properties Handbook* (New York: McGraw-Hill, 1999).
[b]T. Suziki, "Note: Empirical Relationship between Lower Flammability Limits and Standard Enthalpies of Combustion of Organic Compounds," *Fire and Materials* (1994), 18: 333–336 and 393–397.
[c]B. Lewis and G. Von Elbe, *Combustion, Flames, and Explosions of Gases* (New York: Harcourt Brace Jovanovich), 1987.

Detailed Equations for Flammability Diagrams[1]

Equations Useful for Gas Mixtures

In this appendix we derive several equations that are useful for working with flammability diagrams. Section 6-5 provides introductory material on the flammability diagram. In this section we derive equations proving that:

1. If two gas mixtures R and S are combined, the resulting mixture composition lies on a line connecting the points R and S on the flammability diagram. The location of the final mixture on the straight line depends on the relative moles of the mixtures combined. If mixture S has more moles, the final mixture point will lie closer to point S. This is identical to the lever rule used for phase diagrams.
2. If a mixture R is continuously diluted with mixture S, the mixture composition will follow along the straight line between points R and S on the flammability diagram. As the dilution continues, the mixture composition will move closer and closer to point S. Eventually, at infinite dilution, the mixture composition will be at point S.
3. For systems having composition points that fall on a straight line passing through an apex corresponding to one pure component, the other two components are present in a fixed ratio along the entire line length.
4. The limiting oxygen concentration (LOC) is estimated by reading the oxygen concentration at the intersection of the stoichiometric line and a horizontal line drawn through the LFL. This is equivalent to the equation

$$\text{LOC} = z(\text{LFL}). \tag{AC-1}$$

[1]This appendix is reproduced (with modifications) from D. A. Crowl, *Understanding Explosions* (New York: American Institute of Chemical Engineers, 2003). Used with permission.

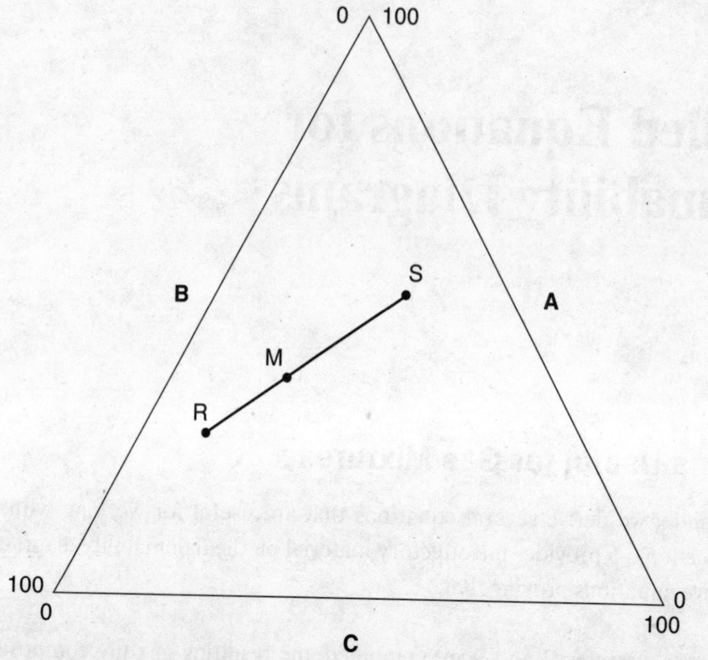

Figure AC-1 Two mixtures R and S are combined to form mixture M.

Figure AC-1 shows two gas mixtures, denoted R and S, that are combined to form mixture M. Each gas mixture has a specific composition based on the three gas components A, B, and C. For mixture R the gas composition, in mole fractions, is x_{AR}, x_{BR}, and x_{CR}, and the total number of moles is n_R. For mixture S the gas composition is x_{AS}, x_{BS}, and x_{CS}, with total moles n_S, and for mixture M the gas composition is x_{AM}, x_{BM}, and x_{CM}, with total moles n_M. These compositions are shown in Figure AC-2 with respect to components A and C.

An overall and a component species balance can be performed to represent the mixing process. Because a reaction does not occur during mixing, moles are conserved and it follows that

$$n_M = n_R + n_S. \tag{AC-2}$$

A mole balance on species A is given by

$$n_M x_{AM} = n_R x_{AR} + n_S x_{AS}. \tag{AC-3}$$

A mole balance on species C is given by

$$n_M x_{CM} = n_R x_{CR} + n_S x_{CS}. \tag{AC-4}$$

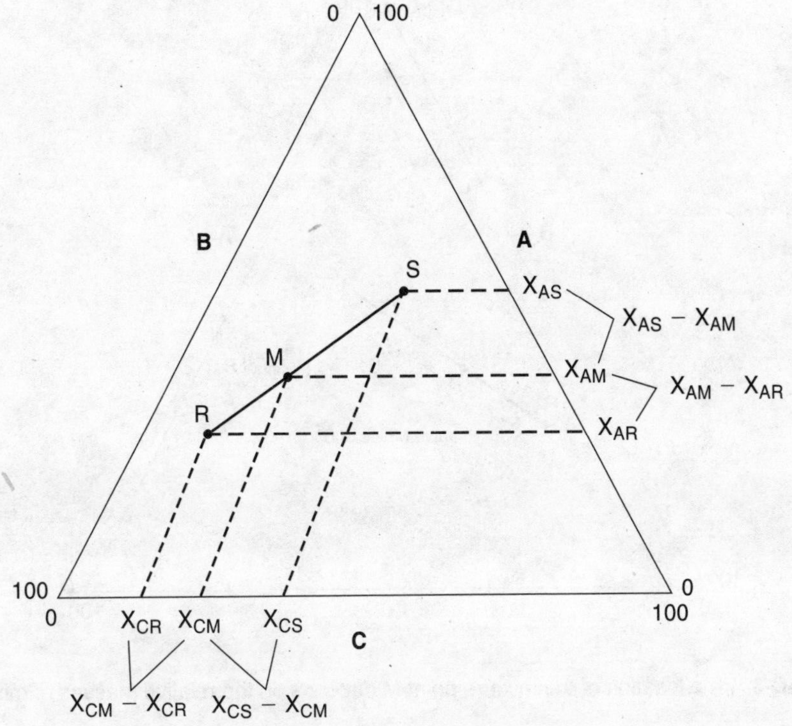

Figure AC-2 Composition information for Figure AC-1.

Substituting Equation AC-2 into Equation AC-3 and rearranging, we obtain

$$\frac{n_S}{n_R} = \frac{x_{AM} - x_{AR}}{x_{AS} - x_{AM}}. \tag{AC-5}$$

Similarly, substituting Equation AC-2 into Equation AC-4 results in

$$\frac{n_S}{n_R} = \frac{x_{CM} - x_{CR}}{x_{CS} - x_{CM}}. \tag{AC-6}$$

Equating Equations AC-5 and AC-6 results in

$$\frac{x_{AM} - x_{AR}}{x_{AS} - x_{AM}} = \frac{x_{CM} - x_{CR}}{x_{CS} - x_{CM}}. \tag{AC-7}$$

A similar set of equations can be written between components A and B or between components B and C.

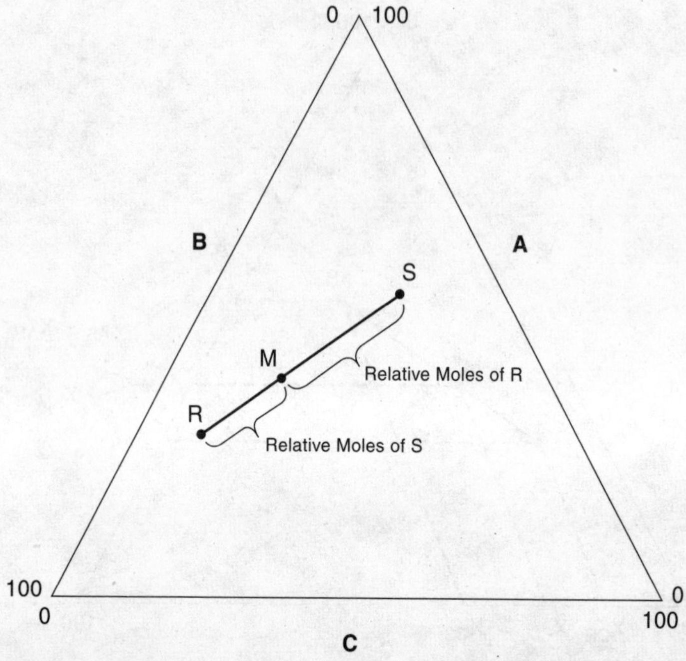

Figure AC-3 The location of the mixture point M depends on the relative masses of mixtures R and S.

Figure AC-2 shows the quantities represented by the mole balance of Equation AC-7. The mole balance is honored only if point M lies on the straight line between points R and S. This can be shown in Figure AC-2 using similar triangles.[2]

Figure AC-3 shows another useful result based on Equations AC-5 and AC-6. These equations imply that the location of point M on the straight line between points R and S depends on the relative moles of R and S, as shown.

These results can, in general, be applied to any two points on the triangle diagram. If a mixture R is continuously diluted with mixture S, the mixture composition follows the straight line between points R and S. As the dilution continues, the mixture composition moves closer and closer to point S. Eventually, at infinite dilution the mixture composition is at point S.

For systems having composition points that fall on a straight line passing through an apex corresponding to one pure component, the other two components are present in a fixed ratio along the entire line length.[3] This is shown in Figure AC-4. For this case the ratio of components A and B along the line shown is constant and is given by

$$\frac{x_A}{x_B} = \frac{x}{100 - x}. \tag{AC-8}$$

[2]O. A. Hougen, K. M. Watson, et al., *Chemical Process Principles,* pt. 1, *Material and Energy Balances,* 2nd ed. (New York: Wiley, 1954).

[3]Hougen et al., *Chemical Process Principles.*

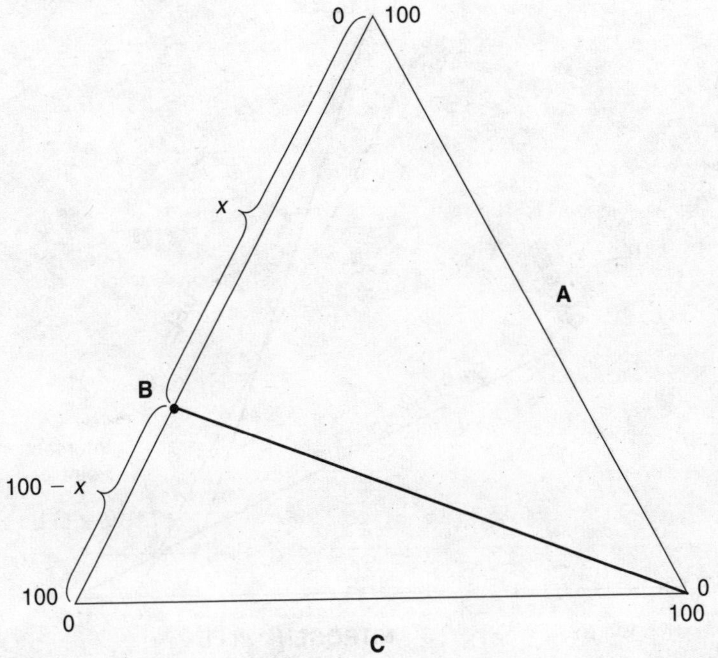

Figure AC-4 The ratio of components A and B is constant along the line shown and is given by $x/(100 - x)$.

A useful application of this result is shown in Figure AC-5. Suppose that we wish to find the oxygen concentration at the point where the LFL intersects the stoichiometric line shown. The oxygen concentration in question is shown as point X in Figure AC-5. The stoichiometric combustion equation is represented by

$$(1)\ \text{Fuel} + z\text{Oxygen} \rightarrow \text{Products}, \tag{AC-9}$$

where z is the stoichiometric coefficient for oxygen. The ratio of oxygen to fuel along the stoichiometric line is constant and is given by

$$\frac{x_{O_2}}{x_{\text{Fuel}}} = z. \tag{AC-10}$$

At the specific fuel concentration of $x_{\text{Fuel}} = \text{LFL}$ it follows from Equation AC-10 that

$$x_{O_2} = z(\text{LFL}). \tag{AC-11}$$

This result provides a method to estimate the LOC from the LFL. This graphical estimate of the LOC is equivalent to the following:

$$\text{LOC} = z(\text{LFL}), \tag{AC-12}$$

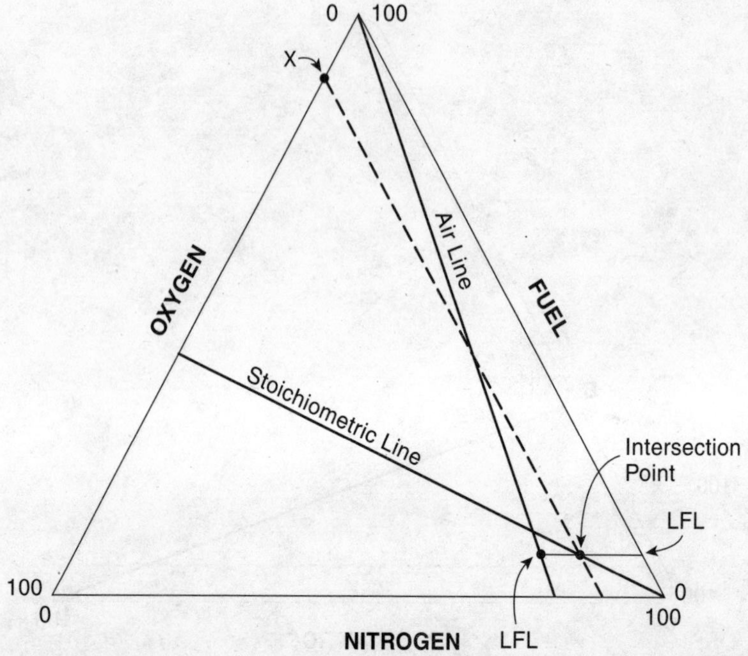

Figure AC-5 Determining the oxygen concentration X at the intersection of the LFL and the stoichiometric line.

where

z is the stoichiometric coefficient for oxygen, given by Equation AC-9, and
LFL is the lower flammability limit, in volume percentage of fuel in air.

Equations Useful for Placing Vessels into and out of Service

The equations presented in this section are equivalent to drawing straight lines to show the gas composition transitions. The equations are frequently easier to use and provide a more precise result than manually drawn lines.

The out-of-service fuel concentration (OSFC) is the maximum fuel concentration that just avoids the flammability zone when a vessel is being taken out of service. It is shown as point S in Figure AC-6.

For most compounds detailed flammability zone data are not available. In this case an estimate can be made of the location of point S, as shown in Figure AC-6. Point S can be approximated by a line starting at the pure air point and connecting through a point at the intersection of the LFL with the stoichiometric line. Equation AC-7 can be used to determine the gas composition at point S. Referring to Figure AC-2, we know the gas composition at points R and M and wish to calculate the gas composition at point S. Let A represent the fuel and C the

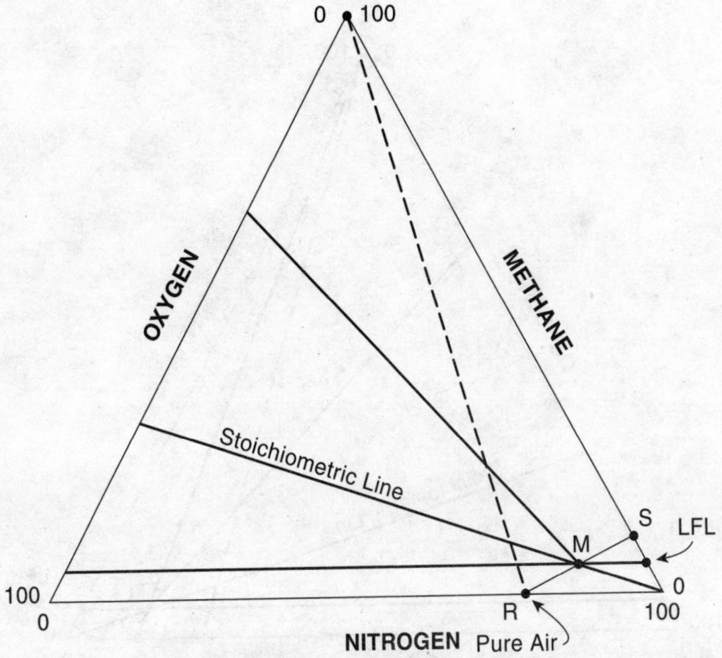

Figure AC-6 Estimating a target fuel concentration at point S for taking a vessel out of service.

oxygen. Then from Figures AC-2 and AC-6 it follows that $x_{AR} = 0$, $x_{AM} = \text{LFL}\%$, x_{AS} is the unknown OSFC, $x_{CM} = z(\text{LFL})$ from Equation AC-11, $x_{CR} = 21\%$, and $x_{CS} = 0$. Then, by substituting into Equation AC-7 and solving for x_{AS}, we get

$$x_{AS} = \text{OSFC} = \frac{\text{LFL}\%}{1 - z\left(\dfrac{\text{LFL}\%}{21}\right)}, \tag{AC-13}$$

where

OSFC is the out-of-service fuel concentration, that is, the fuel concentration at point S in Figure AC-6,

LFL% is the volume percentage of fuel in air at the lower flammability limit, and

z is the stoichiometric oxygen coefficient from the combustion reaction given by Equation AC-9.

Another approach is to estimate the fuel concentration at point S by extending the line from point R through the intersection of the LOC and the stoichiometric line. The result is

$$\text{OSFC} = \frac{\text{LOC}\%}{z\left(1 - \dfrac{\text{LOC}\%}{21}\right)}, \tag{AC-14}$$

where LOC% is the minimum oxygen concentration in volume percentage of oxygen.

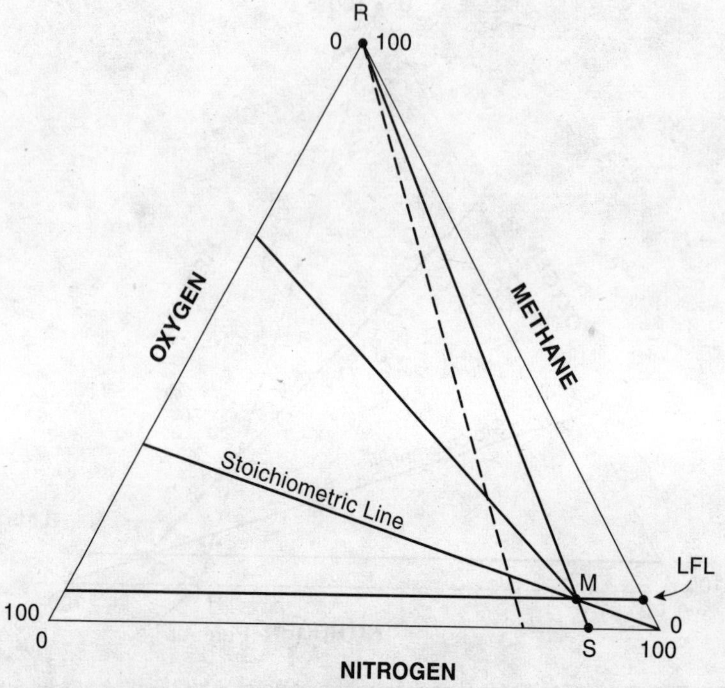

Figure AC-7 Estimating a target nitrogen concentration at point S for placing a vessel into service.

Equations AC-13 and AC-14 are approximations to the fuel concentration at point S. Fortunately, they are usually conservative, predicting a fuel concentration that is less than the experimentally determined OSFC value. For instance, for methane the LFL is 5.0% (Appendix B) and z is 2. Thus Equation AC-13 predicts an OSFC of 9.5% fuel. This is compared to the experimentally determined OSFC of 14.5%. Using the experimental LOC of 12% (Table 6-3), an OSFC value of 14% is determined using Equation AC-14. This is closer to the experimental value but still conservative. For ethylene, 1,3-butadiene, and hydrogen, Equation AC-14 predicts a higher OSFC than the experimentally determined value.

The in-service oxygen concentration (ISOC) is the maximum oxygen concentration that just avoids the flammability zone, shown as point S in Figure AC-7. One approach to estimating the ISOC is to use the intersection of the LFL with the stoichiometric line. A line is drawn from the top apex of the triangle through the intersection to the nitrogen axis, as shown in Figure AC-7. Let A represent the fuel species and C the oxygen. Then, from Figure AC-7 it follows that $x_{AM} = \text{LFL\%}$, $x_{AR} = 100$, $x_{AS} = 0$, $x_{CM} = z(\text{LFL\%})$ from Equation AC-11, $x_{CR} = 0$, and x_{CS} is the unknown ISOC. Substituting into Equation AC-7 and solving for the ISOC results in

$$\text{ISOC} = \frac{z(\text{LFL\%})}{1 - \left(\dfrac{\text{LFL\%}}{100}\right)}, \tag{AC-15}$$

where

ISOC is the in-service oxygen concentration in volume percentage of oxygen,
z is the stoichiometric coefficient for oxygen given by Equation AC-9, and
LFL% is the fuel concentration at the lower flammability limit, in volume percentage of fuel in air.

The nitrogen concentration at point S is equal to 100 − ISOC.

An expression to estimate the ISOC using the intersection of the minimum oxygen concentration and the stoichiometric line can also be developed using a similar procedure. The result is

$$\text{ISOC} = \frac{z(\text{LOC\%})}{z - \dfrac{\text{LOC\%}}{100}}, \qquad \text{(AC-16)}$$

where LOC% is the limiting oxygen concentration in volume percentage of oxygen.

Although these calculations are useful for making good estimates, direct, reliable experimental data under conditions as close as possible to process conditions are always recommended.

APPENDIX D

Formal Safety Review Report for Example 10-4

RESEARCH MEMORANDUM

CHEMICAL ENGINEERING

SAFETY REVIEW FOR PILOT PODBIELNIAK LIQUID-LIQUID EXTRACTION SYSTEM

AUTHOR: J. Doe SUPERVISOR: W. Smith
November 8, 1988

SUMMARY

Chemical Engineering's Podbielniak (POD) liquid-liquid extraction pilot system has been reassembled. It will be used to evaluate the water-washability of toluene. A formal safety review was held 10/10/88. Main action items from that review included (1) padding all vessels containing solvent with nitrogen, (2) grounding and bonding all tanks containing solvent, (3) adding dip legs to all vessels, (4) using elephant trunks at drum openings, (5) adding heat exchangers equipped with temperature gauges to cool hot solvent, (6) purging all vessels containing solvent with nitrogen before startup, (7) changing the emergency procedure to activate the spill alarm in the event of a spill and to trip the sewer isolation valve, and (8) adding receiving drums for all output streams containing solvent.

Subsequently, a few equipment changes were made during initial system checkout and test runs. These changes were made to enhance operability, not safety; for example, (1) the pump (P1) generated insufficient head and a stronger spring was installed; and (2) a light liquid in sample point, a few check valves, and additional temperature and pressure gauges were installed.

ABC chemical	ABC chemical	ABC chemical

DISTRIBUTION:

All

REPORT NUMBER 88-5
SECURITY CLASS None
PROJECT NUMBER 6280
SUPERVISOR(S) APPROVAL(S)

____

____

____

I. INTRODUCTION

A. Process summary

The following procedure is used to wash toluene in the equipment provided.

1. An appropriate amount of solvent is transferred from the solvent storage tank to the emulsion tank.
2. Water is added to the solvent to form an emulsion.
3. The emulsion is heated to 190°F.
4. The emulsion is separated in the centrifugal contactor (POD), which produces a stream containing water-soluble impurities and a stream of washed solvent.

B. Reactions and stoichiometry

No reaction takes place. As far as stoichiometry is concerned, typically one part water is added to one part solvent. Flow rates are based on a maximum of 1000 cc/min solvent to the POD.

C. Engineering data

Toluene has a vapor pressure of 7.7 psi at 190°F. System operating pressures are normally 40–50 psig around the POD, with pumps capable of delivering 140 psig. System temperatures are maintained between 190° and 200°F. Typical viscosities are under 10 centipoise at this temperature.

II. RAW MATERIALS AND PRODUCTS

A. Solvents

The most frequently used solvent is toluene. Toluene boils at 231°F but forms an azeotrope with water boiling at 183°F. Because this is below the system operating temperature, hazards are present because of flammability and volatility. In addition, toluene presents special problems from a personnel exposure viewpoint as a suspected teratogen.

To minimize hazards, the following precautions will be taken:

1. All vessels containing solvent are N_2 padded and grounded.
2. All potential solvent exposure points will be in close proximity to elephant-trunk exhaust ducts for ventilation.
3. All product streams are cooled before discharge or sampling.
4. Colorimetric sampling tubes will be available for ambient air monitoring.

The possibility exists for using other solvents in the system. Safety reviews for each will be conducted as needed.

III. EQUIPMENT SETUP

A. Equipment description (sketches attached)

1. Emulsion tank: The emulsion tank consists of a jacketed, agitated 50-gal glass-lined Pfaudler reactor with N_2 pad and relief valve. Emulsion is heated in the vessel by applying steam to

the jacket. Temperature is controlled by means of a temperature-indicating controller that measures the temperature in the vessel. The controller modulates a control valve in the steam line to the jacket. Emulsion is circulated from the bottom of the reactor to the POD system and back to the reactor top by means of a Viking pump driven by a 2-HP 1745-rpm motor.

A slipstream is fed from this loop to the POD system. Pressure in this circulating loop is controlled by means of a backpressure controller located in the return line to the top of the reactor.

2. Solvent system: The solvent storage tank is a 75-gal stainless steel pressure vessel (112 psi at 70°F) with an integral sight glass, N_2 pad, and relief valve. Solvent is pumped from the bottom of the storage tank to the emulsion tank. The pump is a Burks turbine pump driven by an XP rated, 3/4-HP 3450-rpm motor. A dip pipe is used to vacuum-charge solvent through a dip leg in the vessel where grounding and bonding is secured.
3. POD system: The POD system consists of a Baker-Perkins Model A-1 Contactor (that is, a Podbielniak centrifugal contactor) fabricated in stainless 316. A variable speed drive is capable of rotating the unit at speeds up to 10,000 rpm. The normal operating speed is 8100 rpm.

   The solvent/water emulsion is heated in its subsystem and flows through a Micro Motion mass flow meter. The emulsion is fed to the POD, where the water and organic phases are separated. Through this contact and separation the impurities are extracted into the aqueous phase. This results in a relatively clean solvent.
4. Washed solvent system: The washed solvent tank is a grounded 55-gal drum. An elephant trunk positioned over the bung vents the drum to the exhaust system. Material fed to the drum is cooled from the POD operating temperature of approximately 190°F to 80°–110°F by a stainless steel heat exchanger.
5. Waste water system: The waste water tank is also a grounded 55-gal drum vented to the exhaust system. The heavy liquid out (HLO) stream from the POD system is cooled before discharge into the drum by a stainless steel heat exchanger. Disposal depends on the solvent used, its solubility in water, and environmental constraints.

B. Equipment specifications

1. Emulsion system

   Reactor: 50-gal, glass-lined, jacketed Pfaudler

   Operating pressures: reactor, 150 psi at 450°F
jacket, 130 psi

   Safety relief valves: reactor, 60 psi
jacket, 125 psi

   Agitator: Turbine, 3.6 HP, 1750 rpm, XP rated motor, variable speed drive

   Circulating pump: Viking series HL124, 2 HP, 1745 rpm, XP rated motor

   Micro Motion mass flow meter: stainless steel 316L, 0–80 lb/min mass flow range, accuracy of 0.4% of range, XP rated with electronics unit mounted separately in nonhazardous area.
2. Solvent system

   Tank: 75 gal, stainless steel, rupture disc set at 112 psi

   Pump: Burks turbine, model ET6MYSS; 3/4 HP, 3450 rpm, XP rated motor
3. POD system

   POD: Baker-Perkins A-1 centrifugal contactor, 316 SS; maximum temperature, 250°F; maximum pressure, 250 psig; maximum speed, 10,000 rpm

   Drive: Variable speed Reeves Motodrive, 935–3950 rpm, 3 HP, 1745 rpm motor, XP rated

4. Washed solvent system
   Tank: 55-gal drum
   Light liquid out (LLO) cooler: American Standard, single pass, SS, model 5-160-03-024-001; maximum temperature, 450°F; maximum working pressure, 225 psig shell, 150 psig tube
5. Waste water system
   Tank: 55 gal drum
   HLO cooler: Same as LLO cooler

IV. PROCEDURES

A. Normal operating procedures

1. Purge solvent and emulsion tanks with nitrogen by valves V1a and V1b.
2. If necessary, solvent and emulsion tanks are vented to elephant trunks and into the exhaust system through valves V2a and V2b.
3. Pull a vacuum (15 in Hg) on the solvent storage tank, and charge with solvent by sucking it from the appropriate drum. Check the tank level using the level glass. Periodically check the air for toluene by using colorimetric tubes.
4. Break the vacuum, and pad with nitrogen through valve V1a.
5. Make sure valve V3 is closed from the water head tank to the emulsion tank.
6. Charge the proper amount of softened water through valve V4 to the water head tank located above the emulsion tank.
7. Close valve V4, and pad the water head tank with nitrogen through valve V5.
8. Turn on the emulsion tank agitator.
9. Pump solvent from the solvent storage tank to the emulsion tank.
   a. Line up valves from solvent storage tank through pump P2, to the top of the emulsion tank.
   b. Start pump P2.
   c. Stop pump and close valves when addition is complete.
10. Open valve V3, and add water in the head tank to the emulsion tank. Close valve V3 when addition is complete.
11. Establish circulation in the emulsion system.
    a. Close valve V6 on the feed stream to the Micro Motion mass flow meter.
    b. Line up valves from the bottom of the tank to pump P1 and from the return line back to the top of the vessel.
    c. Start pump P1.
    d. Open steam flow to the jacket of the feed tank.
    e. Bring emulsion up to temperature (190°F).
12. Turn on cooling water to the solvent (LLO) discharge cooler and to the aqueous (HLO) discharge cooler.
13. Line up valves on the HLO and LLO streams from the POD to the coolers and to their respective waste tanks.
14. Open valve V10 to fill the POD.
15. Start the motor for the POD and slowly bring up to the desired rpm.
16. Open valve V6 to begin emulsion flow.
17. Adjust flow to obtain desired rate on Micro Motion flow meter.
18. Control backpressure on the POD LLO and HLO streams by adjusting valves V11a and V11b, respectively.

19. Samples can be obtained from the LLO stream via valve V12a and from the HLO stream via valve V12b.
20. To shut down the POD after a run has been completed:
    a. Close valve V6.
    b. Reduce pressure on the LLO stream (valve V11a), and slowly reduce rotor speed.
    c. Turn off POD motor.
    d. Close valve V10 after the rotor has stopped.
    e. Shut down emulsion system.
    f. Shut off steam and cooling water.

B. Safety procedures

1. The safety concerns unique to this operation are:
    a. The solvent used is volatile and flammable and is also being used at a temperature above its normal atmospheric boiling point.
    b. The materials are all hot (190°F or greater) and capable of producing thermal burns.
    c. Toluene presents a special handling problem because of potential health hazards.
2. The specific procedures to be followed to minimize the risks associated with the above are:
    a. Flammable solvents
        1. Solvents are exposed to atmosphere only with adequate ventilation.
        2. Solvents are transferred into and out of the system only when cold. Do not operate if coolers are not functioning properly.
        3. All solvent-containing process vessels are N_2 purged and maintained under N_2 pad or blanket.
        4. Vapors containing solvent are vented only to the exhaust ducts, never into the worker area.
        5. Initial opening of sample and product valves to atmosphere is done slowly to avoid flashing.
        6. All transfers of solvent-containing streams to or from drums are done in accordance with accepted bonding and grounding procedures.
        7. All equipment is electrically grounded.
    b. Hot material
        1. Avoid contact with hot process lines and vessels. Most lines are insulated for personnel protection.
        2. Wear gloves when working on potentially hot equipment.
        3. Periodically check stream temperatures and cooling water flow to ensure that coolers are working properly.
    c. Health hazards (toxicity, etc.)
        1. Handle potentially hazardous material only when material is cool and when adequate ventilation is present.
        2. Periodically check operating area for leaks with colorimetric tubes.
        3. Repair any leaks immediately.
3. Emergency shutdown
    a. Close solvent valve at bottom of solvent storage tank (if open).
    b. Shut off solvent pump P2 (if operating).
    c. Close valve at bottom of emulsion tank.
    d. Shut off emulsion pump P1.

e. Shut off steam to the emulsion tank jacket.
f. Shut down POD drive system.

4. Fail-safe procedures
   a. Steam failure: No negative consequences.
   b. Cooling water failure: Shut down system.
      1. LLO to washed solvent drum will flash and be sucked into vent system.
      2. HLO to waste drum: Some solvent may flash off and be sucked into vent system.
   c. Electrical failure: Close HLO and LLO valves to protect the unit while it coasts to a stop.
   d. N_2 failure: Stop any operational procedures.
   e. Exhaust system failure: Shut down system.
   f. Pump failure: Shut down system.
   g. Air failure: All steam control valves fail closed. All cooling water control valves fail open.
5. Spill and release procedures
   a. Solvent spill: Follow hazardous spill response as outlined in Safety Manual.
      1. Sound alarm and evacuate if warranted (for example, large drum quantity spill or hot solvent spill).
      2. Vent system on high speed.
      3. Trip sewer isolation valves.
      4. If safe to do so, isolate equipment and ignition sources, and absorb or dike the spill.
      5. Allow excess to evaporate. Check area with explosimeter and colorimetric tubes. Do *not* enter explosive atmosphere.
      6. When safe to do so, sweep up any absorbent material into waste drums for proper disposal.
      7. Consult with Environmental Department if material trapped in sewer system.

C. Waste disposal

The washed solvent is collected in drums for disposal. The aqueous stream, after analysis, can be sent directly to the publicly owned treatment works (POTW). Limits have not yet been set for dumping versus waste disposal in drums. If the solvent being used is a regulated substance (such as toluene), drum disposal of the HLO may be the only acceptable way.

D. Cleanup procedure

Minor spills are soaked up with absorbent material and disposed of in drums. Equipment is washed with hot and/or cold water as necessary.

V. SAFETY CHECKLIST

____ Purge emulsion tank with nitrogen, fill, establish nitrogen pad.
____ Purge solvent storage tank with nitrogen, fill, establish nitrogen pad.
____ Purge washed solvent tank with nitrogen, establish nitrogen pad.
____ Check cooling water flow in two coolers.
____ Vent system operational.
____ Availability of absorbent material and disposal drum.
____ Availability of impervious gloves, goggles/face shield.
____ Sniff area with colorimetric tubes for hazardous solvents.
____ Availability of air line hood.
____ Check all drums for proper grounding.

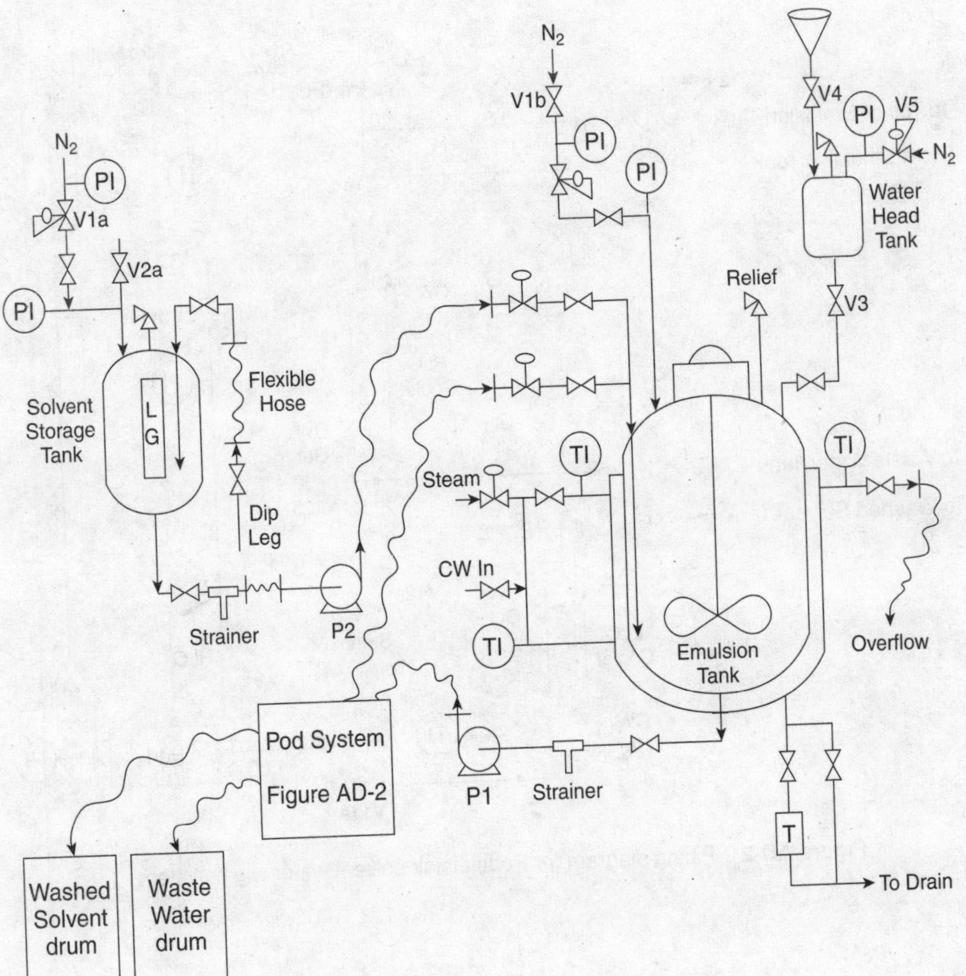

Figure AD-1 Podbielniak extraction system.

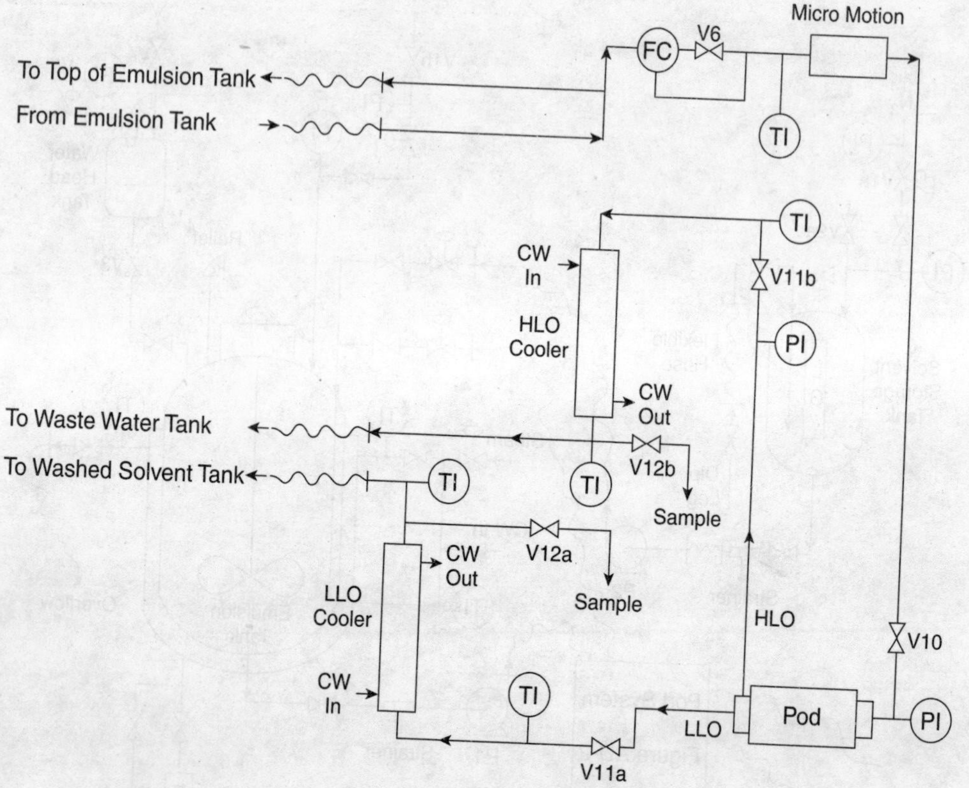

Figure AD-2 Piping diagram for Podbielniak solvent water wash system.

Material Safety Data Sheet

Common chemical name	Physical state	Odor	
Toluene	Colorless liquid	Sweet, pungent	
Synonym	**Molecular weight**	**Odor threshold**	**CAS no.**
Methylbenzene	92.13	2–4 ppm	108-88-3
Chemical formula	**Explosive limits**	**Vapor pressure**	**PEL**
C_7H_8	1.27–7.0%	36.7 mm Hg at 30°C	100 ppm, skin

Toxic Properties[a]

Eyes: Moderately irritating
Skin: Moderately irritating
Inhalation: Central nervous system (CNS) effects
Ingestion: Moderately toxic

[a]Vapors may cause eye irritation. Eye contact with liquid may result in corneal damage and conjunctival irritation that lasts for 48 hours. Inhalation may be irritating and result in fatigue, headaches, CNS effects, and narcosis at high concentrations. Toluene is absorbed through skin. Repeated or prolonged skin contact may result in irritation, defatting, and dermatitis.

Occasionally, chronic poisoning may result in anemia, leukopenia, and enlarged liver.

Some commercial grades of toluene contain small amounts of benzene as an impurity. Benzene is an OSHA-regulated material.

Personal protection

Goggles, impervious gloves, protective clothes and shoes are recommended. Chemical cartridge respirators are sufficient for routine handling. Air-line respirators or self-contained breathing apparatuses are recommended for high concentrations.

First aid

Eyes: Flush thoroughly with water. Consult a physician.
Skin: Wash affected areas with plenty of water. If irritation persists, get medical attention.
Inhalation: Remove to fresh air. Aid in breathing if necessary. Consult a physician.
Ingestion: If swallowed, do *not* induce vomiting. Call a physician immediately.

Special precautions/considerations

This is a flammable liquid. The flash point is 40°F and should be handled accordingly. During transport and storage, protect against physical damage. Outside or detached storage is preferable. Separate from oxidizing materials.

APPENDIX E

Saturation Vapor Pressure Data[1]

$$\ln(P^{\text{sat}}) = A - \frac{B}{C + T}$$

where

P^{sat} is the saturation vapor pressure (mm Hg),
T is the temperature (K), and
A, B, C are constants given below.

Species	Formula	Range(K)	A	B	C
Acetone	C_3H_6O	241–350	16.6513	2940.46	−35.93
Benzene	C_6H_6	280–377	15.9008	2788.51	−52.36
Carbon tetrachloride	CCl_4	253–374	15.8742	2808.19	−45.99
Chloroform	$CHCl_3$	260–370	15.9732	2696.79	−46.19
Cyclohexane	C_6H_{12}	280–380	15.7527	2766.63	−50.50
Ethyl acetate	$C_4H_8O_2$	260–385	16.1516	2790.50	−57.15
Ethyl alcohol	C_2H_6O	270–369	18.9119	3803.98	−41.68
n-Heptane	C_7H_{16}	270–400	15.8737	2911.32	−56.51
n-Hexane	C_6H_{14}	245–370	15.8366	2697.55	−48.78
Methyl alcohol	CH_4O	257–364	18.5875	3626.55	−34.29
n-Pentane	C_5H_{12}	220–330	15.8333	2477.07	−39.94
Toluene	$C_6H_5CH_3$	280–410	16.0137	3096.52	−53.67
Water	H_2O	284–441	18.3036	3816.44	−46.11

[1]Selected from David Himmelblau, *Basic Principles and Calculations in Chemical Engineering*, 7th ed. (Upper Saddle River, NJ: Prentice Hall, 2003), p. 1057.

Special Types of Reactive Chemicals

Reactivity information from R. W. Johnson, S. W. Rudy and S. D. Unwin, *Essential Practices for Managing Chemical Reactivity Hazards* (New York: American Institute of Chemical Engineers, 2003).

Table AF-1 A Few Pyrophoric and Spontaneously Combustible Categories and Chemicals (these materials combust on exposure to air)

Category	Examples
Finely divided metals (without oxide film)	Aluminum, calcium, cobalt, iron, magnesium, manganese, palladium, platinum, titanium, tin, zinc, zirconium
Many hydrogenation catalysts containing adsorbed hydrogen (before and after use)	Raney nickel catalyst with adsorbed hydrogen
Alkali metals	Potassium, sodium
Metal hydrides	Germane, lithium aluminum hydride, potassium hydride, sodium hydride
Partially or fully alkylated metal hydrides	Butyllithium, diethylaluminum hydride, triethylbismuth, trimethylaluminum
Arylmetals	Phenylsodium
Alkylmetal derivatives	Diethylethoxyaluminum, dimethylbismuth chloride
Analogous derivatives of nonmetals	Diborane, dimethylphosphine, phosphine, triethylarsine
Carbonylmetals	Pentacarbonyliron, octacarbonyldicobalt
Grignard reagents (RMgX)	Ethylmagnesium chloride, methylmagnesium bromide
Metal sulfides	Iron sulfide
Miscellaneous	Phosphorus (white), titanium dichloride

Table AF-2 Some Chemical Structures Susceptible to Peroxide Formation (the peroxides formed may become unstable and explode when disturbed)

Chemical structure (not all bonds are shown)	Examples/explanation
	Organic Substances
CH_2–O–R	Ethers with alpha hydrogen atoms, especially cyclic ethers and those containing primary and secondary alcohol groups, form dangerously explosive peroxides on exposure to air and light
CH(–O–R)$_2$	Acetals with alpha hydrogen atoms
C=C–CH	Allyl compounds (olefins with allylic hydrogen atoms), including most alkenes
C=C–X	Halo-olefins (e.g., chloroolefins, fluoroolefins)
C=CH	Vinyl and vinylidene esters, ethers, styrenes
C=C–C=C	1,3-Dienes
CH–C≡CH	Alkylacetylenes with alpha hydrogen atoms
C=CH–C=CH	Vinylacetylenes with alpha hydrogen atoms
	Tetrahydronaphthalenes
(R)$_2$CH–Ar	Alkylarenes with tertiary hydrogen atoms (e.g., cumene)
(R)$_3$CH	Alkanes and cycloalkanes with tertiary hydrogen atoms (e.g., t-butane, isopropyl compounds, decahydronaphthalenes)
C=CH–CO_2R	Acrylates, methacrylates
(R)$_2$CH–OH	Secondary alcohols
O=C(R)–CH	Ketones with alpha hydrogen atoms
O=CH	Aldehydes
O=C–NH–CH	Substituted ureas, amides, and lactams that have a hydrogen atom on a carbon atom attached to nitrogen
CH–M	Organometallic compounds with a metal atom bonded to carbon
	Inorganic substances
Alkali metals, especially potassium, rubidium, and cesium	
Metal amides (e.g., $NaNH_2$)	
Metal alkoxides (e.g., sodium t-butoxide)	

Table AF-3 Chemical Categories Susceptible to Water Reactivity

Category	Examples
Alkali and alkaline-earth metals	Calcium, potassium, sodium, lithium
Anhydrous metal halides	Aluminum tribromide, germanium tetrachloride, titanium tetrachloride
Anhydrous metal oxides	Calcium oxide
Chlorosilanes	Methyldichlorosilane, trichlorosilane, trimethylchlorosilane
Epoxides (e.g., with acid present)	Butylene oxide, ethylene oxide, diepoxy butane, epibromohydrin
Finely divided metals, no oxide film	Aluminum, cobalt, iron, magnesium, titanium, tin, zinc, zirconium
Grignard reagents; organometallics	Ethylmagnesium chloride, methylmagnesium bromide
Inorganic acid halides	Phosphoryl chloride, sulfuryl chloride, chlorosulfuric acid
Inorganic cyanides	Barium cyanide, calcium cyanide, cyanogen chloride, silver cyanide
Isocyanates	n-Butyl isocyanate, methyl isocyanate, toluene diisocyanate
Metal alkyls	Aluminum alkyls, lithium alkyls
Metal amides	Lead amide, potassium amide, silver amide, sodium amide
Metal hydrides	Calcium hydride, lithium aluminum hydride, sodium borohydride
Nitrides, phosphides, carbides	Aluminum phosphide, calcium carbide, gallium phosphide
Nonmetal hydrides	Boron trifluoride, phosphorus trichloride, silicon tetrachloride
Nonmetal oxides	Phosphorus pentoxide, sulfur trioxide
Organic acid halides/anhydrides	Acetic anhydride, acetyl chloride

Table AF-4 Common Water-Reactive Chemicals

This is not an exhaustive list. Reaction with water may be slow to violent. Reaction products may be toxic, corrosive, or flammable. Products may be gaseous and of sufficient quantity to rupture unrelieved containment.

Acetic anhydride
Acetyl chloride
Alkylaluminums
Allyl trichlorosilane
Aluminum chloride, anhydrous
Aluminum phosphide
Amyl trichlorosilane
Benzoyl chloride
Boron tribromide
Boron trifluoride
Boron trifluoride etherate
Bromine pentafluoride
Bromine trifluoride
n-Butyl isocyanate
Butyllithium
Butyric anhydride
Calcium
Calcium carbide
Chlorine trifluoride
Chlorosilanes
Chlorosulfonic acid
Chromium oxychloride
Cyanamide
Decaborane
Diborane
Dichloroacetyl chloride
Dichlorosilane
Diethylaluminum chloride
Diethylaluminum hydride
Diethyl carbamyl chloride
Diethyl telluride
Diethylzinc
Diisobutylaluminum hydride
Dimethyldichlorosilane
Diphenyldichlorosilane
Dipropylaluminum hydride
Ethylaluminum dichloride
Ethylaluminum sesquichloride
Ethyldichlorosilane
Ethyltrichlorosilane
Fluorine
Gallium arsenide
Gallium phosphide
Germane
Isobutyric anhydride
Isophorone diisocyanate
Lithium
Lithium aluminum hydride
Lithium hydride
Methyl isocyanate
Methylaluminum sesquibromide
Methylaluminum sesquichloride
Methyldichlorosilane
Methylene diisocyanate
Methylpentaldehyde
Methyltrichlorosilane
Monochloro-s-triazinetrione acid
Mono-(trichloro)-tetra (mono-potassium dichloro)-penta-s-triazinetrione, dry
Octadecyltrichlorosilane
Phenyl trichlorosilane
Phosphorus oxychloride
Phosphorus pentachloride
Phosphorus pentasulfide
Phosphorus tribromide
Phosphorus trichloride
Potassium
Potassium-sodium alloys
Propionyl chloride
Silicon tetrachloride
Silicon tetrafluoride
Sodium
Sodium dichloro-s-triazinetrione dihydrate
Sodium hydride
Sodium hydrosulfite
Sulfur chlorides
Sulfuric acid
Sulfuryl chloride
Tetraethyl lead
Tetramethyl lead
Thionyl chloride
Titanium tetrachloride
Toluene diisocyanate
Trichlorosilane
Triethylaluminum

Table AF-4 Common Water Reactive Chemicals (*continued*)

Triethylborane	Tripropyl aluminum
Triisobutylaluminum	Vanadium tetrachloride
Trimethylaluminum	Vinyl trichlorosilane
Trimethylchlorosilane	Zirconium tetrachloride

Table AF-5 Typical Oxidizers

Ammonium dichromate	Lithium peroxide
Ammonium nitrate	Magnesium bromate
Ammonium perchlorate	Magnesium chlorate
Ammonium permanganate	Magnesium perchlorate
Ammonium persulfate	Magnesium peroxide
Amyl nitrate	Manganese dioxide
Barium bromate	Mercurous chlorate
Barium chlorate	Monochloro-s-triazinetrione acid
Barium hypochlorite	Mono-(trichloro)-tetra-(monopotassium dichloro)-penta-s-triazinetrione
Barium perchlorate	Nitric acid and fuming nitric acid
Barium permanganate	Nitrites, inorganic
Barium peroxide	Nitrogen oxides (NOx)
Bromine pentafluoride	Oxygen
Bromine trifluoride	Peracetic acid
1-Bromo-3-chloro-5,5-dimethylhydantoin (BCDMH)	Perchloric acid solutions
Calcium chlorate	Potassium bromate
Calcium chlorite	Potassium chlorate
Calcium hypochlorite	Potassium dichloro-striazinetrione (potassium dichloroisocyanurate)
Calcium perchlorate	Potassium dichromate
Calcium permanganate	Potassium percarbonate
Calcium peroxide	Potassium perchlorate
Chloric acid (10 percent maximum concentration)	Potassium permanganate
Chlorine	Potassium peroxide
Chlorine trifluoride	Potassium persulfate
Chlorosulfonic acid	Potassium superoxide
Chromium trioxide (chromic acid)	n-Propyl nitrate
Copper chlorate	Silver peroxide
Guanidine nitrate	Sodium bromate
Halane (1,3-dichloro-5,5-dimethylhydantoin)	Sodium carbonate peroxide
Hydrogen peroxide solutions	Sodium chlorate
Lead dioxide	Sodium chlorite
Lead perchlorate	Sodium dichloro-striazinetrione (sodium dichloroisocyanurate)
Lithium chlorate	Sodium dichloro-s-triazinetrione dihydrate
Lithium hypochlorite	
Lithium perchlorate	

(*continued*)

Table AF-5 Typical Oxidizers (*continued*)

Sodium dichromate	Strontium perchlorate
Sodium perborate (anhydrous)	Strontium peroxide
Sodium perborate monohydrate	Tetranitromethane
Sodium perborate tetrahydrate	Thallium chlorate
Sodium percarbonate	Trichloro-s-triazinetrione (trichloroisocyanuric) (acid all forms)
Sodium perchlorate	Urea hydrogen peroxide
Sodium perchlorate monohydrate	Zinc bromate
Sodium permanganate	Zinc chlorate
Sodium peroxide	Zinc permanganate
Sodium persulfate	Zinc peroxide
Strontium chlorate	

Table AF-6 Some Polymerizing Compounds (these chemicals may polymerize rapidly with release of large amounts of heat)

Acrolein	Methacrylic acid
Acrylamide	Methyl acrylate
Acrylic acid	Methylchloromethyl ether
Acrylonitrile	Methyl isocyanate
1,3-Butadiene	Methyl methacrylate
Butylacrylate	Methyl vinyl ketone
1,2-Butylene oxide	Propargyl alcohol
Butyraldehyde	Propionaldehyde
Crotonaldehyde	Propylene oxide
Dichloroethylene	Styrene
Diketene	Tetrafluoroethylene
Divinylbenzene	Tetrahydrofuran
Epichlorohydrin	Toluene diisocyanate
Ethyl acrylate	Trimethoxysilane
Ethylene	Vinyl acetate
Ethylene cyanohydrin	Vinyl acetylene
Ethyleneimine	Vinyl chloride
Ethylene oxide	Vinyl ether
2-Ethylhexylacrylate	Vinylidene chloride
Hydrogen cyanide	Vinyl toluene
Isoprene	

APPENDIX G

Hazardous Chemicals Data for a Variety of Chemical Substances

Table AG-1 Hazardous Chemicals Data for a Variety of Chemical Substances

Compound	Molecular Weight	Threshold limit value[a] (TLV)			OSHA[b]	NFPA ratings[c]		
		TWA ppm	STEL ppm	C ppm	8-hour PEL ppm	Health	Flammability	Instability
Acetaldehyde	44.05			25	200	2	4	2
Acetic acid	60.00	10	15		10	3	2	0
Acetic anhydride	102.9	5			5	3	2	1
Acetone	58.05	500	750		1000	1	3	0
Acrolein	56.06			0.1	0.1	4	3	3
Acrylic acid	72.06	2				3	2	2
Acrylonitrile	53.05	2			1910.1045[R]	4	3	2
Alkane gases, C_1-C_4	–	1000						
Ammonia	17.03	25	35	50	50	3	1	0
Aniline	93.12	2			5[S]	2	2	0
Arsenic	74.92	0.01 mg/m^3			1910.1010[R]			
Arsine	77.95	0.005			0.05	4	4	2
Benzene	78.11	0.5	2.5		1910.1028[R]	1	3	0
Biphenyl	154.20	0.05	0.15		0.2	1	1	0
Bromine	159.81	0.1	0.2		0.1	3	0	0[OX]
1,3 Butadiene	54.09	2			1910.1051[R]	2	4	2
n-Butanol	74.12	20			100	3	3	0
sec-Butanol	74.12	100			150			
tert-Butanol	74.12	100			100			
Butene	56.11	250				1	4	0
Butyraldehyde	72.1					3	3	2
Butyric acid	88.1					3	2	0
Calcium carbide	64.1					3	3	2[W]
Caprolactum	113.16	5 mg/m^3						
Carbon dioxide	44.01	5000			5000			
Carbon disulfide	76.14	1				3	4	0
Carbon monoxide	28.01	25			50	2	4	0
Carbon tetrachloride	153.84	5				3	0	0

Table AG-1 *(continued)*

Compound	Molecular Weight	Threshold limit value[a] (TLV) TWA ppm	STEL ppm	C ppm	OSHA[b] 8-hour PEL ppm	NFPA ratings[c] Health	Flammability	Instability
Chlorine	70.91	0.5	1		1	4	0	0^{OX}
Chlorine dioxide	67.46	0.1	0.3		0.1			
Chlorobenzene	112.56	10			75	3	3	0
Chloroform	119.38	10			(C) 50	2	0	0
Chlorosulfonic acid	116.5					4	0	$2^{W,OX}$
Crotonaldehyde	70.09			0.3	2	4	3	2
Cumene	120.90	50			50^{S}	2	3	1
Cyclohexane	84.16	100			300	1	3	0
Cyclohexanol	100.16	50			50	1	2	0
Cyclohexanone	98.14	20	50		50	1	2	0
Cyclohexene	82.14	300			300	1	3	0
Cyclopentane	70.13	600				1	3	0
Diborane	27.69	0.1			0.1	4	4	3^{W}
1,1-Dichloroethane	98.97	100			100	1	3	0
1,2-Dichloroethylene	96.95	200			200	2	4	2
Dichloromethane = Methylene chloride	96.95	200			200	2	1	0
Diesel fuel	–	100 mg/m^3				1	2	0
Diethylamine	73.14	5	15		25	3	3	0
Diethyl ether	74.1					1	4	1
Diethyl ketone	86.13	200	300			1	3	0
Dimethylamine	45.08	5	15		10	3	4	0
1,4-Dioxane	88.10	20			100	2	3	1
Epichlorohydrin	92.53	0.5			5	4	3	2
Ethyl acetate	88.10	400			400	1	3	0
Ethyl alcohol	46.07		1000		1000	2	3	0
Ethylamine	45.08	5	15		10	3	4	0

(continued)

Table AG-1 Hazardous Chemicals Data for a Variety of Chemical Substances (*continued*)

Compound	Molecular Weight	Threshold limit value[a] (TLV) TWA ppm	STEL ppm	C ppm	OSHA[b] 8-hour PEL ppm	NFPA ratings[c] Health	Flammability	Instability
Ethyl benzene	106.16	100	125		100	2	3	0
Ethyl bromide	108.98	5			200	3	3	0
Ethyl chloride	64.52	100			1000	2	4	0
Ethylene	28.05	200				2	4	2
Ethylene dichloride	98.96	10			3	2	3	0
Ethylene glycol	62.07			100 mg/m^3	(C) 0.2	2	1	0
Ethylene oxide	44.05	1			1910.1047^{R}	3	4	3
Ethyl ether	74.12	400	500		400	1	4	1
Ethyl mercaptan	62.13	0.5			(C) 10	2	4	1
Fluorine	38.00	1	2		0.1	4	0	4^{W}
Formaldehyde	30.03			0.3	1910.1048^{R}	3	4	0
Formic acid	46.02	5	10		5	3	2	0
Furfural	96.08	2			5	3	2	1
Gasoline	–	300	500			1	3	0
Heptane, all isomers	100.20	400	500		500	1	1	3
Hexachloroethane	236.74	1			1			
n-Hexane	86.18	50			500	1	3	0
Hexane, other isomers	86.18	500	1000					
Hydrazine	32.05	0.01			1	4	4	3
Hydrogen bromide	80.92			2	3			
Hydrogen chloride	36.47			2	(C) 5	3	0	1
Hydrogen cyanide	27.03			4.7	10	4	4	2
Hydrogen fluoride	20.01	0.5		2		4	0	1
Hydrogen peroxide	34.02	1			1			
40% to 60%						3	0	1^{OX}
>60%						3	0	3^{OX}
Hydrogen sulfide	34.08	10	15		10	4	4	0
Iodine		0.01	0.1		(C) 0.1			
Isobutyl alcohol	74.12	50			100	2	3	0

Table AG-1 (*continued*)

Compound	Molecular Weight	Threshold limit value[a] (TLV) TWA ppm	STEL ppm	C ppm	OSHA[b] 8-hour PEL ppm	NFPA ratings[c] Health	Flammability	Instability
Isopropyl ether	102.17	250	310		500	2	3	1
Kerozene		200 mg/m^3				2	2	0
Ketene	42.04	1.5			0.5			
Maleic anhydride	98.06	0.1			0.25	3	1	1
Methacrylic acid	86.1					3	2	2
Methyl acetate	74.08	200	250		200	2	3	0
Methyl acetylene	40.07	1000			1000			
Methyl alcohol	32.04	200	250		200	1	3	0
Methylamine	31.06	5	15.		10	3	4	0
Methyl bromide	94.05	1			(C) 20^S	3	1	0
Methyl chloride	50.49	50	100			2	4	0
Methyl ethyl ketone	72.10	200	300		200	1	3	0
Methyl formate	60.05	100	150		150	2	4	0
Methyl isocyanate	57.05	0.02			0.02^S	4	3	2^W
Methyl mercaptan	48.11	0.5			(C) 10	4	4	1
Naphthalene	128.19	10	15		10	2	2	0
Nitric acid	63.02	2	4		2			
Nitric oxide	30.01	25			25			
Nitrobenzene	123.11	1			1^S	3	2	1
Nitrogen dioxide	46.01	3	5		(C) 5			
Nitromethane	61.04	20			100	2	3	4
Nitrogen oxides						3	0	0^{OX}
Nitrous oxide	44.02	50						
Nonane	128.26	200				1	3	0
Octane, all isomers	114.22	300			500	1	3	0
Oxalic acid	90.04	1 mg/m^3	2 mg/m^3		1 mg/m^3	3	1	0

(*continued*)

Table AG-1 Hazardous Chemicals Data for a Variety of Chemical Substances (*continued*)

Compound	Molecular Weight	Threshold limit value[a] (TLV) TWA ppm	STEL ppm	C ppm	OSHA[b] 8-hour PEL ppm	NFPA ratings[c] Health	Flammability	Instability
Ozone	48.00				0.1			
Heavy work:		0.05						
Moderate work:		0.08						
Light work:		0.10						
<2 hours:		0.20						
Pentane, all isomers	72.15	600			1000	1	4	0
Phenol	94.11	5			5^{S}	4	2	0
Phosgene	98.92	0.1			0.1	4	0	1
Phosphine	34.00	0.3			0.3	4	4	2
Phosphoric acid	98.00	1 mg/m^3	3 mg/m^3		1 mg/m^3	3	0	0
Phthalic anhydride	148.11	1			2	3	1	0
Picric acid	229.11	0.1 mg/m^3			0.1 mg/m^3	3	4	4
Polyvinyl chloride		1 mg/m^3						
Propylene	42.08	500				1	4	1
Propylene oxide	58.08	2			100	3	4	2
Pyridine	79.10	1			5	3	3	0
Sodium	22.9					3	3	2^{W}
Sodium cyanide	49.0					3	0	0
Sodium hydroxide	40.0			2 mg/m^3	2 mg/m^3	3	0	1
Styrene, monomer	104.16	20	40		2 mg/m^3	2	3	2
Sulfur dioxide, liq.	64.07		0.25		5	3	0	0
Sulfuric acid, aq.	–	0.2 mg/m^3			1 mg/m^3	3	0	2^{W}
Tetrachloroethylene	165.80	25	100		2 mg/m^3	2	0	0
Toluene	92.13	20			2 mg/m^3	2	3	0
Trichloroethylene	131.40	10	25		2 mg/m^3	2	1	0
Triethylamine	101.19	1	3			3	3	0
Trimethylamine	59.1	5	15			3	4	0
Turpentine	~136	20			100	1	3	0

Table AG-1 *(continued)*

Compound	Molecular Weight	Threshold limit value[a] (TLV) TWA ppm	STEL ppm	C ppm	OSHA[b] 8-hour PEL ppm	NFPA ratings[c] Health	Flammability	Instability
Vinyl acetate	86.09	10	15			2	3	2
Vinyl bromide	106.96	0.5				2	4	1
Vinyl chloride	62.50	1			1910.1017[R]	2	4	2
Vinyl fluoride	46.05	1				2	4	2
Xylene	106.16	100	150		100	2	3	0

[a]Threshold limit value (TLV) data from American Conference of Governmental Industrial Hygienists (ACGIH), *2009 TLVs and BEIs* (Cincinnati, OH: ACGIH, 2009).

[b]US Occupational Safety and Health Administration (OSHA), www.osha.gov.

[c]NFPA ratings from National Fire Protection Association, *Fire Protection Guide to Hazardous Materials* (Quincy, MA:NFPA, 2002).

(C) Ceiling limit

[OX]Oxidizer

[R]These chemicals have a specific OSHA regulation. See the OSHA document referenced at *www.OSHA.gov.*

[S]These chemicals have an OSHA skin designation. This means that these chemicals can be absorbed through the skin.

[W]Water-reactive.

The absence of data does not indicate non-hazardous properties, just that data are not reported.

Index